W9-ADS-307

Zoology

Third Edition

New York

APPLETON-CENTURY-CROFTS

DIVISION OF MEREDITH PUBLISHING COMPANY

Zoology

by

Alfred M. Elliott
UNIVERSITY OF MICHIGAN

590
EL 5 z

49232
Apr. '65

Preface

With the enormous volume of research that finds its way into the literature each year, it becomes increasingly more difficult to select the meaningful and to present it comprehensively in an elementary college zoology textbook. The process resolves itself into a constant examination of the new which must be weighed against the traditional, and then deciding which has lasting value and should become a part of the knowledge of an educated person, regardless of his ultimate career. This has been the effort in this volume.

The basic organization of this edition, like that of the previous two, centers around organic evolution. Data from field and laboratory studies all over the world continue to supplement our understanding of this unifying concept. Some of the most dramatic and exciting observations are being made at the cellular and molecular level, all of which fortify our concept of the unity of life and its evolution. The principle of organic evolution is so important in understanding life as it exists on the earth today that it cannot be relegated to an isolated chapter, but must occupy the central theme of the entire book, and so it does. The historical approach to the study of organic evolution seems to be the most reasonable one because there is no simpler way to tell the story than to start from the beginning and relate the events as they occurred. In order to follow this sequence, the natural laws must be introduced very early, which means that some aspects of elementary chemistry and physics must be mastered. It is quite impossible to teach modern biology without this background.

The eight parts of the book have been carefully integrated into what amounts to an historical account of the earth and the animals which live upon it. The aim has been to emphasize the salient points concerning animals and their origins without overwhelming the student with detail; to present the best in zoology, some of it complex, in a manner that will fascinate the general education student and challenge the embryo zoologist and preprofessional student.

All of the chapters have been reevaluated in the light of recent knowledge; some have been extensively rewritten, others have been supplemented, and a few remain essentially unchanged. The chapters covering the origin of life, the morphology and physiology of cells, morphogenesis, and genetics required the most revision. These are the fields where research has been most active in recent years. The organization of the invertebrate phyla has been brought into line with recent trends in systematics, and new material replaces or supplements much of the old. The clarity of style, emphasized in the drawings of earlier editions, has been retained in the many new illustrations. Numerous new photographs have also been added. Suggested supplementary readings appear at the end of each chapter, which will encourage further exploration of the topics discussed.

After a brief discussion of the stature of zoology as a science, there follows in Part I a discussion of the scientist, his methods, and the part he plays in the scheme of human endeavor. It is important to know the methods of science and recognize that zoology employs the same disciplines used in other sciences.

The story of evolution begins to unfold in Part II, beginning with the origin of the earth. The elementary principles of chemistry and physics are introduced at this point, because without this knowledge, the later discussions of molecular biology would be meaningless. For those who have had chemistry and physics this section will be easily comprehended; for those without this background some extra effort will be required. For both groups it will be necessary to master this material before going on to later sections. The beginnings of life are considered, and the chemical reactions associated with it are introduced. The story of the origin of living things is described, first from the chemical and physical standpoint, and secondly, the morphological entities are described. Included in this discussion is the gradual construction of the first cells, followed by the details of their function. In Part III we speculate upon the transition from single cells to many cells, and the resulting metazoa. The organization of cells into complex organisms is considered in this section, as well as the problems that arose from this association.

Once the principles involved in organic evolution are well established and the characteristics of the organized animals are understood, a discussion of the animal's relation to its environment is taken up in Part IV. Built upon this foundation, Part V traces the long evolutionary sequence from protozoa to man. Here, animals are described both morphologically and physiologically, with special reference to their origins. The full impact of the evolutionary idea is emphasized in the chapter where the chordates are discussed. This chapter includes a brief history of man.

With this background, the student is prepared for a rather careful study of the organ systems of man, to which Part VI is devoted. Each chapter is introduced with a brief résumé of the organ systems under scrutiny as they appear in the various animal groups. This is done to firmly fix in the mind of the student the origin of the various systems, and to demonstrate that they are not peculiar to man. Because of the importance of the human species, considerable attention has been devoted to this section which, in some respects, will be the most rewarding to students, particularly those who take no more zoology courses.

The continuity of life is taken up in Part VII, beginning with the replication of DNA and protein synthesis and continuing with cell duplication, continuity of the individual and the race. Considerable new material has been added to this section, in order to bring it up to date.

The book concludes in Part VIII with a return to the discussion of organic evolution —its meaning, theories, and mechanisms. Some of the recent concepts supplement the more traditional handling of this subject. Man's place in the whole scheme seems a fitting finale, with the hope that the student will be impressed with the prominent place he now occupies in the living world.

I have relied heavily on colleagues, in this as well as in previous editions, for accuracy in presentation of material from specialized fields. I should like to express again my appreciation to the following specialists who were so kind as to read certain chapters of the previous editions: Professors F. F. Hooper and F. C. Evans (Ecology), J. Hendricks (Parasites), H. van der Schalie (Mollusks), N. E. Hartwig (Amphibians and Reptiles), E. T. Hooper (Mammals), A. C. Clement (Chordates), and N. E. Kemp (Embryology). In this revision, Professor E. E. Steiner read the chapter on Genetics, Professor H. F. Hogg critically reviewed chapters II and III, and Professor L. C. Stuart read the first six chapters. To these specialists I am grateful. The entire manuscript was read by Professor I. J. Cantrall, whose helpful criticism I greatly appreciate. Whatever attractiveness the book possesses is the result of the efforts of a number of artists. Many of the drawings are retained from the earlier editions and are essentially unchanged. These were done by O. J. Ingersoll, D. S. Garlock, Raymond Jansma, William Brudon, and Robert Main. Betty Anthony, Sally Wargelin, Donna Snyder, and Jan Powers prepared the new plates that appear in this edition. In addition to the acknowledgements listed in the back of the book for the photographs, I should like to mention my special appreciation to Professors Keith Porter, Hugh Huxley, and George Rose for the very excellent electron and light microscope micrographs which they so kindly permitted me to use.

I should also like to express my thanks to the staff of our large elementary zoology course here at the University of Michigan, who have been ever on the alert for errors and who have been helpfully critical of my coverage of topics and the manner in which it has been done. In addition, I appreciate the many teachers who have used the earlier editions and taken the time from their busy schedules to share their knowledge and experiences with me in order to improve this edition. Many of their suggestions and criticisms have found their way into this edition. Also, to those students who have given me the benefit of their opinions from time to time, I wish to express my gratitude. I hope that teachers and students who have occasion to read this edition will feel free to let me have the benefit of their criticisms.

A. M. E.

Ann Arbor, Michigan

Contents

x   CONTENTS

PART I

Zoology as a Science

1

The Science of Zoology

OF THE MILLIONS OF PLANETS that exist in the universe, at least one, planet Earth, possesses the necessary physical requirements to support living things. The extent to which this has been accomplished is indicated by the fact that if all of the physical world were swept away, the outline of its crust would be maintained in essentially its present form consisting only of the body framework of living organisms. Possibly the most challenging problems faced by scientists in the past, and even more so today, are those centered around the origin and subsequent history of these living things. The physical world appeared first and life was derived from it at some later time; hence the most obvious classification of objects which make up the world is into nonliving and living. The physical sciences represent the accumulated knowledge of the former, whereas all that we know about the latter comprises **biology,** the science of life. The living world has been arbitrarily divided into **botany,** the study of plants, and **zoology,** the study of animals, the subject of this book.

Physical scientists have made great strides toward understanding many natural laws, particularly in recent decades when the atom has been torn apart and its components examined. As more is understood about the physical nature of matter the more likely it will be that the "riddle of life" will be revealed. Perhaps the most exciting discoveries made today are those at the level where the knowledge of the chemist, physicist, and biologist converge on the problem of the composition of living matter. There is no greater intellectual achievement than the understanding of the laws of nature that initiated and fostered the development of living things on the earth. This becomes more apparent when one considers that these same laws are responsible for the origin of man himself. Few would argue the relative merits of achieving a thorough understanding of the composition and functioning of this one species.

Are the mysteries of the universe being understood? Some of those concerned with our physical world are yielding to our constant probing, and today we are fairly certain of the workings of many natural laws. The atom is gradually yielding its secrets and we are approaching an understanding of the nature of the universe. But what do we know about life? In spite of all of the great accomplishments in chemistry, we have not yet been able to identify the exact composition of the material in which that something called life resides. We do not understand how an animal grows, how a fertilized egg develops into an individual, and we have not the slightest notion how the brain of man works. These and hundreds of other problems are some of the most complex man has so far encountered, but without their solution there can be no understanding of life itself.

In spite of this dearth of knowledge concerning the actual nature of life, there has accumulated a mass of information about animals, particularly about their structure, physiology, and interrelationships. All of these studies are included in the science of **zoology.** Like all scientific knowledge, zoology has become more and more specialized into many compartments, such as **anatomy** (study of gross structure), **physiology** (study of function), **embryology** (study of early development), **genetics** (study of heredity), and many others. In seeking a broad view of the entire field, it becomes necessary to select only the salient parts of each of these segments and fit them into a unified whole. The purpose of this book is to lay these bits of information before you with the hope that you will be able to grasp this unified picture and gain an understanding of animal life as it has come to be what it is today. Most of all, if you can better comprehend your own origin and the place you occupy in this world of living things, you may be able to formulate a more satisfying philosophy of life. If you do, the effort put forth in gaining this knowledge will be well worthwhile and the purpose of this book will have been accomplished.

WHAT SCIENCE IS

Many attempts have been made to define science, and much confusion exists in the minds of most people about just what science is. Science is actually a systematic approach to the solution of problems. It involves observation, the collection of facts and the drawing of verifiable conclusions based on these facts.

Science has come to mean **organized knowledge** which includes all that man has learned about his world. In volume and scope this has become so tremendous that no one person can even read the titles of research papers that appear each day. Indeed, it requires much reading for a specialist to become familiar with the works of others in his own field. One of the critical problems in modern research that must be solved is some way of condensing the current literature that pours from laboratories all over the world and reducing it to such form that it can be read and understood by those working in the field. Many techniques have been devised, such as microfilming and microcarding, but none have been entirely satisfactory.

Science is more than the mere gathering of facts. A fact in itself has meaning only when it is related to a whole body of information. Counting the number of leaves on a tree or the number of hairs on a dog would result in facts, but such information is relatively useless and anyone doing it might be considered queer if not downright "nuts." However, even this information could be useful if one was studying the value of certain compounds to increase foliation in trees or fur quality in animals. Indeed, factual information is essential to the solution of many problems. It is meaningless only when out of the context of related information. In other words, gathering of facts is an essential part of all research and should not be ridiculed. The annals of science are replete with instances where certain isolated facts, dug out of the old literature, have been the key to the solution of some new problem.

The highest level of achievement in scientific thought is the formulation of **theories** which explain observed facts. Theories are particularly gratifying if they can be reduced to simple terms such as mathematical formulas. The physical scientists and astronomers have been able to do this to a remarkably advanced degree, but in biology very few processes or principles can be fitted neatly into a formula. The movement of the planets and forces controlling a falling body obey laws which can be stated in the simplest of mathematical form, but the factors controlling the growth of an embryo cannot be so clearly stated. Biological processes certainly do obey laws, some of which are quite clear today, and a constant struggle is made by biologists to reduce the multitude of complex data that accumulates each day to some sort of working formula. And this may be possible someday, but at present only in a few fields, such as **genetics,** has this been possible.

A good theory is one which explains all of the facts that have been observed but, more important, it makes possible **predictions** of what one might expect in future explorations. In other words, it points the way for future work. It takes the "guesswork" out of one's efforts. For example, if one compound with a certain configuration of its atoms cured a disease in a mouse but was too toxic to be administered to humans even though equally effective in curing the disease, it would be likely that to use other closely related compounds might be highly profitable. One would be more apt to find such closely related compounds to be effective in the treatment of the disease than entirely different chemicals. This is a very simple statement of the use of a theory. Biologists are much happier if theories are sweeping in their scope; for example, a single theory that would explain cancer would be welcomed by all mankind. One of the greatest theories in biology that has had its influence far beyond the limits of biology is the **theory of evolution,** about which we shall have a great deal to say throughout this book.

THE WORKING SCIENTIST

In recent years scientists have figured more in the public eye than ever before for reasons that are quite obvious. Atomic bombs, intercontinental missiles, and very recently space travel have commanded the attention of everyone. The people responsible for these achievements are the scientists. What kind of people are they? They have often been labeled as eccentrics, sophisticated magicians, or men endowed with very unusual powers; in any case, they warrant watching. Actually, scientists are no different from any other group of intelligent, highly motivated people, with one possible exception; they possess a spirit of inquiry which stimulates them to investigate the unknown. They tend to spend most of their lifetime working at their science. The scientist is the modern explorer, the spiritual descendant of Marco Polo or Magellan. He pushes not only out across a wide frontier of unknown ocean or wilderness, but also on to an unknown universe, undiscovered territory which is as full of surprise and adventure as the Indies or the great oceans of the world. He never lacks stimulation; his world is exciting and challenging, and he never tires of exploring it.

Open-mindedness is another characteristic of a good scientist. He must approach all problems with an unbiased viewpoint. Preformed ideas about the ultimate outcome of any investigation are inevitable, but one must be certain that such thoughts do not flavor in any way the facts that are obtained. In biology this tendency is a much greater hazard than in the physical sciences because it is less exact, and oftentimes there is considerable room for interpretation and even speculation, both of which are important in all scientific research; indeed, perhaps the highest level of achievement in science is in the realm of speculation where sweeping ideas, only partially proven, have spurred further investigation. Out of such mental efforts have come our greatest theories and laws, Newton's Law of Gravity and Darwin's Theory of Natural Selection, to give two examples.

A scientist must be critical of all scientific information, particularly his own. It is only by checking and rechecking one another's work that the ultimate truth can be known. Scientists are their own severest critics, and so they should be. Conclusions must be drawn only after the most rigorous tests have been made, and such conclusions must allow for future discoveries which may alter or extend present knowledge. The sole goal of the scientist is to understand as much of the physical and living world as his brain can comprehend.

People not directly associated with the sciences have said that an abysmal gap exists between the humanities and the sciences. Some extremists seem to fear that scientific analysis has driven beauty from the world and, by portraying man as a machine, has destroyed all human dignity and self-respect that were once the pillars of our civilization. Certainly science, if understood in its highest aspirations, is no enemy of the humanities and is not incompatible with the arts. Indeed, science and the arts pursue common goals, in different ways to be sure, but they are both expressions of man's efforts to infuse beauty and understanding into life.

COMMUNICATION AMONG SCIENTISTS

In the early days of science, men often worked alone and in secrecy. This was possible because their tools were simple and for the most part could be made by the worker himself. As the problems became more complex and more and more scientists were working on the same or related problems, it became necessary to depend on one another both for tools, chemicals, and for exchange of ideas. Communication then became a very important aspect of science. Groups of scientists with a common interest formed societies where they could meet at regular intervals to "read" papers, that is, describe their achievements to their peers. The discussions that followed the paper were helpful in evaluating one's work in the light of that of others. The societies usually sponsored a journal in which papers were published for the whole world to read and evaluate. This tradition of publication has remained essentially unchanged to the present.

Publication, as understood by scientists, has a meaning somewhat different from that usually assigned to the word. To the scientist, it means putting down on paper the details of his work in such a fashion that anyone properly trained can repeat his observations at any time in the future. **Repeatability** is the very heart of science, and without publication there would be no opportunity to repeat one another's work and scientific progress would be slow indeed.

It has also become traditional that scientific publications be open to the public. Except in time of strife between nations this has always been true. During war, publications in the basic sciences usually dwindle to the vanishing point. One might ask what purpose does open publication serve? When a great many men in all parts of the world are working on a common problem, the knowledge gained by each is available to all if open publication is practiced. This greatly speeds up the solution to problems and is largely responsible for the meteoric advance of science in the past 200 years.

HISTORICAL BACKGROUND OF ZOOLOGY

From the time man first organized into groups or societies he has had his problems either solved or greatly influenced by certain members of his group who were placed in a position of authority, and whose word was absolute, even to the point of life and death. Conclusions were based on emotions, hunches, and superstition, but rarely, if ever, on observed facts. This cannot be relegated entirely to ancient times, since even today there are countries in the world where similar policies are followed. In this modern world such tactics have led to much bloodshed and may continue to do so.

Historically, we need not go back any farther than **Aristotle** (384–322 B.C.) to find the faint beginnings of a new way of solving problems, indeed, a complete new way of life. Aristotle gave us the **inductive method** of reasoning, which means that generalizations are made from the facts observed. Many facts are collected on the topic in question and after these are all assembled,

certain conclusions are drawn. The counterpart of this method is the **deductive method** of reasoning, wherein the generalization is made and the facts selected to fit the generalization. Most of our great advances in science have come from the utilization of the inductive rather than the deductive method of reasoning. Even when the latter method is employed certain basic facts, frequently mathematical, are used as a starting point. While Aristotle was undoubtedly influential in introducing the inductive method of reasoning to the world, even he was dependent on considerable information that had accumulated during the centuries before his time. It cannot be emphasized too strongly that no man, however great, stands out entirely alone. He always depends to some extent at least on what preceded him.

Aristotle was a man of considerable influence in his day and his stature grew tremendously for centuries after his death; the student of today could hardly miss his name in almost any field of learning. His greatest contribution, perhaps, was his method of approaching problems. Not that he was right in all of his observations, for he made many mistakes, but it was his constant insistence on making careful observations, first hand, and recording them accurately that was important. To be sure, he did rely on accounts by his friends or earlier writers for the description of forms he had never seen. For example, he wrote that there were no neck bones in the lion but merely a fused mass extending from the thorax to the skull. It is obvious that he had not seen a lion's skeleton or he would never have written this account. However, where he made his own observations, such as his description of the development of the chick, he was meticulously accurate. The reader is impressed by his account of the breeding of sharks. On the other hand, his description of the internal human anatomy is inaccurate; one is certain that he was observing the viscera of some lower mammal when he wrote it. His ideas concerning the function of the various parts of the body are rather amusing to us today. For example, he thought that the brain produced mucus and was cold while the spinal cord was hot, that the heart was the seat of intelligence, and that food "cooked" in the digestive tract. He described 520 species of animals that have since been identified. He constructed a crude method of classifying animals, although his system was not accepted by subsequent taxonomists.

Using Aristotle's contribution toward initiating the scientific method of approach to the solution of problems, some progress was made by his followers. But the road was difficult and progress was extremely slow. Of the many men who wrote during the first few hundred years following Aristotle, **Galen,** who lived in the second century A.D., was the most outstanding; he made some rather remarkable contributions to the anatomical studies of the human body (Fig. 1-1). Aristotle's influence probably stimulated Galen to make some accurate observations on the brain and heart particularly. He was denied the use of human bodies for dissection, and his writings indicate that he used the ape and goat for his studies.

Galen was a voluminous writer, having completed 256 treatises during his lifetime, most of which were medical in character. Of these his most outstanding were written on human anatomy. Galen lived at the close of the Age of Classical Culture, just before the Middle Ages, in which all new learning was at a standstill. It was fortunate, for the many generations of medical men who followed, that Galen did produce work of such high grade, because it formed the basis for medical knowledge for the next 1,200 years. His book, *On Anatomical Preparations,* was the standard medical text during this long period, perhaps the longest "run" any textbook has ever enjoyed.

In the next twelve centuries authority

as a source of all information reached its peak. This was very well illustrated in the study of medicine. The professor of anatomy, for example, sat before his class with a large volume of Galen's text before him, and a human body, when it was available, displayed on the dissecting bench some distance below. A barber or two huddled over the body, exposing the various parts, as the professor read about them from the text. The students looked on and absorbed what they could from this crude demonstration. The unquestioning faith in authority of this period was revealed when some portion of the human body did not agree with the description in Galen; the body was always considered at fault, not the text. Such mistakes were common, since Galen's dissections were based on animals other than man. This was typical of the time, even in learned circles, and this profound respect for authority persisted until a few bold men dared strike out to see and learn for themselves some centuries later.

Among the many men who had the ability and courage to fight blind ignorance was **Vesalius,** who was born in Brussels (1514), trained for medicine in Paris, and finally became professor of medicine at Padua in Italy at 22 years of age. During his early medical school days he was a devoted follower of Galen's teachings. But Vesalius was able to secure human bodies for dissection, and as he probed more deeply into the details of human anatomy he discovered Galen's errors. Being an independent thinker, he soon decided that he must write down his own observations concerning human anatomy without reference to the work of anyone else. He secured the services of some of the best artists of his day to illustrate the book that he felt the urge to write. Some recently discovered woodcuts made by Calcar, a student of Titian, were found to be as beautiful as when first used in Vesalius' book, *On the Structure of the Human Body* (Figs. 1-2 and -3). Because he was at variance with Galen, Vesalius

FIG. 1-1. This is a sketch of the human skeleton that appears in Galen's book, *On Anatomical Preparations*. By comparing it with a modern drawing some discrepancies will be noted. Note the shape of the neck vertebrae in the right-hand figure and observe that the coccyx (tailbone) is one piece and peculiarly shaped.

FIG. 1-2. This is a woodcut taken from Vesalius' book, *The Structure of the Human Body*. It depicts Vesalius himself giving one of his public demonstrations of the internal anatomy of the human body.

FIG. 1-3. These are four woodcuts taken from Vesalius' book, *The Structure of the Human Body*. Note the remarkable accuracy with which the superficial and deep muscles were done. The postures and backgrounds were undoubtedly the contribution of the artist Calcar.

soon became the subject of much adverse criticism, which finally forced him to leave his professorial post to become court physician for Emperor Charles V. In this position he apparently was not happy, because some years later he left on a pilgrimage to Jerusalem from which he never returned.

The greatest contribution this energetic man made to the world was his break away from authority and his re-establishment of the old Aristotelian ideal of pur-

FIG. 1-4. These are two of the original sketches made by Harvey in his little book describing the circulation of the blood. The figures demonstrate the valves in the veins that permit the blood to flow only toward the heart.

suing the answer to problems by direct observations. This revolt from authority was furthered by others after Vesalius, but it received its greatest impetus from William **Harvey** (1578–1657), a British physician, who gave us the first experimental approach to biological problems. Educated at Padua, Vesalius' old school, Harvey became interested in the blood vascular system, and went to work eagerly after he left the university, to learn more about this perplexing problem. Up to his time the heart was thought to be purely passive and non-muscular; the blood was supposed to flow into the heart causing it to expand suddenly, which accounted for its audible beat against

the thorax. The blood somehow picked up that intangible "spiritus vitalis" while in the heart, then passed to the liver where the food was changed into blood, thus nourishing the body.

Harvey demonstrated that the heart was a muscular organ and that its contractions were responsible for propelling the blood through the arteries. He experimented with animals and studied normal and abnormal humans for twenty years before he was certain that the blood flowed away from the heart in the arteries, and returned to the heart in the veins (Fig. 1-4). His most important contribution was to prove mathematically that the blood must circulate through the body in this fashion. He went about demonstrating his theory, much the same as it would be done today in a modern research laboratory. He was in error on the capacity of the heart and the rate of its beat. He maintained that it held 2 ounces of blood (it holds approximately 4) and that only one-sixth of this amount was delivered at each beat (almost all of the blood is forced out at each beat). Moreover, he stated that the rate was 33 beats per minute when at rest instead of 72 as we know is the case. The heart actually pumps 20 times more blood than indicated by Harvey's calculations. In spite of these errors his general conclusions were correct. He reasoned that such a tremendous quantity of blood simply had to stay within the body and circulate from one part to the other. He was able to work out the pulmonary circulation quite satisfactorily, but he was forced to guess at the existence of body capillaries because, lacking a microscope, he never saw them. Truly Harvey was a great scientist, and his courage put physiology on its first step toward the profound science it is today. He brought experimentation based on mathematics into the study of biology for the first time, and has been looked upon as the founder of modern physiology.

The values of direct observation and

experimentation gradually became obvious to the intelligent world in the years following Harvey's initial steps. All through the nineteenth century brilliant men added their influence to the growing infant science of physiology until it gained full stature at the turn of the twentieth century, and it has been growing steadily up to the present. During the nineteenth century most biological work was in morphology, that is, the study of form and structure of animals; today physiological problems are receiving most of the attention. Biologists are primarily concerned with the way animals function. In order to find answers they have been forced to rely on the sister sciences of physics and chemistry, for it has become increasingly obvious that in the last analysis these sciences are most likely to give us the solution to our most profound problems.

Using these four men, Aristotle, Galen, Vesalius, and Harvey, as examples spaced over nearly 2,000 years, it is possible to see how the science of zoology took root and grew to what it is today. Men could have been selected from other sciences to demonstrate the same evolution in a way of thinking. In any case, it is obvious that science was slow in developing during its first 2,000 years. It has grown tremendously since then, however, particularly during the past 200 years, and in this century almost explosively. There seems to be no indication of any abatement in its growth at the present time, and if properly guided science will certainly help to make this world of ours a better place in which to live.

WHAT SCIENCE HAS DONE AND CAN DO

Let us consider for a moment what science has done for people of the world, what it is doing today, and what it could or might do in the future. We can use one example,

world population in human beings. Approximately 250 years ago there was a world population of some 600 millions; that number has increased over four-fold up to the present time and is now increasing at an unprecedented figure. This means that within the relatively short period of 250 years there has been a tremendous increase in population compared to the preceding period of approximately 500,000 years which produced the number of people alive in 1700. What has been responsible for this sudden burst of reproductive powers in man? Certainly there has been no physical evolution in man himself in so short a time. It is generally agreed that food is one of the limiting factors in the growth of any population, be it fish or man. Populations always encroach upon the food supply just as closely as they can, often with widespread starvation. This increase in population, then, is due in part to increased food production; increased food production has come about through the application of the scientific method to food production problems. This might be all changed again by a single important discovery, for example, an economical method of producing food from inorganic sources, such as sugar from carbon dioxide and water. A discovery such as this would change the entire food problem of the world overnight. Feeding the half-starved world of today is within the realm of possibility now, although if populations increase at the present rate, it is doubtful that even the best efforts of scientists can keep pace in supplying food.

In colonial days the average life span was under 40 years for a man; today it is well over 65. It is not that men are any better physically today than they were then. It is due almost entirely to the progress made by science in understanding the cause and prevention of infectious diseases. All of the advancements that have been made in medicine have been accomplished through the agency of science. Before the scientific method was employed in the study of medicine medical knowledge was largely based on superstition and mysticism. Since the discovery of the Germ Theory of Disease, aseptic surgery, and anesthesia, many of man's ills have been partially or wholly conquered. There is no doubt that many of the infectious as well as organic diseases that plague man today will eventually be eliminated from civilized societies. If man would follow the scientific approach to the solution of his peacetime problems as avidly as he employs it in the preparation of war machinery, this world would unquestionably soon be a better place to live in. Unfortunately, the hope that he will do this seems rather remote at the present time.

It seems clear that the application of the scientific method to the solution of man's physical betterment has been good and bad. It has lifted many burdens from his shoulders by simplifying the work essential for his physical needs; it has extended his average life span also but, at the same time, has provided him with deadly weapons, such as the atomic and hydrogen bombs. He has for the first time an instrument within his grasp that can annihilate the whole of the civilized world as we know it. Such a situation in an uneasy world certainly is not good when considered from the point of view of survival of a race. Perhaps the application of the scientific method to man's social ills might have some of the success it has had in the alleviation of his physical ills.

With all of the wonders that science has produced, it cannot solve all of our problems. We have found no way to measure love, beauty, or the faith people have in God. By common agreement the scientist deals only with the things he can measure, either with his senses directly, or with instruments that magnify his sensitivity, such as the telescope and microscope. The ultimate purposes and goals of life itself are not within the scope of science and must be left to religion and philosophy.

FIELDS OF THE BIOLOGICAL SCIENCES

There are many facets to the fields of biology, each of which has become very specialized today. The oldest field is concerned with the structure and form of plants and animals, and is termed **morphology.** It has several subdivisions. **Anatomy** has to do with gross anatomical structures that can be studied with the naked eye. **Histology** is the study of the microscopic architecture, and **cytology** is the study of cell structure; both involve the use of the microscope. Another branch of morphology is the study of the development of a plant or animal.

The study of living things in respect to their proper classification is known as **taxonomy.** The field which concentrates on the distribution of plants and animals geographically is **biogeography,** and the study of fossil remains is **paleontology.**

Physiology is the study of the manner in which living things function; this phase of biology is more recent and occupies the attention of a great many people in all branches of biology today including agriculture and medicine. It is probably the most fruitful of all in regard to the improvement of our physical shortcomings. **Genetics** is the study of the mechanics of inheritance.

A study of the relation of plants and animals to their environment is known as **ecology.** This is an important phase of biology because it provides the knowledge for the rehabilitation of stocks of wildlife. The science of the mind alone resolves itself in the field of **psychology** and when the study includes the entire animal and its interrelationships, the field is known as **sociology.**

The science of biology is so vast and so specialized that a biologist may spend his entire life effort on one small phase of the subject. For example, the **entomologist** concentrates on insects and may be fairly familiar with a large number of them, but a **dipterologist** is an expert on flies, one order of insects. Likewise, a **parasitologist** may have a nodding acquaintance with many animal parasites, but a **helminthologist** is a specialist on worms, and a **malariologist** confines his work to causative organisms of malaria, which are protozoan parasites. The **mycologist** studies fungi, whereas the **bacteriologist** concentrates on one group of the fungi, namely bacteria. Bacteriologists are further specialized into those that spend their lives studying only one group of bacteria, indeed, perhaps only one species. It is obvious that there are many small segments of the science of biology that occupy the attention of biologists today, and it is from this concerted effort that our knowledge is going forward at a tremendous rate. The possibility for future benefits to mankind is almost limitless, providing man has sufficient intelligence to utilize this knowledge for the advancement of the human race rather than for its destruction.

SUGGESTED SUPPLEMENTARY READINGS

BEVERIDGE, W. I. B., *The Art of Scientific Investigation* (New York, W. W. Norton & Co., 1957).

CANNON, W. B., *Way of an Investigator: A Scientist's Experiences in Medical Research* (New York, W. W. Norton & Co., 1945).

COHEN, I. B., *Science, Servant of Man* (Boston, Little, Brown & Co., 1948).

CONANT, J. B., *Modern Science and Modern Man* (New York, Columbia University Press, 1952).

GABRIEL, M. L. and FOGEL, S., *Great Experiences in Biology* (Englewood Cliffs, N.J., Prentice-Hall, Inc., 1955).

GARDNER, M., *Fads and Fallacies in the Name of Science* (New York, Dover Publications, 1957).

FULTON, J., *Selected Readings in the History of Physiology* (Springfield, Ill., Charles C Thomas, 1930).

HALL, T. S., *A Source Book in Animal Biology* (New York, McGraw-Hill Book Co., Inc., 1951).

HARVEY, W., *Anatomical Studies on the Motion of the Heart and Blood,* translated by C. D. Leake (Springfield, Ill., Charles C Thomas, 1931).

JOHNSON, W. H. and STEERE, W. C., *This is Life* (New York, Holt, Rinehart and Winston, Inc., 1962).

NORDENSKIOLD, E., *The History of Biology* (New York, Alfred A. Knopf, Inc., 1933).

SINGER, Chas:, *A History of Biology* (New York, Schuman, 1950).

PART **II**

Life: Its Beginnings and Nature

2
Early History of Life

THERE IS general agreement among biologists that life originated on the earth and that all of the elements that compose living things have come from the earth and its enveloping atmosphere. Speculations as to how this came about will be considered a little later, but at this point it might be well for us to give a little attention to the components of the earth and the forces that operate which, together, have made life possible. The crust of the earth, where all living things exist, is made up of many elements and compounds, some of which have become an integral part of all living things. The water and the gases which occur abundantly at the surface of the earth are also important, not only in the composition of organisms, but also in influencing their activity. All of the nonliving world obeys certain physical laws, most of which are well known, and these laws also operate within living things. It is important, then, for us to first try to understand how the physical world is put together before we attempt to learn something about the far more complex living objects that exist in such great profusion at its surface.

ORIGIN OF THE EARTH

Astronomers generally agree that our planet was born at least five billion years ago, probably at the time the entire universe came into existence, possibly as a result of one terrific explosion. Along with millions of other solar systems, our particular sun was formed out of a very large, flattened, and highly rarefied mass of gas and dust. Smaller masses of these gases separated from the sun and became the planets which rotated about it. As the rotation proceeded, with the regions nearest the sun moving faster than the outer regions, whirling eddies must have formed in different parts of this tenuous nebula. Although most of the gases and dust probably escaped the solar system, the larger and denser of these whirlpools were able to coalesce by the forces of gravitation and to attract additional matter into them (Fig. 2-1). After some millions of years, these planetary nuclei had grown slowly and steadily by accretion (addition of particles from the outside) into the solid planets that we observe today.

Planet Earth, like all planets and the sun as well, probably started as a glowing mass of various gases, the most abundant of which was hydrogen, the lightest of all atoms. All of the gases existed only in the form of atoms, owing to the tremendously high temperatures that they had attained when the sun and planets were first formed. The sun today is still primarily atomic hydrogen gas and is extremely hot. As a result of gravitational forces the heavier atoms moved toward the center of the sphere and the lighter ones formed shells at succeeding distances from the center. Geophysicists today believe the earth to be composed of three main concentric spheres (Fig. 2-1). The core consists of molten iron, with some nickel, of about 4,000 miles in diameter. This is surrounded by a shell, known as the "mantle" which is 2,000 miles

thick and reaches almost to the surface. It is composed of an iron-magnesium silicate, a heavy green crystalline substance, and even today remains hot throughout. The next solid layer is very thin (10–30 miles in thickness), about the same proportion as the skin of the apple is to the fruit, but this is the only part of the earth with which man has some firsthand information. Its inner portion is composed of basalt (black rock) which provides the floors of our deepest oceans, and the surface consists of granite. The density of these materials decreases as the surface is approached, which means that our continents are essentially floating on the material below.

Even before the earth became a solid sphere, the lightest atoms, such as hydrogen, nitrogen, oxygen, and carbon, remained at the greatest distance from the center. With gradual cooling these atoms reacted among themselves to form molecules. Since hydrogen is the most active it was more likely to combine with the others than they were with one another. Consequently, the first atmosphere was probably composed primarily of water (H_2O), ammonia (NH_3), and methane (CH_4). The energy which was necessary to cause atoms to combine to form molecules probably came as radiant energy from the sun, although the earth itself was still sufficiently hot to provide part of the energy for this fusion.

The early atmosphere probably consisted primarily of water in the form of steam which existed as a thick gaseous layer covering the entire planet. As the steam pushed upward into the cooler regions, condensation occurred, causing dense fog and torrential rains. Eventually, after still further cooling, the rain drops penetrated the heat and reached the hot rocks below, only to evaporate as steam once more. Finally, however, with further cooling, water stayed in the depressions of the earth's extremely wrinkled surface, forming the

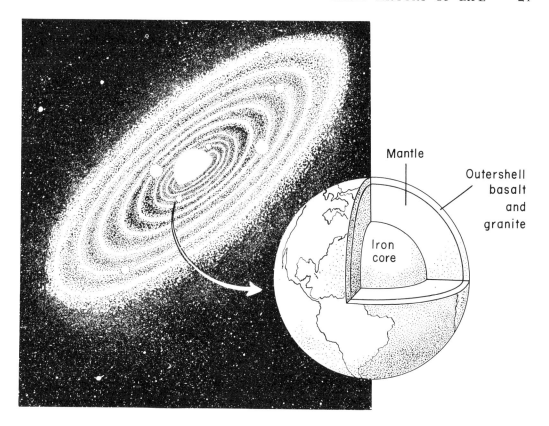

Mantle

Outershell
basalt
and
granite

Iron
core

FIG. 2-1. Planet Earth is one of several planets formed by the condensation of dust clouds encircling the sun. Later it cooled and became a rigid ball. Its inner structure today may be revealed by cutting an imaginary section as indicated. The outer shell is 10–30 miles thick and the mantle about 2,000 miles. The core consists of molten iron.

infant oceans of the world. Hot rivers formed, of course, which were forever rushing to fill the oceans, carrying with them any minerals of the substratum that would dissolve. These substances were deposited in the young oceans, resulting in a constant increase in the chemical composition there. Water evaporated from their great surfaces, just as it does today, leaving the heavier salt particles behind and thus continually raising their total salt content. That is why the ocean water of today is salty. The importance of these great bodies of water lies in the fact that undoubtedly life originated in them sometime during this early period.

The physical and chemical forces operating in the atmosphere and oceans at this early period made it possible for life

to appear later. These warm seas contained an abundance of minerals, but more important they contained dissolved ammonia and methane, two key compounds that, together with water, were the starting molecules for the first living things.

Here, then, we see a spinning new world, sufficiently far from the sun to be warm in most of its parts and fixed in an orbit that insures evenly spaced seasons. Most of its surface is covered with water and that which is exposed consists of rocks, gravel, and sand. No soil has been produced at this early period. A homogeneous gas, rich in nitrogen, envelops its surface, with clouds of water vapor moving slowly with the air currents. This is the setting in which life started, and once started, it spread over most of the earth's surface, becoming ever more diversified as time passed. Among the tremendous numbers of living things that arose, only one, man, evolved who can contemplate his own origin.

THE PHYSICAL NATURE OF THE EARTH

In order that we may understand the origin and nature of life, it is essential that we discuss its chemical composition and the physical laws that operate in the universe. Knowledge of these must precede any discussion of the beginning and subsequent development of life because all living things were derived from the inanimate world, and to study living things without this knowledge would be meaningless. The following discussion involves only the most elementary information in the fields of chemistry and physics. For some students this will be a review, and for others it may be the first contact with these fields. In the latter case some extra effort will be required to master the elementary principles set forth in the following pages. For both groups it is important that these principles be mastered before biological principles are considered.

Matter

Everything in the universe is composed of **matter,** which occupies **space** and has **mass.** Mass may be defined as the amount of matter in a body which can be measured in terms of resistance to change of motion. This is more meaningful when it is considered in the light of attraction between bodies. Bodies attract one another according to their respective masses. For example, the earth has a greater attraction (gravity) for a man than does the moon because the earth has greater mass. We have a convenient method of measuring this attractive force between bodies; we call it **weight.** Weight, of course, changes, depending on where it is taken. A person weighing 180

pounds on the earth would weigh 30 pounds on the moon, although his mass would be the same. Weight simply measures the pull of **gravity.**

Animal bodies are constructed to compensate for the pull of gravity. For example, small animals, such as mice, have relatively light skeletons in comparison to their weights, whereas larger animals, such as the elephant, have much heavier skeletons with respect to weight. This fact limits the size of animals, for should they go on increasing in bulk, they would reach a point where the skeleton alone could not bear its own weight. If life, as we know it, occurs on other planets, it too would show relation to weight. Animals on Jupiter, for example, would have to be constructed on an entirely different plan from those on the earth, because the pull of gravity is so much greater. They would probably be heavily boned animals and greatly flattened.

One cannot mention the motion of matter without referring to another force that operates on bodies, namely, **inertia.** When a swift elevator starts up, one is conscious of a sudden increase in weight; likewise, when it comes to rest, one seems suddenly and momentarily lighter than usual. There may be a simultaneous peculiar feeling in the mid-section as the internal organs respond to the effects of inertia. This force is the resistance of a body to change in its rate of motion. If standing still, it resists movement; if moving at a certain rate of speed it resists any change in this rate. That is why we need low gear and good brakes on our cars—it requires more power to get started or to stop than to keep rolling.

Most animals are little affected by inertia except when suddenly stopped, such as a bird flying into the side of a building. The sudden cessation of forward motion can be fatal to bird or man, as attested by car accidents. Another modern machine that brings the effects of inertia into prominence is the airplane. Pilots often "black out" because their forward motion is suddenly changed, as in coming out of a power dive. The blood, being fluid, tends to follow the forward motion it has attained and is thus pulled away from the head, causing the "black out" or faint. The normal movements of animals are little affected by inertia, and the problem arises in man only when he steps into one of his mechanical contrivances which carry his body faster than it was made to go.

Surface Phenomena

The behavior of matter depends to a large extent on its surface area. Large bodies have smaller surface areas in proportion to volume than do small bodies. A mouse has more surface area in respect to its volume than does an elephant. This can easily be computed by simply measuring the surface area of a cube, say 10 inches on a side or 600 square inches, and then its volume, which is 1,000 cubic inches (Fig. 2-2). This is a ratio of 0.6 square inch of surface to every cubic inch of volume. If a cube one inch on a side is cut out of the larger cube, and the surface computed in respect to the volume, it will be found that each inch cube will have 6 square inches of surface, a tenfold increase. Since chemical reactions may take place at surfaces, it is obvious that the activity will be much greater as matter is divided into smaller and smaller particles. This is a very important physical property, as we shall see when we discuss enzyme action and many other activities that go on within the animal body. This principle is also important in body heat loss in animals. Large warm-blooded animals have little difficulty in securing sufficient food to maintain their constant body temperature; but very small animals, such as the shrews, must eat the equivalent of their own body weight in food each day in order to remain active and keep warm. The relatively large surface area in proportion to volume of these tiny creatures results in an extremely rapid heat loss. The shrew

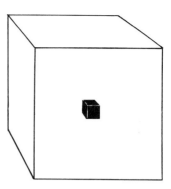

Fig. 2-2. Two cubes, one with dimensions 1/10th of the other. In proportion to volume, the smaller has 10 times the surface area of the larger.

probably has reached the limit in small size for a mammal.

Particles of matter, especially small particles where the effect is more apparent, attract one another of the same kind and also have an attraction for other particles of a different sort. The first is given the name **cohesion,** and the latter **adhesion.** Particles of matter such as water tend to cling together to the extent that they actually form a film at their surfaces. This gives the effect of a stretched membrane and is spoken of as **surface tension.** Water has a rather high surface tension, but mercury surpasses it by a considerable margin. It is well known that when mercury is dropped it breaks up into hundreds of small perfect spheres. Water gives a similar but lesser response when dropped on a dry, dusty surface. Rain drops are usually near-spheres. Liquids, when free of external forces, will assume the shape of a sphere because the cohesive forces of the particles of which they are made form a surface membrane. This fact makes it possible for certain species of insects to walk on the water (Fig. 2-3). Their bodies are light and the weight is distributed over a large area, so that the cohesive force of the water is sufficiently strong to keep the membrane intact.

Adhesive forces are simultaneously at

FIG. 2-3. Some insects, like the water strider, can walk on water because their evenly spread weight is not sufficiently great to break the surface tension.

work with cohesive forces. These have no significant influence on large bodies, but on small particles they become very important, just as important as gravity is to the larger bodies. Certain gaseous molecules, for example, will adhere to carbon particles so tenaciously that it requires high temperatures to remove them; this is the principle of the gas mask and certain purification processes. It is important in biological systems where enzymes, for example, adhere or **adsorb** (the process is called adsorption) to food particles, thus enhancing digestion. This physical property of matter manifests itself in many ways in the bodies of animals.

Composition of Matter

The ancient Greeks conceived of the universe as being composed of four **elements:** fire, air, water, and earth. This idea persisted until the eighteenth century when it was shown that water could be separated into two components, hydrogen and oxygen, both gases and neither one resembling water. Likewise air was found to be composed of several gases, the two most important being nitrogen and oxygen. From these experiments it was obvious that the meaning of element had to change to something less than originally thought. The term still persists today and is defined as the simplest form of matter that possesses specific chemical properties. An element cannot be de-

composed into simpler particles with unique "chemical" properties. However, the reduction of elements to lesser particles has been accomplished, but that will be discussed later.

Atoms. The universe is composed of 92 naturally occurring elements, although scientists have produced eleven more in the laboratory. The **atom** is the smallest unit of matter that possesses all of the chemical properties of an element. Physicists have been occupied in recent years studying the structure of atoms; consequently we know a great deal about these units. The atom is composed of still smaller particles, units which have been weighed, counted, checked for speed, and measured for their electrical properties. The signi-

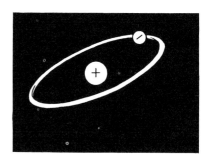

FIG. 2-4. The possible structure of the hydrogen atom. The proton with its positive charge lies at the center and the negatively charged electron revolves about it.

ficance of atomic structure came to the attention of everyone when physicists were able to manipulate atoms in such a manner as to have them release tremendous amounts of energy in the form of atomic explosions.

One might think of the atom as a miniature solar system with its relatively large heavy **nucleus,** the "sun," and its revolving **electrons,** the "planets" (Fig. 2-4). Reminiscent of the universe, the most striking characteristic of an atom is the vast amount of space between the various particles of which

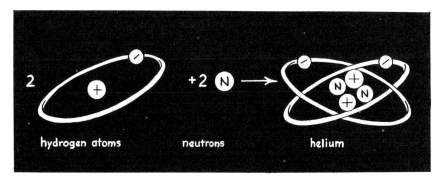

FIG. 2-5. A hypothetical explanation of how helium is formed by the combination of two neutrons with two hydrogen atoms.

it is composed. If we imagine the atom to be the size of a balloon 100 feet in diameter, it would appear as a hazy, transparent sphere. At the center would appear a nucleus, the only clearly visible part, about the size of a small marble. The electrons would be invisible, but because of their terrific speed they would appear as a dim blur, giving a vague limit to the entire structure. In some atoms there would be other concentric rings within the outer shell and these would appear as hazy as the outer shell; they might be intertwined with one another. Only the speed of the electrons would make these limits apparent, because the electrons themselves seem to have very little, if any, mass. They are "intangible units of energy," whirling at unimaginable speeds, yet maintaining remarkable stability. Atoms can be "smashed," as we all know, if unbelievable amounts of energy are directed at them. As a result of "smashing," the nature of the atom itself changes.

The nucleus of the atom consists of a dense cluster of positively charged particles, **protons,** and uncharged particles, **neutrons** (Fig. 2-5). These are held together by some unexplained intra-nuclear force. The protons and neutrons make up almost all of the mass of the atom. For every positively charged particle (proton) in the nucleus there is an **electron,** which carries a negative charge, in one of the orbits. Thus the total atom is neutral, that is, it carries no apparent charge. It is interesting to note that all of the 92 elements are made up of these units, differing one from another only because of the relative number and arrangements of protons, neutrons, and electrons.

A specific atom behaves the way it does because of the number of protons and neutrons in its nucleus and the number of electrons in its orbits. While there is always the same number of protons in the nucleus as there are electrons in the orbits, there may be a varying number of neutrons present in any specific atom. Since the chemical characteristics of the atom are controlled by the electrons in the outer shell or orbit, and since the number of electrons is controlled by the number of protons at the center, any additional neutrons will be without effect on the chemical properties of the atom. The only difference will be in its weight. Physicists have found that they can add or knock out neutrons as well as electrons, and thus change the physical properties of the atom itself. When only the number of neutrons is changed the resulting atom is called an **isotope;** isotopes have the same **chemical properties** as the naturally occurring atom but they have different weights, and therefore can be identified or "tagged." Tagging atoms has made it possible to trace various chemicals through the animal body. This has been very helpful in determining what happens to certain substances in normal life processes. If the isotope happens to be radioactive, that is, if it happens to give off radiations that can be detected with a sensitive instrument (Geiger counter) or by some other means, then the problem of tracing the chemical becomes less difficult. We are gaining a great deal of knowledge today from this type of so-called tracer research, and the future holds out much promise in this field of investigation.

It would seem simple, then, to arrange all of the various elements in a series from 1 to 103, according to the number of electrons (or protons) in each individual atom. This has been done and we call such an arrangement the **periodic table.** It is possible to diagram this atomic sequence (Fig. 2-6). The **atomic number** corresponds to the number of electrons in the orbits, or the number of protons in the nucleus, limited in range, of course, from 1 to 103. The **atomic weights** are arbitrary figures assigned to each atom, and they depend on the number of protons and neutrons in the nucleus. Oxygen has been assigned the figure 16 and others all vary in respect to it. Since a single atom cannot be weighed, these figures must be based on measurements that include a great many individual atoms, and hence are not absolute figures.

There are seven possible concentric

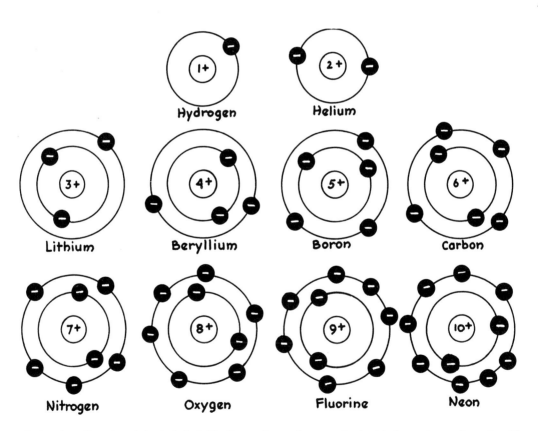

FIG. 2-6. A small portion of the Periodic Table. The number at the center (nucleus) indicates the atomic number. The electrons lie in the orbits, of which only two are shown here. The inner orbit requires only two electrons while the second needs eight, which is satisfied in neon. Of the ten elements indicated, hydrogen, carbon, nitrogen, and oxygen are important constituents of living material.

rings of electrons among all of the atoms, the one closest to the nucleus containing two electrons, and each of those beyond having varying numbers. Hydrogen has one proton and one electron but contains no neutrons. It has the atomic number 1. Helium, the next in the series, has two electrons and, therefore, the atomic number is 2. However, it has an atomic weight of four, because it also has two neutrons in its nucleus along with the two protons. Lithium starts a new outer orbit containing one electron; thus, with its two inner electrons and the one in the outer orbit, it has three altogether, giving it the atomic number 3. Sodium (not shown in Fig. 2-6) is the first atom that has a third ring, with 11 electrons in all. Usually the inner ring must be completed before the next one is formed. Following this principle the numbers of protons, neutrons, and electrons of nearly all 103 elements have been determined.

When the number of electrons in the outer orbit is less than half the total number it can hold, it may lose them, or if it has more than half, it may gain others to complete the ring. Any change in these numbers of electrons changes the electrical nature of the atom; if it gains electrons it becomes negative, and if it loses electrons it becomes positive. Whenever the atom is out of balance in respect to its electrons it is an **ion;** if it possesses an excess of electrons it is called an **anion** (because if placed in an electrical field it will move to the positive pole, the anode); if it has lost electrons it is known as a **cation** (because it moves to the negative pole, the cathode). A solution containing ions will conduct an electric current and the compound producing them is called an **electrolyte.**

Of all the atoms in living things, carbon certainly is the most important. This may be due in part to its physical make-up. It possesses just one half the maximum number of electrons in its outer shell, which means that it does not lose or gain others.

It unites with a large variety of other atoms by simply sharing its electrons. This arrangement permits combination with other carbon atoms to produce long chains or rings which may then join up with a large variety of other atoms to produce immense molecules. It was undoubtedly this nature of carbon that made it the central atom around which life was built. We find it an integrated part of all biological systems and playing important roles, not only in the construction of living materials, but also in storing and releasing energy which is essential in life processes.

Molecules. Atoms almost never exist singly in nature; they are usually found in combination with other similar atoms or with different atoms. When such a combination of like or unlike atoms occurs a **molecule** is formed. For example, hydrogen in the gaseous state consists of two identical atoms, hence is designated as H_2; likewise, the gas produced by living things called carbon dioxide is composed of one atom of carbon and two of oxygen, hence is designated as CO_2. Molecules that are composed of two or more different atoms are called **compounds.**

It is useful in studying compounds in living things to be able to express them quantitatively. This can be done in very precise terms. As mentioned earlier the atomic weight is the sum of the masses of the protons and neutrons. When this number is expressed in grams, it is referred to as the **gram atomic weight.** The number of atoms in a gram atomic weight is 6.02×10^{23}, a fantastically large number. The usefulness of this number becomes apparent when we learn that the atomic weights of all elements have exactly the same number of atoms. For instance, one gram of hydrogen has the same number of atoms as does 16 grams of oxygen. This information is useful in computing the composition of compounds. For example, we know that in CO_2 one atom of carbon combines with 2 atoms of oxygen. Both carbon and oxygen have the same number of atoms but since their gram atomic weights are 12 for carbon and 16 for oxygen, it will require 32 grams of oxygen to react with 12 grams of carbon. Similarly, the **molecular weight** is the sum of the atomic weights of the atoms in a molecule. When this is expressed in grams, it is referred to as the **gram molecular weight,** or **mole.** This means that the number of molecules in a mole of any compound is equal to the number of atoms in a gram atomic weight of that compound; for example, 32 grams of oxygen has the same number of molecules as does 44 grams of CO_2 or 18 grams of water. The value in this observation is that when one compound reacts with another in a ratio of one to one, it becomes possible to calculate the weights of the reacting compounds. Consider the reaction that takes place when carbon dioxide (CO_2) is bubbled through water (H_2O), forming carbonic acid (H_2CO_3). Chemists have devised a kind of shorthand to express this reaction:

$$H_2O + CO_2 \rightarrow H_2CO_3$$

A reaction expressed in this form is called an equation because the compounds on one side of the arrow are equal to those on the other side. This equation can be read to mean that one mole of water reacts with one mole of carbon dioxide to give one mole of carbonic acid. By substituting gram molecular weights the equation reads: 18 grams of water reacts with 44 grams of carbon dioxide to produce 62 grams of carbonic acid. The usefulness of this information is obvious when certain unknowns are present in the equation because one can compute their exact quantities. Reactions always occur in whole-number proportions of moles; that is 1:1 or 1:2, etc., regardless of the molecular weights of the compounds. Now let us consider how atoms combine to form molecules.

Molecules, under certain conditions, tend to dissociate into their constituent ions. For example, in water the electrons shared by hydrogen and oxygen are more firmly attached to the oxygen atom than the hydrogen (Fig. 2-7). Because of the high rate of velocity of their spin there is a slight tendency for the molecule to fall apart. As a result the nucleus (proton) of one hydrogen atom separates leaving the remainder of the molecule which consists of an oxygen atom, a hydrogen atom, and the surplus electron. This is indicated as follows:

$$H_2O \rightleftarrows H^+ + OH^-$$

These products are referred to as the **hydrogen** (H^+) and the **hydroxyl** (OH^-) **ions.** The hydrogen ion is simply a proton. Both ions wander about in the water independent of one another. Water dissociates into its ions only very slightly (at any one time in pure water, one molecule out of 200 million) and since they are always equal in number any effect they might have goes unnoticed. Since all living things are composed of large quantities of water one might expect that any unequal quantities of these two ions might be detrimental, which is the case.

In some hydrogen-containing compounds there is a much greater tendency for the protons of hydrogen to separate from the remainder of the molecule than is the case with water. Such ionized compounds are called **acids,** and they are classified as strong or weak depending on the percentage of protons produced. Sulfuric (H_2SO_4), nitric (HNO_3), and hydrochloric (HCl) are strong acids because each molecule yields a proton since they dissociate completely in water. In weak acids such as acetic acid (CH_3COOH), only 0.1 per cent of the molecules dissociate.

Hydroxyl ions are likewise produced when compounds which contain them are dissolved in water. Such compounds are called **bases** and they react with acids to produce **salts.** For example, sodium hydroxide ($NaOH$) when dissolved in water dissociates completely to form sodium (Na^+)

and hydroxyl (OH⁻) ions. If these are then mixed with hydrochloric acid the hydrogen and hydroxyl ions react to form water and the sodium and chloride ions remain in solution. If the water is removed by evaporation salt crystals (NaCl) will form.

Living things will not tolerate even small excesses of either hydrogen or hydroxyl ions. This is understandable since they are composed primarily of water which contains very few of these ions; those that are present exist in equal numbers. For this

in excess the solution is said to be acid and are indicated by (pH) numbers less than 7.0; numbers higher than 7.0 indicate a basic solution, that is, a solution in which the OH⁻ ions are in excess. An indication of the importance of these figures becomes clear when we note that human blood has a pH of 7.45; if it rises to 7.6 or drops to 7.2, death results.

Chemical Reactions. Let us recall the structure of atoms. Atoms will unite to form

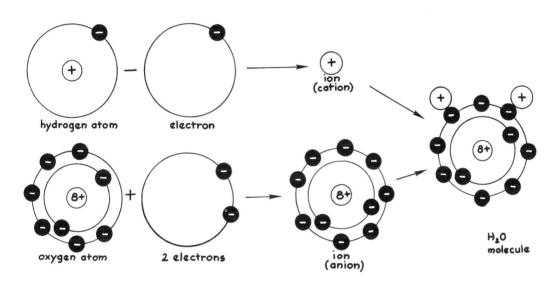

FIG. 2-7. A possible explanation for the formation of a molecule of water from two atoms of hydrogen and one of oxygen. Note that the hydrogen ion is a naked proton, and the oxygen ion is formed by the addition of two electrons. The union of the two kinds of ions produces the molecule of water.

reason biologists have found it necessary to find some method of detecting these ions in a very precise manner. This is done by several methods, the most precise being to measure the electrical conductivity of the solution. Such an instrument is called a pH (hydrogen potential) meter, which measures the number of hydrogen ions (protons) present at any specific time in solution. An arbitrary pH scale extends from 0 to 14, in which a pH of 7.0 means that the numbers of H⁺ and OH⁻ ions are equal, as they are in pure water. When the H⁺ ions are

molecules depending on the number of electrons they can deliver or consume in their ionic state. For example, the potassium atom has 19 electrons; when it loses one electron it becomes a potassium ion. The bromine atom lacks one electron in its outer shell; when this is gained it becomes a bromide ion, an anion (p. 27). When the potassium and bromide ions are present in the same system, they are brought together because "unlike charges attract"; since bromine requires one electron to complete its outer shell, one potassium atom is required to do the job. The result is a molecule of potassium bromide, a stable compound. In general the reaction takes place between different atoms because certain combinations of electrons associated with specific atoms are more stable than others. Among the most common elements found in organisms, stability is accomplished when the number of electrons is two, ten, or eighteen. Those with fewer or greater are the most reactive because in acquiring or losing electrons, they become stable. Reactions always move in the direction to provide stable end-products. For example, sodium with 11 electrons, tends to react with chlorine which has 17, the former having one more electron than the stable number (10) and the latter, one less (18). They react and satisfy the deficiency of each, producing a stable compound, sodium chloride (table salt). The sodium chloride is found to weigh exactly the same as the sodium and chlorine from which it was derived; hence, nothing was gained or lost. This is the **law of the conservation of matter.**

Chemical reactions also obey another rule, called the **law of the conservation of energy,** which means that neither mass nor energy can be created or destroyed. This can be observed by measuring the amount of heat that is liberated when hydrogen combines with oxygen to form water; indeed this may be an explosive reaction because both atoms are very unstable. In this reaction energy is released and when this happens it is called an **exergonic reaction.** On the other hand if electrical energy is applied by means of electrodes (electrolysis) to water the molecule can be degraded into its component parts, namely hydrogen and oxygen. However, this requires as much energy as was released when the gases combined to form water. This type of reaction is called an **endergonic reaction.** Since there is no loss or gain in energy in these reactions it is obvious that the law of conservation of energy holds. Whereas this law per-

tains to all living systems, scientists in recent years have been able to convert matter to energy by changing the nuclei of atoms, which has been most spectacularly dramatized in atomic bombs. Since these reactions have little to do with living things (except in the destruction of them) we shall not consider them in our discussion.

It will be noted that the conversion of water to hydrogen and oxygen, or the opposite reaction, the combination of hydrogen and oxygen to form water, is a so-called **reversible reaction.** This is theoretically true of all reactions. This concept then can be written symbolically:

$$A + B \rightleftarrows C + D$$

in which A and B are the starting compounds and C and D the final products. The significant aspect of this concept is that energy is consumed or released depending upon which way the reaction goes. If energy is required for it to move to the right, the same amount of energy will be released when it goes to the left. This is an important principle with which we shall be confronted again and again in living systems.

Properties of Matter

Matter exists in space in one of the three forms: **solids, liquids,** or **gases.** Water is a convenient example of matter. Below freezing ($^-0°C$) it exists as ice, a solid; between freezing and boiling (0°C and 100°C at sea level), it exists as water, a liquid; above boiling (+100°C at sea level) it exists as a vapor or steam, a gas. In all of these states the substance is still water, its chemical composition is unchanged. The particular state in which matter exists depends on the speed of the movement of the individual molecules. In the solid state they vibrate, but stay in fixed positions within the solid; in the liquid state they move faster and are free to move about within the liquid, whereas in the gaseous state they attain high speeds, so high that they exceed the intermolecular attractions and separate from one another to become independent free-moving bodies. The rate of molecular movement is reflected in the phenomenon of **temperature.** Molecules move faster in hot bodies than in cold ones. When there is no movement the body is as cold as it is possible to get, a condition called **absolute zero** ($-273°C$).

All specific chemical substances exhibit the same changes in state that water does, although they are not always so easy to observe. There are thousands of different kinds of matter, each composed of a specific kind of molecule, such as oxygen, hydrogen, or water. Since life is composed of matter, it must then also be composed of different kinds of molecules, and the properties of these molecules must be reflected in the properties of living things.

It is the various combinations of elements that make up all the thousands of chemical substances existing naturally or that can be produced in the laboratory. For example, glucose (blood sugar) is a complex molecule. It is written this way: $C_6H_{12}O_6$, which means that it is composed of 6 atoms of carbon, 12 of hydrogen, and 6 of oxygen. It is obvious that with 103 building units millions of combinations of atoms are conceivable. Many of these molecules appear in living things and it is necessary to know something about their individual behavior in order to have some understanding about their combined effect as it occurs in a cell. Chemists have been studying these for a long time, and their knowledge is so significant to the study of animals that today zoologists are dependent to a large extent on this information to aid them in solving some of their complex problems.

The arrangement of atoms in a molecule gives to that molecule its properties. Sugar is sugar because of the arrangement of the atoms in its molecule. If any of the atoms are removed or even changed in their respective positions within the molecule, the substance is no longer the same; the properties are different. For example, if the hydrogen and oxygen in the water molecule are separated, we no longer have water but two gases, neither of which acts like water in any way. When the molecules are all alike, we speak of the aggregate as a **substance;** if, however, there are several different kinds of molecules or substances present, we refer to the combined material as a **mixture.** A lump of sugar is a substance; when it is placed in a cup of coffee, the result is a mixture. The sugar exhibits specific properties which are always the same, whereas a mixture displays variable properties. Living things are composed of mixtures and therefore respond as mixtures. Mixtures are much more difficult to understand than substances, and because life exists in a mixture, a very complex mixture, it likewise is difficult to understand.

With this background let us now discuss how life might have come into existence on the earth.

ORIGIN OF LIFE

Once the earth reached a relatively stable condition, the stage was set for the beginning of this most remarkable drama, the inception and subsequent unfolding of life in all of its variety and complexity. It was once thought that life might have come to earth through interstellar space, originating from some other planet. This seems unlikely because of the intense heat it would endure en route. Life as we know it certainly would be destroyed by such high temperatures. One of the greatest problems facing space scientists today is the so-called re-entry problem. Once a body enters the atmosphere at high speeds it burns to incandescence, thus destroying any life that might be inside. However, with continued success in the realm of space travel, a new interpretation of the origin of life on earth may be considered.

It is possible that life evolved to a very high state on other planets, resulting in organisms with very high intelligence who travelled freely in space. Such intellectuals could have visited our planet when it was young and inhospitable. Finding it uninhabitable they departed, leaving behind spores of certain forms of life which subsequently gave rise to all life that we see today through the process of evolution. Perhaps with this in mind scientists are urging the sterilization of rockets intended for the moon or the planets. Of even more importance, the rocket on the return trip should be free of all life that might contaminate our earth.

Whereas the above notion is certainly possible, let us speculate as to how life might have originated on the earth without reference to extraplanetary influence. Geologists tell us that there was a time about 2 billion years ago when conditions were such that life could have started. Those conditions do not exist today, so it is unlikely that life is being generated now. Assuming that life did take its inception a very long time ago on this planet, let us consider the most logical steps that could have taken place. Many scientists, among the first of whom were Oparin (a Russian) and Haldane (an Englishman), have given a great deal of thought to this problem and together have formulated a theory which is backed up by some experimental evidence. Let us follow their thinking and in doing so we shall learn a great deal about the fundamental nature of living things. As plausible as this theory may seem, it is far from proven, and it is improbable that satisfactory proof will ever be forthcoming.

From our earlier discussion we learned that the first atmosphere contained large quantities of water (H_2O), ammonia (NH_3) and methane (CH_4) and that the young oceans contained the latter two gases as well as dissolved minerals. It was in these bodies of water that reactions among the numerous contained chemicals took place, from which the first living forms emerged.

Carbon Compounds. The versatile carbon atom (Fig. 2-6) was the element around which life was initiated. It has a bonding capacity of 4, as illustrated with methane:

Any one or all of the H atoms can be replaced with other atoms, for example:

Methyl chloride   Chloroform   Carbon tetrachloride

Obviously these are all radically different compounds. Other atoms may replace the H atoms, producing a large variety of compounds. Methane also may react with itself, forming short or long chains, or the end carbons of a chain may combine forming a ring:

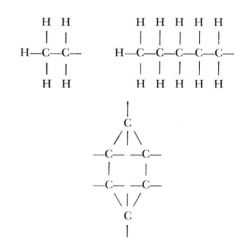

The chains may branch and be combined with other chains or with rings occupying three as well as two dimensions. The free bonds of these carbon skeletons combine with other atoms, thus making innumerable complex compounds each with its own distinctive properties.

The opportunity was present in the young oceans for these reactions to take place and we assume that they did. Methane was in great abundance at this time which made possible the linkage of carbon atoms to one another and to other substances, indeed such combinations still go on in living things. Such carbon-containing compounds occur almost exclusively in matter which either is alive or has been alive at one time. Consequently, such molecules are called **organic** compounds to distinguish them from **inorganic** compounds which contain no linked carbon atoms, such as metals, salts, water, and minerals. The nonliving world is composed of inorganic compounds, although some of them have become a part of living matter and play a very important part in the fabric of all living things.

Prelife Compounds. Whereas a great many compounds were undoubtedly formed in the early seas, a few became precursors to life. These can be grouped into four classes of compounds all of which are conspicuous in living things today. They probably were very simple at first but with time they became very complex as they formed the structure of living matter, which itself became complex.

Sugars and Polysaccharides. Perhaps some of the first and simplest reactions were those between methane and water producing short carbon chains and involving only the atoms C, H, and O. Since the latter two came from water the ratio of 2 H's to 1 O was maintained. These compounds are called **carbohydrates,** two of the most familiar being **glucose** and **fructose.** They are composed of a chain of 6 carbons to which 12 atoms of hydrogen and 6 of oxygen are combined in the following configurations:

Glucose

Fructose

Most sugars (called **monosaccharides**) contain 6 carbons, although some very important ones have only 5 as we shall soon see. Moreover, sugars may combine with one another by the simple process of losing a molecule of water, which is called **condensation.** For example, a molecule of fructose and one of glucose can combine to form one molecule of **sucrose,** a **disaccharide** (double sugar) as follows:

$$C_6H_{12}O_6 + C_6H_{12}O_6 \underset{+ H_2O}{\overset{- H_2O}{\rightleftharpoons}} C_{12}H_{22}O_{11}$$

Fructose   Glucose   Sucrose

Incidentally, the sucrose molecule can fall apart by the simple addition of water. This process is **hydrolysis** which, as we shall see later (see p. 522) is important in digestion. Many glucose molecules, as well as other sugars, can combine in this fashion forming huge molecules, called **polysaccharides.** Some familiar polysaccharides are **starch** (plants) and **glycogen** (animals). These molecules are important as building materials and as sources of chemical energy for living matter.

Glycerol, Fatty Acids, and Fats. Several other compounds were formed from C, H, and O atoms. The simplest of these is **glycerol,** consisting of 3 carbons to which

8 hydrogens and 3 oxygens are attached. Another group of compounds are the **fatty acids** in which the carbon atoms are arranged in chains, from 2 to 18 or even more. There are many fatty acids and in all of them H atoms are attached to all of the carbon atoms except the last one to which 2 O atoms are attached, one of which is combined with another H atom. In water a hydrogen ion is freed which gives the molecule its acidic properties. Glycerol and a general fatty acid have the following configurations:

$$
\begin{array}{c}
H \\
H-C-OH \\
H-C-OH \\
H-C-OH \\
H
\end{array}
$$

Glycerol

$$
\begin{array}{c}
H\ H\ H \qquad\qquad H\ H \qquad\quad O \\
H-C-C-C ------ C-C-C \\
\qquad\qquad\qquad\qquad\qquad\qquad\quad OH \\
H\ H\ H \qquad\qquad H\ H \qquad\ H
\end{array}
$$

Fatty acid

Fatty acids and glycerol may have combined in the early oceans to form **fats** of various kinds. Fats are complex molecules which were used in the architecture of living material and served as excellent sources of energy. They possess less oxygen than the polysaccharides.

Glycerol and fatty acids combine to form **fats** by the loss of water, just as sugars do to form polysacharides. Likewise the fat molecule can be degraded to fatty acids and glycerol by the addition of water.

$$
C_3H_8O_3 + 3\ C_{18}H_{36}O_2 \underset{+H_2O}{\overset{-H_2O}{\rightleftarrows}} C_{57}H_{110}O_6 + 3\ H_2O
$$

Glycerol   Stearic acid   Fat

Amino Acids and Proteins. Another group of compounds formed which was composed of not only C, H, and O atoms but N atoms as well. These are called **amino acids.** They are identified by the presence of at least one NH_2 group, the **amino group,** which probably came from NH_3 (ammonia) by the loss of one H atom. These may be illustrated by the simplest one, glycine:

$$
\begin{array}{c}
H \qquad H \qquad O \\
N-C-C \\
H \qquad H \qquad OH
\end{array}
$$

Glycine

Amino acids also combined in many ways forming the most highly complex of all compounds, the **proteins.** These molecules became the most important of all in the fabrication of living material. Today we find over 20 amino acids which make up the structure of all living things; hence in the early days of the earth at least this many were formed. Amino acids can combine in a large variety of patterns, forming an almost infinite number of proteins. Since they can possess thousands of amino acids, protein molecules reach great sizes, indeed they are the largest and most complex of all molecules. This is important because we see in the proteins a means by which a great variety of living matter can be constructed; hence through the building of protein molecules a system was initiated from the very beginning by which living things could be different from one another, and this they are.

Proteins are formed from amino acids in much the same way that polysaccharides and fats are formed, namely by the loss of water. However, the linking together of the amino acids is done in a special way which we shall discuss later (see p. 53). For simplicity at this point we shall merely say:

$$
\text{Amino acids} + \text{amino acids} \underset{+H_2O}{\overset{-H_2O}{\rightleftarrows}} \text{Proteins}
$$

Some special protein molecules which are an integral part of the process that brought about living matter must have come into existence at this early period. These we now call **enzymes** and we shall have much more to say about them later. At this point we need only consider the fact that in order for reactions to take place high temperatures are often required, temperatures that far exceed those compatible with life. If the reactions we have been talking about and many others occurred, some conditions other than heat must have been present. In the laboratory we can create necessary conditions by the use of **catalysts** which are substances that speed up reactions. Enzymes are such catalysts which operate in living systems; indeed these special proteins must have appeared as some of the very first proteins because they were essential in bringing about the multitude of reactions that were to follow in the synthesis of the first living things.

Purines, Pyrimidines, and Nucleotides. Other compounds were formed which contained molecular skeletons composed of rings; these were the **pyrimidines** with one ring and the **purines** with a double ring, thus:

Pyrimidine

Purine

These compounds combined with two other substances, a sugar with 5 carbons and phosphate (PO_4), forming complexes called **nucleotides.** They may be designated as **pyrimidine-sugar-phosphate** and **purine-sugar-phosphate.** This tendency to combine continued with nucleotides uniting with one another forming highly varied and exceedingly complex macromolecules called **nucleic acids.** Finally, as you might expect, a pinnacle was reached in chemical synthesis when the tremendously complex nucleic acids united with the equally complex protein molecules to form **nucleoproteins.** We may indicate these steps as follows:

Pyrimidines + sugar + phosphate $\longrightarrow$ nucleotides
Purines + sugar + phosphate $\longrightarrow$ nucleotides
Nucleotides + nucleotides $\rightarrow$ nucleic acids
Nucleic acids + proteins $\rightarrow$ nucleoproteins

It was with the formation of the nucleoproteins that the probability of life was assured, because as we shall see later, they were sufficiently complex for a living system to be built around them. As plausible as this story so far may seem, it would be helpful if some experimental evidence could be found that would support it.

It would seem feasible to simulate in the laboratory the conditions that existed during early geological time and to attempt to find some of the molecules that were synthesized then. This Professor Urey and his students did. They heated the gases ammonia, methane, and hydrogen in the presence of water and an electrical discharge simulating lightning which produces ultraviolet light (Fig. 2-8). After several weeks of this treatment a number of amino acids, as well as other organic compounds were recovered from the contained fluids. This simple experiment offers convincing evidence for the assumption that life could have been synthesized from simple compounds.

The energy source for synthesis was primarily ultra violet light which could come both from the sun and from lightning

To
Vacuum
Pump

H₂
CH₄
NH₃
H₂O

Electrical
Discharge

Steam

Cooling
Jacket

FIG. 2-8. The apparatus built by Urey and Miller to simulate conditions at the surface of the young earth.

screening effect of the atmosphere. Consequently, fewer and fewer organic molecules were formed, and a time was reached when there must have been complete cessation of chemical synthesis. This situation once reached might have stayed that way indefinitely had not the nucleoprotein molecules begun to reproduce themselves. Just how this is done we shall discuss in detail in a later chapter. Once this happened the simpler molecules, such as sugars, amino acids, fatty acids, etc., served as raw materials in the manufacture of the larger nucleoprotein molecules. Today we would think of them as nutrients, the food essential for life. Because no more of these food molecules were being synthesized one would imagine that within a period of time the oceans would contain only nucleoproteins. This, however, was not the case, as we shall see later.

Nucleoprotein molecules are very complex, consisting of thousands of atoms. It is not difficult to imagine that occasionally, one molecule might be formed with one or more of its atoms misplaced or deleted completely. Such a molecule might not be able to assemble its molecular food in producing more nucleoprotein molecules quite as effectively as other molecules. Or, conversely it might be able to do the job better. In any case it would be different from the majority and thus have an advantage or a disadvantage in reproducing itself. This would mean that it would be more or less successful than its fellows and would either increase or decrease in numbers disproportionately. The end result would be that those that were more successful in gathering food and in reproducing would gradually replace those that were less successful in these two important functions.

What we have just been discussing is the essence of **organic evolution,** which biologists believe is the underlying principle that has been responsible for the development of life from the simplest to the most complex forms.

which was violent as the earth was cooling. Whereas in the experiment mentioned above, which took place in three weeks, only relatively simple compounds were formed, it is conceivable that if comparable conditions existed for millions of years a great variety of simple as well as very complex compounds would be formed (Fig. 2–9). It is assumed that in this manner complex supermolecules were synthesized into nucleoproteins.

As time passed the source of energy gradually diminished owing to decreased electrical activity in the clouds and the

Energy Sources. When the ultraviolet decreased to a point where it could no longer serve as a source of energy for the synthesis of the food molecules, a new energy source had to be utilized if organisms were to survive. We are familiar with the fact that the combination of oxygen with other molecules (oxidation) is an excellent source of energy but at this early period there was probably no free oxygen in the atmosphere. It is thought that oxygen appeared after living things were well established on earth. Previous to the dawn of life all oxygen was tied up in the form of oxides, water, and organic compounds. One source of energy available to the nucleoproteins for reproduction at this early period was that locked up in smaller molecules already in existence. The most likely candidates

were the energy-rich sugar molecules because they could be easily broken apart releasing their stored energy.

Fermentation. Splitting the sugar molecule into two fragments we now call **fermentation,** and this process might well have been the first by which energy was released from molecules. The manner in which this is done can be written this way:

$$C_6H_{12}O_6 \rightarrow 2C_2H_5OH + 2CO_2 + Energy$$

sugar   ethyl   carbon
     alcohol   dioxide

The energy released in this reaction could be used by the large protein molecules in producing more of their kind. It is interesting to note that organisms on earth today which depend on fermentation exclusively for their energy source have never achieved

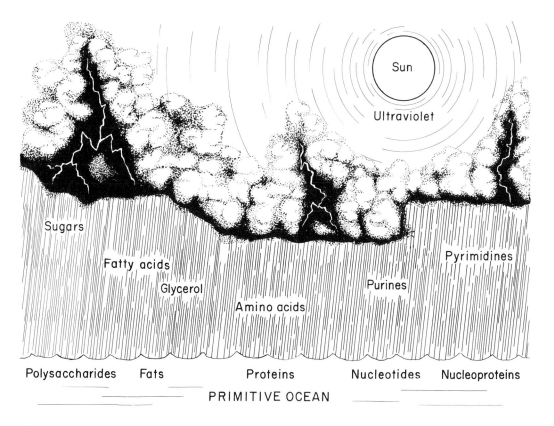

FIG. 2-9. Ultraviolet light from the sun, together with that produced by violent electrical storms, brought about the synthesis of complex molecules which accumulated in the primitive oceans.

a high state of development; they are all lowly microorganisms.

Photosynthesis. Since no more molecules of energy-rich compounds (sugars) were being formed, sooner or later all of them would have been used up; and if some new source of energy had not been found the entire ingredients in the "soup" would have gradually disintegrated and thus the end would have come to this "preliving" material. Fortunately, this catastrophic day did not come because a method of trapping the sun's energy evolved. This we call **photosynthesis.** It is simply a method of storing the sun's energy in the sugar molecule, in the presence of a green plant pigment, **chlorophyll,** using as raw material carbon dioxide and water, two compounds very abundant in nature. It can be written like this:

$$\text{Energy (sun)} + 12\ H_2O + 6\ CO_2 \xrightarrow{+\ \text{chlorophyll}} C_6H_{12}O_6 + 6\ O_2\uparrow + 6\ H_2O$$
$$\text{glucose}$$

It is clear that the energy from the sun is locked up in the sugar molecule by this process. Green plants probably initiated this method of storing energy and have retained it. They are the ultimate source of all utilizable energy on earth today, atomic energy excepted.

Respiration. When did animals come into this story? Once the photosynthetic process was able to supply all of the energy needed for protein synthesis, it would have been possible to produce enough plants to cover the surface of the earth, or until the CO_2 was used up. However, this never had a chance to occur because of the emergence of animals. The first animal was probably a degenerate plant, a plant that could not make sugar; therefore it became dependent on the green plants for a source of energy. The only way it could get the energy out of the sugar molecule was to burn or oxidize it, that is, permit the union of the

now abundant oxygen in the atmosphere (put there as a by-product of photosynthesis) with the sugar molecule, thus degrading it once again to carbon dioxide and water. This process we now call **respiration,** the opposite to photosynthesis, and it goes like this:

$$C_6H_{12}O_6 + 6\ O_2 \rightarrow 6\ CO_2 + 6\ H_2O + \text{Energy}$$

By this means the animal could reproduce itself and do all the other things animals have learned to do. Once this basic principle had evolved, there was a balance between plants and animals. A cycle was established which has operated rather satisfactorily up to the present and is likely to go on smoothly for a long time to come.

Up to this point this story presents a plausible explanation of the chemistry that was necessary during these early days, but what about the morphology of these primitive entities? What did they look like and do they have counterparts in existence today? Let us try to answer these questions.

First Morphology. During the following discussion it will be helpful to refer to Figure 2-10. It is impossible to say what the first 'prelife' looked like but we are quite certain that it contained large nucleoprotein molecules, probably in combination with other molecules. As a result of competition among these molecules some must have been selected out which were sticky and tended to aggregate into masses. Modern proteins, and nucleoproteins in particular, are sticky compounds as anyone knows who has observed the white of an egg or certain types of glue. This property of stickiness would make it possible to collect materials in the immediate vicinity of the nucleoprotein aggregate. If these materials should consist of nutrients, molecular aggregates that possessed a high degree of cohesiveness would have an advantage over those with less, since having nutrients in close proximity would cer-

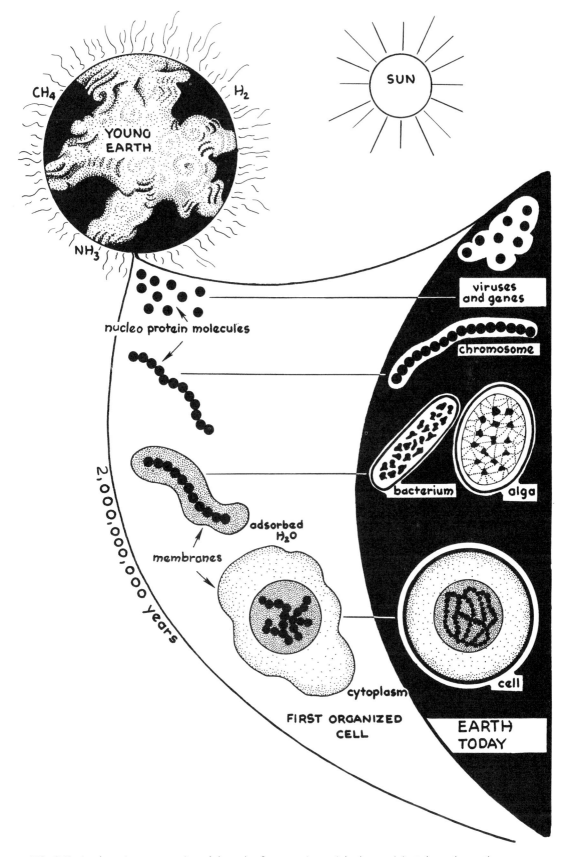

FIG. 2-10. A schematic representation of how the first organisms might have originated on the earth.

FIG. 2-11. Pictures of viruses taken through an electron microscope. (Top) Poliomyelitis virus Type II [X75,000]. Note the regular arrangement of the particles. (Middle) Influenza A virus [X35,000]. (Bottom) T⁴ bacteriophage [X50,000], a virus that attacks bacteria. Note the characteristic head and tail.

tainly be an advantage in the business of reproduction. Thus such molecular aggregates would gradually dominate the population of molecules in the young seas.

Do we see anything resembling such bodies as we have just described on earth today? The first one that comes to mind is the modern **virus,** the invisible (under light microscopy but visible under the electron microscope) organisms, so minute that they pass through the pores of a porcelain filter (Fig. 2-11). They cause many plant and animal diseases, including such dread maladies as poliomyelitis, yellow fever, and many others. Viruses are composed of nucleoprotein molecular aggregates surrounded by a shell of protein molecules. They vary widely in morphology, some being spheres and perhaps like the first viruses, and others possessing tails which may be an advanced form. One would expect evolution among them as we see in all living things that followed.

Viruses certainly have all of the prerequisites of our postulated preliving material. They reproduce readily inside of cells where raw materials are supplied by the cell which is sacrificed in the process. One might think of the cells of plants and animals as similar to the primeval oceans, both serving as a source of nutrients for reproduction of the virus. In the early days the primitive viruses could find an adequate supply of food molecules in the oceans but later this source disappeared. In the meantime cells had evolved and if the viruses were to survive they were forced to make their way inside the newly formed cells, thus becoming the first parasites. Such viruses may well have been the ancestors of those that we find today.

The question often arises, are viruses alive? As we shall see later (p. 42) they do not possess all of the characteristics we assign to living things. They also demonstrate characteristics which living things do not possess. For example when properly treated, at least one, the tobacco mosaic virus about which we know a great deal, will form crystals and remain inactive for indefinite periods of time. Living things may hibernate (p. 116), form resting cysts (p. 117), or otherwise remain relatively inactive for periods of time, but such vital processes as taking in oxygen and giving off carbon dioxide are still observable although at very low levels. The crystalline virus does not demonstrate these properties. Indeed, for all purposes it seems to belong to the inanimate world. Moreover, it is possible to fragment the virus; that is, break it into its component parts and some time later, reassemble the parts into the original virus. When dissociated, the fragments show none of the properties of the whole virus; but when put back together again the resulting compound differs in no way from the original virus, either chemically or in its ability to infect and grow in tobacco leaves. No truly living thing will withstand such treatment. We can say then that, whereas viruses do not possess all of the properties of life, they certainly constitute the borderline forms which were the first to split off from the nonliving world and became the precursors to all life that followed.

The First Cells. The process that brought about the aggregation of nucleoprotein molecules and their protein shells to form the first viruses could have continued in a much more complicated fashion. In addition to protein, other molecules, both organic (particularly lipids) and inorganic, could have accumulated at the surfaces of the nucleoprotein core. Many of these molecules would function as nutrients at first but later serve other functions. For the sake of efficiency these organized molecules could be walled off from the surrounding environment by means of a thin membrane, thus forming tiny packages of diverse molecules, each with one or more nucleoprotein aggregates. These could have been the first cells, endowed with the properties of life.

FIG. 2-12. A picture of bacteria (*Pseudomonas fluorescens*) taken with an electron microscope [X22,000]. Note the long hair-like flagella that are used to propel the cell through the water.

These cell prototypes retained all of the properties of the viruses but they added some new ones. Their nucleoproteins endowed them with the capacity of reproduction, mutation, and evolution. They were able to withdraw food from the surrounding sea and to synthesize these raw materials into their own structure. With the newly added diverse molecules they developed the remaining functions which brought them to the level of living single-celled organisms. Do we see such primitive cells on earth today?

Let us first consider the anatomy of various kinds of cells that can be examined in the laboratory. We shall consider only those parts that are pertinent to our discussion, later we shall go into a very detailed study of cells. The simplest kinds of cells are the **bacteria** (Fig. 2-12) and **blue-green algae.** They consist of an outer **membrane** which encloses a watery fluid in which **chromosomes** and a large variety of molecules and molecular aggregates are suspended. The chromosomes are composed of nucleoprotein aggregates (Fig. 2-13), not unlike viruses in chemical composition. The nucleoprotein aggregates that make up the chromosome include the **genes** (p. 697). Many of the surrounding molecules are the raw materials which are used by the nucleo-protein molecules for reproduction, not only of themselves but of the entire cell. Here we see in bacteria and certain algae counterparts of our postulated first cell. It is possible to select a series of algae which demonstrate succeeding stages from completely dispersed chromosomes to those with the chromosomes centrally located.

The next step in the path toward greater complexity was the accumulation of more materials from the environment in the immediate vicinity of this primitive cell, forming a second shell including a limiting **membrane**. The material trapped in this outer shell constitutes the **cytoplasm** and with this addition the 'modern' cell came into being (Fig. 2-14). It consists of a **nucleus** which is not unlike bacteria and algae mentioned earlier, and cytoplasm. We have seen then, with the evolution of these first complete cells requiring at least two billion years, the transition

FIG. 2-13. Chromosomes are composed primarily of nucleoprotein molecules which become brightly colored when fruit fly salivary gland cells are stained. The colored bands of nucleoprotein probably correspond to the location of the genes.

from the nonliving to the living world. Further evolutionary steps involved aggregation of cells, which was another remarkable series of steps that resulted in all the organisms we see on earth today.

THE NATURE OF LIFE

We have discussed at some length the origin of life but have not attempted to define it. When we attempt a definition we are confronted with an extremely difficult task. All of us at times have been confronted with the problem of defining something complex. We say we know what it is but are hard pressed to formulate a satisfactory definition. Biologists have the same difficulty in defining life, hence the definition resolves itself into a description of living things and how they function. This turns out to be the goal of this entire book, the contents of which could hardly be called a definition. Nevertheless, this is what we are forced to do although at the end of this chapter we shall try to sum up our thinking in a few sentences.

The basic pattern of life was laid down in the first cells and all forms that followed merely varied this pattern. Certain characteristics became incorporated in these first cells which distinguish all living things. Whereas most of them are simulated in the inanimate world, only living things possess all of them simultaneously. Let us consider them now.

Metabolism. In a broad sense metabolism includes **nutrition, respiration, synthesis** and **excretion**. All living things must have the raw materials (or nourishment) to carry out the processes that are essential for life. The incorporation of raw materials is the process of nutrition. The raw materials come in the form of large insoluble molecules which must be degraded to smaller soluble molecules that can be utilized as a source of energy or as building materials (Fig. 2-15). Animals and some lower plants

FIG. 2-14. A phase contrast photograph of a living tissue culture bone cell of a 14-day-old chick cultured for 26 days. The parts of the cell shown are Golgi body (Go), nucleus (N), nucleolus (nu), mitochondria (M), and secretory droplet (sd).

are equipped with digestive enzymes which bring about this degradation. The molecules that are destined to be used as a source of energy are burned by the process

FIG. 2-15. Living things take in food from which they derive energy to carry on their life processes.

of respiration, releasing the energy which is required in all vital processes. This is often referred to as **catabolism,** or **destructive metabolism.** Some of the energy is

utilized to transform other molecules into the physical structure of living matter. This process of synthesis is referred to as **anabolism** or **constructive metabolism.** This constant turnover of energy and synthesis is called **metabolism.** The removal of waste products of metabolism such as carbon dioxide and nitrogenous wastes is called **excretion,** which is an integral part of metabolism.

Metabolism may be simulated by inanimate machines. For example, a machine utilizes fuel (nourishment) and the energy released from the burning fuel could operate the mechanism to manufacture its own parts, and perhaps even put them together in the form of the parent machine. Even the replacement of worn out parts might be built into the design. Such a machine has never been built but it seems within the realm of possibility. Therefore metabolism may be simulated in the inanimate world. However, there are other characteristics which definitely separate the animate and the inanimate world. As a result of metab-

FIG. 2-16. This type of movement is charactersitic of living things.

olism energy is available for other living processes to be carried out.

Movement. Some of the energy resulting from metabolic processes is utilized in movement, a characteristic of all living things, from the imperceptible movement of plants to the flutter of the grouse's wings in flight (Fig. 2-16). To be sure, water moves in a river, stones roll down hill, a car moves along the highway, but all of this movement results from forces acting externally. The water in the river bed flows, the stone rolls down hill, both as a result of the pull of gravity; the car moves because the exploding fuel within the engine drives the wheels, causing a forward movement of the vehicle. The movement seen in the vibrating wings of the grouse or the slow movements of an opening flower are quite different. The energy for such movement comes from within the organism, as a result of oxidizing food molecules. This type of movement is said to be **autonomous,** that is, independent of all outside control. While this is not absolutely true (all life is dependent to some extent on outside controls), it certainly can be easily distinguished from the type of movement seen in the inanimate world.

Irritability. Responsiveness or irritability was implied in the preceding paragraph, all living things respond to their surroundings, that is, their environment. If living things are to profit by their association with their environment they must at all times be aware of the nature of their immediate external world. They are, therefore, equipped with the means to sense its characteristics and respond to them. The information comes to the organism in the form of **stimuli** to which **responses** are made that are appropriate for the preservation of that organism. The rapid response an organism may make to an external stimulus is illustrated by the runner waiting for the discharge of the pistol which is the signal

FIG. 2-17. Living things are irritable. They respond to their environment in very definite ways.

for him to start the race (Fig. 2-17). At other times the response may be very slow, as when with the onset of cold weather, the activities of the cold-blooded animals are gradually retarded. Animals move into favorable environments and out of unfavorable ones owing to their ability to respond to certain physical properties of those environments. Such responses play a very important role in the survival and ultimate success of a species. Most animals are equipped with an elaborate set of sense organs that permit them to keep in constant contact with their external world; the functioning of these organs make the difference between life and death of the species.

This capacity to respond to both internal and external stimuli provides the organism with controls to maintain a so-called **steady-state** within itself without which it would die. These steady-state controls operate to supply the organism with nutritive materials when it is hungry and to adjust the oxidation and synthetic rates in keeping with the demands of the organism at any particular moment. In addition they operate in self-preservation of the organism by swift movements in offense or defense. When injury occurs steady-state controls initiate a complex series of reactions that bring about the repair of damaged parts. Many parts of the organism are constantly being replaced which also come under these steady-state controls. Man has not yet reached the point in his technological knowledge to be able to build a machine that will operate as a self-repairing and self-healing instrument, although he has constructed some remarkable self-feeding and self-adjusting machines. Organisms became self-preserving millions of years ago and this accomplishment separates them from the inanimate world.

Growth. Steady-state controls also permit another characteristic of all living things to operate. When the synthetic forces of an organism exceed the destructive forces there is a net gain in body mass, which is called **growth** (Fig. 2-18). This is typical of all organisms, particularly during their early life. However, a stage is reached where there is a balance between these two forces, and this is referred to as **maturity;** at the time of maturity the organism merely holds its own, becoming

neither larger nor smaller. As life continues the synthetic forces fail to keep pace with the destructive forces, and the entire bulk of the organism loses ground and eventually dies. This involves the processes of aging, the nature of which is not well understood. In its final demise it is likely that only one or two aspects of the steady-state control mechanism break down, but these are of such importance that the entire machinery collapses, a process we call **death.**

FIG. 2-19. All living things reproduce and the offspring resemble the parents in most respects.

No machine has been built, or perhaps ever will be built, that grows. A crystal may grow in size by the addition of other similar crystals to its own bulk, but the pattern and the method of executing it are quite unlike that of a living organism. The crystal merely adds other crystals to its external mass (accretion), as a mason adds bricks to a wall; whereas the living organism takes the raw materials within, and there makes them an integral part of its own structure (intussusception).

Reproduction. We mentioned earlier that the failure of certain vital processes results in the death of the organism. This would mean the end of the organism if some method of continuing its life had not interrupted this inevitable course. With the

FIG. 2-18. Growth is a characteristic of all life.

raw materials and energy supplied the organism has grown in size, which in itself permits subdivision and subsequent growth in numbers (Fig. 2-19). This is reproduction. The young are composed of materials just as old as the parent; but for some reason not at all understood, the young takes on renewed vigor, it is said to be **rejuvenated.** Moreover, the young usually are smaller than the parent and frequently quite unlike it in structure. As it matures it undergoes changes which we speak of as **development,** the details of which we shall consider in a later chapter.

One of the remarkable outcomes of reproduction is the continuity of pattern from generation to generation. Offspring are endowed with structural and physiological characteristics that are almost exact duplicates of those found in the parents. The transmission of these characteristics from parent to offspring is known as **heredity,** another subject which we shall consider in some detail in a later chapter.

There is nothing in the inanimate world that reproduces in any manner similar to that seen in living things. No machine has been built that reproduces itself (a worthy goal for inventors) to say nothing of one that undergoes development and demonstrates rejuvenescense.

Adaptation. Even with all of the characteristics so far described, living things must have added one more in order to survive through the rigors of past ages. With time the face of the earth has constantly changed and with it the environment in which organisms must survive. A basic pattern set down in the bodies of the first organisms which satisfied their needs adequately at that time may be quite unsatisfactory several million years later when the environment has drastically changed. If these ancient characteristics were faithfully reproduced in the offspring generation after generation, it is obvious that the time would be reached when the organisms could no longer survive. This indeed happened to many, but some acquired the capacity to change and so fit more closely their changing environment. This capacity is called **adaptation,** a characteristic of all living things. Here again we see nothing in the inanimate world that possesses this characteristic. The possibility of building a machine with this capacity seems highly unlikely, although we must never underestimate the ingenuity of man.

We have attempted to describe the characteristics of living things and any structure that possesses these characteristics is said to be alive. We still need to learn more about the nature of life, and this can be done by studying its physical state.

PROTOPLASM

Life resides in material given the name **protoplasm** over 100 years ago. The word means the first form (**protos**—first, **plasma** —form). If tiny pieces of any plant or animal are examined under the microscope, they will be found to be composed of **cells,** each of which contains protoplasm. Recalling our earlier discussion of the origin of life, it must be concluded that protoplasm is very complex. It is so delicately adjusted physicochemically that any attempt to find out how it behaves or of what it is made means instantaneous loss of the very thing sought for. It can be handled only with the utmost care without killing it. A dead cell or animal no longer possesses protoplasm, because, by definition, protoplasm encompasses that "something" called life. At the outset it would seem impossible to study protoplasm. This is not quite so because some ingenious biologists have been able to build delicate pieces of apparatus that will permit a study of this fascinating material. One of these is the phase contrast microscope (p. 71), with which it is possible to examine the insides of cells, thus

FIG. 2-20. A living amoeba, when viewed under the light microscope, gives us some clue as to the nature of protoplasm. Note the clear protoplasm that constitutes the pseudopods. Tiny particulate matter floats about in the body of the cell, conveying to it a gray color.

observing protoplasm and its constituent parts.

One of the easiest cells to study is the common protozoan, *Amoeba,* since it is large (barely visible with the naked eye) and rugged (Fig. 2-20). Its protoplasm appears grayish in color and is usually moving about within the limits of the organism in a more or less haphazard manner, even though the general flow is in the direction the amoeba is going. Many different kinds of particles are suspended in this semifluid, semisolid material, some of which are uniform in shape, while others are variable. Among them is the large flattened **nucleus,** several **food vacuoles,** and a clear **contractile vacuole.** These are a part of the protoplasm of the amoeba, but for this discussion we are interested only in the material in which they are suspended.

In order to learn more about protoplasm, a simple experiment will be helpful.

If we drop a little alcohol or mercuric chloride on it, all activity abruptly stops and the entire cell becomes rigid, much like the white of an egg when cooked. The cell has died and, in so far as we know now, this is an irreversible reaction. If we raise the temperature momentarily to the boiling point of water, the same reaction occurs. We no longer have protoplasm, instead only a carcass. Actually we have learned very little about the nature of protoplasm, owing to our inability to design experiments that will give us more information. Lacking these, we may speculate a little further, using our knowledge of molecules and their behavior. Let us suppose that we could magnify the protoplasm of an amoeba until its molecular structure became visible. The most striking characteristic would be the violent activity of molecules of many shapes and sizes. By far the most numerous would be the water molecules, which because of their small size, would move faster than the others. The outer limits of the cell would be made up of huge molecules bound together, thus forming a continuous network perforated with holes of different sizes. This would be the plasma membrane, through which the water molecules pass freely in both directions. Many other molecules pass through also, but some are stopped because of their large size, whereas others are stopped because they possess electrical charges that prevent them from getting past the electrical charge on the membrane. Oxygen molecules enter freely, uniting with fragments from the large glucose molecules which suddenly break into smaller water and carbon dioxide molecules. The smallest particles that result from this process are the hydrogen atoms which exist only momentarily before combining with other molecules. Many other molecules would be moving about performing duties that are essential in the life of the cell, but which we do not understand.

Protoplasm, then, is this mass of molecules in endless motion, constantly changing, adding new molecules, losing others, combining and separating. The molecules obey the same laws as similar molecules found in the inanimate world. It is only when they come together in the combination found in protoplasm that they exhibit the characteristics we associate with life. Even though much of the foregoing discussion is based on speculation, it is becoming increasingly obvious, as more evidence comes from research laboratories, that perhaps these speculations are close to the truth. Let us see what can be learned from a study of the chemistry and physics of protoplasm.

CHEMICAL COMPOSITION OF PROTOPLASM

No matter what the origin of protoplasm is,—rat,—bee, cow, or plant; we would find, from a careful chemical analysis, that it is composed of molecules and atoms. Moreover, no matter what function of protoplasm we study we shall always find that it can be explained in the light of the chemical and physical properties of molecules and atoms. It is the combination of atoms and molecules that gives protoplasm its unique characteristics. We learned something about atoms and molecules earlier in this chapter when we discussed the ·origin of life. Let us now consider the chemical and physical properties of the most prominent ones found in protoplasm.

If we examine protoplasm derived from a number of plants and animals, including man (Fig. 2-21), we will find a remarkable similarity in their chemical composition. The four principle elements are carbon (C), hydrogen (H), oxygen (O), and nitrogen (N). Carbon is the core element of the complex molecules found in protoplasm, probably because of its physical nature which was discussed earlier (p. 32).

Additional elements regularly present in protoplasm are phosphorus (P), calcium (Ca), iron (Fe), potassium (K), sulfur (S), iodine (I), magnesium (Mg), sodium (Na), and chlorine (Cl). There are many others existing only as traces but nevertheless essential for the normal activities of protoplasm.

The chemicals found in protoplasm may be divided into **inorganic** and **organic,** the characteristics of which were described earlier. We learned that the former make up most of the earth, whereas the latter are always derived from living things. The inorganic compounds that are important in protoplasm are **water, inorganic salts,** and certain dissolved gases, such as **oxygen,**

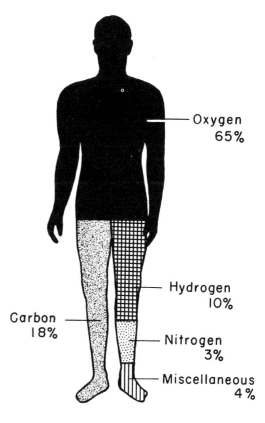

FIG. 2-21. Percentage of various chemical elements in man. Numerous lesser elements are included in miscellaneous elements.

nitrogen and **carbon dioxide.** The important organic compounds are **carbohydrates, fats, proteins** and **nucleoproteins.** Let us consider these inorganic and organic compounds as they contribute to the properties of protoplasm.

Inorganic Compounds in Protoplasm

Water. Of all the inorganic compounds in protoplasm the most important and most abundant is water, the substance in which all other materials are suspended and transported. Life without water would be impossible, because there would be no means of mixing and dispersing the energy-yielding and building materials of protoplasm. Water is important in protoplasm because of its many unique properties.

Water **dissolves** more substances than almost any other liquid. This property of water makes possible the mixing of a large variety of substances that would not dissolve in any other liquid. Hence, the great complexity of protoplasm has come about because so many different substances could come together and mix freely in one common medium. Furthermore, interactions occur more readily between substances in a fluid condition where ample freedom of movement of the molecules is permitted.

Water has a high capacity for **holding heat.** It is "reluctant" to take on or lose heat, a physical property that is very important in living things. Anyone living near large bodies of water is aware of their tempering effect on the climate of the surrounding areas. Since our bodies are primarily water (approximately 65 per cent), we respond to heat much the same as water does. If this were not the case, it would be almost impossible for us to tolerate changes in temperature.

Water possesses some interesting **chemical properties;** for example, it has more ability than any other substance to dissociate molecules into their **ions** (see p. 28). Salts such as sodium chloride (NaCl) ionize readily in water; others such as

sugars and starches do not ionize at all. Water itself ionizes slightly forming hydrogen (H^+) and hydroxyl (OH^-) ions (p. 28). Both H^+ and OH^- ions are extremely active and for this reason they seem to be tolerated only in very small numbers by protoplasm; that is, any increase of either over the other brings about prompt changes in the activity of protoplasm, and any marked increase or decrease terminates life. Protoplasm is approximately neutral all of the time, the numbers of each of H^+ and OH^- ions being approximately the same.

Salts. Many inorganic salts of sodium, potassium, calcium, and magnesium exist in protoplasm. Inorganic acids are also found in small concentrations. The role played by these various compounds will come out in later chapters.

Gases. Because of their diffusing qualities, gases tend to enter protoplasm the same as they enter other material. Since the atmosphere contains over 20 per cent oxygen, considerable quantities of this gas are found in protoplasm. **Oxygen,** of course, is very important in the release of energy. **Nitrogen,** on the other hand, is even more abundant, but because of its chemical inertness it takes part in no reactions that are important in metabolism. However, certain soil bacteria do convert atmospheric nitrogen into nitrates which are essential for plant growth. **Carbon dioxide** exists in small amounts both in the atmosphere and in protoplasm.

Organic Constituents of Protoplasm

The carbon atom is the starting point for all organic compounds as we have already learned. We have also learned that very complex molecules can be built when carbon atoms bind with other atoms and with themselves, forming chains and rings. These organic compounds not only form the fabric of protoplasm but also hold and release the energy that makes all activity possible. Some of the important organic compounds in protoplasm are carbohydrates, fats, proteins, including enzymes, and nucleoproteins. Let us consider each of these briefly.

Carbohydrates. We have referred earlier to the atomic composition of carbohydrates, from glucose to such complex molecules as starch and glycogen. In the plant leaf, CO_2 and H_2O unite under the influence of the sun's rays and in the presence of a green plant pigment, called **chlorophyll,** to form glucose (p. 125). By condensation of the 6-carbon sugars (glucose and fructose) with the loss of water, the disaccharide sucrose is formed. Further combining, called **polymerization,** results in the formation of the huge polysaccharide molecules such as starch (plants) and glycogen (animals). Carbohydrate molecules are found in protoplasm and are all involved in the storage and release of energy. Just how this happens will be discussed in the following chapter.

Fats. These include all of the **fats, oils,** and **fat-like substances** (lipids) identified by a greasy texture. They are relatively insoluble in water, but soluble in hot alcohol, ether, and chloroform. With a few exceptions they all contain C, H, and O like carbohydrates, the chief difference being their low oxygen content. This is easily illustrated by examining the formula of a common fat taken from beef tallow, $C_{57}H_{110}O_6$. Note that there are only 6 oxygen atoms as compared to 57 carbon and 110 hydrogen atoms. This means that when fats burn, they require more oxygen than does glucose. It also means that the molecule can release more energy per gram when burned. Their insolubility makes fats desirable material for the storing of energy.

The fat molecule is composed of **glycerol** ($C_3H_8O_3$) and fatty acids. A common fatty acid is **stearic acid** with the formula $CH_3(CH_2)_{16} \cdot COOH$. This is called an acid because the carboxyl group (COOH) can liberate one hydrogen ion when dissolved in water. It can be written as indicated below.

Going back to the plant leaf again, fatty acids are joined with glycerol to form oils (fats) of different kinds. This is done by the loss of water, as shown below.

stearic acid (from beef fat)

| 1 molecule glycerol | | 3 molecules stearic acid | | 1 molecule fat | | 3 molecules water |

As in the case of starch, the reverse action, hydrolysis, takes place during digestion when water is added, splitting the fat into fatty acids and glycerol.

There are other fats such as **steroids** and **phospholipids,** the latter of which has phosphate and a nitrogen compound in place of the fatty acid. They resemble fats in many ways, but have other characteristics that tend to set them off in a group by themselves. Some of them play their role in the plasma membrane where they are responsible for the selective action of this delicate structure. They are also important in some of the intricate chemistry of the animal body which we shall touch on later.

Proteins. As you learned earlier (p. 34) proteins are composed primarily of C, H, O, and N; in addition they usually contain sulfur (S) and phosphorus (P). They are huge molecules and, like starch and fat, can be hydrolyzed to **amino acids.** There may be hundreds or thousands of amino acid molecules in a single protein molecule; but when broken down, it yields about 20 amino acids, all of which are not usually found in any one kind of protein. The proportion of the different amino acids will depend on the nature of the original protein molecule.

The formula for a simple amino acid, glycine, was mentioned earlier (see p. 34). Let us now consider the general formula which will identify all amino acids:

$$H-\underset{\underset{COOH}{|}}{\overset{\overset{R}{|}}{C}}-NH_2$$

where R represents the main portion of the molecule. The remainder is found in virtually all amino acids. You will note that, in addition to the **amino group** (NH$_2$),

there is another group, the **carboxyl group** (COOH). These two groups are responsible for the behavior of amino acids. It is obvious that the presence of the carboxyl group gives the molecule acidic properties, just as is true of any organic acid. Strangely enough, an amino acid can also act like a base owing to the presence of the NH$_2$ group. It responds like a base by removing hydrogen ions, not by delivering hydroxyl ions. This is demonstrated by the following equation:

$$R \cdot NH_2 + H^+ + Cl^- \rightarrow R \cdot NH_3 + Cl^-$$

In the presence of an acid, then, an amino acid acts like a base by absorbing or removing the hydrogen ions. On the other hand, in the presence of a base it acts like an acid by delivering hydrogen ions from its carboxyl group, thus:

$$R \cdot COO^- + H^+ + Na^+ + OH^-$$
$$\rightarrow R \cdot COO^- + Na^+ + H_2O$$

A substance that responds in this fashion is said to possess **amphoteric** properties. It therefore always has a tendency to bring a solution to neutrality, that is, to balance the number of hydrogen and hydroxyl ions. For this reason, amino acids tend to prevent too much fluctuation in the number of hydrogen and hydroxyl ions in a solution. Such a substance is spoken of as a **buffer;** amino acids are good buffers.

Amino acids unite to form proteins in the plant leaf by the same process that starch and fats were produced, namely, by the loss of water. Likewise, in every cell of the animal body proteins must be assembled from the amino acids that come to it through the blood stream. Just how this is done puzzled chemists for a long time, but it is thought to occur through the so-called **peptide linkage.** The following will illustrate how this occurs:

In this manner the various amino acids are tied together to form molecules that range in size from several hundred to several thousand atoms. Their size can be estimated by the relative molecular weights. For example, glycine has a molecular weight of 75, whereas that of the oxygen-carrying protein of the crayfish's blood (hemocyanin) is over 5 million. Obviously, by combining the 20 amino acids in various ways, limitless numbers of different proteins can be formed. That is why the proteins of every animal or plant differ from those of every other animal or plant. Proteins are the most characteristic and most abundant material (exclusive of water) in protoplasm. Besides forming the actual supporting structure of protoplasm, proteins afford excellent material in which the large variety of chemical reactions essential for life take place.

Nucleoproteins. The possible origin of these supermolecules, as well as their composition, was discussed earlier in this chapter (p. 35). At this point we shall concern ourselves only with certain components of these molecules, namely the nucleic acids. Nucleoproteins hydrolyze to protein and nucleic acids, the latter existing in two forms, **ribose nucleic acid** (RNA) and **deoxyribose nucleic acid** (DNA). DNA is located within the nucleus and constitutes the information-carrying part of the chromosomes (genes);

and RNA exists primarily in the cytoplasm although some is found in a special body, the **nucleolus,** within the nucleus, as well as in the chromosomes in very small quantities. We shall have much more to say about both of these compounds in a later section. At this point we merely wish to note their occurrence in protoplasm.

Enzymes. Enzymes are protein molecules which are called **organic catalysts** and may be defined as substances that hasten a chemical reaction at living temperatures but are not themselves consumed by the reaction. As pointed out earlier (p. 35) they arose early in the evolution of life and have played an essential part in all reactions that go on in protoplasm ever since. Without enzymes protoplasm loses its ability to start and maintain the multitude of activities that go on within it. They are essential in the business of living but the details of their operation are only now beginning to be understood.

A simple experiment will demonstrate how an enzyme works. A watery starch solution is placed in two test tubes, to one of which is added saliva, to the other, nothing. Any attack on the starch can be detected by using an appropriate test for **maltose,** one of the products of polysaccharide breakdown. Within a few minutes this sugar can be demonstrated in the tube

FIG. 2-22. A scheme representing how enzymes work. The substrates A and B are brought into juxtaposition by finding their places on the active site of the enzyme. The enzyme has no effect on substrate C, owing to its wrong configuration. If a molecule (inhibitor) can take the place of the substrate, the enzyme is inactivated.

be possible by the fortuitous collision of these molecules without the enzyme. The enzyme, like all protein molecules, is large and has a vast array of surface configurations, each specific for each enzyme. It apparently is this surface geometry that is the critical point in enzyme action. The surface must be such as to fit precisely the surface of the reacting substances, called **substrates**. For example, in the reaction:

$$A + B \longrightarrow AB$$

A will combine with B in an accelerated fashion under the influence of the enzyme providing the surfaces of both A and B will fit the surface of the enzyme in juxtaposition thus bringing their reacting surfaces close together (Fig. 2-22). Any alteration in the surfaces of either enzyme or substrate will destroy the effect.

The mystery of how certain poisons work has been cleared up by applying this principle. Any substance that has the configuration of the normal substrates, even if only in part of its structure, may take its place on the surface of the enzyme, thus making it unavailable to the substrates. For all purposes the normal reaction stops, which may well be lethal for the organism. On the other hand if the poison incapacitates the enzymes of a disease-producing organism, and at the same time does not affect the enzymes of the organism itself, it can be beneficial. This explains the beneficial effects of many drugs used in the treatment of disease.

The enzyme may be used over and over again to bring about the reaction because the moment the chemical reaction has taken place the combined complex is released and the enzyme is ready to join two more substrates. Hence, we see that the enzyme functions as a very special structure designed for trapping substrate molecules and positioning them so that chemical reactions can take place much more quickly than they would otherwise. Indeed, the breakdown of starch, mentioned

containing saliva, whereas in the tube without it there will be no maltose for many hours. The enzyme **amylase** brings about this reaction. The same breakdown can be accomplished without the enzyme, but it requires drastic treatment with strong acids at high temperatures, conditions that could not be tolerated by protoplasm. It is obvious, then, that enzymes can bring about a difficult chemical change at body temperatures and in a very short period of time. All of this is essential if the many reactions that go on in protoplasm are to occur as quickly and smoothly as they do.

Just how does an enzyme work? It is generally agreed among enzymologists that the enzyme combines temporarily with the reacting molecules, thus placing them in close proximity in order that a reaction can take place at a much faster rate than would earlier, occurs quickly in the presence of amylase, but without the enzyme the reaction hardly takes place at all at body temperatures.

This complexing of enzyme and substrate has been referred to as the "lock-and-key" hypothesis. The enzymes may resemble locks into which only particular keys, substrates, fit. This thought also brings out the precise specificity of enzymes; each reaction is usually carried out by only one enzyme. Since proteins have almost an infinite number of configurations it follows that there can be as many different kinds of enzymes, each specific for every reaction; and there are thousands of these going on simultaneously in every living thing. This does not mean that every protein is an enzyme, only those with configurations that fit specific substrates.

Another characteristic of enzymes is that they accelerate reactions in either direction depending on the concentration of the reacting substances. In all reactions the speed with which it takes place is proportional to the concentration of the participating substances. This is called the **law of mass action.** Let us see how this works in the following reaction:

$$\text{Glycerol} + \text{stearic acid} \xrightleftharpoons{\text{lipase}} \text{Fat} + H_2O$$

The direction it proceeds depends on the concentration of glycerol, stearic acid, and fat at any particular moment. If glycerol and stearic acid are more concentrated than fat, the reaction will go to the right; if fat is higher it will go to the left. If the reaction is started with only glycerol and stearic acid, and no fat, it will move rapidly to the right. As fat forms there will be an ever-increasing movement to the left. Eventually the reactions will be moving in both directions at equal speeds and an **equilibrium** will be reached. There is no net increase of fat and for all purposes the reaction stops since it is moving in both directions at equal speeds. This reaction may be influenced by removing fat from the system.

In that case it will continue to the right until all of the glycerol and stearic acid molecules have combined forming fat. Again the reaction may be pushed to the right by adding a continual supply of glycerol and stearic acid, or it may be forced to go to the left by increasing the amount of fat. The law of mass action operates for all reactions in protoplasm but the reactions are almost never in equilibrium. If the end product is an escaping gas, such as CO_2 when food is burned, the reaction proceeds in one direction continuously until the food is gone; which, of course, never happens if life is to be maintained.

Enzymes are classified in accordance with the substrate they influence; for example, those accelerating reactions of proteins are called **proteinases.** Likewise those involved with carbohydrates are known as **carbohydrases. Lipases** affect lipids (fats and fat-like substances). You will note that the suffix **-ase** denotes the enzyme, although they are also identified by names which describe their action. For example, we may speak of them as synthesizing (synthetases), splitting (hydrolases), or transferring (transferases) enzymes.

The activity of enzymes is controlled by the movement of molecules just as all chemical reactions are. As the temperature rises from o to 40 degrees Centigrade and consequently molecular motion increases, enzyme action increases. With each 10 degree rise in temperature the action doubles, up to a critical temperature of about 40 degrees when all activity ceases. At this temperature enzymes, like most proteins, apparently change their surface geometry and are no longer able to orient the substrate molecules to affect their union or separation.

It is interesting to observe that cold-blooded animals (called **poikilothermal,** that is, those that cannot maintain a constant body temperature, such as insects, frogs, and lizards) are forced into hibernation because at reduced body tempera-

FIG. 2-23. Relative sizes of things that are of interest to the biologist. Magnifications greater than 100,000 are useful to the physicist and chemist.

mal, that is, birds and mammals) are not bothered in this respect because their bodies maintain a constant temperature. It is not sheer coincidence that the body temperature of these animals happens to be the point of maximal activity of the body enzymes.

Enzymes are also very sensitive to hydrogen and hydroxyl ions, as well as certain specific ions such as calcium. Enzymes work most efficiently in solutions with particular pH values, which vary with different enzymes (p. 29). High pressure as well as certain metallic ions stimulate or inhibit the action of enzymes. Here again, the effect is probably due to the alteration of the surface configuration of the enzyme molecule.

We have considered the chemical composition of protoplasm and have found it to be extremely complex. It consists of a great complex of atoms and molecules but the most impressive fact is the constant activity of these components. Highly involved chemical reactions are going on continually and these are integrally related with both internal and external changes. These reactions obey the same physical laws that operate in the inanimate world and we must consider those now.

PHYSICAL NATURE OF PROTOPLASM

We have examined the chemical composition of protoplasm and have found it composed of particulate matter in a vast array of sizes. These particles obey the same physical laws whether in or out of protoplasm. They behave in particular ways when isolated from others of the same kind, or when in close association with those of similar structure. If each particle follows specific laws of behavior when among its own kind it will behave differently when mixed with others of a different sort. Since protoplasm is made up of many kinds of molecules, it follows that the operating

tures enzymatic activity is slowed to a point where normal response is impossible. Warm-blooded animals (called **homiother-**

forces become extremely complex. In spite of this almost hopeless confusion, each particle seems to take its part in a definite pattern so that an orderly procession of reactions occurs. Let us examine some of these physical properties of protoplasm.

Size of Protoplasmic Particles

It was implied in an earlier chapter that the size of particles had a profound effect on their behavior. We should, therefore, have some appreciation of the relative magnitude of the innumerable particles of matter existing in protoplasm.

In order to speak with any degree of accuracy about the size of these tiny particles, it is necessary to apply some unit of measurement to them. Scientists throughout the world employ the **metric system** of measurement almost exclusively. Fractions of the meter, **microns,*** are used by the microscopist because these units are convenient for measuring objects that fall within the range of the microscope. For example, red blood cells in man are about 7 microns in diameter. Smaller objects, such as the particulate matter in protoplasm, are measured in **millimicrons** or Angstrom units. It is possible to measure particulate matter with the same degree of accuracy that can be attained in the macroscopic world.

To demonstrate the relative sizes of objects we may use a cell as the starting point. A large cell of your body, a cell lining your mouth for example, would occupy a space about the size of a needle point (Fig. 2-23). If this were magnified ten times, you would see it quite easily with the naked eye but the parts would not be very well defined. Magnifying it another ten times (100X) brings the nucleus and cytoplasm into full view; even the nuclear structure can be made out. Another tenfold increase (1,000X) shows the chromosomes in out-

* 1 meter (m) = 1,000 millimeters (mm); 1 millimeter = 1,000 microns (μ); 1 micron = 1,000 millimicrons ($\mu\mu$) = 10,000 Angstrom units (Å).

FIG. 2-24. The electron microscope is a precision instrument which makes it possible to observe and photograph the fine structure of cells.

line, but not in detail. A magnification of 100 to 3,000 is the range in which the microscopist works with a light microscope. Any further increase in size must be viewed through the electron microscope, which operates much the same as the light microscope except electrons are used instead of light waves for a source of illumination (p. 70). Of course, there cannot be seen directly with the eye because our eyes are sensitive only to light rays and not to electrons, but such objects can be photographed (Fig. 2-24). Furthermore, the treatment of the material is so drastic that living things cannot be studied under an electron microscope. In order to study any material it must be sliced into extremely thin sections (about $\frac{1}{40}$th micron). With this instrument, magnifications can go up to 100,000 diameters, which will reveal some viruses and the larger molecules such as nucleoprotein molecules.

The electron microscope allows us to see some things in the molecular state. Beyond this, we must rely on methods familiar to the physicist to demonstrate the size and shape of particulate matter, methods that are beyond the scope of this book. Physicists are able to measure the size, shape, and behavior of molecules and atoms, and are now working on the nature of the components of the atoms. For the present discussion, it is only necessary for us to think in terms of the size of particles at the molecular level, because protoplasm is molecular.

Colloids and Crystalloids

If a solid is ground to particles the size of dust, and these placed in water, they will form a murky fluid and after a time will settle to the bottom of the container. If the particles are ground still finer they will reach a size when they remain in suspension and do not settle out even after a long time. These particles are then in the **colloidal state.** Therefore, whether or not a substance exists as a colloid is merely a matter of size. Physicists have set an arbitrary figure for colloids; they state that particles ranging in size from 0.1 to 0.001 micron are in the colloidal state. A **colloidal system** can often be observed with the naked eye. For example, if egg albumin, which is composed of large protein molecules, is placed in water, the solution has an opalescent appearance. Light rays will strike the suspended particles and be scattered, rather than pass directly through as would be the case if the particles were smaller. We do not see the individual particles, only the effect produced by scattered light. However, if the particles are larger than 0.1 micron in diameter, the light will

be blocked altogether and the system will appear opaque, as it does in milk, for example. The larger particulate matter in milk will, of course, separate out (cream on the surface) and is therefore not colloidal.

The large size of colloidal particles also prevents them from passing through an animal membrane. If egg albumin is placed in a loop of frog skin and submerged in water, very little, if any, of the albumin will be found in the water even after hours have elapsed. Furthermore, colloidal particles move slowly when compared to smaller particles such as atoms or ions. This might be expected from our knowledge of the movement of objects that come within our experience. Physicists tell us that the movement of particles is dependent on the absorption of **heat;** the higher the temperature, the faster the movement and the lower the temperature, the slower the movement. Movement is governed by the size of the particle; when the diameter of the particles is halved, the rate of movement is doubled. Therefore, the huge lumbering molecules in a colloidal system move slowly compared to the tiny molecules of a salt solution.

Particles that are smaller than 0.001 micron in diameter are called **crystalloids;** sugar or table salt dissolved in water forms a crystalloid solution. Such systems appear clear and transparent to the naked eye because light passes directly through without being changed in any way by the tiny molecules of salt and sugar. Furthermore, crystalloids pass readily through some membranes and their individual particles move much faster than those in the colloidal state.

Protoplasm contains numerous crystalloidal and colloidal particles in the form of atoms, molecules, and molecular aggregates. The particles remain evenly dispersed and do not respond to the pull of gravity because of their continuous movement. Each particle is being bombarded by others of its own kind as well as by those of a different sort. This can be verified by observing even larger particles, such as certain pollen grains, under the highest powers of a light microscope. They will be seen to jostle about in a random manner, seeming to get nowhere. The apparently aimless motion has been given the name **Brownian movement.** In an aqueous solution much of the activity is due to the bombardment of water molecules which, of course, are much smaller. It requires millions of hits of water molecules to move the huge visible particles, and these must be concentrated more on one side than the other if movement is to occur in any one direction. It is the change in concentration of bombardment that causes the particle to move in the random fashion that is observed. This type of activity is essential in keeping the particulate matter dispersed.

Other factors complicate the behavior of particles in solution. We learned earlier that atoms and molecules may become ionized; that is, they may carry an **electrical charge, positive** when electrons are short, and **negative** when electrons are in excess. We also know that particles of the same charge repel one another while those of unlike charges attract.

The electrical charge on colloidal particles, in addition to Brownian movement, keeps them dispersed. The solid particles of a colloidal system are either positively or negatively charged, hence are kept apart by the charge. If the charge is neutralized by an opposite electrical charge, the colloidal particles will aggregate and settle out (Fig. 2-25). Since protoplasm is primarily a colloidal system, these facts have a profound effect upon its physical nature.

Colloidal particles possess another important characteristic which accounts for the behavior of protoplasm. This is referred to as **phase reversal** or **sol-gel transformations.** This can be illustrated by adding many colloidal particles to a system, or withdrawing water, so that the particles move close together—finally touching. When this happens the particles become intricately entangled, forming a sponge-like network, called a **gel** (Fig. 2-26). The original dispersed colloidal particles become contin-

uous, holding water and other dissolved particles in isolated droplets. As the name implies this has the consistency of Jello or gelatin. It is this property of protoplasm that gives to such fragile forms as amoebas and jellyfish their body shape.

If the particles are withdrawn or water added to a colloidal system, the opposite effect results, that is, it becomes fluid and is said to be in the **sol** state. This alternate switching of the sol and gel states is characteristic of protoplasm. Which state it is in at any one time depends on a number of conditions. As the temperature rises the particles move more rapidly and the gel is converted to a sol, a familiar fact to anyone who has worked around the kitchen. Other factors such as extremes in pH or pressure affect the sol-gel state of col-

COLLOIDAL PARTICLES

A   B   C

FIG. 2-25. Colloidal particles of like charge repel one another and so remain in suspension as shown in A. If particles of opposite charge are added (B) the particles are neutralized and settle out as shown in C.

Sol

Gel

FIG. 2-26. A schematic explanation of the formation of sols and gels. In a sol the elongated molecules flow smoothly past one another in a more or less fluid state. In a gel a latticework effect is produced by the gelation of the emulsion. Such a physical arrangement of the particles produces a semi-solid material.

loidal systems. Colloids also go through a series of changes with time; that is, they are said to **age**. When freshly prepared the particles in a colloidal system attract water molecules to their surfaces. With time this attractive force is weakened so that some of the water within the meshes of a gel flows out shrinking the mass considerably. This is commonly observed when milk sours. The loss of fluids and subsequent shrinking of tissues with advancing years may be related to this process.

When a muscle contracts; an amoeba puts forth a pseudopod; blood clots—to name a few of the thousands of activities that go on within a living organism—the physical characteristics described above are involved.

Limiting Membranes

Protoplasm is always confined within containers which have special properties. The container acts as the boundary between the colloidal system of the protoplasm and the external world which is quite different from the protoplasm itself. It is a physical principle that the region where a colloidal system contacts the surrounding medium (water, air, or another colloidal system), called the **interface**, a **membrane** forms owing to the physical forces placed upon the molecules in this region. They become tightly packed and arranged in a definite orientation that produces the membrane as illustrated by the surface film on boiled milk. Such a boundary on protoplasm is the **plasma membrane**.

The plasma membrane is composed of two protein layers between which is a layer of lipid molecules (Fig. 3-5). The membrane is normally in the gel state, a condition which is maintained only as long as the proportion of calcium and potassium ions are in the proper levels. Any change in the concentrations of these ions, either within or without, drastically affects the membrane. For example, if an amoeba is placed in a solution high in potassium ions and low in calcium ions a new membrane will fail to form if a rent is made in it, whereas in a solution with the proper proportions of these ions a new membrane forms at once. If the concentration is high in calcium ions and low in potassium ion, the entire organism gels, in other words, it loses all of its fluidity and becomes a congealed corpse. Therefore, a careful balance must be maintained between these two ions if a normal membrane is to form around the protoplasmic mass.

Such a sheet of protein and lipid molecules must possess some unique properties if it is to perform the necessary functions of keeping the protoplasm from disintegrating. This is accomplished by the **physical nature** of the membrane itself. The lipid and protein molecules cling together but between them are small openings where they do not fit quite snugly. These openings allow certain molecules to pass through in both directions, whereas others, owing to their large size or chemical nature, are prevented from being transported across. These membranes are thus said to be **selectively permeable** or **semipermeable.**

Water and other small molecules may pass freely from one side to the other. Fat-like particles can dissolve in the lipid molecules forming the membrane, pass inside, then slowly move out of the other side to the interior of the cell. Larger protein molecules cannot penetrate the membrane because the openings are too small to admit them. Glucose and amino acid molecules pass through the openings readily but some of the ions, even though much smaller, are unable to get through owing to the electrical charge which they bear.

Just how the many complex molecules move in and out of the cell is not completely known, but the movement of smaller ones such as water and certain ions is understood.

Diffusion and Osmosis

Diffusion is a process by which molecules tend to move from an area where they are highly concentrated to an area where few of these molecules exist (Fig. 2-27). This occurs in the presence or absence of a membrane as long as the membrane is permeable to the molecules. Molecules which easily pass through the cell membrane will tend to equalize their numbers on both sides of the membrane. Thus, in Figure 2-30A water molecules will move into the cell from the outside of the membrane, since there is a higher concentration of water molecules on the outside. Once the molecules— water, ions or other particles—pass through the membrane of a cell, they diffuse throughout the protoplasmic mass until

they have become evenly distributed, that is, they have reached an equilibrium.

A different situation exists when some of the particles surrounding a membrane cannot penetrate. Under these conditions water molecules will move in order to establish an equilibrium. This unequal movement of water molecules through a semipermeable membrane is called **osmosis.** In a situation where a membrane is permeable to water, but impermeable to large sucrose molecules, the sucrose molecules will constantly strive to intermingle with the water molecules on both sides of the membrane, but since they cannot pass through there will be an uneven distribution of the water molecules on the two sides. The water and sucrose molecules will bombard the membrane with about equal hits on one side; corresponding hits will be made by the water molecules on the other side, but since there

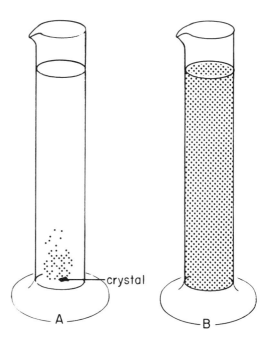

FIG. 2-27. Molecules tend to move from higher to lower concentrations. Thus in A, a crystal of salt is placed at the bottom of a cylinder of water. It immediately begins to dissolve; that is, the molecules mingle with those of the water. An equilibrium is established at some later time as shown in B.

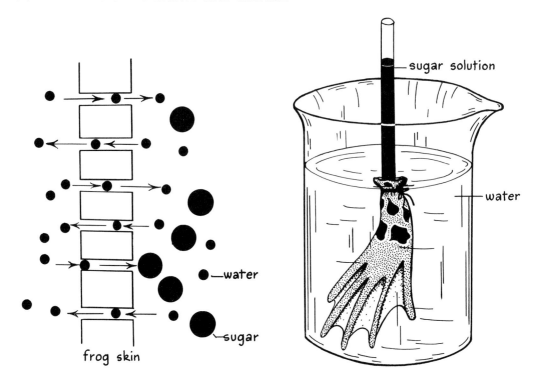

FIG. 2-28. An osmometer is made from the skin of a frog's foot into which a strong sugar solution is poured and a small-bore tube attached. The diagrammatic view at left shows why the membrane is permeable to water and not to sugar.

are only water molecules present, one will pass through for every molecule of sucrose on the other side which cannot get through. The water molecules will be passing toward the sugar side more rapidly than they pass in the other direction, thus building up a hydrostatic pressure on the sugar side (Fig. 2-28).

Osmosis can be easily demonstrated by placing a strong sugar solution in a bag of thin skin, such as frog skin, and tying it to a small-bore tube (Fig. 2-28). The water will pass into the bag, or toward the sugar, thus building up a pressure, the **osmotic pressure,** within the bag which will be registered by the rise of fluid in the small tube. If properly constructed, such an apparatus will demonstrate a rise of the fluid column to many feet, the height being determined primarily by the effective semi-permeability of the bag. Usually such a preparation is

not absolutely semipermeable; some sugar goes the other way, that is, after a time sugar molecules will have wedged their way through the membrane to mingle with the uniform water molecules outside.

The practical significance of osmosis can be demonstrated with red blood cells. These tiny disks have a limiting semipermeable membrane which encompasses a large variety of particles that constitute the internal protoplasm of the cell. While these corpuscles are suspended in the fluid of the blood, water passes in and out of the cell with equal speed, so the membrane is uninfluenced by the movement. Other particles pass in and out, but in so doing there is always an even distribution on both sides of the membrane; that is, for every particle going inside another comes out, so that the numbers, not necessarily the kinds, are approximately the same all of the time. Such a surrounding fluid is said to be **isotonic** to the corpuscles (Fig. 2-29). If the corpuscles are now separated from the fluid portion of the blood and placed in distilled water, a very rapid and sudden change occurs. The water moves into the cell because the dispersed particles are greater (less water molecules) inside than out (where there are more water molecules), so the water flows in, causing the membrane to swell and eventually burst (Fig. 2-29). The water in which the cells were placed is said to be **hypotonic** to the blood cells. Hypotonic

into the blood stream, it might also prove fatal because of the rapid destruction of blood cells. It is important, then, whenever cells are placed in any kind of solution, that the medium have the same number of particles, or, in other words, it must have the same osmotic pressure as the cells themselves, if severe trouble is to be averted.

Another illustration of the effect of osmotic pressure might be cited because of its practical application. Perhaps you have wondered why a person, floating upon vast quantities of water, must die at sea if he

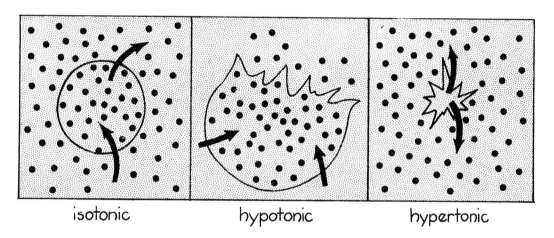

isotonic   hypotonic   hypertonic

FIG. 2-29. The effect of salt solutions of various concentrations on the red blood cell.

solutions should not be injected into the blood stream of an animal because the destruction of red cells, as well as others, could prove fatal.

Again, if the cells were placed in a salt solution in which the numbers of dispersed particles were much greater than on the inside of the cell, the direction of flow would be in the opposite direction, namely, out of the cell, causing it to shrink to only a fraction of its normal size (Fig. 2-29). The reason here is the same as in the previous case. Such shrunken cells are called **crenated cells,** and such a concentrated salt solution is said to be **hypertonic** to the blood cells. If such a hypertonic solution were injected

has no fresh water to drink. Sea water is heavily laden with salts and its osmotic pressure is considerably above that of the blood and tissues of man and all other land animals. If, then, he should take sea water into his stomach it would extract from his stomach the precious water that is already short, eventually filling his stomach so that he would be forced to throw it up. This would leave his body with less water than it had before he swallowed the sea water. That is why drinking sea water can be fatal.

Passive Transport

The movement of particles across membranes is of two sorts depending upon

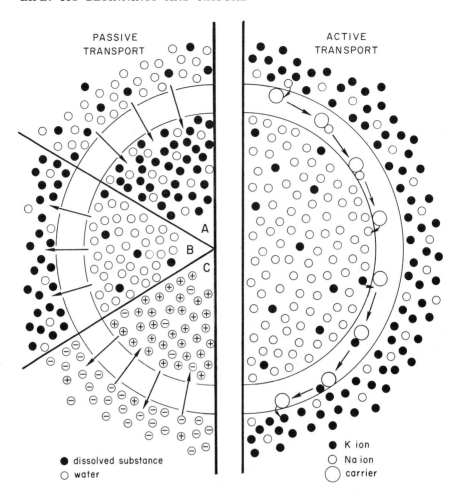

FIG. 2-30. Highly schematic representation of how particles migrate through membranes. See text for explanation.

whether or not energy is required. The movement of water through a semipermeable membrane, as illustrated in osmosis, is spoken of as **passive transport,** because the direction the water migrates depends on the relative concentrations of these and other molecules on each side of the membrane and also because no energy is required. In Figure 2-30A water flows into the cell owing to the fewer molecules of water inside the cell (or conversely, the greater the number of particles of the dissolved substance). Alternatively, in B the water flows out of the cell for the same reason (Fig. 2-30 B). In Figure 2-30 C, however,

the effect of the electrical charge is responsible for the direction of flow of the different ions. If there is a high concentration of positively charged ions on the inside and negatively charged ones on the outside, an electrical potential gradient is established across the membrane. This brings about a gradual migration of the ions across the membrane. Hence, positively charged particles move out of the cell and negatively charged ones move in, eventually establishing an equilibrium.

Active Transport

For the proper functioning of some cells it is necessary to maintain an unequal distribution of ions on either side of the membrane. In such cases, ions must move from an area of low concentration to one of high concentration or against a concentration gradient for which energy is required to counteract the forces of diffusion which tend to bring about an equilibrium of the particles. This type of movement is called **active transport,** because energy is involved in moving particles. The manner in which this is accomplished is shown in a highly schematic fashion in Figure 2-30.

It has been postulated that a carrier molecule located in the membrane itself may pick up a sodium ion from the outside forming a temporary compound, and carry it inside the cell, where it is released. Alternatively, it may transport potassium ions outside the cell. The carrier molecule requires energy supplied by the cell for its action. This active transport system makes possible the maintainence of different concentrations of specific ions on the two sides of a membrane.

IN REVIEW

This discussion of the physical and chemical properties of protoplasm may seem unduly long and to belong more properly in a book of chemistry or physics. It is none the less basic to an understanding of life. Let us summarize briefly to emphasize this once more.

We have seen that protoplasm consists of molecules, atoms, ions, and colloids no different in constitution from similar entities existing in the inanimate world. However, their intricate and complex association in protoplasm bestows upon them the properties that we assign to living things. Although some of the properties of these particles have been described, certainly not all of them have been, nor could they be, because they are not known.

Many people have attributed to protoplasm a vague sort of "something" called life, that suddenly leaves a living thing when it dies. However, attractive though this may be, it is no explanation, at least in the scientific sense. The reason why we have difficulty in explaining life is that we do not know enough about the intricate workings of molecules, atoms, ions, and other particles that go to make up protoplasm. If we had sufficient knowledge about their behavior perhaps we could explain how protoplasm is put together and exactly how it works; indeed, we could explain life itself. That is a far distant goal, but one worthy of the most intensive research.

Can We Define Life? Perhaps we are somewhat closer to a definition of life than we were at the beginning of this discussion some pages ago. We can make a few statements but they need to be shrouded in vague terms which we still do not quite understand. Certainly life involves motion and interaction of particulate matter at size levels from atoms to huge colloids. It includes ceaseless chemical change, with its concomitant consumption or release of energy. Life means chemical and physical organization of pattern and design with a never ending trend toward greater complexity.

SUGGESTED SUPPLEMENTARY READINGS

BALDWIN, E. B., *Dynamic Aspects of Biochemistry* (Cambridge, University Press, 1958).

CALVIN, Melvin, "Chemical Evolution and the Origin of Life," *American Scientist,* 44 (July, 1956), 248.

GAEBLER, O. H. (ed.), *Enzymes: Units of Biological Structure and Function* (New York, Academic Press, 1956).

GREENBERG, D. M. and HARPUR, H. A., *Enzymes in Health and Disease* (Springfield, Ill., Charles C Thomas, 1960).

McELROY, W. D., *Cellular Physiology and Biochemistry* (Englewood Cliffs, N.J. Prentice-Hall, Inc., 1961).

MILLER, S. L., "The Origin of Life," in W. H. Johnson and W. C. Steere, *This is Life* (New York, Holt, Rinehart & Winston, 1962), p. 343.

OPARIN, A. I., *Life: Its Nature, Origin and Development* (New York, Academic Press, 1961).

STEIN, W. H. and MOORE, S., "The Chemical Structure of Proteins," *Scientific American*, 204 (2) (February, 1961), 84.

UREY, H., "The Origin of the Earth," *Scientific American*, 187 (4) (April, 1952), 53.

WALD, G., "Origin of Life," *Scientific American*, 191 (2) (August, 1954), 44.

3
Units of Life—Cells

GOING back to the story of the origin of life, it will be remembered that protoplasm came into being very slowly, and its organization into cells must likewise have required a very long time. All cells, from the free-living one-celled protozoa to the many-celled animals, are extremely complex, and certainly the result of hundreds of millions of years of evolution. All cells perform essentially the same functions whether they are deep in the muscles of an elephant or exist as independent individual units like the amoeba. Before we examine the general cell structure more carefully, a little

of the **historical background** of cell studies may help us in our perspective of modern science.

Long ago, about 1665, an English biologist by the name of Robert **Hooke** cut thin slices of cork and placed them under his newly fashioned microscope. He noted that this material was composed of numerous tiny compartments to which he assigned the name "cells," a name that has come down to the present time. He gave them this appellation because they reminded him of the cubicles in monasteries in which monks of his time lived. Today any beginning biology student can repeat Hooke's experiment and be rewarded with a much better visual image of cells, although he would probably lack some of the enthusiasm that compelled this inquiring man of the seventeenth century to make the discovery.

Everyone who was sufficiently curious to follow the exciting hobby of looking through the newly invented microscope of this early period saw that all parts taken from living things were composed of these tiny "bladders," as **Grew** called them. Their first and only interest seemed to lie in the fact that animals and plants were made up of these tiny units, and they paid little or no attention to the internal parts of the cells for over 100 years. By 1824, **Dutrochet** in France had noted that plants grew by an increase in number and size of the cells of which they were composed. By 1831, **Brown** had seen and described the centrally located body within the cell which he called the **nucleus**. This, together with the increased use of the microscope, centered the attention of investigators on the internal parts of the cell. **Dujardin** saw the universal occurrence of **protoplasm** within cells and gave it the name which it bears today. About this time (1839), two Germans, **Schleiden** (a botanist) and **Schwann** (a zoologist), advanced the **Cell Theory,** which was merely a concise statement of what had been learned by a great many men up to this point, namely, that all living things were composed of cells.

The Cell Theory gave biologists for the first time a tangible theory upon which to base further studies. It meant to them what the molecular theory did to the chemist and physicist, and as a result, biology became more and more a study of cells rather than a study of the organism as a whole. Because cells occupy the central core of studies in embryology, reproduction, growth, heredity, and behavior, they have been given steadily increasing attention through the years by investigators of fundamental

biology. Today there is more activity in this field than ever before. Once a thorough understanding of the cell is acquired, many of our most perplexing problems in biology will be closer to solution.

THE STRUCTURE OF CELLS

Since Robert Hooke saw cells for the first time great strides have been made in the production of instruments which have made it possible to explore the microscopic and submicroscopic anatomy of the intact cell. If we examine the drawing of a cell which interpreted the view of cytologists four decades ago (Fig. 3-1) and compare it to a recent drawing, the difference is striking (Fig. 3-4). The empty regions are now filled with bodies of various dimensions and the structures that were drawn in the earlier sketch now have specific morphology. These changes have come about as a result of improved instruments, particularly in the magnification and resolving power of our modern microscopes. Let us briefly consider a few principles in optics and the instruments that have come into common use which employ these principles.

The main problem in magnification is to distinguish two objects lying close together, which is called the **resolving power** of the optical system. The human eye contains an optical system with a resolving power of 0.05 to 0.1 millimeter, which means that people vary in their ability to distinguish between two objects. Objects with a smaller diameter than this will be invisible and two lines closer together than these distances will be seen as one line. Since the eye cannot magnify we must judge size from past experience. Microscopes, on the other hand, both magnify and resolve. Their capacity depends on the kind of illumination employed. Light microscopes use light, of course; and owing to the nature of light they cannot resolve objects less than one-half wave length,

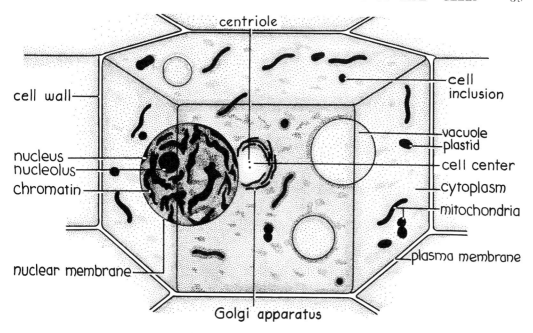

FIG. 3-1. A generalized cell based on light microscope observations.

which is about 0.275 micron (the average wave length of white light is 0.55 micron or 5,500 Angstroms). To obtain this resolution the lens must be perfectly ground and properly corrected. The optical limit of the light microscope was reached many years ago, which meant that particles or structures smaller than 0.275 micron could not be seen. As a result little new information was gained concerning cell structure until an instrument of greater resolution was discovered.

The solution of this problem came about when physicists explored other sources of illumination. Among these the most rewarding has been a beam of high speed electrons which resulted in the **electron microscope.** The design of the electron microscope is compared to the light microscope in Figure 3-2. The source of the electrons is a tungsten filament heated to incandescence by 50,000 or 100,000 volts of electricity. The electrons are focused by electromagnetic lenses so that they pass through the specimen where they are de-

flected or absorbed depending on the density of various parts of the specimen. The resulting black and white image impinges upon a fluorescent screen which makes it visible to the eye. Since we cannot see electrons we must rely on the screen to visualize the image; moreover, the image can be recorded only with a photographic plate for the same reason.

The wave length of a beam of electrons, produced by 50,000 volts, is about 0.005Å. which means that theoretically the electron microscope should resolve objects with a diameter of 0.0025Å. which is less than the smallest atom. In reality, however, it has been impossible to perfect the lens system so that the resolving power is better than 3–4Å., even in the best microscopes. But with this instrument it is possible to magnify objects 20 times more than the best light microscope. The electron microscope has revealed a whole new world for the cytologist. Today he is seeing structures for the first time that were never dreamed of 50 years ago. His experience is reminiscent of

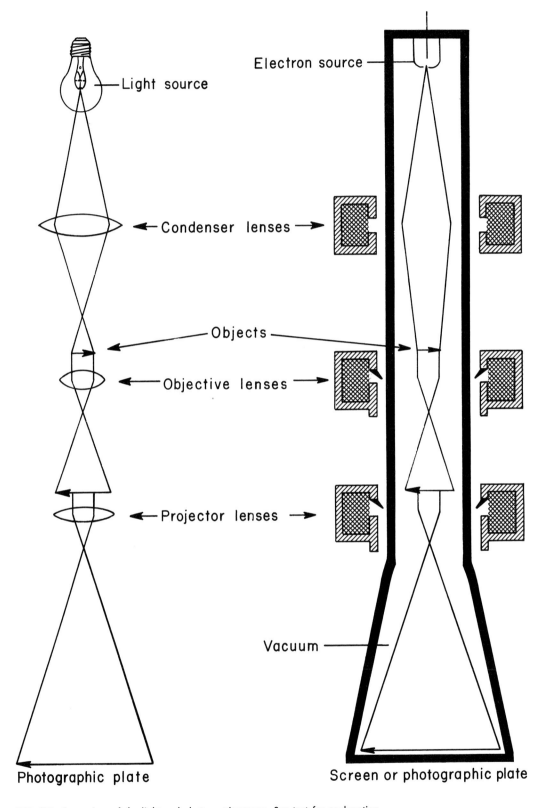

Light source

Electron source

Condenser lenses

Objects

Objective lenses

Projector lenses

Vacuum

Photographic plate

Screen or photographic plate

FIG. 3-2. Comparison of the light and electron microscope. See text for explanation.

that Leeuwenhoek must have had 300 years earlier.

It is obvious that the electron microscope is useful in examining the fine structure of dead cells but is presently of no value in telling us anything about the living cell. In 1932, however, the Dutch scientist, **Zernike,** reported his invention of the **phase contrast microscope,** an instrument designed to permit light to pass through various parts of the cell in such a way as to intensify the slight differences in these parts to a point where they could be seen or photographed (Fig. 2-14). The details of this instrument are beyond the scope of this book; but suffice it to say that this invention has revolutionized the study of living cells, so that we are now aware of many details of living cells which could never have been known with the methods previously employed.

Another method of investigating the structure of living cells is by **microsurgery,** which consists of introducing fine needles, electrodes, and pipettes into cells for the purpose of injecting or removing parts or measuring electrical potentials of various parts under a variety of conditions. The needles and pipettes are operated by an instrument of high precision; indeed, it is so accurate that even chromosomes or nucleoli can be removed from individual cells without destroying them. This instrument has added much information to the essentiality of parts of the cells as well as the physical nature of the protoplasm during different stages in the life cycle of the cell.

Much can be learned from disintegrated cells, that is, cells that have been ground up and the particles of which they are composed separated into "fractions" which are then studied biochemically. This requires a special grinding mechanism which will obtain the desired cell particulates. These are then separated into fractions by centrifugation at carefully controlled speeds. The heavier particles sedi-

ment out at lower speeds than the lighter particles; such fractions contain particles with very little contamination by other kinds of particles. Such fractions can then be tested for their chemical composition and activity. Since they retain their activity for some time it is assumed that their reactions in the test tube are identical to those in the intact cell. In instances where it has been possible to make the same observations on particulates inside the cell and in the test tube this has generally been true.

With this battery of tools cytologists have been making steady progress in unravelling the mysteries of cells. As instruments improve the future holds great hope for an ultimate understanding of the cell although the distance travelled so far is a mere fraction of what is left.

The Morphology of Cells

In order to understand the structure of cells it is essential to study living cells in the intact state as well as isolated particulates. The study of killed, sectioned, and stained cells has been invaluable in adding to our knowledge of cellular architecture. Let us consider what has been learned from the study of both living and dead cells.

Living Cells. Phase contrast microscopy lends itself to the study of isolated cells such as blood cells or protozoa and to cells taken directly from the living organisms. Moreover, with the discovery of **tissue culture** by **Harrison** (1907) and its subsequent development by **Carrel** it is now possible to investigate the cells of many tissues while they are growing in a somewhat normal condition. This method consists in excising small bits of tissue, preferably embryonic tissue, from a living organism and placing it in a medium which contains all of the nutrients required for growth and development of the tissue cells. For a long time this medium consisted of such complex substances as clotted blood plasma or embry-

FIG. 3-3. A young egg cell (Oocyte) of the fish, *Fundulus heteroclitus*. Large spherical nucleus contains several dark, round nucleoli and threadlike chromosomes. Clear inclusions in the cytoplams are yolk vesicles.

onic extracts, but there has been an intense search for more simplified media and only very recently biologists have found a chemically defined medium which supports growth of some kinds of cells.

This tissue culture technique has recently been refined one step further, a step which holds great promise for a better understanding of how cells function. It is now possible to isolate single cells from certain tissues and obtain thousands of cells from this parent cell. This technique is a very old one among microbiologists, but has only recently been successfully employed with tissue cells of higher animals. Such cell-lines are called **clones** and they have the advantage of being genetically alike, hence respond in a manner characteristic of the particular tissue studied. The culturing of clonal cells from various tissues is a great step forward in helping us to understand what molecules go into the synthesis of protoplasm. And what is even more significant it is now possible to examine compounds which accelerate or inhibit the growth and division of cells in the

test tube; this has many advantages over studies involving the intact animal. One can hope for further advances in the next decade or two, in this fertile field of research, from which may come some inkling as to why cells sometimes fail to grow normally and become malignant, such as cancer cells.

When one examines a living cell, say an epithelial cell from tissue culture, with an ordinary light microscope one sees a translucent jelly-like mass of material held together by a membrane, which cannot be seen. Within the cell one may see a body somewhat larger than other bodies which is the **nucleus.** The remainder of the cell, the **cytoplasm,** contains bodies of various shapes which seem to be in constant motion. This is about all one sees under these conditions. However, if we now place the cell under the phase contrast microscope, we observe the same structures, but much better, and, in addition, we see other things (Fig. 2-14). The nucleus contains many small particles of uniform size and one or two large spherical bodies, the **nucleoli.** In the cytoplasm numerous tiny rod-like bodies, the **mitochondria** can be made out. The cell membrane can be seen as a distinct limiting boundary although one still cannot see that it has thickness. Other bodies may be present in the cytoplasm and again movement of the particles is characteristic. If we are going to learn more about the structure of the intact cell we must prepare it in a variety of ways, but in so doing we must kill it.

Killed or Fixed Cells. For over 100 years the detailed structure of cells has been studied from material that has been killed and stained in a very precise manner. There are hundreds of methods for doing this and the methods vary with the type of cell studied. In general, they involve certain common steps. The cells, whether they are single isolated cells or those incorporated in tissues, are killed suddenly with a **fixa-**

tive, which is a chemical compound that coagulates the protoplasm with as little distortion as possible. The cells are then treated in a variety of ways, all very exacting, designed to set off the various parts of the cells in a contrasting manner so that they may be distinguished. This involves cutting the material, if it is tissue, into thin slices which are then stained with a variety of dyes or treated with other compounds which are highly specific, each attacking only a certain part of the cell, thus making that part stand out from other parts. These techniques have been very useful in identifying the internal morphology of cells and are still employed today (Fig. 3-3).

With the invention of the electron microscope various techniques were employed to prepare cells for study. The most popular killing agent turned out to be osmium tetroxide which imposes the least amount of distortion on the cell parts. The most difficult problem to overcome was that of cutting the cells into sufficiently thin sections so that the electron beam would pass through and give a picture. Whereas sections cut 3 to 10 microns thick are quite adequate for the light microscope, they must be $\frac{1}{40}$th micron (250Å) or less for observation with the electron microscope. This requires a cutting instrument (microtome) of high precision. Staining requires merely the deposit of heavy metals on the cellular parts. This causes them to form heavier shadows thereby producing a picture with more contrast. By examining cells with the light, phase contrast, and electron microscopes we can describe rather accurately the morphology of cells. This we shall now consider.

The Generalized Cell

It is quite impossible to designate any one plant or animal cell as representative of all cells, because each cell type has certain unique features; but since all cells have certain parts in common it is possible to construct a generalized cell which will serve for discussing common characteristics. It will be helpful to consult Figure 3-4 during the following discussion.

All cells are composed of protoplasm bounded by a semipermeable **cell** or **plasma membrane,** and within most, there is a **nucleus,** likewise bounded by a membrane, the **nuclear membrane.** The nucleus is suspended in the **cytoplasm** which makes up the major portion of the cell. In addition to the cell membrane, most plant cells are enclosed in a **cell wall** of variable composition, the primary content being the carbohydrate, **cellulose,** which lends support. The cell wall is sufficiently porous to permit the passage of soluble substances through it. We may think of the cell as a factory consisting of a number of subunits, each of which performs specific tasks essential to the existence of the entire cell. Let us examine each of these subunits.

The Cell Membrane. The cell membrane is usually so thin that it cannot be seen in the light microscope, but in the electron microscope it appears as two membranes, consisting of protein, and lying very close together (Fig. 3-5, 3-8). The space between these membranes is filled with a double layer of lipid molecules, the entire cell membrane resembling a "sandwich" of 100Å. in thickness. The protein contributes to the elasticity of the membrane. When the cell grows in size the membrane must possess the property of growth.

The cell membrane is the barrier which isolates the interior of the cell from its external world, and it is across this barrier that all particles must pass into and out of the cell. Hence, it is a most important structure but unfortunately we do not understand exactly how it does its many jobs. We know that it is selectively permeable. Materials pass through the membrane by passive and active transport as mentioned earlier. The combination of these forces maintains the concentration of

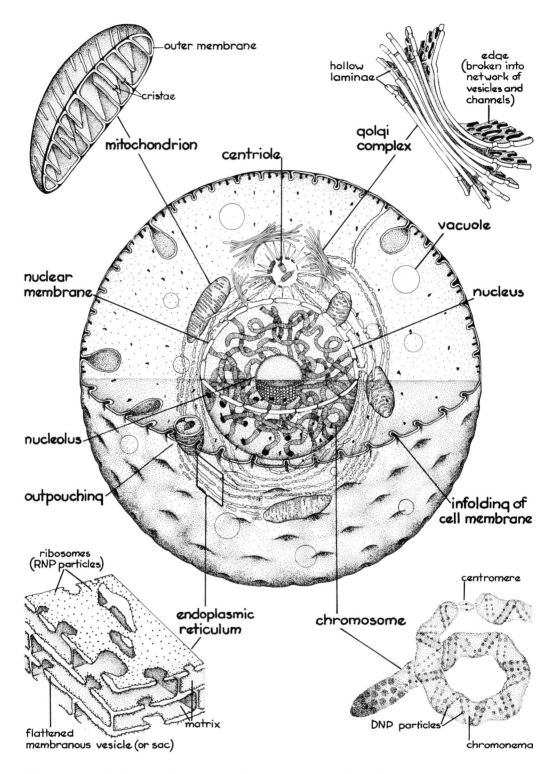

outer membrane

cristae

mitochondrion

centriole

hollow
laminae

golgi
complex

edge
(broken into
network of
vesicles and
channels)

vacuole

nuclear
membrane

nucleus

nucleolus

outpouching

infolding of
cell membrane

ribosomes
(RNP particles)

endoplasmic
reticulum

chromosome

centromere

matrix

flattened
membranous vesicle (or sac)

DNP particles

chromonema

FIG. 3-4. A generalized cell based on electron microscope observations. See explanation in text.

74

FIG. 3-5. An electron micrograph of the bat liver showing the cell membrane (CM), glycogen granules (Gl), Golgi body (Go), mitochondria (M), and nucleus (N). [X11,000]

the essential substances at the proper levels for normal functioning of the cell.

Some cells, however, possess an additional method of bringing substances into their interior. The cell membrane forms tiny pockets or invaginations which draw materials from the environment into the cell, reminiscent of an amoeba engulfing its prey (p. 168). These then pinch off and float free in the cytoplasm where the enclosed material is available for use by the cell (Fig. 3-6). This process is known as **pinocytosis** or **phagocytosis**. These structures can be readily observed with the electron microscope in some cells.

Cytoplasmic Structures. Inside the cell membrane several particles of specific mor-

phology can now be described as a result of electron microscopy which, under the light microscope, appear as tiny granules. Among plant cells we see the large chloroplasts which do not concern us now because they are not present in animal cells. Both plant and animal cells, however, possess mitochondria, which have been called the "power plants" of all living things (Fig. 3-5, 3-7). They have highly organized fine structure and incorporate the enzymes which provide the energy for the machinery of the cell.

The mitochondrion is constructed in such a fashion that the maximum surface area is presented for enzyme action. Inside the outer envelope is a second membrane which is thrown into lamellae which extend toward the interior and may even reach the opposite side. These are called **cristae** and are the sites where oxidation of food molecules probably occurs. Their remarkable uniformity as regards the spacing between the membranes is directly associated with the configuration of the enzymes responsible for oxidation of the substates that provides the energy for cellular metabolism.

Another body of about the same size, but of entirely different structure, can

centrioles, present among lower plant and most animal cells (Fig.. 3-9). With the light microscope these are best seen during cell division, but their structure at all periods in the life cycle of the cell has been described only recently, again as a result of electron microscope studies. It may come as a surprise to learn that they are composed of a cylinder, inside of which are 9 fibers around the periphery. Even more surprising is the fact that cilia and flagella (p. 161) have a similar structure. These vibratile organ-

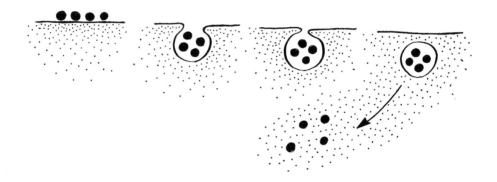

FIG. 3-6. A series of sketches illustrating pinocytosis. Particles on the surface sink into the cell, forming tiny sacs which then become vacuoles and finally diffuse into the cytoplasm.

also be observed under the electron microscope. This is the **lysosome** (Fig. 3-8), which contains hydrolytic enzymes that are capable of breaking down fats, carbohydrates, and proteins into smaller, soluble products that can be burned by the oxidative enzymes in the mitochondrion. It is essential that these powerful enzymes be packaged in the lysosome for once the sac is broken they immediately attack the cell and destroy (lyse) it.

Many other particles such as granules of various dimensions, as well as spherical vacuoles containing storage products, are clearly seen. Of particular interest among these is the **centrosome** with its pair of

elles originate from a body called the **kinetosome** (Fig. 3-10) which resembles the centriole, not only in its structure but also in its reproductive capacity. Both the kinetosome and the centriole are self-replicating entities and probably undergo reproduction in the same manner. We shall consider this problem in more detail later (p. 161).

The earlier drawings of cells indicated a vast, essentially vacant area in the cytoplasm. With the aid of the electron microscope we now see that this region is far from vacant; it is composed of a complicated system of membranes, called the **endoplasmic reticulum** (Fig. 3-7, 3-8). This

FIG. 3-7. An electron micrograph of a rat liver cell showing mitochondria (M), rough endoplasmic reticulum (ER) with dark granules on the surface (ribosomes), smooth endoplasmic reticulum (SER), nucleus (N) and the nuclear membrane showing distinct pores. [X25,000]

is often spoken of as the "cytoskeleton" of the cell. These membranes have been shown in some cells to extend from the inner cell membrane to the outer nuclear membrane thus establishing a continuous channel from the external environment to the nucleus. Some of the membranes are "smooth"; others are "rough," the difference being that the latter possess tiny granules regularly arranged along their external surfaces whereas the former have no such granules. These granules are called **ribosomes** and contain a high percentage of **ribonucleic acid (RNA).** They are the sites of protein synthesis.

Associated with the endoplasmic reticulum is a cluster of smooth membranes that has been seen by light microscopists for many years and has been called the **Golgi body** (Fig. 3-5) after the Italian

cytologist, Camillo Golgi. Their function is questionable but some believe that they may function in secretion and the production of new endoplasmic reticulum. The numerous membranes in cells and their remarkably similar structure has led to the suggestion that perhaps all of the cytoplasmic structures, Golgi, mitochondria, endoplasmic reticulum, originated by invaginations of the cell membrane.

The Nucleus. The conspicuous nucleus is bounded by a double membrane much like the cell membrane, except that it is perforated with **pores,** or holes, through which large molecules may move in or out of the nucleus (Fig. 3-7). As pointed out earlier the outer membrane seems to be continuous with the endoplasmic reticulum thus permitting materials between these membranes to have an immediate passageway to the nucleus where they are used for synthesis of materials within that body.

All of the genetic material, **deoxyribonucleic acid** (DNA), is localized inside the nucleus, packaged in the **chromosomes.** When the cell is not dividing the chromosomes are greatly elongated and are quite invisible under the light microscope—appearing only as **chromatin granules.** These uncoiled chromosomes (see p. 80) provide the maximum amount of surface during the stage when the cell is growing at its greatest rate. This configuration is necessary in order that its contained DNA can carry out the function of replicating itself and producing RNA (Fig. 3-11). In some cells, such as developing amphibian eggs, the extension of the surface is greatly increased by loops extending laterally from the axis of the chromosome which gives it a fuzzy appearance, and for that reason these are termed "lampbrush" chromosomes.

These chromosomes, like all chromosomes, consist of a thin **axial filament,** sometimes called a **chromonema,** to which thick dense swellings, the **chromomeres** are attached. These bodies contain DNA (called DNP particles because they also contain protein) and may well be the genes since they have the proper distribution along the filament. There is no membrane bounding the chromosome as is so often described. We shall say more about the chromosomes when we discuss division.

The nucleus contains one or more conspicuous bodies, the **nucleoli** (singular, nucleolus) which are composed of small granules resembling the ribosomes in the cytoplasm. They, too, are rich in RNA and are centers of protein synthesis. It may be that they are reservoirs for messenger RNA which is cyclically passed to the cytoplasm through the nuclear membrane. There is some evidence for this as will be pointed out later. The chromosomes and

FIG. 3-8. An electron micrograph of a rat liver of two contiguous cells, showing lysosomes (L) in addition to the structures shown in 3-5 and 3-7.

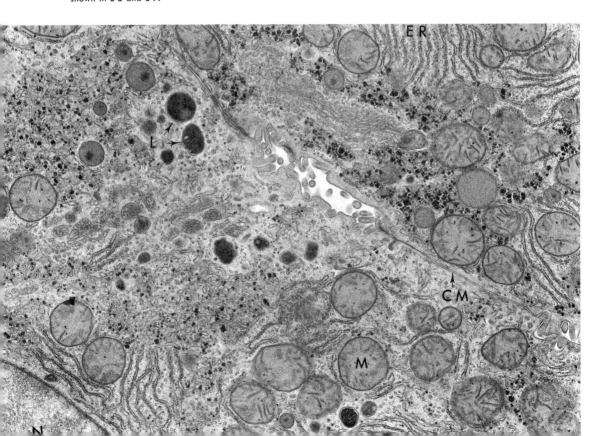

nucleoli are bathed in the **nucleoplasm,** a protein-containing matrix which supplies all the essentials for DNA and RNA synthesis.

Thus we see that we know a great deal more about the architecture of cells than we did even two decades ago. We see that instead of being rather loosely organized it has particulates "positioned," and all movements follow a pattern that is prescribed by the structure of the cell itself. Indeed, this must be so if the functions of the cell are to be integrated and follow some kind of order which we know is essential.

The generalized cell has been considered in this section, but it must be remembered that specialized cells contain additional structures that are designed to do specific jobs assigned to those cells. Furthermore, cells vary tremendously in size, shape, and special functions.

Size. There is as much difference in the size of cells as there is between most animals, an elephant and a mouse, for example. There is no correlation between the size of the animal and the size of its cells. The larger animals simply have more cells. It has been thought that certain species of spherical bacteria, which have a diameter of 1 micron or less, are the smallest cells. Cells must not be confused with viruses, which are not organized into cells and which, in fact, normally live at the expense of cells. Bacteria can be seen only with the best high magnification microscopes. Recently they have been photographed through the electron microscope which has made possible more detailed studies of their internal anatomy (Fig. 2-12). Most cells that compose the bodies of animals are considerably larger than the largest bacteria; on the average they are about 7 microns in diameter. The nerve cells are very long and thin, particularly those reaching from the tip of the toe to the spinal cord in the back. In an elephant

FIG. 3-9. An electron micrograph of a rat liver cell showing a pair of centrioles (C). Note that they consist of tubules. The one on the left is in longitudinal section and the one on the right is in cross section.

or giraffe these cells are 6 or 7 feet long. The largest animal cells are found among bird's eggs, in which what is popularly called the "yolk" is a single cell. The largest living cell known is the yolk of the ostrich egg which reaches a diameter of 2 or more inches. The large quantity of stored food (yolk) in eggs is responsible for their great mass.

Shape. The shape of cells depends a great deal on their function (Fig. 3-12). If they perform a tensile function, such as cells found in tendons, they are long and thin because of the constant stretching action placed upon them. If they are conductive, as in the case of nerve cells, they must also be long and thin. On the other hand, red corpuscles are tiny disks, fitted by shape to float in the blood stream. Smooth muscle cells are spindle-shaped which is the ideal shape for a cell that must shorten or contract. Cells that line the respiratory tract in our bodies are small cylinders with minute, vibratile, hair-like structures **(cilia)** on one end, which function in carrying the mucus along the tract by their whip-like action. Other cells, such as the amorphous white blood cells, resemble tiny bits of jelly that move by rolling along, taking in and destroying bacteria and other foreign particles in the blood and tissues.

Number. A glance through a microscope at a thin slice of tissue taken from any animal will demonstrate the fact that there are a great many cells in even a small animal like the mouse or spider. The larger the animal, the more the cells, although swift-moving and very active animals such as insects and birds usually have fewer cells per unit volume than do sluggish, slow-moving creatures such as the salamander. Every cubic millimeter of human blood contains about 5 million red blood cells,

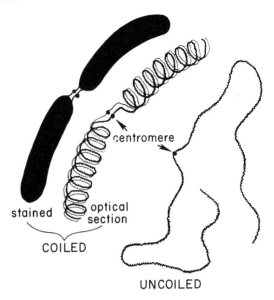

FIG. 3-11. A single chromosome is shown here in the coiled and uncoiled state. Stained preparations observed under the light microscope appear solid black. The chromosome actually is composed of a tightly coiled pair of threads (chromonemata). The uncoiled chromosome loses its major coils but retains the minor ones.

FIG. 3-10. Electron micrograph of a kinetosome (K) and its cilium (C) from the protozoan *Tetrahymena pyriformis*.

and the total number in the entire blood stream approximates 30 trillions. The human brain alone has billions of cells; the number in the whole body thus takes on astronomical figures.

THE FUNCTION OF CELLS

As we have already noted, cells resemble one another anatomically, therefore one would expect that they would also function in much the same manner. This is essentially true; all cells have certain requirements which are satisfied in much the same way. Whereas there may be differences in the way they acquire their food, the processes of utilizing the food are quite the same in most cells. As pointed out earlier these vital processes are included under the term metabolism. Therefore let us consider **cellular metabolism**, remembering that the overall operation of the entire organism, be it a flea or dog, is ultimately at the cellular level. An understanding of metabolism at the cellular level is fundamental to understanding the metabolism of communities of cells as they are found in complex animals such as man.

Nutrition. All of the activities of an organism that have to do with securing, consuming, digesting, and absorbing food may be considered **nutrition** in the broad sense. At the higher organism level this involves a complex of organ systems which need not

The autotrophs include green plant cells and purple bacteria which obtain their energy for building food molecules from the sun. A few bacteria are able to gain energy for food synthesis by oxidizing certain inorganic compounds (chemosynthesis). The raw materials needed by autotrophs to build food molecules (and protoplasm) are very simple compounds, carbon dioxide, water, and a few inorganic ions. Green plants are superb chemists in that they combine these simple compounds into

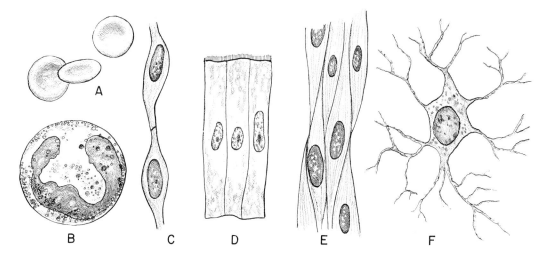

FIG. 3-12. Various kinds of cells. A. Red corpuscles. B. White corpuscle. C. Flat (squamous) epithelial cells. D. Columnar ciliated epithelial cells. E. Smooth muscle cells. F. Nerve cell (neuron).

concern us at this time. We are only concerned with the ways in which a cell may receive nourishment.

There are two methods by which cells acquire food. Those cells that are able to synthesize their own food that is, manufacture all of the complex molecules that are used for building materials and for energy, are said to possess **autotrophic** (self-nourishing) nutrition and they are called **autotrophs.** Those cells that must depend on outside sources for their food are said to have **heterotrophic** nutrition and are identified as **heterotrophs.**

all of the complex molecules that are eventually found in the mature plant, something that the human chemist has found no way of doing as yet.

Heterotrophs vary somewhat in their method of securing food. Some protozoa, the fungi, and most bacteria absorb their food in the form of small soluble molecules directly from their surrounding environment. They are referred to as **saprophytes** (saprophytic nutrition). They possess powerful hydrolytic enzymes which are excreted into the immediate environment. The large fat, carbohydrate, and protein molecules are broken down (digested) to soluble molecules of fatty acids and glycerol, sugars, and amino acids which are then taken inside the cell (absorbed) and utilized.

Other cells such as certain protozoa (amoeba) and those found in simple invertebrates (hydra, p. 210) ingest the large molecules and then digest them while they are enveloped in tiny sacs (food vacuoles) within the cell itself. This has been referred to earlier as pinocytosis (p. 75) and probably occurs much more commonly in cells than was thought at one time. Cells that receive nourishment in this manner, that is eat, are sometimes called **phagotrophs** and the method **phagotrophy** or **phagocytosis,** as well as pinocytosis. This must not be confused with eating by multicellular animals such as a cat eating a mouse, although the end result is the same. In this case the large molecules which compose the mouse are taken into a tube (digestive tract) where enzymes, produced by special cells, break them down to soluble molecules which are then taken up by the cells lining the wall of the tube. This is called **holozoic nutrition** and usually refers to the method of food taking of most animals and will be discussed later.

It may be useful at this point to compare the requirements of a typical autotroph cell (green plant) and a typical heterotroph cell (animal), remembering that there are intermediate types which do not follow the rule. The self-nourishing plant cell requires only water, minerals (including nitrate NO_3), organic carbon in the form of carbon dioxide, and the presence of chlorophyll for photosynthesis. The heterotrophic animal cell also requires water and minerals, but in addition, it must have organic carbon in the form of a complex compound, such as glucose, and amino (NH_2) nitrogen which it usually obtains in the form of amino acids. It cannot make some amino acids, hence requires them in their intact form; these are called

essential amino acids. Moreover, the animal cell requires **vitamins** (p.   ) some of which it also cannot make. The plant can manufacture the vitamins and all of the amino acids; therefore, the animal cell must depend directly or indirectly upon the autotroph to supply these nutritional requirements. The animal cell is only required to provide the hydrolytic enzymes that are necessary to break the plant (or other) molecules to such form that they can be absorbed and utilized. The plant cell, on the other hand, needs nothing from the animal cell (except CO_2) and is therefore self-sustaining.

The basic pattern of nutritional requirements of cells must be very old because we see even among the single celled forms (algae and many protozoa) essentially the same requirements that are found in the multicellular plants and animals. The tree is an autotroph and the dog is heterotroph. One wonders how the animal cell became so dependent upon the plant cell. Perhaps at one time the animal cell may have manufactured most of its requirements through an enzyme system as elaborate as that of the plant cell. With time mutations, perhaps, blocked certain metabolic pathways by destroying the effectiveness of certain enzymes. As long as the animal cell could obtain the essential nutrient which it could no longer make from plants or perhaps other animal cells, it could survive. Any defect caused by mutation would be inherited so that the progeny of the altered cells might continue to exist and even prosper. A continual loss of enzyme effectiveness might persist until further reduction in synthetic capacity could not be tolerated. The state of heterotrophy reached may have been while cells were still in the one-celled stage; and for that reason all higher animals have essentially the same basic nutritional requirements. Hence man, like a protozoan, requires about 10 amino acids and certain vitamins in his diet. To be sure there are minor variations, but many of the same nutrients are required by both men and protozoa.

Regardless of how the cell came by its raw food molecules, once they are inside the cell the process by which energy is released from these molecules and the way products are synthesized are remarkably similar in all cells. Let us consider these now.

Metabolism includes the processes by which energy is released from the energy-rich compounds and building materials are incorporated into the structure of the cell. The business of providing the cells with food and removing the waste products is merely accessory to the real job of extracting energy from the food and using it to build new protoplasm. This process involves a great many enzymes and the chemical reactions are tremendously complicated. The remarkable similarity of these numerous enzymes and their corresponding chemical reactions among all living organisms is strong evidence for common descent of all cells. It seems quite clear that primitive living things evolved a system of obtaining energy and constructing proteins that has remained more or less unchanged up to the present. Undoubtedly thousands of chemical pathways have been "experimented" with through past ages, but long ago the situation, as we see it today, emerged as the most compatible with the environment on this planet and has become firmly established in all cells.

The history of food molecules from the time they enter the cell until they leave as waste products involves some rather complicated chemistry, most of which has become understood only in recent years. We speak of the entire process as **intermediate metabolism**. It has been known for over a century that cells take in glucose and convert it to carbon dioxide and water, yielding energy during the process. But understanding the steps involved in this

degradation of glucose, the intermediate steps, has come to light primarily through the aid of traceable atoms such as radioactive carbon (C^{14}), radioactive phosphorus (P^{32}), and others which have been used to *tag* the large molecules involved in this process. This so-called **tracer** technique is very useful and has been responsible for much of our newer knowledge in biology. Let us attempt to trace some of the major steps that occur during the metabolism of glucose, amino acids, and fats from the time they enter the cell until they leave as waste products.

While studying the following description it will be useful to refer to the accompanying diagrams. Figure 3-13 indicates graphically where the chemical reactions probably occur in the cell and Figure 3-14 shows a skeleton outline of the reactions themselves. Glucose arrives at the cell membrane, following the hydrolysis of starch or glycogen, and passes into the cell where it must first combine with phosphate to form **glucose-6-phosphate**. This is accomplished by the enzyme **hexokinase** and the process is called **phosphorylation**. Since this is an endergonic reaction, energy must be supplied for it to take place. This energy comes from the breakdown of the high energy phosphate compound, **adenosine triphosphate,** called ATP for short. Since this is the primary source for quick energy in all biological systems it is fitting that we discuss it at this time before continuing with the discussion of the metabolism of the cell.

This unique compound supplies the cell with a source of energy that can be called into service instantly. When a muscle contracts, a cell divides, a firefly turns on its light, the energy is supplied from ATP. The primary source of energy goes back to the oxidation of glucose but the usable energy is stored in the form of ATP as we shall see. The structural formula of the molecule is given in Figure 3-15 in which the important part is the "triphosphate"

FIG. 3-13. A schematic representation of the sites of physiological reactions in a typical cell. There remains some doubt about the exact location of some of the reactions.

portion, from which it gets its name. The two chemical bonds that link the phosphate with the adenosine are called the **high energy phosphate bonds.** The uniqueness of this molecule is demonstrated when these bonds are broken. Two or three times as much energy is released when this happens in ATP than when most chemical bonds are ruptured. The bond energy in ATP directly or indirectly drives all the energy-requiring processes of living things.

If you examine the structure of ATP you will note that it is composed of the purine, **adenine** (p. 35) plus the sugar ribose, to which is attached three phosphate groups. The skeleton of the molecule with one phosphate group is a nucleotide (adenylic acid), a compound with which we are familiar since it appeared very early in the evolution of life. Undoubtedly ATP also evolved during this early period and supplied the energy that was essential for

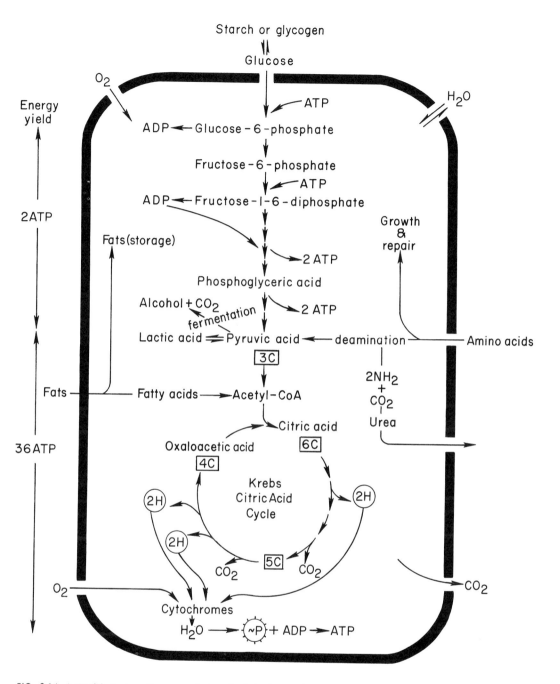

FIG. 3-14. A simplified schematic representation of cellular intermediate metabolism. See text for explanation.

further reactions to take place.

Energy is released from ATP when the terminal high energy phosphate bond is ruptured forming **adenosine diphosphate** (ADP), thus:

$$ATP \rightleftarrows ADP + phosphate + energy$$

As indicated in the equation the reaction is reversible. Obviously it will require the same amount of energy to form ATP as was released. The source of this energy is the oxidation of glucose and now we shall see how this energy is released from the glucose molecule. As you may guess it is not a simple oxidation process and there are many steps involved. It is necessary to

ATP. It must be remembered also that each of these steps requires a separate enzyme.

The series of steps taken so far in degrading the glucose molecule has yielded very little energy and you will note that no oxygen has been used. For that reason we say this is an **anaerobic** process and the overall reaction to this point is referred to as **glycolysis.** Many microorganisms, such as yeast, can obtain energy anaerobically only through the process of *fermentation* which involves the disintegration of glucose and the evolution of gas. They cannot carry the process any further, owing to the lack of specific enzymes to do the job. It is obviously a very wasteful method of ob-

FIG. 3-15. The structural formula for adenosine triphosphate.

degrade the glucose molecule in a slow orderly fashion so that the energy can be stored in ATP at body temperatures. If it were oxidized rapidly the energy would be lost in the form of heat and thus could not be made available to the cell for doing all the necessary jobs that it must do.

Glucose-6-phosphate is converted to **fructose-6-phosphate** and then to **fructose-1, 6-diphosphate,** the latter reaction also requiring energy from ATP. This compound then passes through a series of steps during which it is degraded, finally reaching the three-carbon compound **pyruvic acid.** During these steps 2 molecules of ATP have been used to bring about the reactions, but 4 molecules of ATP have resulted; hence we have a gain of 2 molecules of

taining energy because most of the energy still remains locked up in the waste products, alcohol, lactic acid, or acetic acid. Most cells, however, evolved enzymes to carry the degradation all the way to carbon dioxide and water, thus removing almost the last trace of energy from the glucose molecule. Let us continue our story and see how this is done.

Pyruvic acid, which is the starting point for the next series of reactions, is converted to acetic acid, and then enters a series of reactions which move sequentially in a cycle, yielding energy as acetic acid is converted to carbon dioxide and water. This circular pattern of reactions has been called the **Krebs citric acid cycle,** in honor of the man who first postulated it. The sequence of events starts when acetic acid (in combination with coenzyme A) combines with oxaloacetic acid (a 4-carbon compound) to form citric acid (a 6-carbon compound), which is then converted into seven other compounds, coming back finally to oxaloacetic acid. Each conversion is under the influence of a specific enzyme. If any one of these enzymes is destroyed, the cycle stops at that point, and the compound formed at that time will accumulate. By employing specific enzyme poisons, it is possible to identify each compound in the cycle; indeed, this is one of the methods that was first employed in working out the cycle.

As the Krebs cycle turns, carbon dioxide and hydrogen fall away, and the former is ultimately lost from the cell as a waste product. The process by which hydrogen is released is called **dehydrogenation** and the enzymes involved, **dehydrogenases,** of which there are a number. The released hydrogen ultimately unites with oxygen to form water, but many steps are encountered before this final stage is reached. A number of compounds, collectively called the **respiratory chain,** combine temporarily with hydrogen before it unites with oxygen to form water. Some of these contain the vitamins niacin and riboflavin (p. 529), which is the main reason why they are essential in the diet. After hydrogen is passed along from one vitamin-containing compound to another, it is directly passed to a series of **cytochromes,** protein compounds related to hemoglobin (p. 570), which change color when they accept or lose hydrogen. The cytochromes, of which there are usually three (a, b, c), finally donate the hydrogen to oxygen to form water. It is interesting to note that the oxygen in the waste CO_2 comes from some substrate molecule in the glycolytic and Krebs cycles, whereas the oxygen in released water comes from the oxygen that is taken in when breathing.

The Krebs citric acid cycle has been referred to as the "intracellular energy wheel" because, as the wheel turns, large amounts of fuel (H) is made available for the respiratory chain where it is captured and stored in ATP molecules. This is done by converting ADP to ATP as pointed out earlier.

You will note that whereas glycolysis has produced only 2 ATP molecules, the Krebs cycle has yielded 36. Obviously it was only when cells reached the stage in evolution where they could extract the energy remaining in the molecular fragments left over from fermentation that they really became efficient metabolic machines.

Obviously this entire process is **respiration;** and while we can write it simply:

$$C_6H_{12}O_6 + 6\ O_2 \longrightarrow 6\ CO_2 + 6\ H_2O + \text{energy}$$

which quite amply describes the net result, the intermediate reactions are far from simple. One might ask, why bother with all of these steps when the end result is all that we need to know? This knowledge of the intermediate steps has been necessary in understanding such questions as why certain substances are poisons, why antibiotics work, and many others. Heavy metals, such as arsenic, mercury, and lead, are poisons because they block the activity of many enzymes in the Krebs cycle. Poisons can work one of two ways. One way is to offer the cell a substance that causes the synthesis of a nonfunctional enzyme, say one in the Krebs cycle. This is done with certain compounds, called **analogs,** that are closely related to the vitamins. Hence, the enzyme cannot do the job of converting one compound to the next, as it normally does in the Krebs cycle. The "wheel" stops at this point, respiration ceases, and the cell dies. Some antibiotics work this way. The reason why it is so difficult to find an antibiotic is because it must be able to stop the Krebs cycle in the infective organism (bacterium, etc.), but not in the cells of the host, usually man. A substance that brings the cycle to a stop in all cells is obviously useless as an antibiotic.

Another method of poisoning cells is to offer them a substance which is very much, but not quite, like one of the compounds in the Krebs cycle (Fig. 2-22). The enzyme then accepts the substituted compound; but, of course, it cannot make the conversion that is necessary for the cycle to continue, and death of the cell follows just as surely as with the first method. Such substances are also called analogs, and this type of block is known as **competitive inhibition.** Both methods have proven very effective in studying metabolic pathways in organisms, and the search for analogs of both types is more active today than ever before. One of the reasons for this search is that some bacteria that cause our most serious diseases have "discovered" a way of by-passing the antibiotics and continuing their growth unabated, thus making the antibiotic ineffective. This has meant that new analogs that are effective in other parts of the Krebs cycle must be found if these germs are to be destroyed.

From what we have said so far, it would appear that the only source materials that keep the Krebs cycle going come from glycolysis. If this were true, cells could not utilize amino acids and fats as sources of energy. We know that these foods are used and that animals can live very well on protein and fat, with very little carbohydrate in their diet. This is possible because some portion of the amino acids that enter the cell are **deaminated,** that is, lose their amino groups (NH_2), and the remaining fragment of the molecule, which contains only C, O, and H atoms, is fed into the Krebs cycle via pyruvic acid, thus furnishing material to keep the cycle operating. The amino groups may leave the cell in the form of ammonia, or they may combine with carbon dioxide to form urea (p. 85) and then leave the cell. The amino acids that are not utilized as an energy source are utilized by the cell

for growth and repair of worn-out protoplasm.

The fats that arrive at the cell membrane pass through it and are hydrolyzed to fatty acids and glycerol. The fatty acids then are converted to acetic acid, which moves into the Krebs cycle and is oxidized. Unoxidized fats are stored in the cell for future use. Thus we see that the three foods, fats, carbohydrates, and proteins, are utilized as sources of energy by cells.

Just where do all of these reactions occur? Let us now take another look at the cell with this thought in mind. The site where some of the chemical reactions occur has been ascertained by studying cell fragments and particulates. As was pointed out earlier it is possible to homogenize cells and by centrifugation separate fractions which contain the different parts of the cell. By testing these fractions for the various reactions we have been describing, it is possible to determine where they occur in some instances. However, it is not possible as yet to say where they all occur because not all are completely understood, to say nothing of their position in the cell.

There seems to be no doubt about where the Krebs cycle enzymes are located because oxidative metabolism occurs in mitochondrial fractions. The respiratory chain enzymes are localized on the mitochondrial membranes. Glycolysis apparently occurs, at least in part, in the cytoplasm and is not associated with particles. ATP is found throughout the cell which is understandable because energy is needed for nearly every activity of the cell. Fats are stored in vacuoles and the hydrolytic enzymes are confined to membraned sacs, the lysosomes. The secretory products of the Golgi bodies pass from the cytoplasm out of the cell and perform their function extracellularly for the most part, although they may have intracellular functions as well. Deamination and urea formation probably occur in the cytoplasm with no relationship to particulates. DNA and

FIG. 3-16. This is a comb jelly (*Mnemiopsis leidyi*) found along Cape Cod. The combs are luminescent and this photo was taken using their own light.

RNA are manufactured by the chromosomes inside the nucleus, the latter accumulating in the nucleolus. The smaller molecular RNA, called transfer RNA, passes through the nuclear membrane and migrates to the ribosomes where it functions with the messenger RNA in the synthesis of proteins, including enzymes. Just how this occurs shall be discussed in a later section when cell duplication is considered.

We have seen that cells, while highly variable in size and morphology, all have the same fundamental needs which must be cared for whether they are a part of a many-celled organism or live as isolated individuals. Some cells, however, have additional unique functions, such as the production of compounds like enzymes and hormones, or contraction as in muscle fibers. One very interesting property found in special cells of many organisms is the capacity to produce light. Let us consider

this in some detail leaving other special abilities of cells for later chapters.

Bioluminescence

Light can be emitted by an atom or molecule when an electron changes its energy level, and this can be accomplished by light (photoluminescence), by electrical energy (electroluminescence) and by a chemical reaction (chemiluminescence). Our particular concern is with one type of chemiluminescence occuring in living organisms which is called **bioluminescence**. The capacity of producing light is widespread; indeed, luminous species occur in all the major phyla, except the Platyhelminthes and the Nemathelminthes. The sea is teeming with luminescent bacteria, protozoa, and a large variety of metazoa (Fig. 3-16). These microorganisms, as well as some of the smaller metazoa, cause a brilliant display of light in the wake of a ship on the ocean on dark nights at certain times of the year. Some deep sea forms, particularly fishes, are endowed with **luminescent organs** which provide light in an otherwise eternally dark world. These organs are rather remarkable in that they themselves do not emit light but are really cavities in which luminescent bacteria live. The organ is well supplied with blood vessels to permit adequate oxygen for the bacteria. The bacteria glow continuously but the fish can turn the light off by means of a flap of skin which functions much like an eyelid.

The best known terrestrial luminescent animals are the fireflies and the glow worms, although many others have the ability such as certain beetles, flies, millipedes, centipedes, snails, and earthworms. A very interesting fly (*Arachnocampa luminosa*), living in caves in New Zealand and elsewhere, supplies sufficient light to dimly illuminate these dark caverns. It is actually the **larval** stage that clings to the roof of the cave, sending down threads of mucus as "fishing nets" for trapping midges (insects) living in the river below, their sole food supply. The glowing light attracts the midges which fly up from the stream and become enmeshed in the mucous threads and are then devoured by the larval glow worms. To visit one of these caves is a fascinating experience.

The mechanism that brings about bioluminescence is not understood although a great deal of work has been done with the problem. The solution of this problem could have far-reaching effects in our economy because these organisms produce "cold light" in which very little energy is lost in the form of heat, which is the big problem in our present methods of producing light. In 1887 it was suggested by a Frenchman, Dubois, that the light in the luminous clam, *Pholas dactylus,* was produced when a substance, **luciferin,** was oxidized. We now know that luciferin is destroyed in the presence of the oxidative

enzyme, **luciferase,** and oxygen. This reaction causes the light to be emitted. If the two substances are placed in a test tube in the presence of oxygen and ATP, luminescence occurs. It turns out, however, that luciferin is not a single substance present in all light producing organisms, but occurs in many different forms which suggests that bioluminescence evolved independently many times during the long course of organic evolution. It has been suggested, because of the close chemical relationship between bioluminescense, photosynthesis and vision, that the former is the reverse of the latter two. That is, in vision and photosynthesis the reaction is excited by light and chemical compounds result, whereas in bioluminescence the reverse happens; as a result of a chemical reaction light is produced. Moreover, oxygen is a byproduct of photosynthesis and an absolute requirement for bioluminescence. As more is learned about the energy transformations in these reactions, the evolutionary story will become more clear.

Light emission may have occurred in early times among most organisms as a byproduct of oxidative processes, and have gradually been lost owing to a shifting of the end product to ATP for example. Do modern organisms today make any use of this illumination? It seems quite clear that some do whereas in others its value is questionable. For example, bacteria and fungi make little, if any, use of their light; likewise, what use does *Chaetopterus* (p. 279), living on the ocean floor in a dark tube from which it never escapes, have for a light? On the other hand it has been shown that the intermittent flash of the firefly is intimately tied up with the mating process. The light emitted by deep sea animals could be helpful in recognition of one another or as warning signals for predators. It would be interesting to know what use the remarkable railroad worm of Uruguay has for its row of green lights along its two sides and the two red ones on its head.

Now let us consider the problems which cells had to solve when they aggregated into masses, that is, when they became metazoans.

SUGGESTED SUPPLEMENTARY READINGS

BALDWIN, E., *Dynamic Aspects of Biochemistry* (Cambridge, Cambridge University Press, 1952).

BRACHET, J., "The Living Cell," *Scientific American,* 205 (3) (September, 1961), 50.

CRICK, F. H. C., "Nucleic Acids," *Scientific American,* 197 (5) (September, 1957), 188.

DeROBERTIS, E. D. P., NOWINSKI, W. W., and SAEZ, F. A., *General Cytology* (Philadelphia, W. B. Saunders Co., 1960).

GIESE, A. C., *Cell Physiology* (Philadelphia, W. B. Saunders Co., 1962).

HAYASHI, T., "How Cells Move," *Scientific American,* 205 (3) (September, 1961), 184.

HOAGLAND, M. B., "Nucleic Acids and Proteins," *Scientific American,* 201 (6) (December, 1959), 55.

HURWITZ, J. and FURTH, J. J., "Messenger RNA," *Scientific American,* 206 (2) (February, 1962), 41.

LEHNINGER, A. L., "Energy Transformation in the Cell," *Scientific American,* 202 (5) (May, 1960), 102.

LEHNINGER, A. L., "How Cells Transform Energy," *Scientific American,* 205 (3) (September, 1961), 62.

PUCK, T. H., "Single Human Cells in Vitro," *Scientific American,* 197 (2) (August, 1957), 91.

ROBERTSON, J. D., "The Membrane of the Living Cell," *Scientific American,* 206 (4) (April, 1962), 64.

SCHMIDT, F. O., "Giant Molecules in Cells and Tissues," *Scientific American,* 197 (5) (November, 1957), 204.

SIEKEVITZ, P., "Powerhouse of the Cell," *Scientific American,* 197 (1) (July, 1957), 131.

SOLOMON, A. K., "Pores in the Cell Membranes," *Scientific American,* 203 (6) (December, 1960), 146.

SOLOMON, A. K., "Pumps in the Living Cell," *Scientific American*, 207 (2) (August, 1962), 100.

WILSON, G. B., and MORRISON, J. H., *Cytology* (New York, Reinhold Publishing Corporation, 1961).

PART III

The Organized Animal

4

From Single Cells to Many Cells

ONCE THE FULLY ORGANIZED CELL had become well established on earth, it probably "explored" many possibilities in structural and physiological patterns in order to improve its situation, which usually means better adaptation to its environment. Undoubtedly as numbers increased cells moved into many different environments. Some found niches in which they were "satisfied," where they have remained more or less unchanged, through the succeeding millions of years. We find them still occupying these same, or similar, places today. The demands of their environment remained essentially static, hence they were not forced to change in order to survive. Others, however, were forced into adverse environments which compelled them to change or perish. It was from this group that we might expect to find not only new varieties of single cells but also some that banded together in small groups which apparently enhanced survival. We shall never know why cells aggregated into groups since there are no fossil remains to guide our thinking, but we can speculate a little about some of the advantages that accrue from such assemblages of cells.

First of all, there is the matter of size. Small single-celled forms, moving about with tiny whip-like flagella, have very little control over their movement. Whereas they can orient themselves to a limited extent, they are predominantly under the influence of water currents and must go wherever these currents take them. With increased bulk this influence is diminished; indeed as size increases the organism has more command over where it shall go. Hence, it is likely that those cells which aggregated, increasing their overall bulk, coped better with certain environmental hazards, and therefore were able to survive where single cells would have perished.

An alternative method of increasing size was apparently attempted by some single cells, and to a point it was successful. The cell itself increased in size by adding more protoplasm, resulting in huge cells. We see these today among the ciliated protozoa where some reach a length of a millimeter (p. 163). This increased protoplasmic mass required additional nuclear material to maintain normal metabolism, hence, in addition to an ordinary nucleus they acquired extra nuclear material in the form of the large macronucleus. Even with this bit of accessory equipment size limits were soon reached. These cells are all comparatively small when compared to most animals. The solution to the problem of size limitation had to be solved in some other way. The most obvious possibility was for cells to aggregate into masses and this apparently happened. Just how this came about has inspired considerable speculation on the part of many biologists for a long time. It is worthwhile discussing, briefly, some of their thinking.

Let us assume that during the millennia required for the unfolding of higher animal life, some animals found satisfactory niches and have remained essentially unchanged up to the present. If this is so it should be possible to find such representative animals and to arrange them in the order of their complexity, forming a continuous series from single cells to the most complex animals alive today. We would expect to find gaps between groups, and we would also expect the animals we do find are not to be exact duplicates of the originals. They too would undoubtedly have undergone changes during this long period of time, even though they might have remained in a relatively unchanging environment. By forming such a series the story of evolving life can, possibly, become a little clearer.

Biologists agree that the many-celled living things, both plants and animals, took their origin from single-celled forms. The only part of this story we wish to consider in this discussion is that dealing with the transition from the single- to the multi-celled organisms. Of the several theories that have been formulated by biologists during the past hundred years, we shall consider the two which are currently most popular although neither is completely satisfactory. Consult Figure 4-1 during the following discussion.

The Colonial Theory. Surveying the thousands of unicellular organisms (protozoa and protophyta) the most likely candidates for the most primitive cells are those which bear **flagella** (p.178). Among these the flagellates which contain **chlorophyll,** a green plant pigment, are usually selected as the most primitive and are therefore thought of as the starting point for all subsequent evolution. This group of flagellates contains a large assemblage of those that exist singly to those that exist in groups called colonies. Starting with the single-celled *Chlamydomonas,* one can arrange a graded series where individuals differ only in number of cells that cling together. *Eudorina* is composed of a ball of sixteen cells embedded in a matrix of jelly-like material. Each of the cells is not greatly different from *Chlamydomonas.* The combined beating of their flagella causes the entire colony to roll along in a graceful manner. Another form, *Pleodorina,* is composed of many more cells, clustered in the shape of a hollow sphere; aside from the increased number of cells there is little difference between this one and *Eudorina.* We do note one rather interesting dissimilarity. Not all of the cells are the same size; some are smaller than others, and during reproduction the smaller ones are unable to produce new colonies, in other words, they are **sterile.** Therefore, in this form there seem to be two kinds of cells, **reproductive cells** and sterile or **soma cells.**

A much larger aggregate is illustrated by *Volvox,* a beautiful hollow spherical colony consisting of several thousand cells. Again these cells resemble *Chlamydomonas* in most respects, although there are tiny bridges between individuals which tend to lock them together more securely than the loose jelly of other forms. Most all of the cells are alike although there are some here and there that are larger and have a different appearance. These are the reproductive cells; all others are soma cells. A more careful observation will reveal that the reproductive cells are of several kinds. Some are bundles of tiny bodies, the **sperm** or male cells, while others are large ovoid **egg** cells. These special **sex cells** reproduce the colony by a **sexual process;** that is, the sperm are released into the water where they swim to and unite with the egg. This subsequently becomes a **zygote,** which hibernates in a heavy-walled zygospore. Other reproductive cells merely divide and move into the hollow of the sphere where they become small colonies, known as **daughter colonies.** These eventually burst out, destroying the mother and becoming adult colonies themselves.

Two striking events occurred in this gradual association of cells. First, similar cells aggregated into a mass which appar-

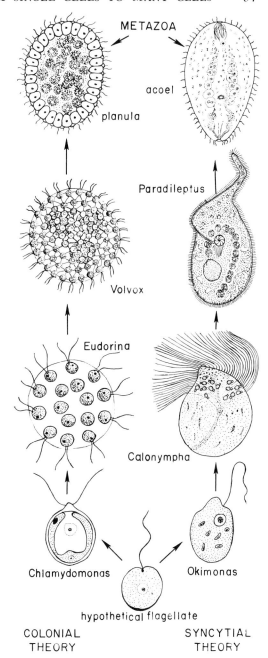

FIG. 4-1. A schematic representation of the colonial and syncytial theories for the origin of the metazoa.

ently succeeded better; that is, there was strength in union probably because of increased size. Second, **division of labor** was initiated among the cells, some becoming sterile and functioning only in locomotion and food-getting, whereas others retained the primitive condition of colony-reproducing. Some of the reproductive cells became highly modified into eggs and sperm while others merely retained their primitive characteristics of reproducing by simple fission. In other words, a differentiation of function took place among the cells of the aggregate, definitely marking it off from the isolated single cells and at the same time creating the first step in the organization of a complex animal through the loss of the power of reproduction by some of the cells. Once this step was taken, differentiation of the soma cells continued in various directions toward greater and greater complexity, and thus to higher animals.

This gradual advance in complexity might be compared to the evolution of our own society. The protozoa may be compared to primitive man who lived alone and was compelled to obtain all of his own food, make his own clothing, and provide his own shelter. Existence by this crude means made chances for survival poor, and mortality high. Later, man associated himself with others in the common interest of survival and of making the drudgery of life less grueling. The first groups were made up of the immediate family; they lived together, hunted together, and made shelters together. In other words, they performed all the duties acting as a group rather than singly as heretofore. Food was easier to secure because they could surround and kill larger animals, their shelters could be more elaborate, and the burdens which fell upon each individual were not as great as when each lived alone. Such aggregation grew to include larger groups until small villages were formed; with the increasing numbers of individuals participating in mass efforts, less responsibility fell to each one, and what was more important, each shared in the results of the

mass efforts. They all lived better and longer. This method of living has finally developed into our modern civilization.

Following this analogy, we can think of primitive society as resembling the single-celled animal and modern society as the complex metazoan, such as the mammal. As the cells began to aggregate into groups, individual cells specialized in particular jobs, and the group as a whole became more complex. There are animals all along the evolutionary scale which represent steps in increasing complexity.

If we look at some of the simplest metazoan animals alive today we may be able to guess which ones were the most likely candidates for the next step toward greater complexity. In order to fulfill the requirements the animal should be some modification of the spherical ball seen in *Volvox*. If such a sphere of cells pushed in on one side (p. 624) it would become a two-layered sac. The coelenterate, *Hydra,* is such an example (Fig. 8-6). We shall study this fascinating creature later in detail; it is only necessary at this point to examine its anatomy briefly in order to carry further the idea of increasing complexity.

Hydra is made up of many cells, mostly soma cells, which are arranged in two layers. Some of the cells in the outside layer (**ectoderm**) have differentiated into "nettle cells" for stinging purposes in defense or offense. Others are able to lengthen and shorten during locomotion and to convey impulses (**neuromuscular cells**). Still others have the ability to give rise to sperm and eggs, and to new individuals by bud formation. Here, then, we see that the soma cells have differentiated into several kinds, while the sex cells remain much like they were in *Volvox*. Division of labor has started among the soma cells which is the next step in the development of more complex animals.

The Syncytial Theory. Whereas the Colonial Theory may seem to be a reasonable

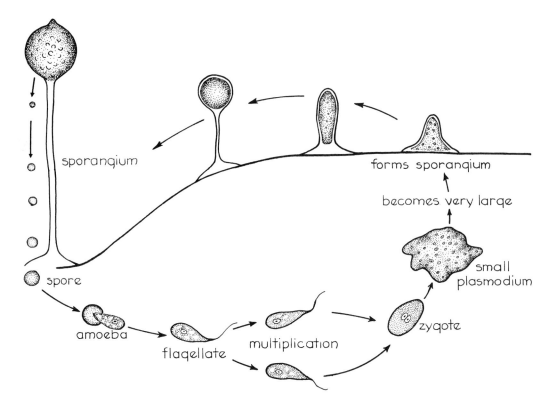

FIG. 4-2. The life history of a slime mold.

explanation for the origin of the metazoa, and most biologists adhere to the hypothesis, still it is not the only one. Let us consider the so-called Syncytial Theory which stems from the fact that there exists a group of microscopic marine metazoan animals, called **acoel turbellarians** (p.233) which possess primitive characteristics (Fig. 4-1). Their bodies are composed of a protoplasmic mass in which nuclei are present with no cell membranes. Such an arrangement is called a *syncytium* and it is not infrequently found among both simple and complex animals. For example, skeletal muscle of vertebrates is a syncytium (p. 104). Among the protozoa there are some multinucleated ciliates, such as *Paradileptus*, which appear to be quite similar to the acoels. They approximate them in size and are covered with short cilia. Going back a step farther

we find among the flagellated protozoa such forms as *Calonympha* which likewise has many nuclei and numerous long flagella. Most protozoologists believe that the ciliates arose from the flagellates and that the ancestral type from which these complex flagellates were derived were the simple colorless flagellates such as *Oikomonas*. The starting point for both theories is a chlamydomonas-like flagellate.

Syncytial organization is also found among lower forms such as the **slime molds** (Fig. 4-2). At one stage in their life history they are single-celled flagellates and while in this stage multiplication by fission results in huge numbers of individuals. At some later time these haploid (p. 659) cells fuse to form an amoeba-like **zygote** (p. 662) which moves about much the same as an amoeba does. Nuclear division occurs without the formation of cell membranes forming a **plasmodium** (syncytium) which grows to be very large (25 centimeters or more). It is this stage that suggests its name. Then a very strange thing happens. The large mass comes to rest and sends up stalks with bulb-like expansions at the top (the whole structure is called a **sporangium**). The nuclei that go to form the stalk produce cells which are quite different from those of the plasmodium. In other words, these sterile soma cells undergo differentiation (p. 631). Reproductive cells are produced in the form of resistant spores in the expanded knob at the tips of the stalks. These are discharged at the proper time and each hatches into a tiny amoeba which soon develops a flagellum and the cycle is completed. The interesting point about this organism is that some cells are produced which die when the reproductive cells have been produced, just as the mother colony (soma cells) dies in *Volvox*. We see in this strange organism the separation of the reproductive and soma cells and differentiation in the latter. The simple flagellate in both is an intricate part of the life cycle and may be considered the starting point. In each the gap between single isolated cells and aggregated masses of cells was bridged resulting in an organism that can be called a metazoan.

It is generally agreed that the fungi did not give rise to higher metazoa or metaphyta, but they do show us how a multinucleate mass of protoplasm can "cellularize" and give support to the Syncytial Theory.

Regardless of which theory is correct, and we shall never know, there is no doubt among biologists that the metazoa arose from protozoan ancestors. Once cells aggregated into masses and began to differentiate, each group of cells performing specific tasks, animals became larger and were able to invade more niches, hence became more varied in form and function. Through this process, the tremendous variety of ani-

mals that live on the earth today have emerged.

From the simplest metazoans to the most complex, division of labor has occurred among the soma cells, resulting in specialized cells. The major types of such specialized cells are not great in number but each type has several kinds. Let us examine these cells and how they are organized in higher animals.

ORGANIZATION OF CELLS INTO TISSUES

Division of labor among the soma cells spread throughout the metazoa until a wide variety of cells was produced, each doing a specific job. Cells of the same kind grouped together in a continuous mass form a **tissue**. A particular kind of tissue is not necessarily limited to one region of an animal body, but usually is found in several different places, where it may or may not perform the same function. There are five major kinds of tissues, **epithelial, supporting, blood, muscular,** and **nervous.** All of the tissues will be discussed in this section except blood which is considered on p. 567. Although tissues are found in all groups of animals except the protozoa, for simplicity let us consider only those found in the vertebrate such as man.

Epithelial Tissues. These are the surface tissues which cover and line not only the outside of the body but the cavities within as well. They are composed of closely fitting cells forming continuous membranes and with very little intercellular material binding them together. Since the jobs performed by epithelial tissues vary greatly, these tissues exhibit a wide variety of form (Fig. 4-3). The tissue is usually named according to the shape of its constituent cells, for example, **squamous** (flat), **cuboidal** (cubes), and **columnar** (columns or pillars). They may also be described in terms of accessory structures such as **flagella, col-**

FIG. 4-3. Epithelial tissue.

lars, or **cilia.** Finally, the tissue may be referred to as **stratified** if the cells have different forms and lie several cells in thickness.

In addition to protection, epithelial cells that line cavities usually have the function of **secretion,** which is the production of special substances used by the organism in various ways. For example, the cells lining the digestive tract are mostly secretory in function. These cells form the secreting portion of **glands,** whether the gland is single- or many-celled. In multicellular glands the secreting cells may lie beneath the surrounding surface forming simple tubes (**tubular glands)** or flask-shaped pockets (**alveolar glands).** Such tubes and pockets may be single structures (**simple glands)** or they may be grouped into aggregates (**compound glands)** (Fig. 4-4).

Supporting Tissues. These are the tissues that give the body form and support. They are composed of cells embedded in a **matrix,** secreted by the cells and usually occupying more space than the cells themselves. The matrix may be composed of fluid, gelatinous material, long tough fibers, or hard mineralized material. There are several different kinds of supporting tissue, all dependent on the type of matrix (Fig. 4-5).

The tough **ligaments** that fasten the bones together and the **tendons** that connect the muscles to the bones are composed mostly of tough fibers forming a matrix about the cells which produce them. Also, many of the internal organs of the body are laced together by sheets of similar tissue called **mesenteries.** In this type of tissue the fibers lie at random with no particular arrangement; this results in a thin layer of tissue that is soft and pliable, yet tough. A similar type makes up most of the deeper portions of the skin lying below the superficial epithelium. It is this supporting tissue that gives the skin the qualities essential for an adequate body covering.

Animals, particularly land forms, require a very rigid skeleton to support their massive weights. This is provided by **bone** and **cartilage,** types of supporting tissue that are composed of large quantities of matrix secreted by isolated cells. In the case of cartilage the matrix is a spongy semisolid mass in which cells are embedded in tiny cavities **(lacunae).** The cells are usually single, although as they divide there may be as many as four in one cavity before they finally separate. Cartilage is excellent material to resist shock; therefore, it is found between bones such as the vertebrae. It also provides ideal support for the tip of the nose and the external ear where retention of shape and pliability are essential. Bone, on the other hand, consists of a mineralized matrix (calcium carbonate and phosphate) which is very rigid, imparting an element of solidarity to the entire structure. In this case also, the matrix is formed from cells embedded in tiny spaces (lacunae) within the matrix itself. These usually take on definite patterns around blood vessels and nerves, called **Haversian systems.** All of the cells have access to a food supply from the blood system by means of tiny canals **(canaliculi),** for these

cells are alive and must be nourished like any other cells (Fig. 4-5).

Tissue in which fat is stored is often classified as supporting tissue, primarily because there seems to be no other category for it. It performs no mechanical function other that to occupy space. The fat is stored within the cell itself and these cells are located under the skin and in the abdominal region as well as other well-known areas of the human body. During periods of starvation it is very scanty, but during good times it may be stored in quantities far beyond any usefulness to its owner, as attested by many overweight people.

Muscular Tissue. This tissue, called muscle tissue, has the ability to shorten, that is, to pull its two ends closer together. This apparently very simple action is responsible for all of the movements of most organisms. Muscle tissue consists of elongated cells or fibers whose internal parts consist of **myofibrillae,** tiny contractile fibrils, lying in a fluid protoplasm called **sarcoplasm.** There are three well-defined kinds of muscle tissue, *visceral, skeletal,* and *cardiac,* each of which differs in its appearance under the microscope (Fig. 4-6).

Visceral muscle is found in the walls

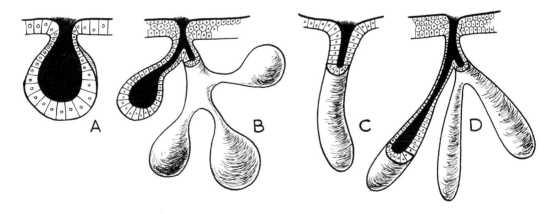

FIG. 4-4. Various kinds of glands that arise from epithelial tissue. A. A simple flask-shaped gland (alveolar) such as that found in the skin of the frog used to secrete mucus. B. A compound alveolar gland such as that found in the salivary glands. C. A simple tubular gland such as that in the lining of the intestine. D. A compound tubular gland such as that found in the stomach lining.

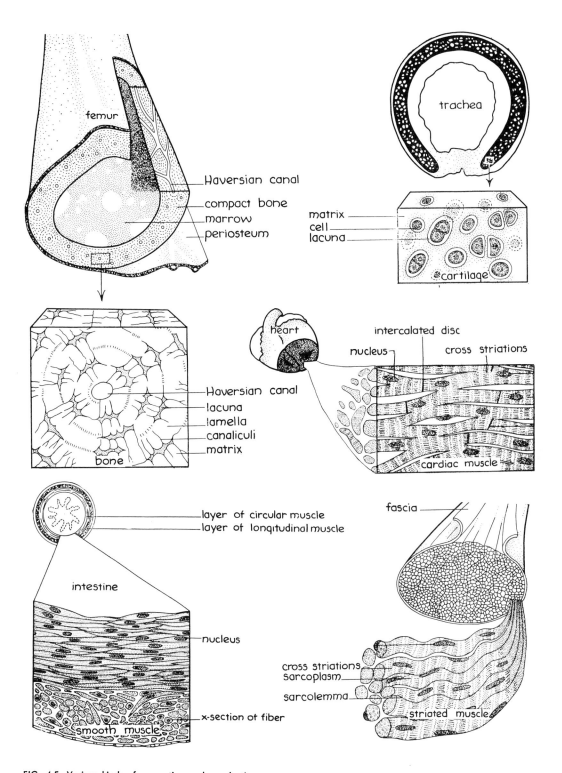

FIG. 4-5. Various kinds of supporting and muscle tissues.

FIG. 4-6. These are photographs of rabbit skeletal muscle taken through the electron microscope. The top picture is a longitudinal section of the fibers showing the numerous bands characteristic of voluntary muscle. Note the numerous tiny fibrils that make up each fiber. The fibers are shown in cross-section in the bottom photograph. Note the regular spacing of the fibrils. It is from such studies that our knowledge of muscular action is continually increased.

of the digestive tract, and other places in the body which are not under voluntary nervous control; its activity is primarily automatic. The cells are spindle-shaped with centrally located flattened nuclei, and with myofibrillae running lengthwise in them. It is the shortening of the myofibrillae that pulls the two ends of the muscle cell closer together. Visceral muscle contracts and relaxes slowly, a behavior which is quite satisfactory for the kind of job it has to do.

The **skeletal** muscles are usually attached to bones and they constitute the large muscles of the body. It is this muscle-bone combination that is responsible for the movement of the body as a whole. These muscle cells are peculiar in that they are not marked off by definite cell membranes, and a single skeletal muscle fiber is composed of many cells whose nuclei lie at regular intervals along the periphery of the fiber just under the surrounding membrane (**sarcolemma**). The fiber is called a **syncytium,** referred to earlier (p. 98). Another marked difference between this muscle and the preceding is that there are dark and light transverse bands extending throughout the fiber. These **striations** identify the tissue as striated muscle (Fig. 4-5). The skeletal fibers contract suddenly with considerable force, an essential feature in moving the body. They can contract rapidly again and again with only momentary rest periods.

Cardiac or heart muscle is characteristic of vertebrates and is not found in the heart of any of the lower forms. It differs from skeletal muscle in that all of the fibers are connected with one another so that the entire organ functions as a unit, that is, as a **syncytium.** This is an apparent advantage because the nature of its job requires almost continuous operation. Striations are present, but the nuclei are located deep within the fibers rather than at the surface as in the skeletal muscle fibers. Cardiac muscle cells are so closely connected with

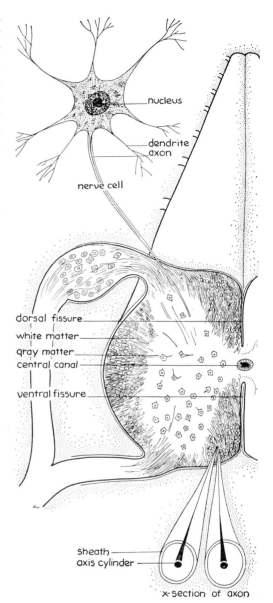

FIG. 4-7. Nerve tissue as found in the spinal cord and ganglia.

one another that a single nerve impulse sets them all contracting at once, thus executing a single powerful contraction. This is obviously very desirable in a pump such as the heart.

Nerve Tissue. This type of tissue is composed of **neurons,** special conducting cells that are found throughout the brains and nerve cords of all animals that possess a centralized nervous system (Fig. 4-7). The nerve cell is composed of a **cell body,** which contains the nucleus and surrounding cytoplasm. Extending out from the cell body are threadlike fibers, consisting of numerous **dendrites** which normally convey impulses to the cell body and a single **axon** which usually conducts impulses away from the cell body. The cell body maintains the nutrition of the entire neuron, and if it is destroyed the fibers die. However, nerve fibers severed from their cell body will usually be replaced by new fibers growing out from the cell body.

Cell bodies are concentrated into masses, the most conspicuous of which are in the **brain** and in the **spinal cord;** other masses called **ganglia** have special locations in the body. The nerves that we see on dissection are made up entirely of fibers, each of which is insulated by a fatty sheath, the **myelinated sheath.** These units go to make up the complex nervous system which we shall study in more detail in a later chapter.

ORGANIZATION OF TISSUES INTO ORGANS AND ORGAN SYSTEMS

By definition any structure which performs a given function is an **organ.** Obviously, a single contractile cell could be an organ under this general definition. However, in the usual, restricted sense, an organ is a group of tissues assembled for the purpose of performing a specific function. The small intestine, for example, is an organ whose function is the digestion and absorption of food. It is composed of layers of different tissues—an outer layer of epithelial tissue covers the gut throughout its length; immediately inside this are two layers of muscle tissue, then a layer of connective tissue, and finally a thin layer, one cell thick, of lining epithelium. Nerves and blood vessels

are interspersed among the other tissues. All of these tissues perform specific jobs in bringing about the greater function of digestion and absorption of food. Even so, the small intestine is not adequate to complete the job of ingestion, digestion, absorption, and egestion as a single organ. This greater function involves a series of organs, the mouth, teeth, esophagus, stomach, small intestine, liver, pancreas, colon, and anus. In other words, the entire job is done by a **system of organs.** Likewise, circulation, breathing, excretion, and indeed all bodily functions are performed by different organ systems. The combined organ systems in integrated action constitute an **organism,** or an **individual.** This can be relegated to the cellular level, as in the case of an amoeba in which all of the activities take place within a single cell. On the multicellular level, tissues, organs, and organ systems have been assembled to make up an organism which functions as a unit, just as the single cell functions as a unit.

The Consequences of Organization

As animals grew in bulk and complexity the problems of transport and coordination had to be solved. Such activities as nutrition, respiration, and excretion, which were performed in a simple manner when the cell was in constant contact with its fluid world, became difficult or impossible when it was separated from this environment by even a few covering layers of cells. Such inner cells would have to depend on diffusion to carry oxygen and food to them and to remove wastes from them. At best this is a slow process and certainly not rapid enough to allow an animal to grow very big or become very active. Therefore, specific organ systems had to be evolved if animals were to grow in bulk and activity.

In the following discussion we shall compare some of the activities of organisms at the cellular and multicellular levels, pointing out the problems involved in becoming complex and indicating how the metazoan animal has solved them. We can use paramecium for the single-cell level, hydra for a simple metazoan, and a mammal for the multicellular level.

Locomotion and Coordination. With increase in size of cellular aggregates the problem of getting around in the environment required a new approach. Flagella were quite inadequate to move a really large animal, although they were quite satisfactory in single-celled forms, even quite large ones, as well as in small metazoans. Moreover, some means had to be established whereby the individual cells could be connected to each other by some communicating system, so that they would do whatever was necessary in a coordinated fashion. Chaos would have resulted had this not been accomplished.

The Metazoa solved the problem of movement through the agency of contractile cells which are called **muscles.** These are very simple fibers distributed in certain strategically located cells of the primitive metazoan; in more advanced forms these cells became highly specialized as you have just seen (p. 102). Their job was to move the organism in all of its parts in an efficient manner, if it was to survive. Indeed, its very life depended on the efficiency of these contracting cells, both in securing food and defending itself against injury. Hence, with increasing complexity a more and more elaborate system of muscles evolved reaching the pinnacle of perfection in such animals as insects and mammals.

Along with the evolution of muscles, other cells specialized into conducting units, called **nerves,** which developed to a high degree the capacity of conveying signals from one cell to another, frequently over long distances. This made possible a closely knit communicating system which was essential if animals of any great size were to succeed. How elaborate this system has become in metazoans is demonstrated by

a careful analysis of the communicating system of large mammals such as the whale or man.

Requirements of Metabolism. At the one-celled level the problems of securing food, digesting it, absorbing it, metabolizing it, and removing the waste products, are a relatively simple procedure. The paramecium (Fig. 4-8) draws its bacterial food supply into its gullet, forming food vacuoles which might be thought of as miniature intracellular "stomachs." Digestion takes place in these tiny sacs and the end products (amino acids, glucose, fatty acids, and glycerol) are absorbed into the surrounding cytoplasm. The food is oxidized and the released energy is utilized by the protozoan in the many ways that are essential for its life.

The simple metazoan, such as *Hydra,* captures and digests its food by the cooperative effort of many cells, some of which are contractile and conducting. The food is captured by the tentacles and conveyed to the body cavity where it is retained until the lining cells secrete enzymes to digest it. The end products are then absorbed directly by the lining cells where some are used for metabolism and the remaining portion sent along by diffusion to the external layer of cells.

In a complex metazoan, such as a sheep (Fig. 4-8), the simple process of diffusion will not suffice to transport the food molecules to the millions of cells that lie great distances from the digestive tract. A **circulatory system** is required in any metazoan of great size. This is provided by a system of tubes in which a fluid (blood) is in constant movement in a one-way path. Some portion of the system has thin-walled tubules which come very close to every cell in the organism and which are so thin that they are no more than one or two cells thick. These tubules are called **capillaries** (p. 556). With such a system it is possible to nourish all the cells in the metazoan.

In *Hydra,* all that is needed is a place where the food can be held sufficiently long so that digestive enzymes pouring into it will have time to break the complex food molecules into their end products. Then proper facilities are needed for absorption, that is, large surface areas are required.

These conditions are met in the digestive tract of all higher animals very satisfactorily. They possess a portal of entry or mouth, which may or may not be armed with teeth for macerating food, and a long tube into which digestive glands empty their food-splitting enzymes. Undigested food leaves through the end of the tube, the anus. Once the food has reached the soluble stage it is absorbed into the blood and transported to each cell, which picks and chooses the particular energy-giving and constructive materials it requires.

Once the food molecules are delivered to the cells, they must be oxidized and this requires oxygen. In *Paramecium* this is cared for very efficiently and simply by diffusion through the cell membrane (Fig. 4-8). Once in the cell, the oxygen diffuses to the food molecules with which it combines, forming carbon dioxide and water as end products. Carbon dioxide likewise diffuses throughout the protoplasm ultimately passing through the cell membrane into the ex-

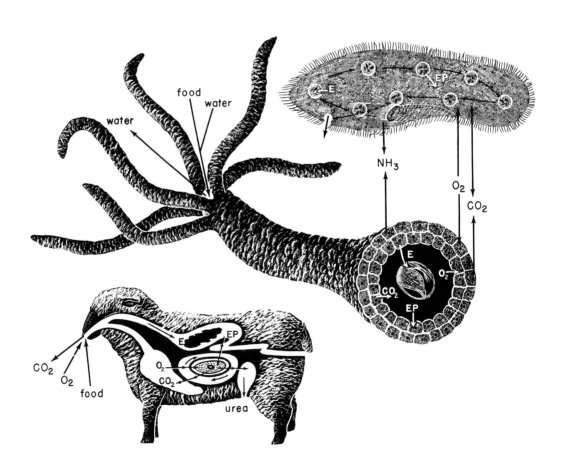

FIG. 4-8. The problem of consuming food, digesting it, burning it, and excreting the waste products is essentially the same at all levels of animal organization. Here it is compared in the single-celled animal, paramecium, the simple metazoan, hydra, and in a highly complex form such as a sheep. The problem is always reduced to the level of the cell and must be solved at that level in all animals. The letters EP refer to end products and E refers to enzymes.

ternal fluid world. The only essential need is sufficient oxygen in the immediate environment.

This gaseous exchange is essentially the same in the simple metazoan where each cell is in contact with its external world. Since water circulates within the cavity the lining cells are adequately supplied with oxygen. Diffusion, therefore, is quite adequate to take care of the gaseous exchange of this simple animal.

In the complex metazoan the same problems arise as were encountered in supplying nourishment to each cell. Since most of the cells lie deep within the organism, there is no possible chance for gaseous exchange by diffusion with the external world, especially since the organism is usually covered with skin which is impervious to such gases. The complex metazoan solves the problem by developing a **breathing system.** This, in combination with the transportation system, would make it possible to deliver and remove the gases from each cell. In aquatic forms such as fish, the breathing organs are **gills;** in land forms such as the sheep, they are **lungs.** Both must meet certain requirements if they are to function as breathing organs. They must be constructed so that oxygen in the surrounding medium (water or air) can pass readily into the transporting medium (blood) which will convey the gas to each body cell. This means that the blood must flow in capillaries very close to the external environment in order that the exchange can be really accomplished. Microscopic examination of a gill filament or lung sac will reveal that this condition is met. Blood flowing through the capillaries passes within two cells of the outside world (Fig. 4-8), which makes the gaseous exchange possible by simple diffusion.

The transporting system delivers oxygen to the cells of the body and collects the carbon dioxide from them. The latter is conducted to the breathing organs where it is lost to the outside environment. Thus,

by the combined operation of the breathing and transporting systems each cell of a complex body consisting of millions of cells can be as readily supplied with oxygen and relieved of its carbon dioxide as can a single cell. This accomplishment removed one of the size limitations on metazoan animals.

Other end products of metabolism must be removed from the cell constantly, if it is to survive. These are those resulting from the metabolism of nitrogen compounds, such as amino acids. They are nitrogenous compounds such as ammonia and urea which are toxic if retained within the cell or its immediate vicinity. They are normally eliminated through the cell membrane (p. 73) and simple diffusion is quite adequate for the single cell. At the multicellular level, however, diffusion is quite inadequate to do the job and without some means of removing these toxic substances the cells cannot survive. Hence, an effective **excretory system** was required in any animal where the cells were located any distance from the surface.

The simple metazoan, like the single-celled animal, gets rid of its nitrogenous wastes by simple diffusion (Fig. 4-8), where there are but two layers of cells, each in contact with the external world, the problem of excretion is readily solved.

In most complex metazoans, an elaborate system of selectively absorbing tubules, in combination with the transportation system, evolved to take care of these waste products (p. 592). By a process involving filtration, selective reabsorption, and secretion, wastes are removed from the blood and conveyed out of the body. Most metazoans above the two-layered animals possess such a system of excretory tubules. In the most primitive animals there are many units scattered among the cells so that fluid bathing these cells can find its way to one of these tubules and be relieved of its load of nitrogenous wastes. In more advanced forms the many excretory units become compactly arranged in a single organ, the **kidney.**

Reproduction. Certain other complications also arose when cells aggregated into huge masses. The single-celled forms depend primarily on increasing their numbers by the process of simple *fission,* that is, the cell merely splits into two offspring, each retaining the exact characteristics of the parent cell. Whenever *Paramecium,* for example, reaches a certain size, it divides and continues growing. The rate at which it can increase its numbers under favorable conditions is limited only by its food supply and its capacity to build protoplasm. The progeny are thus all alike and, barring accidental death, live forever.

Most multicellular animals do not employ simple fission as a means of increasing their numbers, but rely on special cells, **eggs** and **sperm,** which, with a few exceptions, must unite to produce a new individual. This process has the advantage of uniting two lines of protoplasm which results in variation in the offspring. The progeny always possess a combination of the parental characteristics and are therefore different from either. Variation seems to have some advantage in survival of the species and probably has been important in the gradual evolution of complex forms.

These specialized reproductive cells of higher animals are generated in special organs called **gonads.** Eggs are produced in the **ovary** and sperm in the **testis.** To insure the union of the sex cells, special tubules are usually necessary to conduct these cells out of the body, and ultimate union is still more effectively assured in some higher animals by the development of copulatory organs. To insure greater survival, the offspring of many higher animals are either retained within large egg shells or the body of the mother for varying periods of their early development. All of this machinery apparently has survival

value because it is found in complex metazoans.

The Penalty of Organization. What are the sacrifices, if any, that animals have made for becoming complex? The organization of cells into masses and the subsequent specialization of different kinds have resulted in organisms that are able to penetrate many different environments because of their greater motility and intricately adjusted bodies. This means an increased number of species as well as individuals; and we think of this as biological success. Along with all of the benefits derived from specialization, however, has come at least one rather severe penalty, and that is natural death.

Single cells reproducing by simple fission, barring accidental death, live on forever. You will recall that the *Volvox* mother colony and the soma cells of the slime mold died when the reproductive cells were produced. Obviously, death put in its appearance when cells became specialized to function in capacities other than reproduction. Such specialized cells which had lost the power of reproduction were sacrificed and those which retained reproductive capacity were able to continue.

It is difficult to understand why cells that are separate, free from other cells, may continue living forever, whereas others that are bound together into a mass must eventually die even though, apparently, all of their basic needs are satisfied. Perhaps during the process of evolution the organization was not quite perfect; that is, the individual cells were not completely cared for, or perhaps the whole organization slowed down after a certain period of time and could not keep pace with the demands of all the cells. This point has long intrigued biologists and has resulted in some very fruitful research.

If it were possible to grow tissues away from the animal of which they are a part, it would be possible to determine whether or not such cells once released from their intended environment could survive like single isolated cells. In 1907 Ross G. Harrison, succeeded in growing embryonic tissues in flasks by feeding them special nutrients (p. 71). Alexis Carrel, employing similar methods, kept embryonic chick heart tissues alive for over 30 years. At the end of this period of time, about three times the normal life span of a chicken heart remaining with its owner, the cells were active, although some changes had occurred. These cells apparently have the capacity to live forever, just as single-celled animals do. Many tissues have since been kept in culture for years and, whereas slight modifications do occur in their morphology and perhaps in their physiology, they do remain alive. It seems that metazoan cells have retained their immortality, but the subtle changes that occur when removed from the animal may be the same ones that bring about senescence when in the intact animal. Recent studies have shown that cells both in the intact animal and in the test tube gradually change with time. Some protozoa demonstrate a definite life cycle, showing youth, maturity, and old age, each stage demonstrating physiological and morphological change. So we cannot say that all single cells are immortal, although some seem to be. As in most problems in biology, there is no simple answer to aging. The process may vary in different cells in both unicellular and multicellular animals, but until we know a great deal more than at present, the problem remains unsolved.

SUGGESTED SUPPLEMENTARY READINGS

BLOOM, W., and FAWCETT, D. W., *A Textbook of Histology* (Philadelphia, W. B. Saunders Co., 1962).

ROMER, A. S., *The Vertebrate Body* (Philadelphia, W. B. Saunders Co., 1962).

THOMPSON, D. W., *On Growth and Form* (New York, The Macmillan Co., 1942).

PART IV

Animal Relationships

5

The Animal and Its Environment

SO FAR we have considered the origin of animal life in a physical world, centering our attention on the animal itself rather than the environment in which it thrives. Since the animal is closely integrated with its environment, it is necessary to devote some attention to this relationship, which is the study of **ecology.** Our particular emphasis will be on animal ecology, although no ecological study can ignore the role played by the plants.

Great variations in the environments of the world are caused by such physical factors as light, temperature, and moisture, all of which have a profound effect upon the physical and physiological characteristics of animals. These physical factors not only determine the kinds of animals that are able to survive in certain regions but are also instrumental in building up associations between animals and plants. Thus the problem in ecology is twofold: first, to consider the individual animal in terms of certain physical factors in its environment; second, to study the relationship between organisms living together.

FIG. 5-1. Jumping mouse (*Zapus hudsonius*) in active condition (above) and hibernating (below).

PHYSICAL AND CHEMICAL FACTORS IN THE ENVIRONMENT

Temperature

Everyone is fully aware of his own sensitivity to change in temperature. We usually want our houses at a relatively constant temperature of about 23°C and experience discomfort if it deviates a few degrees one way or the other. Our internal environment is even more critical—there a rise of a few

degrees indicates sickness of a serious sort. What is true of man in this respect is equally true of many animals. When we consider that the temperatures known to us range from 273°C below zero to several thousand degrees above zero, it is rather remarkable that life exists in that extremely narrow range of a few degrees above freezing to about 45°C. Even within these narrow limits the physiological processes do their best work at an **optimal point** around the middle, on either side of which the rate of physiological reaction falls off. Animals tend to seek out a temperature that, at least most of the time, will permit their bodily activities to proceed at an optimal rate.

Since animals are found in all parts of the earth, even the polar regions, they must find ways of surviving extremes of temperature with the least amount of discomfort to themselves. Those living in colder regions either have a constant body temperature (**homiothermal**) or else have developed a hardiness to cold that permits them to survive. The internal environment of the warm-blooded animals—birds and mammals—is relatively constant and always maintains the temperature at which physiological activities can proceed at an optimal rate. Cold-blooded animals (**poikilothermal**), on the other hand, vary their internal temperature and rate of reaction in accordance with the external environment. When the temperature drops, the animal becomes sluggish, even to the point of complete inactivity. Some can stand freezing for short periods of time. On a chilly morning in the fall of the year it is simple to capture a cold-blooded animal, from a common housefly to a rattlesnake, but the task becomes more difficult on a hot summer day when the temperature approaches 35°C. Only at the higher temperature are most activities at their maximum.

During cold seasons some mammals undergo a period of inactivity called **hiber-**

nation, when their temperature drops and metabolic processes are reduced to a minimum. Hibernating rodents, such as the jumping mouse (Fig. 5-1), pass into almost complete inactivity, their heart and breathing rates slowing down markedly. Indeed metabolism is just enough to keep the animal alive. The energy to maintain life is derived from stored fat, hence the fat bear in the fall and the lean bear in the spring of the year.

Some cold-blooded animals put forth communal effort to prevent too great a drop in temperature. Bees, for example, become very active on cold winter days, beating their wings almost continuously. This keeps the temperature in the hive above freezing even though the outside temperature may be several degrees below zero. Snakes frequently aggregate in dens in the fall of the year for the apparent purpose of keeping warm. Even though they are cold-blooded, their temperature stays slightly above that of the external environment. By coiling about one another in large masses, the whole group stays a little warmer because the individual heat loss is reduced.

Keeping in mind that all living things are tuned to such a narrow temperature band, try to imagine what would happen if the earth's orbit shifted ever so slightly, just enough to change the average mean temperature on the earth by a paltry 100°C up or down. All life would stop abruptly; every living thing would congeal from either freezing or cooking. Think how precarious our existence is, reckoned in astronomical terms. A slight celestial slip would mean the end of life as we know it.

Moisture

We are already familiar with the importance of water in relation to life processes (p. 50); here we need to consider it as an essential part of the environment. Getting the proper amount of water at the right time is one of the basic problems that con-

fronts animals. This is sometimes very difficult and, as a result, animals are equipped with various means for maintaining their water supply at a constant level. Although too much water is as detrimental to some animals as too little is to others, probably the greatest problem for most animals is the conservation of water.

Even protozoa have provided themselves with a method of withstanding desiccation. Amoeba, for example, forms a resistant cyst which is impervious to water loss (Fig. 5-2). While housed in this tiny container the amoeba can withstand long periods of drouth without ill effects. The eggs of many metazoan animals such as crustacea and rotifers are provided with a thick shell which resists drying. The eggs of many parasitic roundworms are likewise resistant to moisture loss. Some can be blown around in the dust for months and still become active when picked up by the proper host. In fact, some even rely on this period of desiccation to disseminate the species.

Other animals survive periods of intense heat by going into an inactive state called estivation. This is strikingly demonstrated by the African lungfish, which lives in regions that are apt to dry up during the summer months (Fig. 5-3). With the ap-

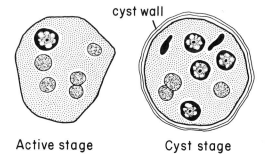

cyst wall

Active stage   Cyst stage

FIG. 5-2. Some protozoa such as the human intestinal parasitic amoeba (*Entamoeba histolytica*) withstand periods outside the digestive tract where there is very little moisture. This it does by secreting a resistant cyst wall that prevents desiccation. It is in this stage that the parasite is transmitted from person to person.

proach of hot weather and desiccation, the fish burrows in the mud and secretes a capsule in which it passes the warm dry months. When the temperature drops and moisture returns, it resumes its active life once more.

Some large animals, desert turtles and lizards for example, never require water in the liquid state; they manage very well on that which is taken in with their food. Camels are notorious for their ability to work long periods without water. They can exist a week or more on dry food, and if green plants are available it is not uncommon for them to go without water for a month. Jack rabbits, mountain goats, jumping mice, and other mammals living in arid regions are very well fitted to conserve their water intake, which is usually

only that provided in the food. Most mammals, however, require a great abundance of water, especially those that perspire, such as man and the horse.

Excessive moisture is fatal for some animals. The earthworm, for example, is driven from its burrows after heavy rains because it cannot get enough oxygen from the water. Even frogs may drown in spite of the fact that they are usually near water and require it in large quantities. High humidity often creates a favorable environment for certain types of parasites which under normal amounts of moisture could not gain a foothold.

Light

The sun emits electromagnetic radiations which are characterized by a definite **wave length** and **energy content** (Fig. 5-4). The wave lengths extend from less than one Ångstrom unit (gamma rays) to more than a thousand meters (Hertzian or radio waves). This entire extension is referred to as the radiation spectrum. The energy content is inversely proportional to the wave length, that is, the longer the wave length the less the energy. Waves that are utilized in radio, television, and radar signals are some of the longest waves and they are also some of the weakest as far as energy is concerned. As the waves become progressively shorter their energy content increases; X-rays and gamma rays contain a great deal of energy and are also penetrating, hence their use in "looking at" the inside of bodies that light does not penetrate.

Human beings are sensitive to only a very small portion of the radiation spectrum, that is, only to the **light waves.** Our photoreceptor, namely the human eye, is the recording instrument by which we measure light waves based on colors. The eye in combination with the brain perceives the longer light wave lengths as red and the shorter ones as violet. Intermediate wave lengths are recorded as orange, yellow, green and blue (from longer to shorter).

FIG. 5-3. The African lungfish (*Protopterus*) undergoes estivation during periods of drought when the waters disappear from its normal habitat. If placed in a container filled with mud it will form its capsule and remain dormant for many months in this condition. Pictured here is such a fish being released from a can of mud. When placed in water the animal immediately breathes by means of its gills like any other fish.

...A case of concealment by acquiring the color ...on of the surrounding environment. Note how ...part of this swamp eel (*Fluta alba*) resembles ...ding eelgrass.

Some of the lower vertebrates, particularly fish and amphibians, have the ability to change color. They usually attempt to match the background upon which they are resting, obtaining the obvious advantage of camouflage (Fig. 5-5). This is done by condensing or spreading out the pigments that are confined to special skin cells called **chromatophores.** Experimentation has shown that at least one mechanism involves the amount of light that enters the eyes of the animal. This is discussed more fully on p. 481.

Environmental Cycles

The very nature of the movements of the earth brings about the recurrence of conditions in a rhythmic fashion. The earth spins with remarkable precision and this periodism impresses itself on the physical as well as the biological matter existing on it. A moment of reflection will reveal the point of this statement. The daily light cycle, as has already been pointed out, profoundly affects plants and animals. Such minute changes as one or two degrees in man's body temperature, which occurs each day (circadian rhythm), the 28-day menstrual cycle, coincident with the moon cycle, are other illustrations of built-in rhythms. The profound effect that cycles in the physical environment have upon all living things will be referred to in later sections. Here let us consider some of these physical cycles.

The Water Cycle. The abundance of water on the earth is striking; over 73 per cent of the surface is covered by it, and all exposed bodies contain water, as well as the atmosphere above the earth. The organisms that live on the planet are primarily water. Its temperature has a profound effect on all objects near it or in it. Much of the sun's heat energy is stored in the oceans, thus moderating the temperature variation from day to night. Equally important is the screening effect atmospheric water has upon

...by means of gills and must, there-...k out damp places which are more ...» be found in dark places than in ...ted regions.

...: reproductive cycle of some ani-...irticularly birds, is definitely influ-...y light. If daylight is supplemented ...cial illumination the reproductive ...are stimulated to work longer, ...nore eggs and young. Farmers ...ken advantage of this fact by ...g in their chicken houses lights ...urn long after the sun goes down. ...with this is the stimulus that causes ...n in at least some birds. Bees are ...o determine direction by the angle ...in (p. 322).

120

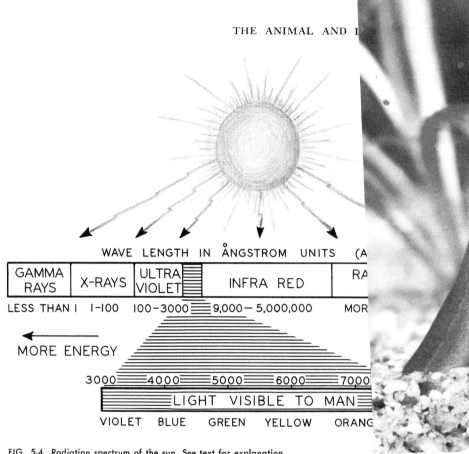

FIG. 5-4. Radiation spectrum of the sun. See text for explanation.

Combined, the entire spectrum of waves visible to man (visible spectrum) appears as "white" light.

Most animals seem to be sensitive to the visible spectrum, although some respond to wave lengths to which we are insensitive. On the other hand, we see wave lengths that some animals are unaware of. Our receptors pick up only about $\frac{1}{125}$ of the total radiation spectrum. Even though light waves make up such a small segment of this spectrum, all animals are profoundly affected by them.

When light energy is absorbed it can be made to do work, providing some mechanism exists which can trap this energy. Plants have such a mechanism in their chloroplasts which has only recently been described. Electron micrographs of sectioned chloroplasts demonstrate laminated bodies, called **grana,** which are the light-

trapping structure
interesting to not
green because the
about 5000 Å., her
this wave length fo
ever, they readily
other wave lengths
Photosynthesis does
are exposed to gree
normally when any
visible light are u
source.

Most animals f
mals orient themsel
intensity. Single-cell
the light intensity
usually neither too
Moths fly toward a li
bright light. The a
may be questionable
the pillbug is relate

high energy radiations coming from space. Without water planet Earth would be uninhabitable, at least with life as we know it. Water follows well-established cycles which play their principle role in establishing climate as it occurs in the various areas of the earth (Fig. 5-6). Let us consider these.

Water constantly **evaporates** from its surface and this is very significant over the oceans, particularly in the tropical regions of the earth because increased temperature hastens evaporation. Water vapor condenses as it rises to form clouds and with subsequent cooling falls as rain or snow. This frequently takes place over the land, particularly on the windward side of mountains. This results in a high rainfall on the oceanside of a mountain range, with very little on the opposite side. The result is fertile valleys on one side of a mountain range and desert on the other. Obviously this movement of water profoundly affects the organisms living in these environments. Most of the rain falling on land eventually makes its way back to the oceans. In mountainous areas the flow is rapid and the resulting torrential streams cut deeply into the earth constantly transforming its surface. As a result of the eroding effect of water new habitats are provided for living things while others are destroyed. Water that seeps into the soil ultimately reaches impervious rock formations which in general conform to the exposed surface of the earth. The underground water, like surface water, finally reaches the ocean only to evaporate again and repeat the cycle.

Within the large bodies of water, such as oceans, massive up and down movements of water, caused by the temperature differential between the hot tropics and the polar regions, bring about a constant shifting of water between the poles and the equator. This results when the cold water of the polar region sinks and the warm water in the tropics rises. These forces, together with the rotation of the earth, as well as wind patterns, create **oceanic currents** which influence the cli-

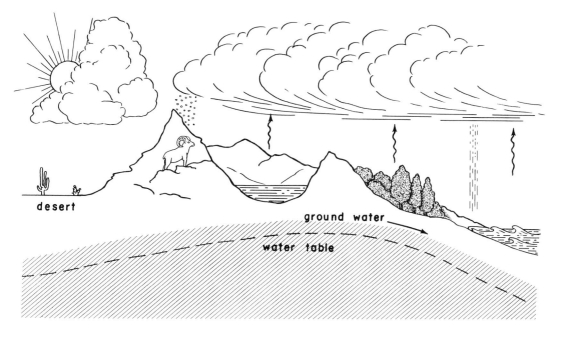

FIG. 5-6. The water cycle.

mate, not only in the sea itself but also on the land masses nearly everywhere on the earth. Again plant and animal life is drastically influenced by such water movements.

The amount of water on the earth is relatively constant but the state it is in has had and is having a marked influence on global climate. The amount of water in the form of polar ice varies over long periods of time, for reasons that are not well understood. Warming and cooling trends come in cycles which last from 60,000 to 200,000 years, during which the polar icecaps recede and expand. During the interglacial periods of geologic history the poles were relatively free of ice; between these the ice moved far south. Consequently the coast lines of the continents are alternately flooded and exposed. Based on careful measurements taken during the last 100 years, it appears that the last ice age reached its peak about 30,000 years ago, and presently there is a warming trend sweeping over the earth. Hotels built at the foot of a glacier 50 years ago are now several miles below it. Plants and animals are gradually moving northward. The ice ages have had a profound effect on living things in the past, and there is no reason to believe that present environmental conditions will not have an effect on living things in the future.

The tremendous mass of protoplasm that exists on earth also has some influence on global climate, and as this mass increases the effect will become more pronounced. Plants and animals release carbon dioxide to the atmosphere in ever increasing amounts, and this is accentuated by the quantity added as waste from industry. As the percentage of this gas increases, the atmosphere will become a more effective heat insulator and result in a warmer global climate. Such a change will affect all life in one way or another.

Chemical Cycles

The elements of which all organisms are composed come from the environment and return to the environment upon the death and subsequent decomposition of the organism. There is, then, a constant cycle of the elements. An atom of carbon residing in a protein molecule that goes to make up one of our muscle cells, let us say, may have been incorporated into any carbon-containing molecule of thousands of plants and animals before us, and will become a part of thousands of living things following us. It might be thought of as a kind of "reincarnation," so to speak, but not the variety that usually comes to mind when this word is mentioned. All elements found in protoplasm follow specific cycles, two of which—the **carbon** and **nitrogen cycles**—will be discussed briefly.

Carbon, being the core element of protoplasm, is conspicuously present in all living things and, like all elements, follows a cyclic pattern (Fig. 5-7). Plants utilize the carbon in carbon dioxide to manufacture fats, carbohydrates, and proteins, as well as many other essential food products. These foods are eaten, digested, and absorbed by animals, and the carbon becomes a part of the body of the animal. During metabolism carbohydrates are burned, releasing carbon dioxide into the air again. Similarly, carbon dioxide is released at night by plants as they oxidize carbohydrates to obtain energy. It must be pointed out, however, that plants also produce carbon dioxide during the daytime, but because it is utilized immediately in the process of photosynthesis, its release is obscured. The burning of organic matter and decaying of dead plants and animals also release carbon dioxide into the air. Such is the extent of the carbon cycle.

The nitrogen cycle (Fig. 5-8) is somewhat more complicated than the carbon cycle, primarily because plants cannot utilize atmospheric nitrogen. Nitrogen in the

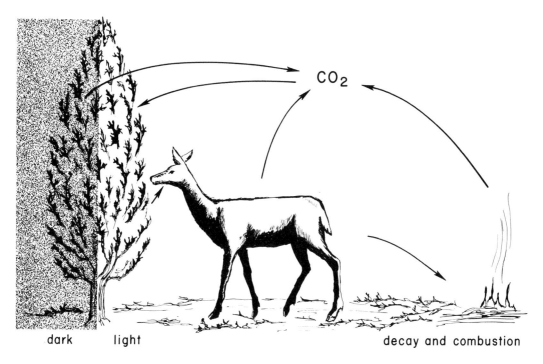

FIG. 5-7. The carbon cycle.

air must be converted first to **nitrites** (NO_2) and then to **nitrates** (NO_3) before the plants can make use of it in producing proteins. This conversion is brought about by N-fixing bacteria some of which are in the nodules that protrude from the roots of certain leguminous plants, such as beans and clover. Again the plant proteins are consumed by the animals and converted into their own proteins, or reduced to urea and lost from the body. Urea, as well as the dead body of an animal or plant, decomposes to form either atmospheric nitrogen or nitrates which are then used by the plants. Bacteria play an important part in the nitrogen cycle. If all bacteria suddenly disappeared from the earth, we would soon be short of nitrates and eventually of the basic materials that produce protoplasm.

Nutrition: Food Chains

All animals with the exception of a few protozoa depend ultimately on plants for their food. This is illustrated in Figure 5-9, where we see that the plant manufactures fats, carbohydrates, and proteins, and the animal breaks these down for its own use. The plants, therefore, are continually building up the organic world while animals are constantly tearing it down. It is apparently a well-established relationship, and one that we hope will endure for a long time to come.

Solar energy that has been stored by the plant passes to the animal that eats the plant. However, it does not always expend itself completely in a passage that involves only two organisms. Often there are many intermediates which transfer the energy through a **food chain,** in which one animal after another is eaten until the energy can be released only by the death of the last animal in the chain. All of the food chains in a given community constitute a **food cycle.** Let us consider several food chains.

In an abundantly populated fresh-water pond, plants and animals are constantly dying, falling to the bottom, and decomposing. This disintegrating organic material forms a source of energy for the growth of bacteria. In addition many algae (simple plants) grow by the utilization of simpler substances, just as all plants do. These two then, bacteria and unicellular plants, form the basis of food for tiny organisms such as protozoa. Small protozoa are eaten by larger ones, these in turn are eaten by rotifers, then crustacea, aquatic insects, and finally by fishes—first smaller fish, then larger ones. The latter either die or are eaten by fish-eating mammals such as mink, bear, or man. In the first case the chain ends with the death of the fish, in the second by the death of the mammal. A somewhat shorter pond cycle would be one starting with a snail eating a leafy plant, such as is depicted in Figure 5-10. The snail is then eaten by a crustacean, the crustacean by a small fish, the small fish by a larger one. Here the food chain ends unless, as before, the fish is eaten by bird or mammal.

On land a food chain may follow a similar pattern (Fig. 5-10). In this case a cricket feeds on plants and is then eaten by a lizard which is consumed by a snake, which, in turn, is devoured by a road runner. As the road runner grows older and loses some of its faculties, sooner or later it falls prey to another carnivore (flesh eater). This transfer of energy may go on almost endlessly.

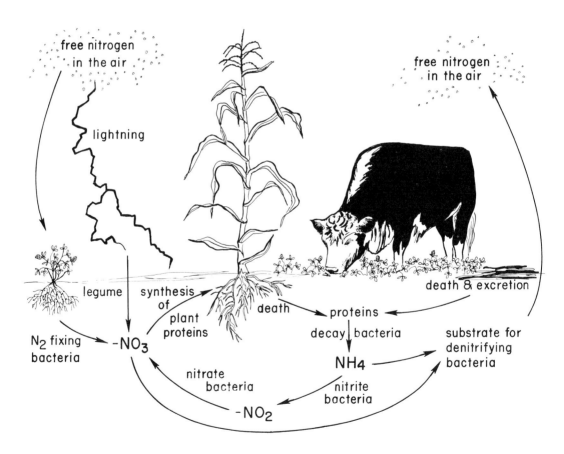

FIG. 5-8. The nitrogen cycle.

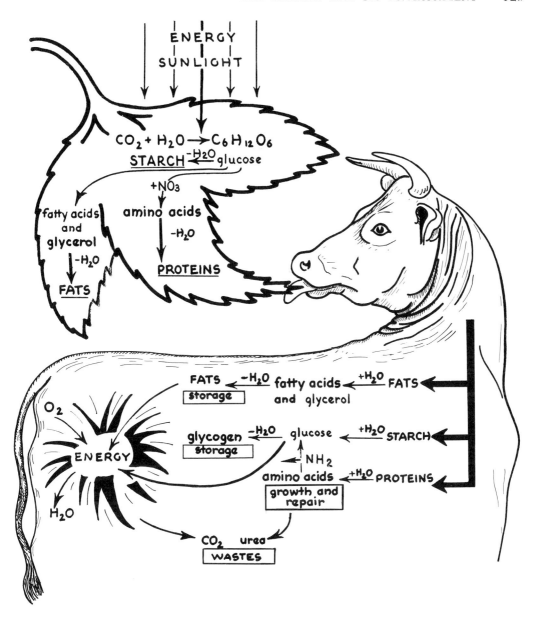

FIG. 5-9. Solar energy is incorporated into the foods manufactured by plants. This energy is released from the foods by animals for their own use.

Ecological Pyramids

In any group of organisms, whether they are in the ocean, on land, in the forest, in the soil, or elsewhere, there are usually a great many small organisms associated with a few large ones. This natural arrangement is often thought of as taking the shape of a pyramid, those organisms at the base representing the large number of smaller ones and those toward the apex indicating the few larger ones (Fig. 5-11). The smallest organisms at the base supply the food for those just above them, and these in turn are fed upon by the ones higher in the pyramid and so on to the animals at the top. It is also quite clear that the actual protoplasmic mass (biomass) as well as the numbers decrease as we ascend the pyramid —that is, to produce a given amount of human protoplasm, a great deal more calf protoplasm is required; similarly, a unit weight of calf protoplasm depends on a much greater weight of alfalfa. One can also see the same principle if one measures the energy involved in each of these layers. Just as in the food chains, useful energy is

lost in the transfer through each step from the smaller organisms to the larger. The pyramids of biomass describe graphically the over-all effect of the food-chain relations for the entire ecological group.

RELATIONSHIPS AMONG ORGANISMS

Up to this point we have considered the physical environment and the energy cycles involving organisms in that environment. Now we must think about the relationships among organisms. Organisms do not live alone; they are always associated with

FIG. 5-10. Food chains. The chain always starts with plants which are eaten by herbivores. These in turn are eaten by a series of carnivores, in one case ending with the road runner and in the other with the large fish.

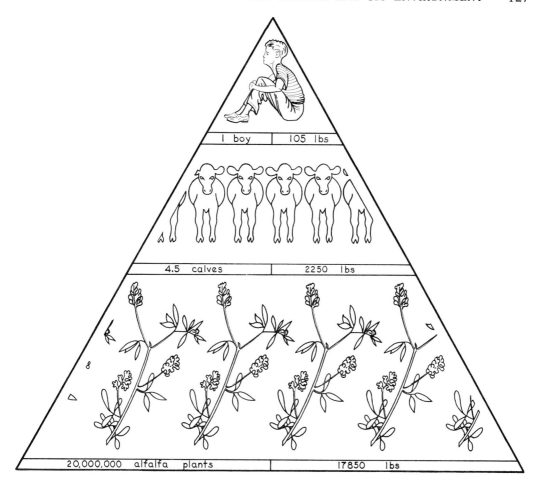

1 boy	105 lbs
4.5 calves	2250 lbs
20,000,000 alfalfa plants	17850 lbs

FIG. 5-11. A schematic representation to illustrate ecological pyramids of numbers of organisms and protoplasmic mass (biomass). A large amount of plant material is required to support a few calves and these, in turn, are more numerous and massive than the boy at the top of the pyramid who is supported by their protoplasm.

members of their own kind and other species associated together in areas known as **biotic communities.** Such communities are more or less definite units held together by the interdependence of their individual members. Within communities, smaller groups whose members are closely associated with each other form units which are called **populations.** A population may be made up of one species or it may consist of one to several species, and these need not be closely related. There is no hard and fast separation between population and the community, but they may be con-

sidered levels of organization above that of the individual that can be studied more or less separately.

Two other terms used by ecologists, **habitat** and **niche,** should become a part of our vocabulary before we go into this complex study of ecology. The habitat of an organism is the place where it lives. For example, the habitat of the earthworm is moist humus soil. This is where you would go to find it. The habitat includes other organisms as well as the nonliving environment. The ecological niche, on the other hand, is the "status of an organism in its community." Biologically speaking, one might say that the habitat is the "address" of the organism, whereas the niche is its "profession." Continuing with this analogy, if it is desired to become acquainted with a person, it would be a simple matter to look up his address. This would be insufficient information to really know the person. To do this we would need to know his occupation, his interests, and his function in the community. A similar situation exists with organisms; we usually want to know more than just where they can be found. We must discover what their activities are in the community, what they eat, their movements, and their effect on other associated organisms. Referring again to the earthworm, it is a simple matter to find the earthworm in moist humus soil, but with this information we know very little about this organism. To really understand the animal we should know something about its diet, the parasites that live within its body and how it may affect other organisms in the community, what effect it has upon the soil, and many other things. The description of ecological niches of organisms is one of the most important aspects of ecology, because it is from such knowledge that an understanding of the community can be had.

Another term used by ecologists and which is important as a concept is the ecological system or **ecosystem.** It is defined as a natural unit of living organisms which, together with the organisms' nonliving environment, forms a stable system through interaction; the exchange of materials between organisms and environment follows a circular path. The ecosystem is the largest functional unit in ecology, since it includes both the nonliving environment and the organisms, each contributing to the other and both essential for the continuance of life as we find it on earth.

Populations of Single or Similar Species

The study of population alone has proved valuable not only in the control of insect pests and predators, in increased game and fish, and other redistributions of animal life, but it has also been very important in business and government, as for example in the formulation of insurance and retirement plans. During every census more and more information is gathered about people in order to learn what is happening to our population. This makes it possible to predict future trends and also sheds some light on what might be done to influence the ultimate outcome. This is a hopeful field of investigation and shows promise of being of great value as time goes on.

When organisms of a single or similar species are numerous, they take on characteristics of the population which are not those of single individuals of that population. Some of these characteristics are **population density, birth rate, death rate, age distribution,** and **reproductive potential.** Both birth and death are characteristics of the individual, but birth and death rates are not; for they are found only in populations.

The success or failure of a population is dependent on **population density,** which means the number of organisms per unit of area or volume—the protozoa in a liter of lake water or the meadow mice per acre of land. This is often very important to know, especially when one is trying to determine the capacity of a certain area to support certain species of plants or animals, or to know the effect of one species on another. For example, one grasshopper per acre of a farmer's land would have little effect on his cereal crop, but one million per acre would.

It is also important to know not only the density of a population but also whether or not it is changing and at what rate. This is possible by counting the number of fish that swim past a certain point per hour or the number of animals caught in a trap in a certain specified time. Another method is to catch a certain number of animals in a trap, say 100, tagging them by clipping the tail, for example, and then releasing them. This may be repeated again at some later time and the number of tagged animals noted in the traps. If in the second sample of 100, 10 were found with tags, then the population (P) in this area would be $100/P = 10/100$, or $P = 1,000$. This is a rather accurate method of estimating populations and has been extensively used.

Populations also grow in a characteristic manner, and when the numbers are plotted against time we arrive at a so-called **population growth curve.** We might start by considering how growth occurs in single cells, protozoa, for example. If one or only a few protozoa are placed in a flask containing complete nutrients for this particular cell, in a short time there will be mil-

lions. Since they are single cells, we may count them at regular intervals during this period of increase and from this information construct a curve which will tell us something about how growth occurs (Fig. 5-12). Such a curve is said to be **sigmoid,** because it is S-shaped. At the beginning the cells fail to divide for a time, as indicated on the curve by the so-called **lag phase;** just why this occurs is not known. They then begin to divide at a rapid and uniform rate. This is called the **logarithmic phase** of growth because the cells increase in a geometric manner, that is, 2, 4, 8, 16, and so on. Once they reach this phase they continue dividing at a uniform rate, so the curve is straight. As the limits of food in the culture are reached or the accumulation of wastes inhibits further divisions, the growth rate gradually falls off until the population finally reaches a plateau. Either the organisms no longer divide, or if they do, they die as fast as they are produced, for the total number remains the same.

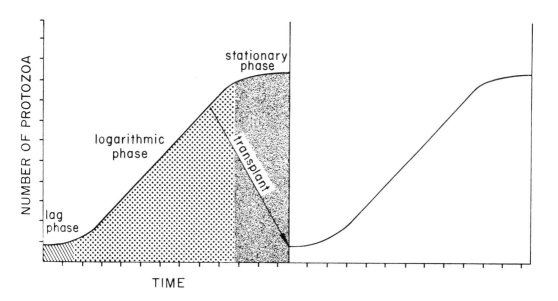

FIG. 5-12. Growth of cells, such as protozoa in a flask of nutrients, follows very precise stages. During the initial stage there is little increase in numbers (lag phase). This is followed by a rapid uniform rate of increase (logarithmic phase) that continues until the food becomes exhausted or the accumulated wastes become toxic, or both factors operate simultaneously. Growth then remains at a plateau for a time (stationary phase). This cycle can be repeated any number of times by transplanting some of the cells to a fresh medium.

This is called the **stationary phase.** This curve can be repeated again and again by simply taking some of the organisms in the stationary phase and placing them in fresh medium. If the medium is continually changed, the culture can be kept in the logarithmic phase indefinitely. Apparently, these cells can continue to grow and divide at a uniform rate with no sign of aging. Aging then may be only the exhaustion of food or the accumulation of wastes in any community of cells.

Whether one studies the growth of protozoa or human beings, the curve is essentially the same. Such curves have been invaluable in predicting the outcome of certain populations in environments where conditions are favorable to unlimited growth.

Natality or **theoretical birth rate** is the innate capacity of a population to increase. This capacity usually far exceeds the actual birth rate because adverse environmental conditions drastically influence the actual numbers of offspring produced. The theoretical birth rate can be determined under optimal conditions rather accurately, and it is usually found to be rather constant for each species. This capacity to produce young is often helpful in making predictions about the possibility of a species overrunning a new environment once released in it. For all practical purposes, the actual birth rate is more important in any given situation because it determines the ultimate numbers of any species in any constant environment.

Mortality is the antithesis of natality, that is, it refers to the death of organisms per unit of time in a population. Here again there is a minimum mortality which refers to the number of deaths that would occur owing to the ravages of old age. This is an ideal figure which is constant for a population but in actuality rarely occurs. Environmental factors, including the composition and size of the population, greatly influence this ideal figure. It is possible to plot a so-called **survival curve** to indicate graphically the number of individuals that actually survive in a community (Fig. 5-13). By plotting the number of survivors out of 1,000 against percentage of total life span, one can compare the survival of organisms with quite different life spans. Rotifers live a short time, then nearly all die at once. Oyster larvae, on the other hand, die in great numbers very early in life, and only those that become attached to a rock or shell survive and mature. The locust is typical of most plants and animals, since a relatively constant number die throughout the life span. Even though mortality in man is more frequent in the first five days of life than during the following several years, it is still relatively low. Survival is high until in the mid-forties when once again the death rate increases until nearly all are gone at the hundredth year. The curve plotted for man applies only to civilized man and is influenced by modern medicine. It would be somewhat modified for primitive populations.

Another characteristic of a population

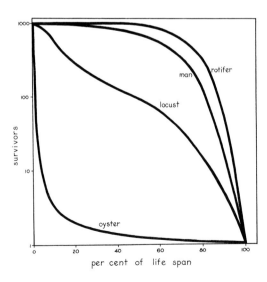

FIG. 5-13. Several types of survival curves indicating the numbers of individuals out of 1,000 that survive in a community. Numbers of survivors are plotted on a logarithmic scale and age in percentage of total life span.

is **age distribution,** which influences both natality and mortality. Reproduction is usually restricted to the middle-age groups of animals, and mortality varies with age, some dying earlier than others. For this reason, the ratio of the various age groups in a population more or less determines the capacity of the population to reproduce itself. In general, a rapidly expanding population contains a greater proportion of young members, whereas a declining population has a higher percentage of old individuals. A stationary population consists of a more or less even distribution of animals of different ages. The progress of a population can sometimes be determined by observing the age of its members. The age of fish, for example, can be determined by counting the growth rings on the scales, thus making it possible to know the numbers of fish in each age group. This information is important to commercial fishermen in deciding whether or not a fish population is expanding or declining. They can then control their fishing practices accordingly.

One of the most important pieces of information one needs to know about any population is its power to increase its numbers when the age ratio is stable and the environment is optimal. Ecologists call this characteristic of a population its **reproductive potential.** Obviously this power must be kept in check, and the factors that do that are collectively spoken of as **environmental resistance.** These two antagonistic forces maintain a balance in nature which is observed in any community of organisms.

Although each species of animal has the potentiality of overrunning the earth, it actually never does. Populations grow in size and die out just as individual organisms do. Indeed, the number of individuals in a given population rarely remains constant but *fluctuates* in time. The many interrelations that exist between a given population and the populations of other species may act as a regulatory mechanism and serve as a system of checks and balances to keep numbers of individuals within relatively narrow limits. Such controlling mechanisms may be competition for food, infectious disease, predation, and many others. Moreover, a single species may fluctuate widely from season to season. Grasshoppers may be very numerous one year, devouring all vegetation over large areas, whereas the next year there may be few. Barring man's intervention, this may be caused by unseasonal weather during the young stages when the organism is sensitive to adverse conditions. Ruffed grouse may increase steadily for several years until they reach great numbers, then suddenly decline, much to the disappointment of the hunter. Indeed, this rise and fall in the population of certain species is so regular that it can be predicted. Sometimes animals reach tremendous numbers, then go into a decline from which they never recover, and eventually become extinct. The passenger pigeon is a good example. In other cases, like the American bison and the whooping crane, an attempt is being made to save them from extinction by the animal who nearly caused it in the first place, namely, man. Our efforts have been so successful in the case of the bison that each year a considerable number of animals must be killed to keep the herds within the limits of the food supply. It is questionable whether or not the remaining 25 whooping cranes can be saved, in spite of the protective measures that are being taken to preserve them.

If the reproductive potential of a species is permitted to express itself to any great degree, the results are sometimes unfortunate. One example will suffice. The English sparrow was first introduced in Brooklyn, New York, in 1850 and 1852 for the purpose of controlling certain insect pests that were destroying the shade trees of the city. In England the bird was desirable and because of its natural enemies existed in modest numbers. In America, however, it was free from its predators and the full powers of its reproductive capabilities came into play. Within a few years it became a pest. Instead of eating the insect pests, it fed on garden produce and cereal grains, man's own food, and in addition destroyed other insect-eating birds. By 1886 it had spread to Salt Lake City and today its distribution is continent-wide. One interesting fact has been noted about the English sparrow: it no longer populates the streets of our cities as it did a generation or two ago when the horse and buggy was a common means of transportation. Grasshoppers and other insects clinging to the car radiator are a poor substitute for the horse droppings that dotted the streets some years past.

Such mistakes as the one just described have been made on numerous occasions by man. Sometimes injurious animals are imported into new regions because they have escaped border inspections and have subsequently become established, later to become serious pests. Great care is now taken to prevent this from happening. Many states have inspections on railroads and highways to keep any injurious pests out. Airplanes must be carefully inspected when they fly from one region to another, particularly when the two are great distances apart. The danger of introducing certain disease-carrying insects, such as mosquitoes, into a new environment is obvious.

Man has intentionally introduced some animals to prey upon others with excellent success. One good illustration is that of the ladybird beetle introduced from Australia a few years ago to destroy the cottony scale which was playing havoc with the citrus crops of California. This required the research efforts of an entomologist who studied the enemies of the cottony scale in its native Australia. The ladybird was finally decided upon and when brought to

this country proved very successful in partially controlling the pest. It has not, as yet, become a pest itself.

Our economic zoologists are well aware of the great precaution that must be exercised in interrupting the delicate balance of life in any environment. For example, when the insecticide DDT was first available for public consumption, many enthusiastic laymen wanted it spread from airplanes over wide swamp areas in order to destroy mosquitoes as well as other insects that have mostly a nuisance value. If our practical zoologists had not prevented that procedure, the damage might have been so tremendous that it would have taken several generations and perhaps many millions of dollars to repair. Think of the destruction to honeybees as one example. Besides destroying them as a source of honey, there would be untold damage to orchards due to unpollinated flowers. Birds, amphibians, and reptiles feed largely on insects, to say nothing of the aquatic life that subsists on these very numerous little animals. We can tamper with the environment only in small areas for specific purposes; any large-scale operation must be carried out with utmost caution so that the balanced plan of the community of animals is not disturbed.

A very interesting relationship among animals, and one that is very evident in all social orders even human societies, is the hierarchy displayed by groups of animals of the same species. This has been observed in many animals from fish to monkeys, but perhaps is best known among birds, particularly chickens. A Norwegian psychologist, T. Schjelderup-Ebbe, discovered that in a flock of hens there was always one hen that could peck all other hens and was pecked by no hen, whereas at the other extreme there was one hen that was pecked by all of the others and could peck no hen. All gradations existed between these extremes, but each hen was very much aware of the hens she could peck and those that were privileged to peck her. This is often spoken of as the *peck-order*. This same descending hierarchy exists among male chickens. W. C. Allee has shown that injecting male hormone into a hen increases its aggressiveness so that it will fight its way up the social ladder, finally becoming the top hen in the flock. The female hormone, on the other hand, causes hens to be more submissive, resulting in their social decline. The peck-order has a direct bearing on sexual behavior and, of course, has great practical value to poultrymen. The rooster highest in the social order mates most frequently with the hens and therefore passes his traits on to the next generation, whereas the male lowest in the social order may not mate at all, thus greatly influencing the genetic constitution of the next generation of chickens. It is quite clear that a poultryman must study his breeding stock if he is to obtain the characteristics he desires in his flock.

Populations of Two Interacting Species

Populations of two different species may interact with one another in a number of ways. Broadly speaking they may (a) compete for food, space, or other common needs, or (b) live in close association, either benefiting or harming one another (symbiosis). These are not clear-cut distinctions and one is sometimes hard put to be certain what the relationship is between two closely associated populations. We shall consider several relationships which are fairly well defined.

Competition. When two populations of interacting species occupy the same habitat, competition and a concomitant decrease in number of both populations result. The two populations compete primarily for food

and space; hence, something must happen in a relatively short time. One possibility is that the less endowed competitor dies or is forced to move to another niche leaving the other to occupy the area. The second possibility is that both populations survive but with a reduction in numbers in both groups. Obviously, since populations are bound to overlap at their boundaries, competition to a greater or lesser extent will occur in these regions. It becomes extremely difficult to determine at what point two populations are in equilibrium or in competition. This problem has stimulated considerable research and some pertinent observations have been made.

The Russian ecologist, Gause, concluded on the basis of field and laboratory observations, that each niche is occupied by only one species. Even though niches overlap, each one is filled by a single species. One of Gause's own experiments with protozoa illustrates the principle. When two species of Paramecium, *P. caudatum* and *P. aurelia,* are grown under identical cultural conditions in separate containers their growth rates are quite different—*P. aurelia* grows much faster than *P. caudatum*. When the two species are grown together, *P. aurelia* outstrips *P. caudatum,* indeed completely eliminates it after about two weeks. Apparently, *P. aurelia* utilizes food more efficiently, hence is the more successful competitor when both occupy the same niche. Thus *P. aurelia* and *P. caudatum* occupy different niches.

Again using protozoa, the presence or absence of a micronucleus seems to determine the success or failure of ciliates of the same species (Fig. 5-14). When equal numbers of two strains of *Tetrahymena pyriformis,* one with a micronucleus and the other without one, are inoculated into a tube of culture medium and permitted to grow for several days, a marked difference in their relative numbers is noted. The amicronucleate cells are far more numer-

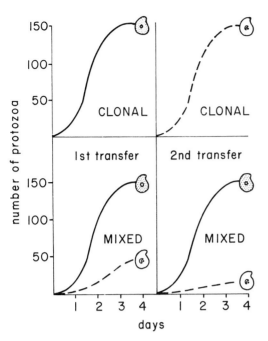

FIG. 5-14. Gause's principle illustrated by the protozoan, *Tetrahymena pyriformis*. Competition between micronucleate and amicronucleate in the same environment. The latter always over-grows the former.

ous than those with micronuclei. If a small sample of this culture is transferred to a second tube which is then permitted to grow for several more days, the difference in numbers of the two strains is even more striking. When this is done a third time, it is difficult to find even a single micronucleate cell among thousands of amicronucleate protozoa. In this case, even though these two strains have identical morphology, other than the presence or absence of a micronucleus, they seem to occupy different niches, at least in a test tube. Whether or not this situation occurs in nature is not known.

Gause's principle has been examined with many competing populations both in the laboratory and in the field. Flour beetles have been used in laboratory studies. When *Tribolium* and *Oryzaephilus*

are grown together the former always exterminates the latter owing to the fact that it is more aggressive in destroying the immature stages of the former. Both populations will survive, however, if glass tubes are provided in the flour because the larvae of *Oryzaephilus* have a place to hide. Therefore, by introducing a second niche both populations survive owing to the reduction in competition. If this can be carried over to natural conditions it becomes clear that the more the niches the greater the number of species that can survive.

Many examples can be drawn from field studies. At first these may seem to be exceptions to Gause's principle but upon more careful scrutiny, the principle holds. One example will illustrate the point. In Africa two species of flamingos feed side by side in shallow lakes and would certainly appear to be in direct competition with one another for food. However, upon closer examination of the anatomy of the screening mechanism in the mouth region, it becomes quite clear that one feeds only on microscopic algae whereas the other can take larger food particles such as small animals. These birds, then, though mingling in the same habitat, occupy different niches.

A great deal of evidence has accumulated from both laboratory and field studies which seem to confirm Gause's contention that only one species can occupy any one niche.

Symbiosis. Some very interesting interrelationships between organisms have been established, primarily for the purpose of obtaining energy, although some seem to have other functions. Collectively, these relationships are spoken of as **symbiosis.** They range all the way from a loose, more or less haphazard association to a closely knit relationship in which the two or more organisms are forced to live together. These may be associations between plants, between animals, or between plants and animals. The antithesis of symbiosis is **antibiosis,** which is also common among certain organisms, particularly the lower plants. Instead of living together, some organisms produce substances (antibiotics) which insure that others, at least certain others, remain at a safe distance. A famous example is the mold *Penicillium notatum* which secretes a substance that has the property of preventing growth of a large variety of bacteria and, because of its nontoxic effect when taken into the body, has become a very important medicine in the treatment of infectious diseases. There are many other examples of this type of antibiosis. One might even consider the toxic substances produced by certain amphibia or the odoriferous secretions of the skunk as antibiotics. Some of these interrelationships are almost fantastic and have fascinated biologists for centuries. Let us consider several cases of symbiosis, particularly among animals.

Commensalism. This is a loose association of two animals in which one derives benefit from the combination whereas the other does not. These associations vary greatly in degree; indeed it is often difficult to be certain of the exact effect of the relationship on the members involved. One example will illustrate this type of association. A flatworm, *Bdelloura,* can usually be found on the gills of the king crab (Fig. 5-15). From this association the flatworm is able to pick up bits of food which are dispersed into the sea water as the crab tears up its prey. It is doubtful that the crab receives any particular benefit from this association, although it seems to suffer no inconvenience from the presence of the worms.

Mutualism. A situation where animals live together with benefit to both is called **mutualism,** and this arrangement seems to be far more common than commensalism. There are all gradations of this association, from those who only casually meet and become associated to those that are always found together and, indeed, cannot live apart. One interesting example is that of certain jellyfish (*Physalia,* Fig. 5-15) and several species of small fish. The fish live among the tentacles of the jellyfish which offer protection by their stinging cells. On the other hand, the jellyfish benefits by the fact that the tiny fish act as lures by attracting larger fish to come within shooting distance of the deadly stinging darts. Thus both cooperate in the kill and both benefit. A similar relationship exists between certain large sea anemones and several species of small fish (Fig. 5-16). Whereas these associations frequently occur, they are probably only temporary; neither party is forced to live with the other.

Another illustration of a temporary association is that of the hermit crab and sea anemones (Fig. 5-15). In this case the sea anemone, attaching itself to the shell occupied by the crab, gets free transportation to areas which the crab finds attractive because of an abundance of food. In return for the ride the sea anemone acts as a camouflage, making the shell resemble the rest of the ocean floor. In addition, because of its powerful battery of stinging cells, it functions as a line of defense against possible enemies of the crab. Some primitive chordates (prochordates) have adopted the same association with hermit crabs (Fig. 5-15).

Another interesting association, where the relationship is more or less compulsory, is the case of the metazoan hydra and a unicellular plant, an alga. The algae live in the hydra's inner layer of cells (endoderm) where they carry on photosynthesis, releasing oxygen which is utilized by the hydra. The hydra in turn releases carbon dioxide which is used by the algae. While in nature this situation usually exists, it has

FIG. 5-15. Plants and animals became associated intimately in many ways. Here are some illustrations. See text for explanation.

been possible to separate them in the laboratory and each can survive without the other.

In some cases of mutualism the association of two animals is so intimate that neither can live without the other. The best illustration of this is among the termites, or white ants (Fig. 5-15). This association came to the attention of biologists when it was thought that termites could survive indefinitely on pure carbohydrate. They feed on wood alone, receiving only the small amount of nitrogenous compounds that are present in wood. Upon investigation it was found that great hordes of complex protozoa inhabit the termite's intestines. If the termite was warmed up a bit the protozoa died and such defaunated termites lived only a short time. Likewise, the protozoa could not survive outside the body of the termite. Apparently the protozoa produce enzymes that digest cellulose to sugars which are utilized by the termite. The termite, on the other hand, provides a good abundant home for the protozoa.

Parasitism. This is also a forced relationship between two animals, but it is a one-way proposition. The **parasite** lives at the expense of the **host,** taking all and giving nothing in return, possibly even causing injury to the host. An ideal parasite withdraws just enough nourishment from its host to maintain itself in good health and in reasonable numbers. If the parasite removes too much from its host, so that the latter becomes sick and dies, then the parasite too is destroyed. Many parasites reach a satisfactory balance with their host in which the latter merely contributes a home for the parasite and is not apparently injured by it.

Parasitism probably arose shortly after life originated on the earth. Some animals soon found that they could live to advantage either in or on the body of another. Perhaps at first the relationship was a perfectly harmless one, something like commensalism, but as the association persisted the parasite became more and more dependent on the host for its existence. It modified its body both morphologically and

FIG. 5-16. Several species of small fish live among the tentacles of certain large sea anemones. This one (*Amphiprion*) was found on the Great Barrier Reef. It spends most of its time nestled among the tentacles, coming out only when food is available. If pursued by a larger fish it dashes among the tentacles, sometimes completely disappearing into the gastrovascular cavity of the sea anemone.

physiologically in accordance with its parasitic habit. In earlier relationships the parasite probably clung to the outside of its host, later going into the shallow cavities such as the mouth and cloaca. Some, of course, were inadvertently swallowed with the food, and these after a time became adapted to life in the gut where all of their food requirements were provided for. Others that learned to live in the bodies of insects, such as mosquitoes, also learned to thrive in the blood of vertebrates because they were dumped into that environment every time the mosquito feasted on a blood meal.

Through similar food chains, parasites must have learned to live first in one host, then in another, and sometimes in a third, all in sequence, in order to complete their life cycle. This arrangement had the advantage of spreading the species but it also had the serious disadvantage of depending not only on three hosts but also on the necessity that the hosts be sequentially arranged in time and space. Should any one of the hosts die out, the parasite would likewise be destroyed because it could not complete its cycle. In fact, this is a most effective way to control certain dangerous parasites. Killing mosquitoes in order to control malaria is a familiar example.

Parasites have been so intimately tied to their hosts for so many millions of years that ecologists today can often trace the history of certain species by comparing their parasites. In the subsequent chapters we shall study several different kinds of parasites as they occur in the various animal groups.

Predation. Parasitism should be distinguished from **predation,** in which one animal also lives at the expense of another. A predatory animal feeds upon another by eating its entire body, frequently at one sitting. A parasite might just as surely destroy the host, but it does so in an entirely different manner. A cat kills and eats a mouse; the cat is living at the expense of the mouse. The cat has a tapeworm inside its intestine; the tapeworm is living at the expense of the cat. The first case is predation, the second, parasitism. "The difference between a predator and a parasite is simply the difference between living upon capital and income, between the burglar and the black-mailer. The general results are the same although the methods employed are different." (Elton)

BIOTIC COMMUNITIES

A biotic community, as defined earlier, is any collection of populations existing in a defined area or habitat. It is not a closely organized unit, but it is sufficiently well defined to possess characteristics of its own which are different from those of its individual and population components. It consists of the living organisms of the ecosystem and it may be large or small. The concept of the community implies that widely diverse organisms live together in an orderly fashion, not as independent self-sufficient organisms. Thus it is possible to study the different types of communities and determine their characteristics, which can be very important when one wishes to alter them in such a way as to encourage or discourage the growth of one particular species. For example, mosquitoes can be effectively controlled simply by changing the water levels where they breed at the proper time of year. This is much more economical than using expensive poisons to kill the larvae.

There is wide variation in the importance of the many species of plants and animals that inhabit a community, some having much greater influence than others. Usually a relatively few species exert the major controlling influence owing to their numbers, size, or activities. For example, in a pasture, bluegrass and cattle may be the dominant organisms, therefore the controlling influence in this community. In all

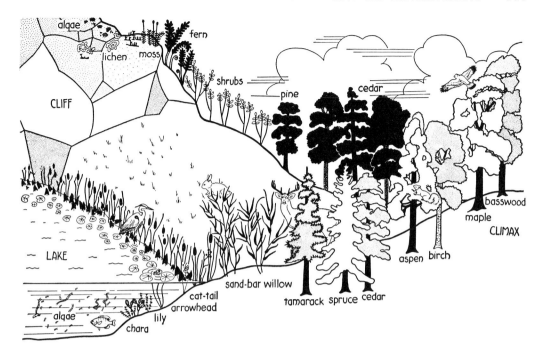

FIG. 5-17. A sketch showing ecological succession from two different younger communities to the stable climax community. See text for explanation.

communities there are usually a very few dominant species and these are responsible for the principal characteristics of that community.

Ecological Succession. In nearly all communities there is an orderly process of change in which one community replaces another in a given area. In a typical ecosystem, community development begins with a **pioneer stage** which is gradually replaced by several sequential stages, each more mature than the preceding one, until a **climax** is reached where the community becomes relatively stable. An interesting point about ecological succession is that it is directional; a careful examination of a community will reveal the stage it is in at any one time, and a reasonably accurate prediction can be made as to what will happen to it in the future. This type of prognostication is extremely helpful in making plans for the development of areas.

The early development of pioneer stages is often very gradual but the intermediate stages may progress rapidly; indeed each year may bring different organisms into the community. Gradually the process slows down until the climax is finally reached. We usually think of the organisms as changing, but they also bring about changes in the environment. As a matter of fact, the action of the community on the habitat tends to make the area less favorable for itself and better suited for other groups of organisms, which follow in sequential order. When the climax is attained, the community changes but little until some catastrophic event occurs which greatly alters the whole environment, as in forest fires, the draining of lakes, and flooding of the land.

Succession can be clearly seen in many aquatic environments such as lakes (Fig. 5-17). "Young" lakes contain very little plant and animal life, but later as they begin to fill in with sediment, increasing numbers and kinds of living things appear and disappear in succession. The lake depicted in Fig. 5-17 is relatively "old" and is characterized by the presence of rooted vegetation, bluegills, and frogs. Cattails and arrowhead constitute the principal vegetation around the edges of the water. A few years later this lake would contain more and more rooted vegetation and it would also grow smaller and smaller in size as the sediment produced by the plants and animals filled up the basin. Bluegills would be replaced by catfish and golden shiners. Finally the lake or pond would become a swamp and then dry land on which a continued sequence of vegetation and animals would follow with time. The swampy regions would support willows, tamarack, spruce, and cedar. Later these would be replaced by aspen and birch, and finally the climax of this par-

ticular region would consist of maples and basswood trees. Along with this plant succession occur succeeding associations of animals, the invertebrates, fish, amphibia, birds, deer, and squirrels.

A recently exposed pioneer area such as a rocky cliff is suitable only for primitive plants such as algae and lichens, later to be replaced by mosses and ferns (Fig. 5-17). These plants, together with a few animals, gradually change the rocky region to one containing a thin soil. Erosion washes most of this soil into the valleys, beginning the slow process of filling them. Farther down the mountainside the soil supports shrubs; still farther down where the soil is deep, trees such as pines thrive. With time these communities gradually change, and this change is always toward the climax vegetation and the associated animals.

Another characteristic of biotic communities is **vertical stratification** of the or-

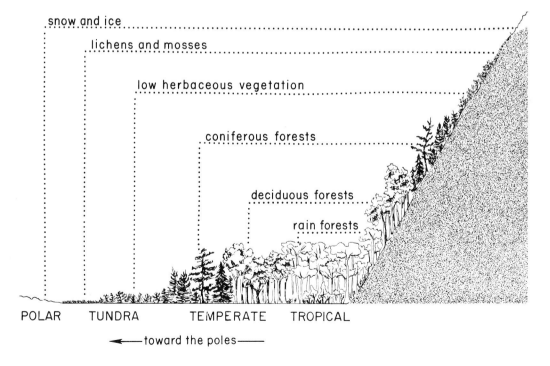

snow and ice

lichens and mosses

low herbaceous vegetation

coniferous forests

deciduous forests

rain forests

POLAR   TUNDRA   TEMPERATE   TROPICAL

←—— toward the poles ——

FIG. 5-18. A sketch demonstrating the life zones at different altitudes and latitudes. Note that the successively higher habitats support the same types of vegetation as are found at successively greater distances from the equator.

ganisms of the community. This is owing to the vertical differences in such physical factors as temperature, light, oxygen, and so on, as well as to the composition of the underlying soil. Stratification of organisms makes possible many more niches in a community, thus reducing interspecific competition and permitting a more effective use of the solar energy reaching the area. A good illustration of stratification is found in many lakes of the temperate regions of the earth. During the summer the water is stratified temperature-wise, the circulating surface layer being oxygen-rich and warm, the deeper layers of cold water with a lower oxygen content. Fish such as the large mouth bass inhabit the surface waters, the walleye and sauger the deeper layers. By measuring the depth, oxygen, and temperature, one can predict where the fish may be found, a very helpful bit of information for the eager fisherman.

Latitude and Elevation. As one moves north from the equator a striking difference is noted in the plant and animal life. The same observation is made when climbing a mountain (Fig. 5-18). Temperature and precipitation more or less correlate between these two axes and consequently the habitats are bound to be similar. At the base of a mountain in the tropics one finds typical tropical rain forests, deserts, or grasslands, and as one moves up the slope one encounters in succession, deciduous forests and temperate zone grasslands, then coniferous forests, then low shrubby growths, and finally nothing but mosses and lichens. Beyond this point there is no plant or animal life, merely snow and ice. One finds essentially the same sequence when moving from the equator to the poles.

The mountains in the temperate zone and farther north have vegetation at their bases similar to that generally found in the latitude where the mountain is located, and on their slopes, vegetation that exists still farther north. We see then that the farther north a mountain is located the fewer habitats it provides for plants and animals. Consequently, in the extreme north where polar ice exists, there is almost no life at all.

The wrinkling of the earth, its turning on its axis, and its spacial relationship with the sun create a wide variety of habitats at its surface. Plants and animals have invaded these rather generally, and ecosystems have been established. These may be as large as the great oceans, plains, deserts, or as small as ponds or brooks. The limits of space preclude a coverage of each of these but we can take a brief look at two of them.

ECOSYSTEMS

We are already familiar with the ecosystem concept. Now let us examine two ecosystems, a fresh-water pond and a desert. A consideration of these two diverse ecosystems may provide some appreciation of their complexity.

A Fresh-Water Pond. A pond is defined as a small body of fresh water, usually not more than two or three meters in depth, its temperature being approximately the same throughout (Fig. 5-19). Many animals and plants live in such a limited environment, and even within its confines there are definite regions which support specific animals. The open water is largely devoid of both fish and rooted plants, but the shores support a variety of animal and plant life, depending on the relative amounts of mud, sand, or rocks.

If the bottom is muddy, many plants, such as water lilies, grow in profusion. In protected places around the edge there may be several varieties of fish, principally bass and pickerel. Crayfish and small fish may be seen darting here and there in search of food. Tadpoles can be found near the bottom. The water teems with tiny crustacea and larvae of insects like midges (small

FIG. 5-19. A typical fresh-water pond. The association of plants and animals in such an environment is extremely complex.

gnat-like flies in the adult stage), which form the basic food for young fish. By scooping up some of the mud in a fine mesh net, many other animals can be noted, including snails of various sizes and shapes and perhaps a few leeches.

Many different kinds of flying insects make their home around the edge of the pond. The dragonfly (Fig. 13-21) and May fly larvae can be found. An occasional diving beetle (Fig. 5-20) may be picked up. This is an interesting insect because it is so well adapted to aquatic life even though it must breathe air. It carries a film of·air under its wings which acts as a reservoir for underwater maneuvering. The hind legs are large and beautifully designed for swimming under water.

The water boatman also carries a similar air film. Its long hind legs covered with bristles, when in operation, remind one of a man rowing, hence its name. Other insects such as the water strider and the whirligig beetle skim over the surface of the water, depressing but never breaking the surface film. Their food consists of airborne insects that are blown out over the water and accidentally fall on the surface. The whirligig beetle possesses unique eyes which are divided into two parts; the lower part enables it to perceive objects in the water and the upper half gives it a clear view in the air.

The pond may include a sandy shore where animals of a different kind live. Snails, different from those found on the mud bottom, crawl over the sand from which they remove the small plants growing there. Frogs, toads, and turtles may live around the edge of the pond, and birds such as the redwinged blackbird may inhabit the vegetation along the shore. Although these animals do not live in the water, they do contribute to the combined interrelationships of the community. They seek at least some of their food in the water and when they die their bodies may fall into the water where they are eaten by animals living there.

It is obvious that there must exist many complex food chains in such a well-defined community. The chief occupation of each living thing is to nourish itself, a need that results in a severe struggle for existence. Rarely does an animal die a natural death, for the moment it wavers it is pounced upon and destroyed by another, thus becoming a part of a long or short food chain. There is, however, a complete food cycle for the entire community which involves certain general groups of plants and animals. The green plants always provide the beginning of such a food chain. In the case of the pond, the water plants extract their simple needs from the water and manufacture food which is consumed by **plant feeders,** such as the tiny crustacea that feed on algae and the snails that eat larger plants. These animals are pursued and eaten by a large variety of carnivores such as the predaceous diving beetles. These predators are eaten by larger carnivores such as fish. Some, like the midge larvae and May fly larvae, are content with the dead bodies of plants and animals, and are known as **scavengers.** Finally, the organic matter that remains after all animals are through with it is decomposed by bacteria, known as **decomposers,** so that the inorganic compounds that are needed by the plants are restored to the water. Thus the cycle is completed.

Seasonal changes occur in the pond community and the animals living there must adjust to them. Usually there is an abundance of water in the pond during the spring of the year, but as fall approaches there may be very little water left. Consequently animals must migrate to other ponds or go into a resting stage until conditions improve. The sheet of ice which covers the pond during the winter excludes most of the light, which results in less photosynthesis, hence less oxygen. If animals are to survive the winter they must be able to get along on minimum quantities of oxygen as well as withstand low temperatures. Each animal living permanently in such a pond community is able to meet these situations and is found year after year in the same locality.

A Desert Plain. In contrast to the pond, the desert environment supports only those

FIG. 5-20. Aquatic insects are modified in many ways for life in the water. The predaceous diving beetle (*Dytiscus*) shown here has its hind legs fringed with hairlike bristles which serve to increase the effectiveness of these appendages when used in swimming. As a result, it is an excellent swimmer. The insect also stores reserve air under its wings for use while submerged.

FIG. 5-21. Because of the exacting environmental conditions of a desert plain, few plants and animals subsist there. But even here there is an intricate relationship between them.

plants and animals that can survive on very little or no water, except that taken with the food. If we study the life existing on the plains of our own Southwest, we find a strange group of plants and animals, all of which are adapted in one way or another to life in a hot dry climate (Fig. 5-21). This region is not truly desert; it is about half-way between grassy plains and true desert. The vegetation is composed chiefly

FIG. 5-22. Life on Heron Island, one of the thousands of islands that make up the Great Barrier Reef. (Left) A scene from the reef looking back at the exposed island at low tide. The scattered corals appearing above the water are the dead skeletons; living corals are below the water. (Right) A mutton bird (*Puffinus pacificus*), one of the thousands that nest on the island. This confused bird laid its egg on the ground; normally they are laid in burrows in the coral sand.

of cacti, yuccas, and other plants particularly well adapted to prevent loss of water through transpiration. They also possess water-holding devices which permit storing of water during the brief wet seasons to be used when moisture is reduced to minimal levels. They are protected from the marauding attacks of hungry and thirsty animals by their sharp stiff spines and tough outer coverings.

Desert animals possess some very interesting adaptations to life in this dry climate. Scarcity of water forces them to conserve it in every possible way. The tough impervious integuments of reptiles such as snakes and lizards reduce water loss to a minimum. Moreover, they excrete **uric acid** (birds do likewise) which is essentially dry and in the form of crystals. Mammals, on the other hand, excrete **urea** which requires considerable quantities of water to flush it out of the body. In spite of this "fault" some, such as the kangaroo rat and the pocket mouse, can live indefinitely on dry seeds and do not require drinking water. Moreover they do not use water for temperature regulation and their urine is extremely concentrated. By day they remain in their burrows where the relative humidity is 30–50 per cent as compared to 0–15 per cent above ground. They are abroad at night when the relative humidity is about the same as it is in the burrows. Those desert animals that require drinking water and cannot survive on dry food manage to quench their thirst by eating the succulent cacti and other desert plants that have the capacity to store water. The largest carnivores of the desert are foxes, coyotes, and bobcats, all of which feed on the lesser creatures, which are primarily vegetarians.

Compared to the pond situation, the desert food cycle is rather simple, as would be expected where there are fewer organisms. Like the food cycle in any ecosystem, the desert cycle begins with the plants. These are preyed upon by the various herbivorous animals, which in turn are eaten by the carnivores, which probably also eat one another. Eventually death overtakes them and the elements of which each is composed return to the soil to be used again by the plants.

Other Ecosystems. There are a great many other ecosystems in a wide range of habitats. Some of these are ocean, grassy plains, tundra, forest, and mountains. One of the most interesting communities of the ocean ecosystem is the coral reef (p. 222), the largest of which is the Great Barrier Reef off the northeast coast of Australia. Of the thousands of islands which make up this 1,200-mile-long reef, one, Heron Island located at the southern tip, has been studied quite extensively owing to the fact that a biological station is located there. The vegetation consists of a few plants and the Pisonia tree (Fig. 5-22). The Noddy Tern nests in these trees and the Mutton Bird or wedge-tailed Shearwater burrows in the coral sand

FIG. 5-23. Heron Island. (Left) A giant female loggerhead turtle (*Thallassochelys caretta*) laying eggs. She digs a hole with her hind flippers, deposits the eggs, and then covers them so expertly that they cannot be detected. The warm sun incubates the eggs. (Right) Once she has laid her eggs, she makes her weary way back to the sea.

where it lays its single large egg. The enormous green and loggerhead turtles seasonally lay their eggs in the coral sand (Fig. 5-23). Whereas the exposed island itself is only several hundred feet across, the reef extends about 5 miles and is covered by shoal waters that vary in depth with the tides. At low tide the biologists can have a most delightful experience studying the vast array of coral life. There is probably no greater concentration of life in any other ecosystem and the variety in color, form, and activity is fantastic.

In the ecosystems of the world many niches have developed, inhabited by certain species of plants and animals which are similar as regards specific needs. Together they constitute the complex life pattern of the earth.

SUGGESTED SUPPLEMENTARY READINGS

ALLEE, W. C., EMERSON, A. E., PARK, O., PARK, T., and SCHMIDT, K. P., *Principles of Animal Ecology* (Philadelphia, W. B. Saunders Co., 1949).

BARTHOLOMEW, G. A., and HUDSON, J. W., "Desert Ground Squirrels," *Scientific American,* 205 (5) (November, 1961), 107.

BATES, M., *The Forest and the Sea* (New York; Random House, 1960).

CARSON, R., *The Sea Around Us* (New York, Oxford University Press, 1951).

CHANDLER, A. C., and READ, C. P., *Introduction to Parasitology* (New York, John Wiley & Sons, Inc., 1961).

COLE, L. C., "The Ecosphere," *Scientific American,* 198 (4) (April, 1958), 83.

DEEVEY, E. S., "Life in the Depths of a Pond," *Scientific American,* 185 (4) (October, 1951), 68.

DIETZ, R. S., "The Sea's Deep Scattering Layers," *Scientific American,* 207 (2) (August, 1962), 44.

ELTON, C., *Animal Ecology* (New York, The Macmillan Co., 1939).

NICHOLAS, G., "Life in Caves," *Scientific American,* 192 (5) (May, 1955), 98.

NOBLE, E. R., and NOBLE, G. A., *Parasitology, The Biology of Animal Parasites* (Philadelphia, Lea & Febiger, 1961).

ODUM, E. P., *Fundamentals of Ecology* (Philadelphia, W. B. Saunders Co., 1960).

RYTHER, F. H., "The Sargasso Sea," *Scientific American,* 194 (1) (Jan., 1950), 98.

WENT, F. W., "The Ecology of Desert Plains," *Scientific American,* 192 (4) (April, 1955), 68.

6
Orderliness Among Animals

To THE casual observer the plants and animals on the earth may seem to exist without order, being so varied in shape and size that it would be useless to try to arrange them in any kind of order. Early scholars were confronted with this problem and many attempted to place organisms into groups, that is, classify them. It seems to be man's innate tendency to catalog everything about him when it exists in sufficient numbers. The first recorded effort to classify plants and animals was made by the Greek scholars Aristotle and Theophrastus. According to their scheme, they divided the plants into herbs, shrubs, and trees; the animals into land-dwellers, water-dwellers, and air-dwellers. This system served the single purpose of arranging organisms so that one might find the name of any one of them, so long as the number was small, but with increasing knowledge it became cumbersome and almost useless. It was not until the sixteenth and seventeenth centuries that significant steps were taken to find a better system of classification. John Ray in England in the seventeenth century and Carolus Linnaeus in Sweden in the eighteenth century established **taxonomy** (the science of classification) on a firm footing. We may remember Ray for defining the category **species,** which previously had meant a rather unclear group of organisms. He described a species as a closely related group of organisms whose parents were similar and who passed their characteristics on to their offspring. Once the species concept was established, an entirely new approach was taken in classifying plants and animals.

Linnaeus (1707–1778) is generally recognized as the father of taxonomy because he gave us the system of classification that is in current use today (Fig. 6-1). He was a Swedish physician who developed an interest in natural history that continued from childhood throughout his lifetime. In his early youth he recognized the need for a better system of classification and soon set down the basic principles on which he later built a satisfactory method of cataloging plants and animals. Linnaeus had the insight to select important fundamental characters as bases for his classification. This was fortunate because not only did he give us a system which was workable and sound for an infinite number of additions, but it also closely corresponded to the theory of evolution which became widely accepted after 1859. Linnaeus' is a branching type of system, just as evolution is, so the two are compatible, although not actually intended to be so by Linnaeus.

Linnaeus used such fundamental structures as the skeleton, scales, hair, feathers, and so forth in classifying the larger animals; for the soft-bodied invertebrate types he used characters like the foot of the mollusk, the body segments and exoskeleton of the arthropods. Likewise with plants he placed those bearing flowers in a group distinct from those without this structure.

All animals and plants in this system of classification were given two names, a **generic** (a noun) and a **specific** (an adjective) name. This is now known as the **binomial system of nomenclature.** The ge-

FIG. 6-1. Carolus Linnaeus (1707–1778) is considered the father of taxonomy because he initiated a system of classifying plants and animals that is still in use today.

neric name is comparable to our own family name, whereas the specific name is like our given name. Linnaeus decided that these names should be written in a universally familiar language that would cause the least amount of international jealousy and therefore selected Latin.

Plants and animals that are most alike were placed in one species, such as *sapiens,* the specific name for all men alive today —there have been other species of men but they are all extinct. Likewise, man also belongs to the genus *Homo;* there have been other Homos but they, too, have been extinct many thousands of years. Under the Linnaean classification, therefore, man is known as *Homo sapiens.*

Linnaeus grouped all the various **genera** (plural of genus) into larger groups which he called **orders;** while these organisms resembled one another in certain respects, they differed much more than did the various species in the separate genera. He further grouped the orders into six **classes,** his largest category. Since his time, of course, a great many biologists have unearthed information about more and more organisms so that it became necessary to enlarge his classification extensively. This was done by adding two more groups, namely, **families** (between genera and orders) and **phyla** (the largest group of all). Furthermore, each group has been subdivided again and again, so that we now have the following general categories: phylum, subphylum, class, subclass, order, suborder, family, subfamily, genus, subgenus, species, and subspecies. However, not all of these divisions are necessary in the classification of every organism.

The differences are less and less as the selection moves from the phylum to the species. For example, the differences between the horse and the earthworm are various and striking; each belongs to a separate phylum. The differences between the horse and the alligator, while many, are not nearly as numerous as those between the horse and the earthworm; they belong to the same phylum but not to the same class. They show more differences than are observed between the horse and the dog, both mammals, belonging to the same class. The differences between the dog and the horse are sufficient, however, to place them in different orders, families, genera, and species.

In many cases, however, the problem of separating species is much more difficult. In fact, a point is reached where biologists are frequently in doubt as to whether or not a given organism is actually a separate species at all. This is what one would expect if the theory of evolution holds, namely, that plants and animals have originated and are indeed still originating from a common ancestral stock. Undoubtedly new species are forming at the present time and will continue to do so as long as there is life on earth.

The following example illustrates the use of the Linnaean system in classifying man according to his distinguishing characteristics and in outlining the basis of his relationship to other animals:

Phylum Chordata—notochord, gill slits, nerve cord
 Subphylum Vertebrata—backbone
  Class Mammalia—mammary glands, hair
   Subclass Theria—marsupium and placenta
    Infraclass Eutheria—true placenta
     Order Primates—superior nervous system
      Suborder Anthropoidea—flattened or cupped nails
       Family Hominidae—no tail or cheek pouches
        Genus Homo—manlike
         Species sapiens—present-day man

Thus *Homo sapiens* includes all living men today. To distinguish between different colors and other characteristics of men, the subspecies is given. The scientific name then becomes trinomial, such as *Homo sapiens africanus,* which identifies a particular race of living men, the African Negro.

MODERN TAXONOMY

As you would guess a great deal has been learned about animals since Linnaeus' time; consequently much new information is available for the taxonomist to work with. Moreover, our idea of species has changed. Whereas Linnaeus conceived of species as immutable, today we are certain that species are constantly evolving, forever changing. This idea, though very old, was crystallized by Charles Darwin when he supplied abundant evidence that species are constantly evolving. We shall discuss his theory of evolution in some detail later on (Chapter 27). All we need say now is that all modern taxonomists have completely abandoned the idea that a species is static, and have developed an entirely different interpretation of the Linnaean Binomial System.

Today, the systematist (taxonomist) conceives of the species as a population strongly influenced by ecological and genetic factors. Instead of one animal or plant being the taxonomic unit, he now considers the entire population when he speaks of a species. This requires a great deal more knowledge on the part of the systematist because he must be familiar with statistical methods and understand the role genetics plays in an ever-changing population. He must also possess a thorough knowledge of morphology in order to recognize subtle differences in organisms, morphology still being very important in describing species.

Perhaps the best definition of a species is based on genetics, namely, a species is a population of interbreeding organisms. This is a straightforward definition that has the possibility of proof. The difficulty is that it is not practical to carry out cross-breeding experiments with every species that is or has been described. Unfortunately only one in ten thousand species has been so tested, hence this definition will probably never be completely satisfactory. Structural characteristics as well as behavior, physiology, and distribution are now relied upon for describing species.

Using interbreeding populations as a criterion for species has certain pitfalls. For example, among the ciliated protozoa there are some morphological species that have among them a number of interbreeding populations. This is true of *Paramecium aurelia* and *Tetrahymena pyriformis*. In the latter there are at least ten interbreeding populations, called **varieties,** which are genetically isolated from one another, even though two or more may inhabit the same environment. Morphologists agree that they are very similar in structure. It has been suggested that such populations be called

syngens, which identifies the genetic species, leaving the term species for the morphologist's species. Since this problem is still in a state of controversy it is best that we use the term species where it includes both genetic and morphological characteristics.

The modern systematist studies the structure of organisms from the point of view of relationships, that is, he searches for **homologies** between structures when he is describing a taxonomic category **(taxon).** Homologous structures are those parts that are similar in form and number in different organisms and can be arranged in a continuous series showing only slight differences from one to the next. This is usually illustrated by comparing the anterior appendage of vertebrates, for example, the frog, man and the horse (p. 737). A species, then, is a group of organisms that share the greatest number of homologous structures. The number of homologous structures become fewer and fewer in each succeeding higher taxon. The dividing line between taxa, of course, becomes a matter of the taxonomist's judgment and must be arbitrary; this cannot be avoided. It has been said that a system of classification is no better than the taxonomist who designed it.

In searching out homologous structures in organisms the taxonomist is actually observing evolution. Hence, the scheme that results in using this procedure reflects evolutionary change, and is a "natural classification" not greatly unlike the one provided by Linnaeus. The interpretation of it, however, is quite different from Linnaeus' interpretation of his scheme.

SOME BASIC CHARACTERISTICS OF ANIMALS

The whole scheme of animals has been studied by biologists for centuries in an effort to set down certain characteristics that can be used to separate large groups into

radial

hydra

bilateral

planaria

FIG. 6-2. Two kinds of symmetry.

types of symmetry, and (3) **kinds of body cavities,** if present. We shall consider each of these briefly.

Grade of Organization. This merely indicates the way cells are arranged in an animal, whether the animal is single-celled or multicellular. The unicellular Protozoa are distinct entities with the exception of the colonial protozoa, which give indications of some sort of organization among individuals in the colony. The Porifera, distinctly metazoan, demonstrate the **cellular** grade of organization, whereas all higher metazoa represent the **tissue** grade of organization. All animals can thus be separated into these large categories.

still smaller categories. Is it possible to determine certain characters which can be found in many phyla and which will establish relationships among them? As more animals have been studied, it has been possible to establish a few fundamental categories which are agreed to be sufficiently basic to include all animals living today. These are: (1) **grade of organization,** (2)

Types of Symmetry. As cells became organized into groups, they formed definite relations to one another, imposing upon the resulting animal a particular shape that can be described in terms of symmetry (Fig. 6-2). Symmetry refers to the arrangement of parts in relation to points, planes, and

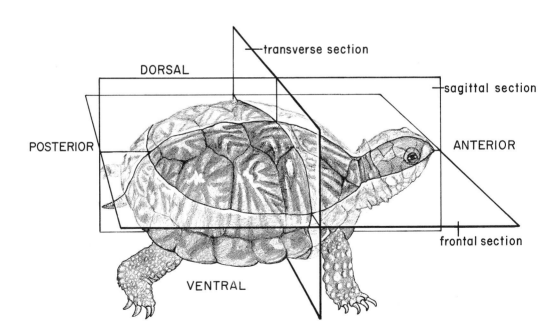

transverse section

DORSAL

sagittal section

POSTERIOR

ANTERIOR

frontal section

VENTRAL

FIG. 6-3. Orientation of an animal possessing bilateral symmetry.

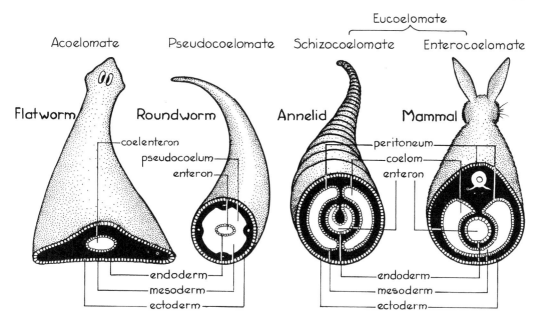

FIG. 6-4. Various types of animal cavities.

straight lines. The metazoa can usually be conveniently divided into two types of symmetry. Probably the first to appear in evolution was **radial symmetry**, which is characteristic of the Coelenterates and the Ctenophores. These animals are distinguished by a principal axis around which the parts are arranged in a radiating fashion. All higher forms possess **bilateral symmetry**. In these one can divide the animal by a plane which results in two approximate mirror halves. Such animals are usually oriented into an **anterior** end, or head, a **posterior** end, or tail, a **dorsal** side, or back, a **ventral** side, or belly, and a **right** and **left** side (Fig. 6-3). These terms are handy in locating organs and parts of animals.

In general, there is a correlation between types of symmetry and modes of life of the organisms. Primitive and attached animals possess radial symmetry, whereas higher and active animals are bilaterally symmetrical. Sessile forms require a body form that permits them to explore their food-laden world in all directions, whereas

an animal that pursues and apprehends its prey can succeed in this task much better with a body that permits one-way movement, a head equipped with numerous sense organs to locate the prey, and some means of propelling itself, such as appendages. These latter features we see in nearly all bilaterally symmetrical animals.

Kinds of Body Cavities. Whereas several body cavities developed in the most primitive metazoa, such as the gastrovascular cavity of the coelenterates, we wish to consider here only those animals with bilateral symmetry which either possess or do not possess a cavity surrounding the digestive system (Fig. 6-4). Those that have no such cavity are called **acoelomate** animals (nemertines and flatworms), and those with such a cavity are termed **eucoelomate** animals. The cavity of this latter group is usually spoken of as a true **coelom,** which is a cavity lined with a thin layer of mesodermal cells called the *peritoneum*. A few animals such as the nematodes and the rotifers have a cavity, but it is not lined with meso-

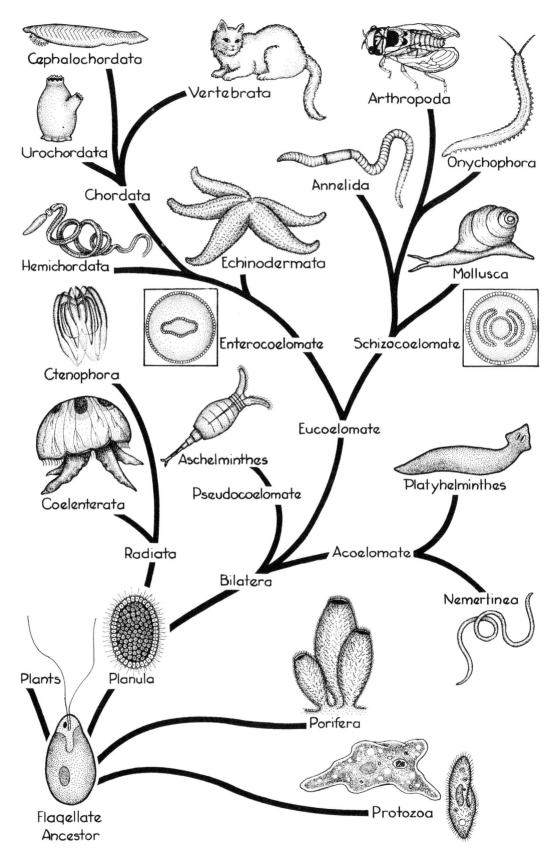

FIG. 6-5. Phylogenetic relations of animals.

154

derm, hence is not a true coelom. These are called **pseudocoelomate** animals.

The eucoelomate animals may be divided into two large groups: (1) those in which the coelom is formed from solid mesoderm (**schizocoelom**) and (2) those in which it forms from mesodermal pouches from the gut (**enterocoelom**) (Fig. 6-5). The manner in which the coelom forms is evident only during early embryology. In the schizocoelomates the mesoderm arises as a solid mass of cells which very early develops a cavity, the coelom. The coelom of the enterocoelomates is present when the outpocketing of the endoderm, or primitive gut, first appears to form the mesoderm. The end result in both cases is the same.

With these three general categories it is possible to show the evolutionary relationships of the entire animal kingdom in the form of a branching system, as shown in Fig. 6-5.

Now let us discuss in some detail the various kinds of animals that have evolved since the inception of life on earth. As we gaze upon the great profusion of plant and animal life today, we should remember that each living thing has survived following a struggle by its forebears to provide a plant or animal organization able to cope with an environment that has been changing through the millennia. Millions have perished along the way, but these species you see today have survived the struggle and, even now, are fighting to maintain their place on the crowded earth's crust. The nature of the struggle and the path which each species has followed will probably never be known, but as one of these species, we can appreciate the magnitude of the problem.

SUGGESTED SUPPLEMENTARY READINGS

BORRADAILE, L. A., POTTS, F. A., EASTMAN, L. E. S., and SAUNDERS, J. T., *The Invertebrata* (Cambridge, Cambridge University Press, 1958).

HYMAN, LIBBIE H., *The Invertebrates,* Vols. I, II, III, IV, V (New York, McGraw-Hill Book Co., Inc., 1940, 1951, 1951, 1955, 1959).

MAYR, E., LINSLEY, E. G., and USINGER, R. C., *Methods and Principles of Systematic Zoology* (New York, McGraw-Hill Book Co., Inc., 1953).

ROMER, A. S., *The Vertebrate Story* (Chicago, The University of Chicago Press, 1959).

SCHECHTER, V., *Invertebrate Zoology* (Englewood Cliffs, N.J., Prentice-Hall, Inc., 1959).

SIMPSON, G. G., *The Principles of Animal Taxonomy* (New York, Columbia University Press, 1961).

PART V

The Rise of Animal Life

7

The First Animals—Protozoa

Up to this point we have considered the physical world and the laws that operate in it, the origin and nature of the first living things, the origin of the metazoa and the problems associated with organization on the multicellular level, the animal and its environment, and finally classification of animals. We shall now examine in some detail the various kinds of animals that have arisen through the millions of years since the first life appeared on earth.

Let us start our discussion of the rise of animal life with the most primitive animals and then continue through the animal kingdom in the order which most zoologists agree these animals appeared on the earth. There is little doubt that animals started from simple one-celled forms and gradually increased in complexity of structure and function. Of the 1,200,000 different species that have been described we are obliged to consider only one or two representatives of the major groups with the hope that some understanding will be gained of the process of evolution. It is important to keep in mind the story that is being told, rather than the details concerning individual animals. Specific facts are

first cell

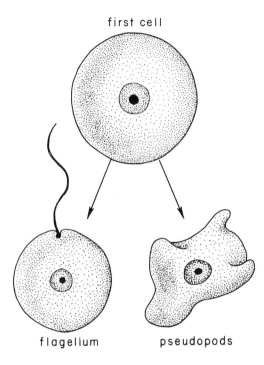

flagellum   pseudopods

FIG. 7-1. Two methods of movement evolved among the first cells, one by means of a vibrating flagellum and the other by pseudopods.

required about representative animals, but the panoramic view is more important than isolated details, no matter how fascinating they may be.

At one stage in the evolution of living things the predominant type was in the form of single cells. These explored all the available niches where they might survive and increase their numbers. With time competition for favorable niches undoubtedly occurred resulting in diversity of form and function within the limits of one cell. One of the first problems that must have faced these first cells was that of getting from place to place to secure food or to secure protection (Fig. 7-1). This apparently was accomplished in two ways; which came first is a matter of conjecture.

One way to move was by means of a vibrating, flexible, thread-like structure, which we now call a *flagellum* (plural—flagella) or *cilium* (plural—cilia). The sim-

plest type of flagellar movement is illustrated in Figure 7-2. As a result of active bending and straightening of the flagellum a wave-like motion passes down the flagellum which exerts a force on the surrounding fluid causing the cell to move forward. This type of flagellar movement was gradually improved upon as indicated by the fact that only the simplest cells observed today employ it.

Another type of movement, employing the same thread-like structure, is ciliary movement. In this case the numerous cilia are short and beat much like the back and forth movement of the oars in propelling a boat. The power stroke exerts a backward force on the surrounding fluid which causes the cell to move forward as shown in Figure 7-2. This type of mechanism is em-

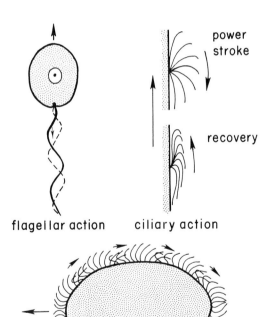

flagellar action   ciliary action

ciliate

FIG. 7-2. Flagellar movement requires that the flexible "thread" (flagellum) undulate, thus creating a force against the surrounding fluid which results in pushing or pulling the cell. Cilia move the cell by paddle-like action.

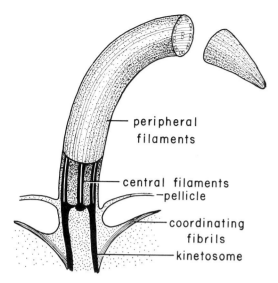

FIG. 7-3a. A schematic representation of the cilium. Note that the cilium arises from the kinetosome. The peripheral filaments originate from its walls whereas the central filaments arise from a dense body at the level of the pellicle. The filaments are enclosed in a covering which is a continuation of the outer membrane. The coordinating filaments probably function in bringing about unified action of all the cilia.

ployed by many single cells and is also found among the metazoa, which we shall consider later.

How can a structure so small as a flagellum or cilium bend on itself, performing the complex movements that we observe under the light microscope? Considerable light was thrown on this problem when electron micrographs became available. They show that these structures consist of tiny filaments and a covering (Fig. 7-3). There are nine pairs located around the inside of the membrane and two at the center often spoken of as the "9 + 2" arrangement. This exquisite fine structure was not dreamed of by early microscopists. Now that we are familiar with this delicate anatomy, the question still remains as to how they work. There has been some speculation on this matter.

The simple power and recovery strokes of the cilium may be brought about by five of the filaments contracting simultaneously thus bringing about the effective stroke. The remaining four filaments are idle during this part of the cycle, but slowly begin to contract during recovery. The two central filaments might act as conductors which carry the signal for contraction to the outer filaments. Thus the cilium or flagellum (both have basically the same structure) turn out to be highly complicated structures in themselves. Moreover where many of them are beating rhythmically there must be some sort of communication between them. Such a coordinating system has been clearly identified in several ciliated protozoa as a result of electron microscope studies.

Quite a different method of locomotion must also have appeared in the very earliest of cells. This is by means of **protoplasmic flow,** or as we refer to it, by **pseudopods** (p. 166). The principle involved in this type of movement is based on the sol-gel phase reversal referred to earlier (p. 59). When one observes a cell such as an amoeba "flowing" along it appears to be the simplest type of movement, yet it is so complex that biologists are still arguing about the mechanism. Let us consider one explanation with a brief reference to another, remembering that neither may be completely right.

FIG. 7-3b. An electron micrograph of the cross section of two flagella from *Trichonympha,* a protozoan living in the gut of the termite. Note the arrangement of the filaments [X150,000]

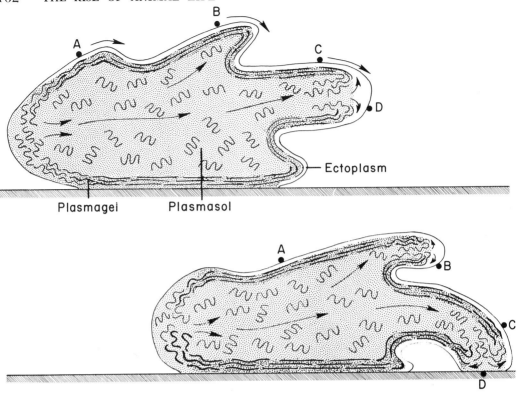

FIG. 7-4. A schematic representation of amoeboid movement. Note that the particles (A, B, C, D) move forward as the amoeba advances (top figure to bottom figure). Plasmasol changes to plasmagel at the anterior end and the reverse action occurs at the posterior end.

The first indication of pseudopod formation is activity in the protoplasm at a specific point (Fig. 7-4). The **ectoplasm** then flows out into this region. Simultaneously, the temporary posterior end gives up its position, and the protoplasm in this region moves forward, filling the region left by the protoplasm that is actively forming the new pseudopod. Thus the entire cell slowly moves in the general direction of the advancing pseudopod. In order to understand this entire process we must examine the different regions of the protoplasm more carefully.

The ectoplasm is clear and seems to have little to do with movement. The **endoplasm**, on the other hand, is made up of two parts, the outer **plasmagel** and the inner **plasmasol.** These two may quickly change from one phase to the other, a change which is responsible for movement. Precisely, the plasmasol flows in the direction in which the pseudopod is to form, and changes to plasmagel as it spreads out at the tip. This describes what happens but why does the plasmasol flow in the direction the pseudopod forms? There are two popular theories offered to answer this question.

The explanation that has been accepted for some time now is that the plasmagel in the rear and around the sides contracts forcing the sol forward in the manner of squeezing tooth paste from a tube. A more recent view is that the contraction of the plasmagel occurs near the anterior portion of the pseudopod thus pulling the plasmasol forward. Regardless of which theory is correct the question still remains as to what causes the phase reversal to occur as it does. The answer to this puzzling question must wait for further research.

You may wonder why biologists worry so much about how the amoeba moves, it hardly seems worthwhile. This would be true if it were not for the fact that if we could understand all of the steps involved in amoeboid movement we would be much closer to an answer to the fundamental question of contractility in general, and to such problems as muscle contraction. All organisms move by one means or another and perhaps there is one underlying answer to the process. Hence, studies of the amoeba will continue and perhaps someday the answer will emerge.

Flagellar and amoeboid movement probably originated in cells when they were isolated individuals. Once established, however, these "patents" were retained throughout all higher groups of animals that were to follow. For example, we see amoeboid movement in the white blood cells of man as well as ciliary movement in the cells lining his trachea (p. 538). We would expect to observe these types of locomotion in modern single cells, and we do.

Before going on to the study of these first animals, perhaps we should discuss their place among microorganisms. Microscopic cells exist in a large variety of forms, illustrated by bacteria, yeasts, molds, algae, and protozoa. Some are marked off by rather well-defined characteristics, but others show close affinities; indeed it is often difficult to be certain in which category they belong. Some have plant-like characteristics, that is, they resemble higher plants, whereas others are definitely animal-like and still others seem to possess both animal and plant characteristics. One has no difficulty in distinguishing between a tree and a cat, but at the unicellular level frequently one is hard pressed to clearly separate these microscopic organisms into distinct categories. To overcome this difficulty, and for convenience, some biologists have created one large taxon to include all these unicellular organisms. They call this group *Protista* and the individuals, *protists*. Since we are dealing in this book only with animals, we shall have little need to refer to this term and will confine our attention to the animal-like protists, the protozoa.

PHYLUM PROTOZOA

The protozoa display the full potentialities of protoplasm within the confines of a single cell. With few exceptions they are unicellular, yet in spite of this limitation they have explored almost every possible design in form and function so that we see them doing nearly all the things multicellular animals do. They exist in a vast array of sizes, shapes, and habitats. It has been estimated that there is at least one protozoan associated with every metazoan, either as a commensal or a parasite, and since commensals and parasites are usually host-specific, each host harboring a different species, it would appear that there must be several million species of protozoa. They range in size from 3 to 15,000 microns and live in almost any environment, from soils to the red blood cells of vertebrates.

Biologists have argued for a long time over the question of whether or not the protozoa fit the definition of a cell, that is, are they equivalent to the metazoan cell. Quite obviously a metazoan cell is only a part of a greater unit and each cell plays a particular role in the operation of the whole organism, whereas in protozoa the cell is the organism. Many prefer to call protozoa **acellular,** leaving the term cell for the units making up many-celled organisms. Those who prefer to think of them as **unicellular** argue that most of them contain a nucleus and other structures found in all cells and this is sufficient evidence to call them one-celled animals. Since all functions are performed within the confines of

FIG. 7-5. This ciliated protozoan, *Tetrahymena pyriformis*, has many of the nutritional requirements of higher animals, including mammals, and for that reason has become valuable in research. The study of microorganisms has become an important field of research where the fundamental workings of protoplasm are under investigation.

tive animals one might expect that they possess many, if not most, of the characteristics of animals and that it might be profitable to study them in solving problems in basic biology. Actually the protozoa are becoming more popular as experimental tools in cellular research. Cells possess common biochemical and morphological characteristics whether they reside in the body of a man or as single individuals such as a paramecium or an amoeba. It is frequently difficult or even impossible to study individual cells of a higher organism in the manner that is required for understanding its basic mechanisms, whereas isolated protozoans in a test tube might yield the desired information which then can be extended to metazoan cells. For example, the ciliate *Tetrahymena pyriformis* (Fig. 7-5) has proven to be an excellent cell for

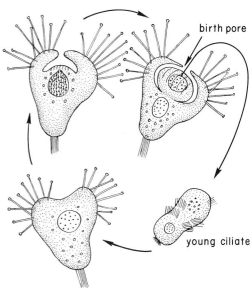

FIG. 7-6. This protozoan, *Tokophrya*, remains attached by means of a stalk throughout its adult life and feeds through sucking tentacles. It is unique in that it gives rise to a free-swimming offspring which forms as an internal bud, is "born" through a birth pore, swims about for a time, then becomes attached by its caudal cilia, grows a stalk and tentacles, and loses its cilia as it metamorphoses into the adult.

the single cell numerous structures have evolved within protozoa, some far more elaborate than those found in any metazoan cell. In other words differentiation has developed at the one-cell level, just as it developed later among the cells of the multicelled organisms.

The question of what the protozoa should be called can be reduced to a matter of semantics and need not concern us here. For convenience we shall refer to them as unicellular.

Since the protozoa are the most primiresearch in nutrition, metabolism, cytology and genetics. Several species of paramecium have been utilized as experimental animals for studies in genetics, and amoeba has had a long history as an ideal cell for the study of behavior, cytology, movement, biochemistry, and many other problems in biology. Such protozoa as *Stentor* and *Tokophrya* (Fig. 7-6) are ideally suited for studies of embryology. The latter organism is unique among one-celled organisms in producing internal buds which become "embryos," mature, and are "born," a process reminiscent of higher animals. Such organisms provide excellent research material for studying the way new cells are formed from parent cells. Many other protozoa are currently being used in a great variety of experiments which are designed to solve problems in basic biology. As more is learned about handling these tiny animals in the laboratory, they will become more and more useful in research.

When one attempts to classify this heterogeneous group of organisms into any sort of logical system, he is at once faced with some difficult decisions. The older biologists utilized the very obvious character of methods of locomotion as the single criterion for assigning groups. At first it appears to be rather easy to separate protozoa into groups which possess flagella, cilia, pseudopods, and no obvious means of locomotion. However, it has become increasingly clear as more knowledge accumulates that certain fallacies exist in this method of classification. For example, it is now known, as a result of electron microscope studies, that cilia and flagella are structurally the same (p. 161). The fact that cilia are usually short and numerous is not a distinguishing characteristic either, because there are flagellates which possess numerous flagella and ciliates without cilia. Even more damaging to such a simple system is the fact that a few protozoa may possess flagella at one period in their life

cycle and cilia at another time. For example, the protozoan, *Tetramitus rostratus,* exists as an amoeboid form under certain cultural conditions and when these are changed it transforms into a four-flagellated organism (Fig. 7-7). Moreover, many protozoa which appear to be without means of locomotion, such as the malarial parasite, do have stages in their life cycles which are motile.

In spite of these difficulties, the presence of various types of locomotor organelles is used as a criterion for separation of protozoa into rather well-defined taxa. The taxonomy of the protozoa is presently undergoing some rather drastic changes but until there is general agreement as to how it shall be done, we will adhere to the generally accepted groupings.

Owing to their great diversity it is impossible to obtain more than a glimpse of the phylum protozoa as a whole. We can, however, study two representatives in some detail in order to have some understanding of their morphology and how they function. Later we can describe representatives of the various groups in a cursory fashion to gain some notion of their diversity. We have selected **amoeba** as a simple form and **paramecium** as one of the most complicated protozoans. Both of these are ubiquitous in their distribution and because they are easily handled have been classic material in biology classes for many years.

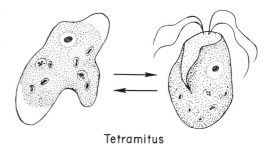

Tetramitus

FIG. 7-7. The life cycle of *Tetramitus* involves both amoeboid and flagellated stages indicating the close affinities of these large groups, the sarcodinids and mastigophorans.

AMOEBA

The common amoeba, *Amoeba proteus* (Fig. 7-8), spends its life today, as it probably has for many millions of years, in an aquatic environment from which it receives all of its nourishment and into which it deposits all of its wastes. Its continual search for food keeps it on the move, crawling over vegetation on the bottom of ponds and streams. It resembles an amorphous blob of nearly transparent jelly and its chief outward manifestation of animal behavior is its movement, which appears mysterious because there seems to be no propelling mechanism.

Locomotion

The amoeba moves by means of lobe-shaped projections of its protoplasm, called **pseudopods** (false feet). We have already discussed the mechanism involved in their formation (p. 161). The **ectoplasm** which surrounds the entire cell is completely transparent and is separated from the surrounding fluid environment by a thin membrane, the **plasmalemma.** The remaining protoplasm is the **endoplasm** which consists of

FIG. 7-8. This is a micrograph of a living amoeba taken through the light microscope. Note the highly granular nature of the protoplasm in the main body of the cell and the clear regions where the pseudopods are forming.

two parts, the free-flowing internal **plasmasol** and the external **plasmagel.** The most obvious indication of movement is the flowing of the numerous crystals suspended in the plasmasol. The large oval **nucleus,** as well as **food vacuoles,** also flows freely during movement. The **contractile vacuole** is conspicuous by its rhythmic pulsations.

The first indication of pseudopod formation is activity in the ectoplasm at one specific region (Fig. 7-9). A bulge forms as a result of the plasmasol flowing forward, pushing the ectoplasm ahead of it. Simultaneously, the temporary posterior end gives up its position and the whole organism moves in the direction of the newly formed pseudopod. Pseudopods form vertically and anteriorly, that is, in the direction of the cell's general progress. The amoeba is able to "step over" particles which are not food and to engulf those which are a part of its diet. Most descriptions of this process point to the fact that the pseudopods form in several directions at one time. There follows a "tug-of-war" until finally the pseudopods on one side or the other accumulate the bulk of the protoplasm, causing the others to retract and follow the cell body in a specific direction.

Ingestion of Food

The activity of the amoeba is about the same during locomotion and during food-getting, with one or two minor exceptions. When it approaches a motionless particle of food, such as an immotile alga, the pseudopods are spread around and over the plant cell in close proximity until they meet, forming a **food vacuole.** If the food is active, as in the case of a small protozoan, the amoeba spreads its pseudopods over a larger area in order to capture the organism first before closing in on it to form the vacuole (Fig. 7-10).

Once the food vacuole is within the cell body, digestion begins, much the same as it begins in man's stomach when a morsel of food is swallowed. The surround-

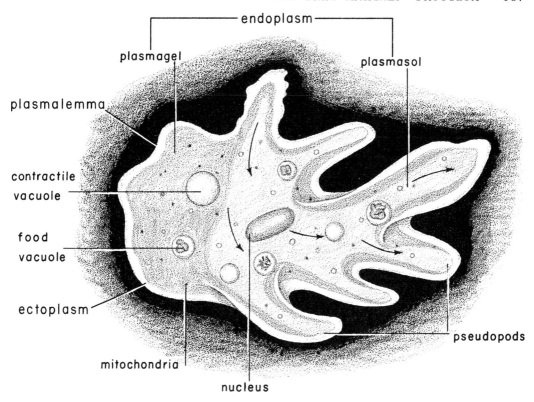

FIG. 7-9. Amoeba with internal anatomy shown in detail.

ing protoplasm secretes enzymes into the vacuole where they proceed to digest the captured food. This interesting process can be observed under the microscope. A captured protozoan, for example, slows down in its activity and finally ceases movement altogether. It then begins to disintegrate and after a time there is very little left of the original organism, except the undigested parts which, incidentally, are left behind as the amoeba moves on its way. The digested food passes into the protoplasm where it is metabolized. This is the source of energy which enables the amoeba to keep continuously on the move and which also provides the materials from which it is able to grow and reproduce.

Respiration and Excretion

The exchange of oxygen and carbon dioxide is a simple business in amoeba. Oxygen moves into the protoplasm of the cell by diffusion whenever the concentration of the gas is greater outside than inside. Likewise carbon dioxide diffuses out of the cell into the surrounding water when it forms as a result of metabolism within the organism. Since this little creature demands an abundance of oxygen continuously, you would not expect to find it in stagnant water where there is little or no oxygen.

As a result of the metabolism of nitrogen-containing compounds (amino acids), poisonous wastes tend to accumulate in the cell. These are removed by diffusion to the outside fluid world also. They are not allowed to accumulate because of their toxic effects.

There is a prominent organelle (little organ) located variously in the cytoplasm of the amoeba which requires some explanation. It is the **contractile vacuole.**

avoids injury

avoids bright light

avoids
injurious chemicals

engulfs food

ACTIVITIES
OF
AMOEBA

"walks"

side view

FIG. 7-10. Amoeba responding to various conditions in its environment.

This is a small, clear, spherical area which forms in the cytoplasm, soon grows to maximum size, then suddenly disappears. It forms and disappears at regular intervals. Those who have studied this carefully believe that the contractile vacuole probably functions only as a device for getting rid of excess water that accumulates inside the cell. In other words, it acts like a bailer who works to get rid of the water that is constantly flowing into a leaking boat. Because of the hypertonicity of the amoeba, water is constantly flowing into its protoplasm. If it were not removed the little animal would soon become waterlogged. Furthermore, if the concentration of dissolved substances in the surrounding water is increased (hypertonic), as it is in sea water or in a solution with high salt content, the contractile vacuole disappears. If the marine amoeba, which has no contractile vacuole, is placed in fresh water, vacuoles form very soon. All evidence points, therefore, to the fact that the contractile vacuole functions merely as a hydrostatic organelle, a mechanism that controls the flow of water out of the amoeba.

Behavior

Another innate quality of amoeba which makes possible its survival is its responsiveness to changes in its external world. It responds usually to protect itself from harm or to lead itself to a rich food area. This is spoken of as its **behavior.** Although gradual changes in intensity of light elicit very little or no response, intense, sudden light causes it to send out pseudopods in such a way as to withdraw and move away from the light source (Fig. 7-10). Likewise, if a concentrated salt solution is placed near the amoeba, a definite response is noted. If it is floating free in the water and one of its pseudopods contacts a surface, it at once adheres to the substratum. However, if a sharp point is pressed into its protoplasm at the surface, an immediate avoiding reaction follows. Amoeba thrives

best at room temperature. If it is subjected to lower temperatures, all of its activities slow down and cease altogether as the freezing point is reached. Activity also ceases if the temperature is raised to approximately 30°C.

In general, then, the behavior of amoeba is geared to its needs and is responsible for its survival. If more were known about the amoeba's response to its external world, problems which arise in the more specialized animals would be easier to solve.

Reproduction

Amoeba, like all other living things, reproduces itself. It does this in the simplest way, namely, by dividing into two equal parts, a process known as **binary fission** (Fig. 7-11). After the cell has grown to a certain size, it rounds up into a ball. The nucleus divides first, then the entire cell cleaves into two parts which are usually spoken of as "daughter cells" (they are called daughter cells perhaps because they give rise to other cells; "son cells" would be unable to do this). The amoeba seems to have to reach a certain size before dividing, for if a small piece of cytoplasm is

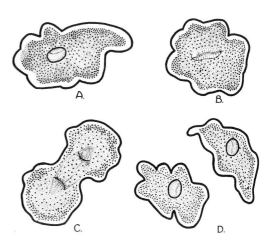

FIG. 7-11. Amoeba undergoing binary fission.

FIG. 7-12. Paramecium has been studied perhaps more than any other protozoan. It is large (100–200 microns in length) and very easily cultured in the laboratory.

cut off periodically as the amoeba grows, never allowing the animal to reach the proper size, it will not divide.

Amoeba is "immortal," as was pointed out in an earlier section. If death occurs, it comes only through accident. Occasionally its watery environment may dry up, leaving it to desiccate and die; however, provisions were made for it to exist through periods of adverse conditions. When such times come, the amoeba (there seems to be some question about *A. proteus* forming a cyst although other amoebas do) secretes an impervious outer covering called a **cyst** (Fig. 5-2), which allows life to continue at a very low ebb until it is once more submerged in water. The cyst then splits open and the amoeba resumes its active life. This provision has made it possible for the animal to survive long periods of unfavorable conditions and has been an important factor in its survival.

PARAMECIUM

Not all protozoa are as simple as amoeba. A study may now be made of a protozoan which is perhaps one of the most complicated of all single cells—paramecium, the "slipper animalcule" (Fig. 7-12). This form has been experimented upon and studied as much as, if not more than, the amoeba, and a great deal of fundamental biological information has been derived from it.

As one might guess, the animal is shaped like a slipper, pointed at the posterior end and blunt at the anterior end (Fig. 7-13). A groove extends throughout most of its length and the **mouth** or **cytostome** (cell mouth) is formed in the groove on the oral side, about two-thirds back from the anterior end. Paramecium has an outer covering, the **pellicle,** which is sufficiently rigid to maintain a constant shape. Careful examination with excellent optical equipment shows that the covering is made of minute hexagonal plates, and that the middle of each plate is perforated by a

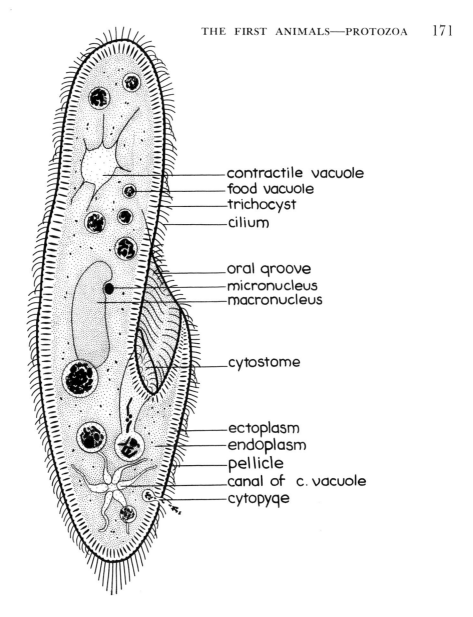

contractile vacuole
food vacuole
trichocyst
cilium

oral groove
micronucleus
macronucleus

cytostome

ectoplasm
endoplasm
pellicle
canal of c. vacuole
cytopyge

FIG. 7-13. Paramecium with internal parts shown in detail.

central opening through which a **cilium** passes. The animal moves by the combined rhythmic beating of these cilia. At the junction of the plates are other tiny holes through which threads are thrust when the animal is disturbed. The threads originate from small bodies lying just beneath the pellicle, called **trichocysts.** They are apparently used in defense and perhaps also in attaching the animal to detritus in the water. Adding a small amount of acetic acid to the water near the paramecium discharges them.

Locomotion

The power stroke of the cilia is diagonal, so that the animal turns on its long axis. Since the cilia in the oral groove are larger and beat with more vigor, the anterior end describes a circle and causes the animal to

FIG. 7-14. Path taken by paramecium when moving freely through the water.

the equivalent of a miniature "brain." If this is destroyed experimentally, the cilia fail to beat in a coordinated manner, and the animal loses all control of its movements. Clearly something similar to the nervous system in multicellular animals exists in paramecium, which makes it possible for this tiny cell to carry on in such a complicated manner.

Ingesting of Food

A simple experiment can be performed to demonstrate how paramecium feeds. Some yeast cells that have been heavily

FIG. 7-15. Movement of paramecium when attached at posterior end.

swim in a spiral manner (Fig. 7-14). When the posterior end is stationary, the long axis of the body describes a cone (Fig. 7-15). When the animal is confronted with an obstacle, the cilia reverse their effective beat so that the cell moves backward a short distance, turns slightly, then moves forward again. If it meets the obstacle again, the process is repeated until the animal passes around and goes on its way (Fig. 7-16). This is known as an **avoiding reaction.**

In order to discover how the cilia operate in such perfect coordination, biologists have made careful studies of the mechanism involved. It has been found that the cilia are attached to one another by tiny fibrils just beneath the pellicle. The fibrils concentrate at a focal point in the region of the gullet where the protoplasm must form

stained with Congo red (a dye) are placed on a glass slide containing a drop of paramecia. By studying the region of the gullet, one can see the cilia beat in such a way as to pass the yeast particles along its oral groove and down into the gullet. There they are rounded up into a mass which finally pinches off into the cytoplasm as a **food vacuole.** Once in the cytoplasm the yeast cells remain deep red for a time, but gradually begin to turn blue as they approach the anterior end. This means that the contents of the food vacuole are alkaline at first (Congo red is red in alkali, blue in acid), just as the mouth of man is alkaacetic acid

responds
positively to acetic acid

10°c

avoids an object

selects
certain temperatures

23°c

ACTIVITIES

OF

PARAMECIUM

37°c

responds to an
electric current

FIG. 7-16. Paramecium responding to various conditions in its environment.

line. As digestion proceeds, the vacuoles become acid as indicated by the blue color; the human stomach is acidic as well. The digested material passes through the wall of the vacuole and out into the protoplasm where it is metabolized, the same process that was noted for amoeba. Finally the undigested portions left in the vacuole pass through a tiny opening to the outside, the **cytopyge,** which is equivalent to an anus in higher animals.

Some species of ciliates are able to receive nourishment from dissolved organic matter in the medium. In fact, one species, *Tetrahymena pyriformis* (Fig. 7-5), a small paramecium-like ciliate, grows in a culture medium entirely free from bacteria or other microorganisms. This tiny animal has about the same food requirements as higher animals, including man himself. It has been demonstrated that to grow it requires a diet containing amino acids, sugar, salts, and vitamins. This seems to indicate that even a single-celled animal maintains metabolic processes almost as intricate as man's.

Respiration and Excretion

Respiration and the excretion of nitrogenous wastes take place in paramecium much the same as in amoeba. The **contractile** or **pulsating vacuoles** which lie at either end of the cell contract alternately at about 15-second intervals. Several **radiating canals** empty into each contractile vacuole, becoming most obvious when the vacuole is nearly empty. Each vacuole discharges its contents to the outside through a minute **pore** in the pellicle. The rate of contraction varies with temperature, activity of the animal, and the concentration of salts in the surrounding medium. As in the amoeba, the contractile vacuole functions normally as a bailer to rid the animal of excess water constantly entering the cell.

Behavior

Paramecium is very sensitive to the relative acidity and alkalinity of its environ-

ment (Fig. 7-16). It responds positively by going toward an acid environment, even though the acid may be of sufficient strength to destroy it. If a drop of weak acid, for example acetic acid, is placed on a slide containing paramecia, they will move toward the acid region and remain there. If they get away from this region and approach a less acid surrounding, the paramecia display the avoiding reaction, by returning to the more acid medium. This sensitivity is probably due to the fact that, in large numbers, paramecia give off carbon dioxide in such quantity that the water in the immediate vicinity becomes weakly acid.

Paramecium selects a temperature optimal for its activities, usually around 23°C (Fig. 7-16). If given a choice, it seeks this temperature. If placed in an electrical field of direct current, it responds in a very definite manner, always orienting itself with respect to the flow of the current (Fig. 7-16). It moves toward the negative pole, indicating that externally it is positively charged.

Reproduction

Paramecium maintains its numbers by dividing transversely across its long axis (Fig. 7-17). The first sign of division is in the tiny **micronucleus** which moves out from the large **macronucleus** and undergoes a change in shape from a sphere to a spindle-shaped body (Fig. 7-18). The micronucleus functions as a carrier of hereditary traits, but the exact function of the macronucleus is uncertain. Only the macronucleus is indispensable for life of the paramecium as well as some other ciliates; this is borne out by the fact that some ciliates have been kept alive, dividing normally, for many years without micronuclei. Once the micronucleus has spun out into two equal parts and these deposited at the two ends of the cell, the macronucleus divides by pinching into two parts. A second gullet and two more contractile vacuoles then appear, followed by indentations in the mid-region where ultimate separation is to occur. Other structures also duplicate before the two daughter cells finally separate. After a growth period they are ready to divide again. Under optimal conditions, division occurs about every six to twelve hours. If division took place under these conditions and all individuals survived, 200 billion animals would be produced within a month. Under natural conditions they very soon cease dividing, owing to the accumulation of wastes, lack of food, or other adverse environmental factors.

Under partially starved conditions, paramecia periodically undergo a sexual process called **conjugation** (Figs. 7-18, 7-19). During the process two individuals interchange micronuclear material, which means that genes, hence genetic factors, are involved. This is similar to sexual reproduction in that there is a fusion of genetic material, although there is no immediate increase in numbers as the term *reproduction* usually implies. A controversy has gone on for many years over whether or not conjugation is essential for continued asexual reproduction of at least one species of paramecium. Professor L. L. Woodruff, long ago, separated paramecia after each fission so that conjugation was impossible. He followed individuals through 15,000 generations over a period of 25 years without observing conjugation. It is now known, however, that this organism does undergo a type of self-fertilization, called **autogamy**, at regular intervals. Moreover, it seems that unless autogamy or conjugation occurs periodically, certain species of paramecia cannot continue dividing and finally die. Another ciliate, *Tetrahymena pyriformis,* has been maintained in continued culture for over 35 years with neither conjugation nor autogamy taking place. Therefore, nuclear reorganization seems to be essential in some ciliates but not in others.

The process of conjugation is well

FIG. 7-17. Paramecium divides by binary fission as shown in this photograph of stained specimens.

known for a large number of ciliates and, in a few, "**mating types**" have been found. Mating types are distinguished from one another by their conjugation reactions and have been identified for convenience by Roman numerals. Thus, an animal designated as mating type I will mate with ciliates of mating type II, but not with others like itself, that is, mating type I. This might suggest sex in these protozoa, male and female. The difficulty arises when other information is considered. Jennings and his co-workers found as many as eight different mating types in *Paramecium bursaria,* and more recently ten have been found in one variety of *Tetrahymena pyriformis.* Since two sexes are usual in both plants and animals, it is perhaps better

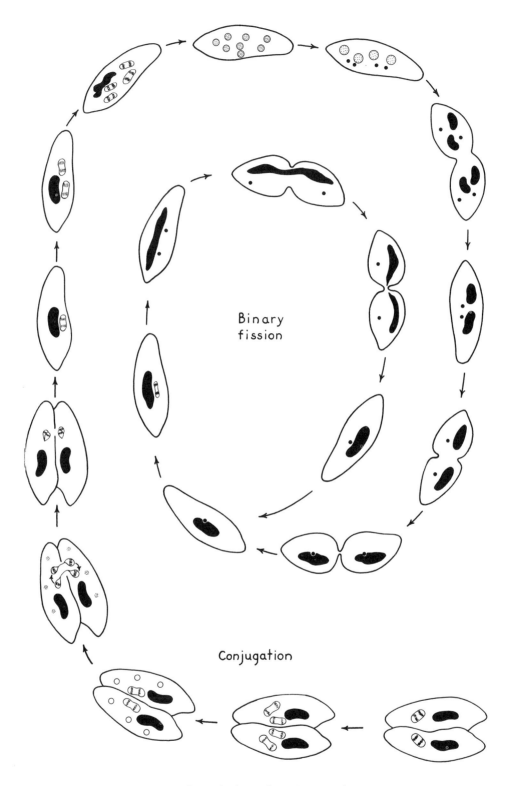

Binary fission

Conjugation

FIG. 7-18. Conjugation and asexual reproduction by binary fission in paramecium.

that we retain the designation *mating types* for this unusual condition found only among the ciliates and a few lower plants.

Conjugation in ciliates involves a series of rather precise steps. In *Paramecium caudatum,* for example, when animals of opposite mating type are mixed under proper conditions, the surface membranes of the cells seem to become sticky which causes them to adhere together in pairs, rather securely attached at their oral grooves where a narrow protoplasmic bridge extends from one to the other (Fig. 7-18). Very shortly thereafter, the micronuclei in both animals divide twice forming four micronuclei; during one of these divisions the chromosome number is reduced to one-half, which is equivalent to meiosis in metazoa (see p. 658). At this time the macronucleus and three of the newly formed micronuclei disintegrate and disappear, leaving one micronucleus which then divides once more giving rise to two micronuclei each containing half the number of chromosomes possessed by the original micronucleus. A significant event now takes place—one of these micronuclei from each animal migrates across the protoplasmic bridge into the opposite cell and fuses with the micronucleus remaining there. The migratory micronucleus is sometimes thought of as a *sperm cell* and the stationary one as an *egg*, although they are not comparable to their implied counterparts in higher forms. The **fusion nucleus** now possesses the full number of chromosomes, one-half from the migratory micronucleus and one-half from the stationary micronucleus. The paired cells now separate and the fusion nucleus undergoes three successive divisions producing eight micronuclei, four of which remain micronuclei and four become new macronuclei. Both paramecia then divide twice, producing eight individuals in all, each one of which resembles the original parents. These then undergo ordinary asexual fission until conjugation is once more induced.

OTHER PROTOZOA

This brief introduction to two different protozoa gives us a basis for considering the importance of the group as a whole in respect to numbers, variety, and classification. Over 50,000 protozoa have been described as distinct species, and in numbers of individuals they exceed all other animals. They live in water of all kinds, in soil and dust, in and on the bodies of plants and animals. Some of them cause the most destructive diseases known to man, malaria, for example. Most protozoa are free-swim-

FIG. 7-19. Conjugating paramecia which have been killed and stained. Note the large macronuclei and the smaller micronuclei.

ming, although some are sessile; most live singly, some form colonies. Many form a source of food for aquatic animals such as fish, but they are of little value to man, except a few which are useful in sewage treatment. They are such a large and varied group of animals that some biologists have considered placing them in a group larger than the phylum, that is, a subkingdom.

The protozoa are divided into two subphyla and five classes, based on their means of locomotion. The subphylum **Plasmodroma** includes those that move by means of flagella and pseudopods, in addition to those that have no means of locomotion in the adult stage. The protozoa that move by means of cilia belong to the subphylum **Ciliophora.** The first subphylum includes the classes **Mastigophora, Sarcodina,** and **Sporozoa;** and the second subphylum includes the classes **Ciliata** and **Suctoria.** The student is already familiar with representatives of two of these classes, the Sarcodina (amoeba) and the Ciliata (paramecium). There is some evidence to show that the protozoa may have evolved in the order indicated by the classification, although there undoubtedly was some overlapping and there is no precise indication as to which types actually preceded other types. For our purposes, the order above will be followed; that is, we shall consider the Mastigophora as the most primitive and the Suctoria as the most complex.

SUBPHYLUM PLASMODROMA

Class Mastigophora

This is a widely diverse group of protozoa in which some members are colored and live independently like plants, whereas others are colorless and require food from the outside, such as the parasites living in the intestinal tract of termites.

Colored Flagellates. Although there are wide divergences in structure and habitat of flagellates, a brief description of *Euglena* (Fig. 7-20) will help in understanding the group as a whole.

Anatomically, euglena is quite different from amoeba. It has a rather definite general shape, which is something like a spindle, although it is sufficiently elastic to be able to undergo animal-like movements when confined to a small space (Fig. 7-20). It moves by means of a single, hair-like, vibratile **flagellum** (plural, *flagella*) which, when active, pulls the organism through the water in a spiral path. In its cytoplasm euglena bears bodies known as **chloroplasts,** which contain the green plant pigment, **chlorophyll.** Because it is able to live on the simple elements that plants utilize, and at the same time possesses certain animal characteristics of behavior, euglena is thought to be intermediate between the plant and the animal world, and is frequently referred to as a **plant-animal** type.

The anterior end of euglena is usually more blunt than the posterior end; in fact, the latter is pointed in some species. There is a **reservoir** at the anterior end, the walls of which give rise to the flagellum, and lying near the reservoir is the **contractile vacuole.** In the immediate region of the reservoir is the **stigma** or **eye-spot,** a conspicuous red dot which apparently functions in aiding the cell to find the proper light intensity for photosynthesis. In order to manufacture its own food, euglena must receive the proper amount of light, hence the significance of the eye-spot. Euglena can, however, live in the dark providing nutrient materials are present in the surrounding medium, in which case it absorbs its food directly. Under favorable conditions euglenas are frequently found in such numbers as to produce a green scum at the surface of the water. As some species grow old they produce a red pigment called **haematochrome** in their cytoplasm. If this happens when they exist in great numbers, a visible red layer appears on the surface of

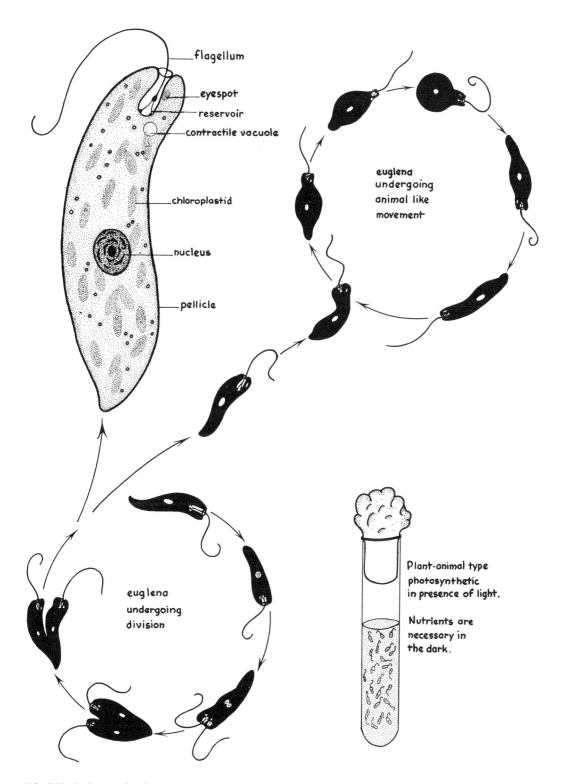

flagellum

eyespot

reservoir

contractile vacuole

chloroplastid

nucleus

pellicle

euglena
undergoing
animal like
movement

euglena
undergoing
division

Plant-animal type
photosynthetic
in presence of light.

Nutrients are
necessary in
the dark.

FIG. 7-20. Euglena in detail and undergoing some of its life processes.

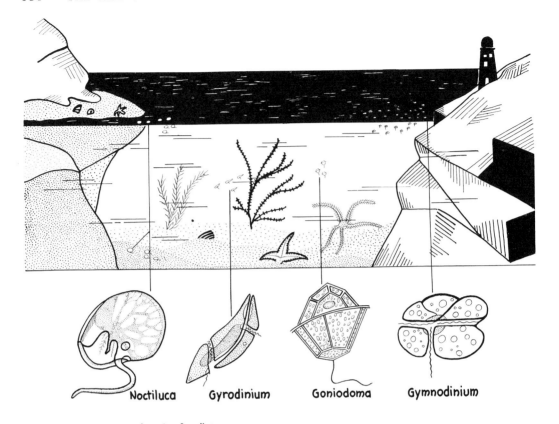

Noctiluca   Gyrodinium   Goniodoma   Gymnodinium

FIG. 7-21. Various types of marine flagellates.

the water. This has sometimes given rise to the name "bloody pools."

Euglena divides longitudinally, that is, in an anterio-posterior direction, splitting the cell into two equal parts (Fig. 7-20). In a rapidly growing culture, cells can be observed in all stages of division. Because this protozoan can be grown in sterile cultures, that is, free from all other microorganisms, it has been used in experimental work in an effort to determine its basic nutritional needs. It is an example of the increasing use of protozoa as experimental animals in fundamental biological research.

Other Colored Flagellates. All kinds of fresh water as well as the oceans are teeming with free-living flagellates. The **dino-**

flagellates, for example, live in the oceans for the most part and constitute a large portion of the diet of small crustacea and other animals. Some members, such as *Noctiluca* (Fig. 7-21), possess luminescent properties which cause them to glisten in the dark when the surface of the water is disturbed. This is a particularly attractive sight in the wake of a boat. Another interesting dinoflagellate, *Gymnodinium brevis* (Fig. 7-21), has appeared several times during the past hundred years along the Florida coast in extremely large numbers (50,000,000 per liter—a normal count is about 100,000 for all kinds of protozoans). Furthermore, this protozoan apparently secretes a by-product which is lethal to all other kinds of animal life in the vicinity. In 1947 half a billion fish were destroyed

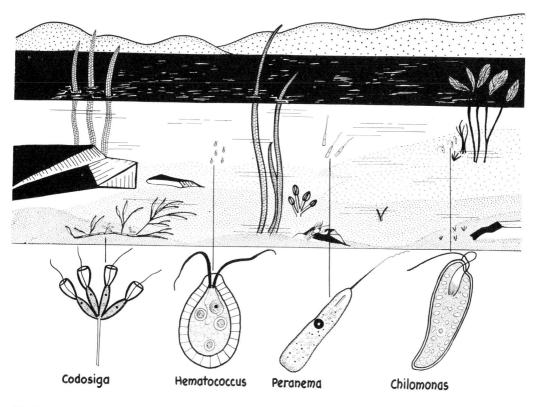

Codosiga   Hematococcus   Peranema   Chilomonas

FIG. 7-22. Various types of fresh-water flagellates.

along the Florida coast, presumably by this toxin.

Fresh water, particularly that containing a considerable amount of decomposing organic matter, supports a large variety of flagellates (Fig. 7-22). Many of them play a very important function in providing food for aquatic animals, especially during their early life when their mouths are so small that no other food but a protozoan could be ingested. Without these tiny animals there would be no fish in many of our lakes and streams. Some, like *Haematococcus pluvialis* (Fig. 7-22), are bright green in color and can reach unbelievable numbers in small pools. Like euglena, they produce haematochrome at certain times of the year, imparting a reddish color to the water. In some Alpine passes they have

been responsible for the so-called bloody snow, a familiar sight to mountain climbers.

Many form colonies, some of which we have already referred to (p. 97). None is more beautiful than the large *Volvox* which contains up to 50,000 cells (Fig. 7-23). It tumbles over in a graceful fashion as it moves through the water. In spite of the fact that it seems to roll in a random fashion, careful studies show that it always turns in such a fashion that certain cells lead the colony. In other words it actually possesses an orientation along one axis so that it demonstrates radial symmetry (p. 152). Another common colonial flagellate is *Synura uvella* (Fig. 7-24), each cell of which contains a brown-yellow chromatophore. When it accumulates in large numbers in drinking water supplies, it conveys a foul odor which often renders the water unpalatable.

Colorless Flagellates. Some colorless forms, such as *Peranema* and *Chilomonas* (Fig. 7-22), live in stagnant water where they feed upon bacteria or other smaller protozoa. Although in its normal environment *Chilomonas* seems to live on a complex diet, it can be grown in a test tube on a diet consisting of ammonia, as a source of nitrogen, and carbon dioxide, as a carbon source. Here apparently is an organism that in nature lives much like an animal but in the laboratory can be forced to live like a plant, or even more simply, since it does not require nitrogen in the form of nitrates. This may mean that *Chilomonas* has a full set of enzymes to utilize very simple food sources for the construction of its protoplasm, but since it is not forced to use them normally, has taken up the animal type of nutrition. This would mean that this small organism had a very simple beginning and has not changed much through millions of years of evolution.

Most colorless flagellates live as single cells, although some live in colonies, such as the branched and stalked form, *Codosiga* (Fig. 7-22). This colony possesses a collar at the anterior end of each cell from which the flagellum emerges. With this exception, collared cells such as these are found only among the sponges. This group of protozoa may well have given rise to the sponges.

Parasitic Flagellates. The flagellates have been very successful in making their way into the tissues, blood, and body cavities of almost every group of animals. They are particularly common in the digestive tract and the blood of vertebrates, including man. Some have become serious parasites and today cause untold misery in many parts of the world, not only because they infect man directly but also because they destroy many of his domestic animals. Among the most common offenders is a closely related group of tiny elongated flagellates called *trypanosomes*. They are polymorphic, that is, they change body structure during their life cycle (Fig. 7-25). The four body forms are designated as *leptomonal, crithidial, trypanosomal,* and *leishmanial.* The parasite may exist in one or more of these forms, passing readily from one to the other depending on which host it occupies. Most of these parasites are transmitted from one vertebrate to another by means of an intermediate host, by either a blood-sucking insect or some other arthropod. Moreover the leptomonal and crithidial stages are usually found in

FIG. 7-23. Photomicrograph of *Volvox* colonies, many of which contain daughter colonies.

the invertebrate host, whereas the trypanosomal and leishmanial stages infect the vertebrate host. The disease is usually recognized and named after the organism found in the blood of the vertebrate. We shall consider several of these parasites because of their medical importance in the tropical parts of the world where many nations are presently emerging.

One of the most common and well-known diseases of equatorial Africa is sleeping sickness caused by two species of trypanosomes (*T. gambiense* and *T. rhodesiense*). These tiny parasites possess a single flagellum which lies in a fold of the outer membrane throughout its length, forming an *undulating membrane* (Fig. 7-26), an effective propelling apparatus in blood and other body fluids. This parasite normally lives in the large wild animals, being transmitted from one to the other by means of the *tsetse fly;* man becomes infected when the fly bites him. Unless treated in its early stages the disease is usually fatal after several months or years. The fact that the tsetse fly carried the parasite was known long before the parasite was discovered. By 1909 it was established that the fly was not only the mechanical vector but an intermediate host in which the parasite went through a definite life cycle.

The trypanosome is sucked up into the gut of the fly during its blood meal (Fig. 7-27) where it transforms to crithidial and leptomonal stages. It finally makes its way into the salivary glands, a common procedure among parasites of blood-sucking insects. Some time later, if the fly bites another person, the parasite is injected along with the saliva. It remains free in the blood for a time but eventually reaches the cerebral-spinal fluid. In this stage the metabolic products of the parasite cause paralysis resulting in the characteristic drowsiness of the victim. He finally falls into a fatal coma.

Vast regions of Africa are denied to man because of the ravages of this disease.

FIG. 7-24. A plastic model of the colonial brown flagellate, *Synura.*

The parasite is harmless, however, to the local wild animals, which act as reservoirs, always keeping it circulating in substantial numbers. For this reason the wholesale destruction of the tsetse fly is the only satisfactory control measure; even such insecticides as DDT have been ineffective in destroying this carrier.

The future development of a large fertile area of Africa must await the control of this disease. This has become an urgent need in the face of an expanding world population. It was once thought that the white man could not thrive in the tropics, but data collected during the last war, when large numbers of white men lived in tropical countries for several years, have disproved this conjecture. There is no reason why he cannot be as successful in the tropics as elsewhere, once control is gained of the tropical diseases to which the white

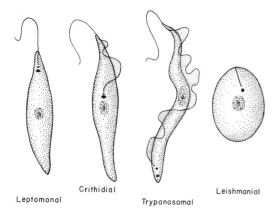

Leptomonal   Crithidial   Trypanosomal   Leishmanial

FIG. 7-25. Closely related parasitic flagellates which cause serious diseases of man and other animals.

man is very receptive. The other races living in the tropics are constantly subject to the murderous attack of many kinds of parasites, an important factor in their inability to thrive.

Another tragic disease that incapacitates millions of people in the world is *Kala azar* caused by *Leishmania donovani*, a member of this group of flagellates. It occurs in large sections of North China, various parts of India, the Sudan, and South America. In the past it has ravaged

FIG. 7-26. These tiny leaf-like trypanosomes live in the blood of vertebrates and other animals. This is a blood smear showing the parasites among the red blood cells.

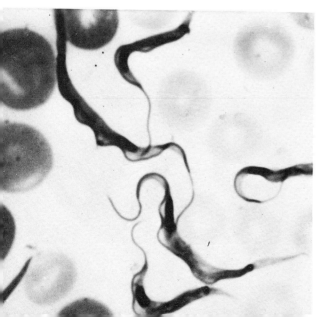

the inhabitants but with the advent of knowledge concerning epidemiology, diagnosis, and treatment, many of the evil effects of the disease have been greatly reduced.

Leishmania are tiny (2-4 microns) ovoid parasites which attack the cells of tissues associated with the circulatory system, including the spleen and liver. Upon entering the cells it multiplies (Fig. 7-28) until eventually the host cell bursts and the released parasites attack other cells. Some enter the blood stream where they are picked up by the intermediate host, the sand fly (*Phlebotomus*). In the gut of this insect they become flagellated and change considerably in shape. When the insect bites another person, some time after it has received the parasite, the flagellated forms are injected directly into the blood where they attack the lining cells of the blood vessels and the cycle is complete. Like most blood-sucking insects, the sand fly introduces a small amount of saliva, which has an anticoagulating effect on the blood. If this were not introduced, a blood clot would shortly interrupt its meal. However, the parasite in introduced along with the saliva, through no intent on the part of the sand fly.

The disease runs its course in a matter of months or several years, frequently ending in death. It has been shown that the flies also bite dogs, which in turn act as reservoirs for the disease. So the problem of eradication consists not only of preventative measures and treatment of infected persons, but also control of the dog population of any affected community. The most common method of prevention is the destruction of the breeding places of the fly as well as the fly itself.

Class Sarcodina

Although members of this class resemble the amoeba to some extent, there is wide variation in form and structure in the group as a whole. Among the fresh-water

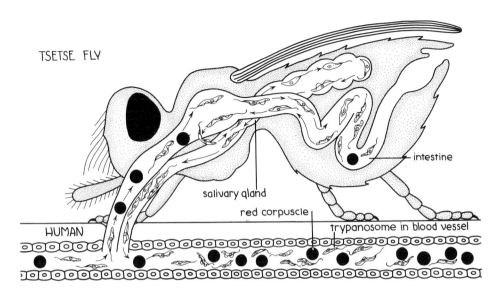

FIG. 7-27. Life cycle of a trypanosome causing African sleeping sickness.

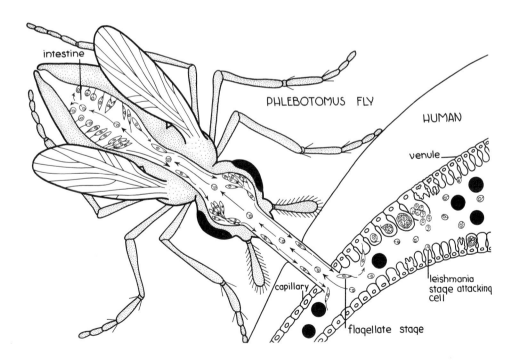

FIG. 7-28. Life cycle of a *Leishmania* causing kala azar.

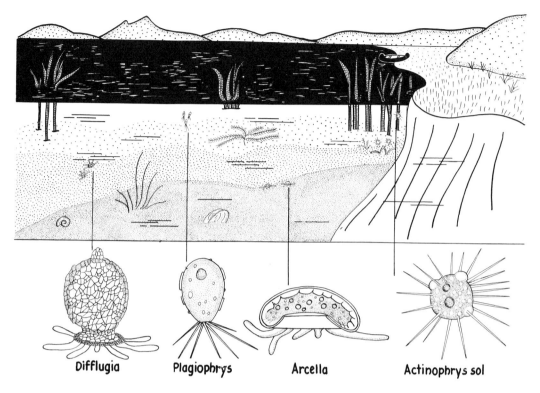

Difflugia   Plagiophrys   Arcella   Actinophrys sol

FIG. 7-29. Various types of fresh-water sarcodinids.

forms there are those, such as *Difflugia* (Fig. 7-29), that build houses for themselves. This tiny animal gathers grains of sand and cements them together to form a pear-shaped outer covering into which it may retreat when in danger. *Plagiophrys* and *Arcella* (Figs. 7-29 and 7-30), likewise, build houses for themselves, but in this case they are secreted by the animals. When observed through the microscope, the shell of Arcella resembles a doughnut. Corresponding to the hole in the doughnut is the opening through which the amoeboid form passes as it retracts or extends itself from the shell.

Another fresh-water sarcodinid of interest is the "sun animalcule," *Actinophrys sol* (Fig. 7-29), which resembles a miniature sun when it is floating in the water. The radiating, ray-like pseudopods seem to have a paralyzing effect upon other protozoa, such as euglena, which serve as a food source. There are many relatives of this spectacular protozoan. Together they con-

stitute the order *Heliozoa,* a group that is commonly found in the oceans of the world. One, *Oxnerella* (Fig. 7-31), is a particularly beautiful heliozoan.

A large group of forms resembling Heliozoa form the order *Radiolaria*. These are also distributed throughout the oceans of the world and float near the surface of the water. Most of them possess a siliceous skeleton (Fig. 7-32) which sinks to the ocean floor when the animal dies, forming a thick, mucky layer called "radiolarian ooze." This is particularly extensive in the Pacific and Indian Oceans. Skeletons of these animals are also found in rocks and have been used by geologists in learning about the history of the earth.

Marine sarcodinids that have even greater significance to geologists are found in the order *Foraminifera*, which secrete shells of almost pure calcium carbonate. They have a rather complicated life history as illustrated by the pelagic (floating at the surface) foraminifer, *Tretomphalus sp.* (Fig. 7-33). The cycle includes an orderly succession of sexual and asexual generations in which two distinct types of individuals and three kinds of shells are involved. The asexual generation (microspheric stage) consists of a large individual with many chambers in its shell. It produces many small individuals asexually which become the sexual generation (megalospheric stage). These grow and produce a gas-filled chamber which permits them to float at the surface of the sea. When mature they become associated with another of the opposite mating type and remain united until they produce prodigious numbers of biflagellated gametes which fuse to form zygotes. These settle and become attached to vegetation where they develop into tiny amoeba-like forms which then grow into the microspheric stage. Thus the

FIG. 7-30. This amoeba-like protozoan (*Arcella*) carries around a "house" into which it may retreat when its life is endangered. The shell is brown in color and, because the opening through which the animal passes lies in the center, it resembles a doughnut. Note the long pseudopods protruding out from the shell. This is a plastic model.

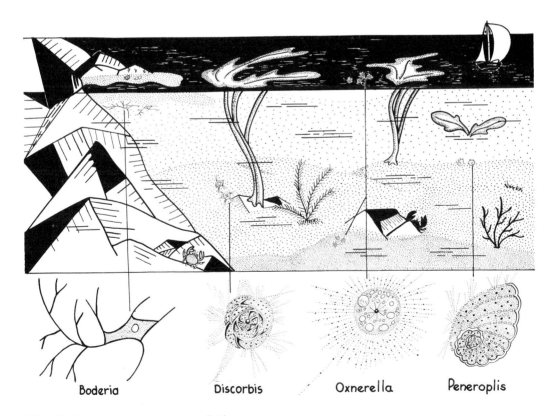

Boderia   Discorbis   Oxnerella   Peneroplis

FIG. 7-31. Various types of marine sarcodinids.

FIG. 7-32. The oceans of the world are teeming with radiolarians and foraminiferans which upon death leave beautiful skeletons, as shown by these two photographs. (Top) The siliceous skeleton of a radiolarian. (Bottom) The calcium carbonate skeleton of a foraminiferan. Note the snail-like nature of the shell.

cycle is completed and starts over again.

Most of the marine foraminifers form shells, and these are highly varied, although some, such as *Boderia* (Fig. 7-31), possess extremely thin, delicate outer coverings. The variety of shell forms is illustrated by *Discorbis* and *Peneroplis* (Fig. 7-31). These many-chambered, snail-like shells are produced as the animals grow larger and are perforated with tiny holes through which the fine pseudopods project. When they die their skeletons, like those of the Radiolarians, form a "globigerina ooze" (named after the most dominant form, *Globigerina*). This eventually becomes chalk many hundreds of feet thick. The Cliffs of Dover are an outstanding example of this phenomenon. Wherever this chalk appears on land, one can be certain that it was once at the bottom of the sea. Globigerina deposits appear in certain strata of the earth's surface and have a definite relation to the formation of petroleum. Therefore, knowledge of foraminiferans has been useful to geologists in predicting the location of oil deposits.

Parasitic Amoebae. Some amoebae, like some flagellates, have become adapted to life in the body cavities of many different animals, including man. Of the half dozen or so amoebae that inhabit the various cavities of man, only one, *Entamoeba histolytica,* causes any great harm. This amoeba is responsible for the well-known **amoebic dysentery.** Though not common in the population as a whole, it became an important disease among our armed forces fighting in the tropics in the past war. Native villages were often infected 100 per cent, providing a rich source of parasites for spreading the infection to newcomers.

The parasites are transmitted from person to person by contaminated food and water (Fig. 7-34). There may also be an indirect transfer by way of flies and other insects that pick up the infective stages on their feet and proboscis, carrying them di-

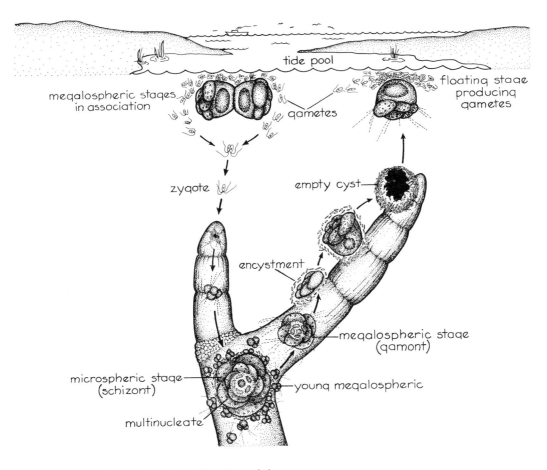

FIG. 7-33. The life history of the foraminifer, *Tretomphalus.*

rectly to food and water. Hence, the obvious method of control is to instigate sanitation in respect to human excreta and to destroy the flies. Both of these measures can easily be accomplished in civilized communities, but not among primitive peoples where both the knowledge and the facilities are lacking.

Some notorious outbreaks of amoebic dysentery have occurred in the United States which have been traced directly to faulty plumbing. Studies among groups in retarded areas of this country show an infection rate as high as 23 per cent, although for the nation at large it is around 5-10 per cent. Varying degrees of success have been achieved with a great many substances in attempts to combat the disease. Of the antibiotics, **aureomycin** and **terramycin** have proven the most effective.

Class Sporozoa

This class includes a large and heterogenous group of organisms, all parasites, which have puzzled taxonomists for a long time. They show relationships to such diverse organisms as the fungi and some of them are so bizarre that they are included among the sporozoa for want of a better place to put them. Sporozoa are usually immotile, although many have flagellated stages, and they usually lack contractile vacuoles. They reproduce asexually by a process called **schizogony.** At some stage in their complex life cycle they produce sex cells, **macro-** and **microgametes,** which fuse to form **zygotes,** and then by a process of **sporogony** form resistant **oocysts.** The asexual stage gives rise to the sexual stage in a cyclic manner, resulting in alternation of generations spoken of as **metagenesis.** We will have occasion to study this phenomenon in metazoa a little later. Some sporozoa complete their life cycle in one host, others require two hosts, the parasite being transferred from one to the other in cycles. They parasitize animals from protozoa to man, invading cells, fluids and cavities. Some seem to cause little damage to their hosts whereas others are devastating; for

example, millions of fowl are destroyed each year by sporozoa and malaria is the most important single disease of man.

The class is divided into three orders, based on the nature of their life cycles. We shall discuss representatives of each.

Gregarinida. Members of this order either invade cells or live in body fluids. A common example is *Monocystis lumbricis,* which parasitizes the seminal vesicles of earthworms (Fig. 7-35). The worm becomes infected by eating spores which are enclosed in a capsule, the oocyst. These pass down the digestive tract where they "hatch"

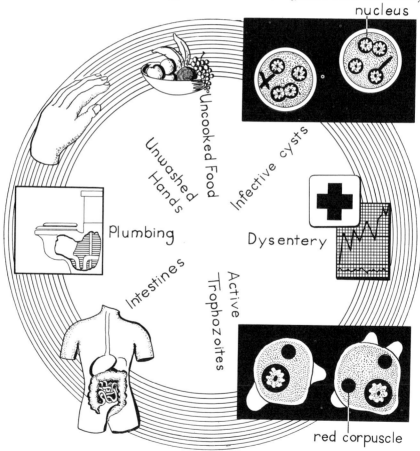

FIG. 7-34. Life cycle of the dysentery amoeba (*Entamoeba histolytica*). Infective cysts are carried on the hands of food handlers and thus transmitted directly to uninfected people on uncooked food. The trophozoites emerge from the cysts in the intestine, where they multiply and feed on the tissues and blood of the host, thus producing serious illness.

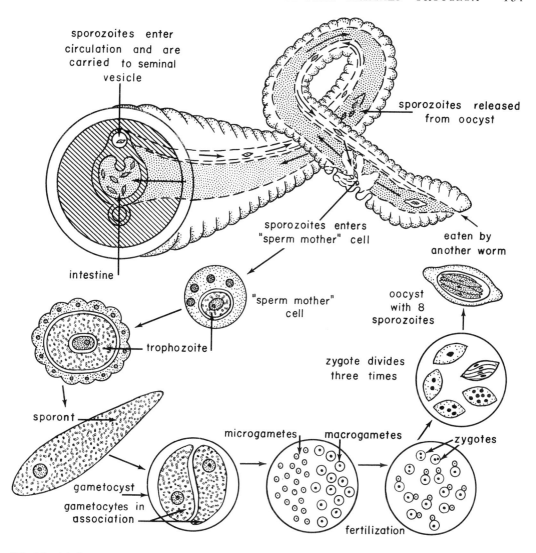

FIG. 7-35. Life history of *Monocystis lumbricis*.

and become active **sporozoites** which move through the digestive wall into the blood stream. They are carried to the seminal vesicles where they invade the "sperm mother" cells, growing at their expense to become the **trophozoites.** Some of the potential sperm-producing cells of the earthworm are thus destroyed, but not enough to interfere effectively with its reproductive powers. At maturity the trophozoites are freed as **sporonts** which become associated in pairs (syzygy) as **gametocytes** inside a gametocyst. Nuclear division (sporulation) then occurs followed by a partitioning off of the cytoplasm by cell walls thus producing numerous microgametes and macrogametes. These then unite forming the zygotes which are soon encased in a hard shell, the oocyst. Three nuclear divisions occur producing eight nuclei, each of which acquires cytoplasm and cell membranes to become the sporozoites. The oocysts containing the sporozoites are left behind in the burrows in some way that is not clear, where they are picked up by another worm and the cycle continues.

Coccidia. Members of this order inhabit epithelial cells of many vertebrates and a few invertebrates. Their chief infection site is the lining cells of the intestine, although they are also found in other organs. Multiplication of the organism takes place by schizogony and sporogony. Infection with these parasites is called **coccidiosis** which is frequently fatal. Domestic animals such as poultry and barnyard mammals, as well as their relatives in the wild, may be heavily infected. Rabbits are frequently infected by the coccidian, *Eimeria stiedae*, whose life cycle is typical (Fig. 7-36).

Rabbits become infected by eating vegetation contaminated with oocysts. The action of the digestive juices releases the sporozoites which then enter the epithelial cells where they undergo rapid multiplication by schizogony producing **merozoites.** These break out into the lumen and repeat the cycle by entering other cells. This permits the production of millions of sporozoites, and with each cycle more and more of the epithelial cells are destroyed thus causing the disease. After several cycles some of the merozoites become gametocytes which then develop into macro- and microgametes. These unite to form zygotes which shortly secrete an oocyst. The oocysts pass out of the body of the rabbit with the feces

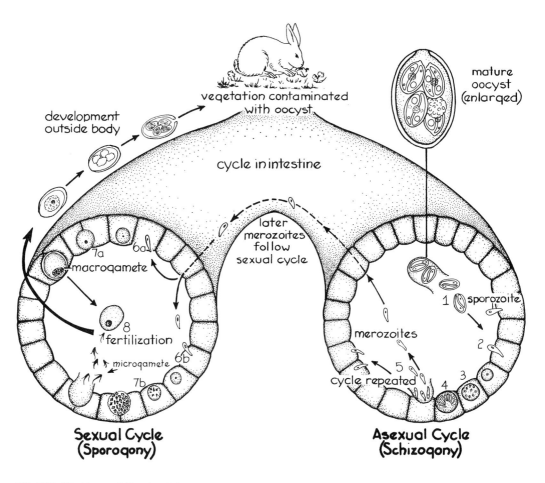

FIG. 7-36. Life history of *Eimeria stiedae*.

and undergo further development. Two divisions occur producing four spores, each containing two sporozoites. This is the infective stage and when taken in with food by another rabbit it continues the cycle.

Haemosporidia. Members of this order infect the blood cells of tissues of birds and mammals. Unlike members of the previous two orders the haemosporidians do not produce resistant spores but are transferred directly by blood-sucking arthropods in which a part of the life cycle takes place. The best known example of this group is *Plasmodium,* the causative agent of malaria.

The malarial parasites (*Plasmodium vivax* is the most common) infect large numbers of warm-blooded vertebrates besides man. In fact, the life cycle was worked out originally in birds by Ronald Ross in 1898. The widespread occurrence of the disease in human populations is indicated by the fact that prior to 1945 over 300 million people were infected all the time. It has been estimated that 3 million die of malaria each year—over half of all the deaths in the world. This certainly places it in the number one position among deadly diseases. These figures come as a surprise to most Americans because we now have the disease under control, although a hundred years ago it was responsible for a great many deaths in the South. During World War II it once again became a very important health problem for men in the tropics, and the large number of men continuing to suffer from the disease attests to the fact that we were not altogether successful in our preventive program.

Two factors are necessary for the propagation of malaria, a large population of the appropriate species of *Anopheles* mosquito and infected humans (Fig. 7-37). Only female mosquitoes bite. In order to become infective the female anopheles must bite a person suffering from the disease and with-

draw blood that contains gametocytes. There are two kinds of gametocytes, male and female, both of which must be taken into the stomach of the mosquito, where each type of cell undergoes certain modifications. One remains pretty much as it is, producing a single large macrogamete, whereas the other produces 6 or 8 smaller motile, threadlike microgametes. The macrogametes and microgametes unite in pairs to form zygotes which are able to bore through the stomach wall under their own power. In the outer part of the stomach wall each zygote multiplies many times, producing a great many tiny infective sporozoites. These swollen zygotes protrude from the outside walls of the mosquito's gut like tiny beads. They puzzled Ross when he first saw them, and one can imagine his surprise when he squeezed them and saw thousands of spindle-shaped bodies emerge. Normally they burst into the blood which fills the space between the gut and the body wall, and via the blood the sporozoites make their way into the salivary glands. With each bite of the mosquito from this time on, sporozoites are injected into the blood of the next host.

After entering man's blood stream the sporozoites seem to disappear for a few days. This fact puzzled biologists for many years until it was discovered that they undergo their early multiplication stages in various tissues of the body, notably certain cells of the liver. At any rate, within ten days some of the parasites are in the blood stream, each entering a red blood cell where it grows and multiplies by schizogony. After a remarkably regular period of time—namely, 48 hours in *P. vivax,* the most common form of malaria—the infected red cells burst, each releasing 10–20 merozoites. These immediately enter other cells, and so the infection keeps increasing in intensity. When there is a sufficient number of infected cells, the person suffers chills just before and a fever just following the bursting of the red cells which occurs at 48-

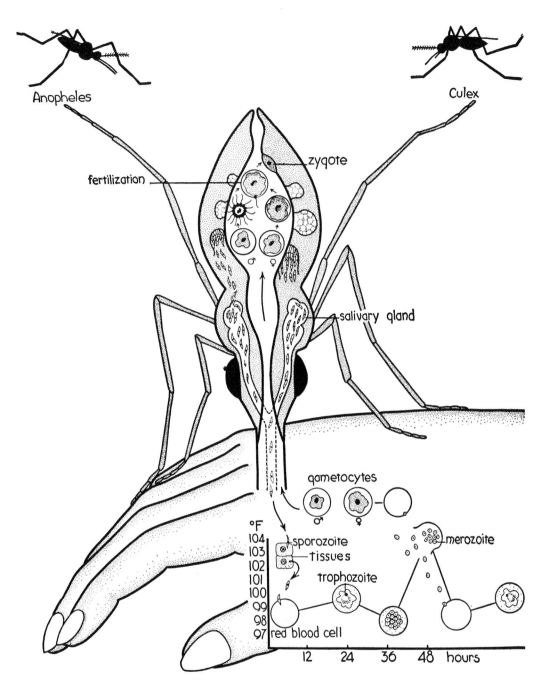

Anopheles

Culex

zyqote

fertilization

salivary gland

gametocytes

°F
104
103 — sporozoite
102 — tissues
101
100
99
98
97 red blood cell

trophozoite

merozoite

12   24   36   48   hours

FIG. 7-37. Life cycle of the malarial organism, *Plasmodium vivax*. The female Anopheles mosquito assumes a typical stance (upper left) which is quite different from that of the harmless Culex (upper right).

hour intervals. The symptoms become more intense for the next two weeks when either the person is unable to combat the infection and dies, or he is able to and lives, although intermittent chills and fever continue for a long time, sometimes for several years. During this time some of the merozoites become modified into gametocytes. If some of these are taken up by the mosquito with its blood meal, they pass to the stomach and thus complete the cycle.

The treatment for malaria has an interesting history. About 1640 a countess visiting in Peru became ill with malaria and when given extracts from the bark of a tree, since named cinchona in her honor, she recovered. She was so impressed with the drug that she brought some back to Europe where it was shown to be extremely effective in the treatment of malaria. From that time to the present **quinine,** the effective drug in cinchona bark, has been used as a specific treatment for malaria. It has probably saved more lives and relieved more suffering than any other drug ever discovered by man, the recent antibiotics included. During the past war our supplies of quinine were cut off, so we had to rely on substitutes such as **atabrine** and **plasmochin.** The attempt to synthesize quinine continued during the war years with unrelenting vigor until finally the synthesis was successfully accomplished at the end of the war. A constant search is made for a new specific for malaria and some success is reported from time to time. Perhaps the ideal one will be found in the future.

The best and most successful methods have been to destroy the mosquito. This has been so effective that today there are about 100 million cases of malaria as compared to over 300 million fifteen years ago. World health groups predict that by 1975 the disease may well be eradicated from Europe, the Americas, North Africa, and a large part of Asia.

SUBPHYLUM CILIOPHORA

Class Ciliata

The members of this class are distinguished by the possession of **cilia** and two or more nuclei. These characteristics were observed in paramecium, which is a representative of this group. The class has been subdivided according to the arrangement of the cilia into four orders; the more interesting members of three of these will be described briefly.

Those belonging to the order **Holotricha** possess evenly distributed cilia over most of their body. Paramecium is typical.

Didinium is an interesting member of this group because of its carnivorous habits. It is oval-shaped, with two bands of cilia encircling the anterior and posterior regions (Fig. 7-38). Protruding from the anterior end is a formidable-looking **proboscis** which is an effective organelle for impaling paramecia prior to engulfing them. The magnitude of this feat can be realized by imagining a man eating a full-grown horse at one sitting. This is only one illustration of the voraciousness of these carnivorous ciliates which abound in almost any stagnant water.

The order **Spirotricha** includes a large variety of diverse ciliates, one of which, *Spirostomum,* is a veritable giant among the protozoa. This cell reaches a length of 3 millimeters and can easily be seen with the naked eye. In fact, when first observed, it might be mistaken for a tiny worm because of its apparent crawling movements. Another large form, *Stentor* (Fig. 7-39), vase-shaped and colored a beautiful greenish blue, is a spectacular sight for the microscopist.

This order also includes several species in which the long cilia are fused into stiff bristle-like organelles called **cirri.** Cells of this type are flattened dorso-ventrally and seem to use their cirri in "walking" along the substratum. One of these is *Stylonichia*

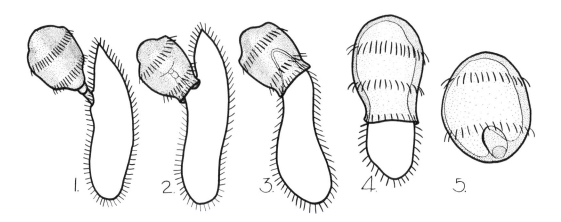

FIG. 7-38. Some ciliates are voracious carnivores. *Didinium*, for example, is able to engulf a paramecium much larger than itself.

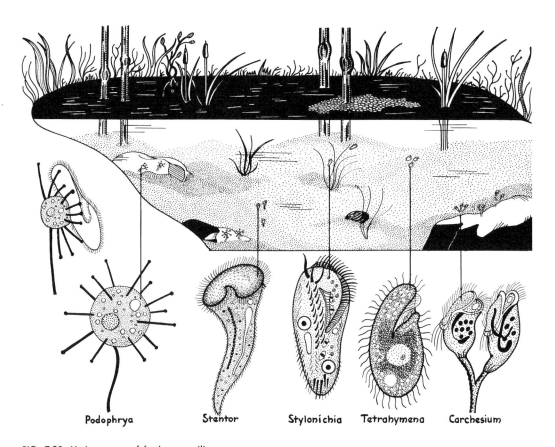

FIG. 7-39. Various types of fresh-water ciliates.

(Fig. 7-39), which is about the size of paramecium but whose actions are quite different. It moves along in a jerky fashion, darting forward and backward, and sometimes crawling along on the bottom. Professor C. V. Taylor, working with a closely related ciliate, *Euplotes,* some years ago, was interested in how this cell controlled the cirri in locomotion. With the use of a delicate dissecting instrument he was able to cut the tiny fibrils that connect each of the cirri with the others. Such an operated animal lost control of its cirri and was unable to coordinate its movements sufficiently to move in any one direction. Thus he discovered that even this tiny animal possesses some kind of coordinating system resembling the nervous system of higher forms. Recent observations with the electron microscope demonstrate conclusively that these tiny animals do possess an elaborate system of fibers which undoubtedly function in coordinating its movements.

Ciliates belonging to the order **Peritricha** have their cilia conspicuously arranged in the anterior region. Most of these forms are vase-shaped and many are stalked. Common examples are *Carchesium* (Fig. 7-39) and *Vorticella* (Fig. 7-40). Of the two, the latter is more common and is familiar to anyone who has persisted in examining stagnant water under the microscope. It was seen and described for the first time by Antony Leeuwenhoek in Holland during the seventeenth century (Fig. 7-41). Vorticella is usually attached to the substratum by means of its contractile stalk. When disturbed or sometimes for no apparent reason, it suddenly contracts and at the same time the cilia around the funnel-shaped mouth disappear and the entire cell rounds up into a ball. Shortly, it emerges again and starts its oral (mouth) cilia beating so that food particles floating by are wafted into its mouth.

Class Suctoria

This class includes a very peculiar group of stalked protozoa which possess long "tentacles" instead of cilia in the adult stage. *Tokophrya* is an example (Fig. 7-6). The young stages, however, resemble other ciliates in that they possess cilia and are free-swimming. It is because of this evidence that the suctoria are placed with the ciliates. The adults have no mouth but acquire their food by means of the knob-tipped tentacles. When other ciliates which serve as food touch the tentacles they are immobilized and their internal parts drawn through the tentacles into the suctorian, much like fluids sucked through a straw. They are voracious feeders and may be seen withdrawing nutrients from several ciliates simultaneously. They reproduce asexually by fission and internal budding.

FIG. 7-40. A stalked-ciliate, Vorticella, in various stages of its life history. The two animals to the left are undergoing division while on the extreme right is the free-swimming stage which enables the species to spread to new environments. The fine contractile thread which can be seen in the stalk makes it possible for them to suddenly become coiled as some of the organisms here. This is a plastic model.

FIG. 7-41. Antony Leeuwenhoek (1632–1723) was the first man to see and describe many protozoa as well as other microorganisms. He was not trained in science, but his devotion to the disciplines of the field places him among the foremost scientists of his day.

We discussed the latter method earlier (p. 165). The young swim about for a time and then become attached to debris losing their cilia and developing tentacles as they transform into the adult stalked stage.

Parasitic Ciliates. Very few ciliates have developed the parasitic habit. Only one, *Balantidium coli,* infects man. However, there are a fantastic number of ciliates living in the two parts of the complex stomach of ruminants and in the colon of other herbivorous animals. There may be as many as 10 billion in the stomach of a cow.

These ciliates feed on plant fragments and bacteria and when they die they serve as nourishment for the host. Even though they seem to be consistently present in ruminants the protozoa are not essential for the health of the host because they can be experimentally removed (copper sulfate) without detectable injury to the cow. The ciliates are highly variable in structure and size; one, *Epidinium ecaudatum* (Fig. 7-42), will illustrate their general anatomy. It is one of the most complex of ciliates, even exceeding paramecium in complexity. It has a mouth surrounded by membranelles which are attached to a collar that can be protruded or retracted. This is accomplished by the action of **myonemes** which function like muscles. It has a terminal opening, the **anus,** through which waste products are removed from the body. In addition, the most complete coordinating system of any protozoan, consisting of a **nerve center** with connecting fibers, is found in *Epidinium.* This protozoan maintains its form by means of **skeletal plates,** and most of its body is devoid of cilia.

The *Epidinium* illustrates how far differentiation can go within a single cell. It maintains organelles for locomotion, feeding, swallowing, digestion of food, egestion of wastes, excretion, and continuity of its germ plasm by means of its nuclear structures. This exhausts all the accomplishments metazoan cells have achieved, as we shall see in the next chapters.

From this cursory survey of the "first animals" one is impressed with their diversity of form and habits of life. We shall now examine animals composed of many cells and observe how they fit into the numerous habitats on the earth's surface, and how they have diversified to accomplish this. The parallelism between them and the protozoa from which they sprang is striking.

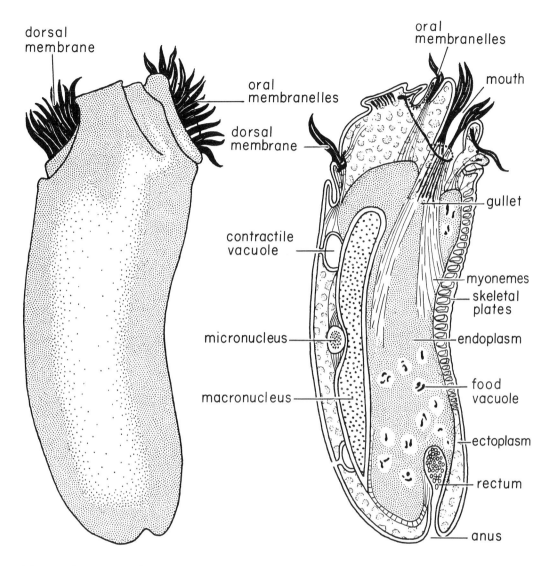

FIG. 7-42. This protozoan, *Epidinium ecaudatum*, lives in the digestive tract of ruminants. The external anatomy is shown in the left drawing and the internal structure in the right.

SUGGESTED SUPPLEMENTARY READINGS

ALLEN, R. D., "Amoeboid Movement," *Scientific American*, 206 (2) (February, 1962), 112.

ALVARADO, C. A., and BRUCE-CHWATT, L. J., "Malaria," *Scientific American*, 206 (5) (May, 1962), 86.

CORLISS, J. O., *The Ciliated Protozoa* (New York, Pergamon Press, 1961).

DOBELL, C., *Antony Van Leeuwenhoek and His "Little Animals"* (London, John Bale Medical Pub., 1932).

HALL, R. P., *Protozoology* (Englewood Cliffs, N.J., Prentice-Hall Inc., 1953).

HYMAN, L., *The Invertebrates,* Vol. I, *Protozoa through Cteno-phora* (New York, McGraw-Hill Book Co., 1940).

JAHN, T. T., and JAHN, F. F., *How to Know the Protozoa* (Dubuque, Iowa, Wm. C. Brown Co., 1949).

KUDO, R. R., *Protozoology* (Springfield, Ill., Charles C. Thomas, 1954).

MACKINNON, D. L., and HAWES, R. S. I., *An Introduction to the Study of Protozoa* (Oxford, The Clarendon Press, 1961).

MANWELL, R. D., *Introduction to Protozoology* (New York, St. Martin's Press, 1961).

SATIR, P., "Cilia," *Scientific American,* 204 (2) (February, 1961), 108.

TARTAR, V., *The Biology of Stentor* (New York, Pergamon Press, 1961).

WOLKEN, J. J., *Euglena* (New Brunswick, N.J., The Rutgers University Press, 1961).

WICHTERMAN, R., *The Biology of Paramecium* (New York, The Blakiston Co., 1953).

D. C. SNYDER

8

Sponges and the Radial Animals—Coelenterates

WE DISCUSSED at some length the origin of the metazoa in an earlier chapter (p. 95). In this chapter we shall describe the most primitive metazoan forms which are predominantly simple sacs consisting of two well-defined body layers, **ectoderm** and **endoderm,** with the beginnings of a third layer, the **mesoderm.** Even though simple, these animals are very successful, abounding in the waters of the world (Fig. 8-1). Some live in fresh water, but by far the greatest number still occupy their ancestral home, the salty oceans. They have done well through the millions of years since their beginnings, in numbers of both individuals and species. They have moved into most of the habitats of the oceans; they cling to rocks in the shallow waters and are able to survive in the abysmal seas. Many are floaters at or near the surface and some can even propel themselves to some extent. Some have become highly differentiated, such as *Physalia,* developing bizarre modes of life. Some produce limy deposits (corals) which have been important in reef-building in the tropical seas of the world. Most of them are colorful and give beauty to the sea as the floral plants do to the land.

201

PHYLUM PORIFERA

This unique group of animals is not in the direct line of ascent to higher forms, therefore are thought of as "blind alley" animals, that is they apparently reached their present stage of development millions of years ago and there is no evidence that they gave rise to higher forms. The word *porifera* means "pore bearer" which is a characteristic of the group. The flagellated collared cells, **choanocytes,** that line their cavities resemble one group of protozoa (p. 182) indicating their close affiliation with these one-celled animals. Digestion is wholly intracellular and, except for simple epithelia, there are no tissues. For this reason sponges are considered to have gone no farther than the **cellular grade of organization.** Unlike the protozoa where the single cell carries on all activities, the sponge demonstrates division of labor where the cells are specialized to perform different functions; some support the body while others gather food and still others function in reproduction.

Living sponges have a gelatinous texture, quite different from the familiar bath sponge sold on the market. Being sessile, they are easily mistaken for plants. Sponges assume many shapes, vary in height from 1 millimeter to more than a meter, and are usually drab in color. Some forms, however, take on shades of red, yellow, blue, black, or green, the last being caused by the green alga, *Chlorella,* living in the body cells. Their most common habitat is a number

FIG. 8-1. A few sponges and coelenterates that live in the oceans.

of feet below the tidal zone of the sea (upper and lower limits of the tide) (Fig. 8-1), although some, like the glass sponge (Fig. 8-2), live as much as three and a half miles below the surface of the ocean. Fresh-water forms are also known, some of these attaching themselves to twigs and rocks in the streams (Fig. 8-3).

Morphology of a Simple Sponge

In order to have some knowledge of the morphology of the sponge, it is best to discuss a simple sponge, *Leucosolenia*, as an example. It lives beneath the low tide level in the sea and consists of many slender upright tubes which are joined at their bases in a many-branched common tube (Fig. 8-4). The upright portions are thin-walled sacs perforated with hundreds of microscopic holes (**incurrent pores**) and one large opening, the **osculum (excurrent canal)**, at the upper tip. The cavity of the sac is called the **spongocoel.** Its wall is made up of an outer **epidermis** or skin-like layer of flat cells, and an inner continuous layer of the flagellated collared cells (**choanocytes**). A third jelly-like layer, the **mesenchyme,** lies between these two, and in this layer several kinds of amoeba-like cells, called **amoebocytes,** are present. This layer also contains the skeleton formed by **spicules,** which resemble crystals. In the glass sponge the spicules consist of silicious material and in horny sponges, of fibers and spongin. In most forms, however, they are composed of calcium carbonate. A combination of spicules and fibers also occurs.

Scattered among the ordinary epidermal cells are the tubular **pore cells,** each with a central canal or pore. A pore cell, together with "helpers" surrounding it, controls the flow of water into the sponge. The vigorous beating of flagella on the collared cells lining the spongocoel causes water to move in through the pores and out through the osculum. This movement causes a constant stream of water, heavily laden

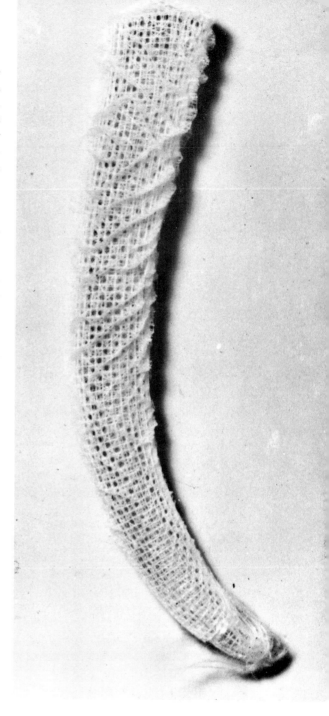

FIG. 8-2. The skeleton of the glass sponge, *Euplectella*. Note the fine bridging of the fibers to form the skeleton.

with microscopic organisms, to pass within reach of the choanocytes. The manner of beating of the flagella in the collared cells

FIG. 8-3. A fresh-water sponge collected in a Michigan stream; it measures about 14 inches long and is a green-gray in color owing to the presence of unicellular algae growing in the body cells.

propels tiny food particles to the cell body which engulfs it, forming food vacuoles much like amoeba. Any food not needed by the choanocytes is passed to the amoebocytes for further distribution. Waste products are borne out through the osculum in this same current of water.

Sponges in General

Sponges reproduce asexually by means of internal and external buds, as well as sexually by means of eggs and sperm. Buds form on the outside of the sponge and sometimes move away, but as often remain a part of the parent sponge. During unfavorable conditions, as in drought or cold winters, sponges develop internal buds, called gemmules, which are merely masses of cells with a hard outer covering. They drop to the bottom of the stream or sea during these adverse conditions and grow into sponges the next season when circumstances are again favorable.

Some sponges are monoecious (of one household), that is, both sexes are present in one animal; others are dioecious (of two households), the sexes being found in separate animals. There are no special sex organs, and the sperm and eggs simply develop from certain of the amoebocytes in the middle layer or mesenchyme. Fertilization occurs in situ (in place) and is followed by rapid division until a blastula is formed with many flagellated cells (future choanocytes). The flagella are directed inward toward the central cavity, the blastocoel. A hole appears later and the embryo turns inside out, bringing the internal flagellated cells to the outer surface. In this stage, called the amphiblastula, it leaves the mother sponge through the osculum and swims around for a few days, finally settling and attaching itself to a rock or some other solid object where it grows into a sponge (Fig. 8-4). The larger cells of the larva overgrow the flagellated cells and completely surround them. The cell layers of the sponge seem to be the reverse of those found in higher forms and for that reason are not comparable to them.

Some very interesting cases of commensalism are found among the sponges. They occasionally strike up a friendly relationship with animals such as crustaceans,

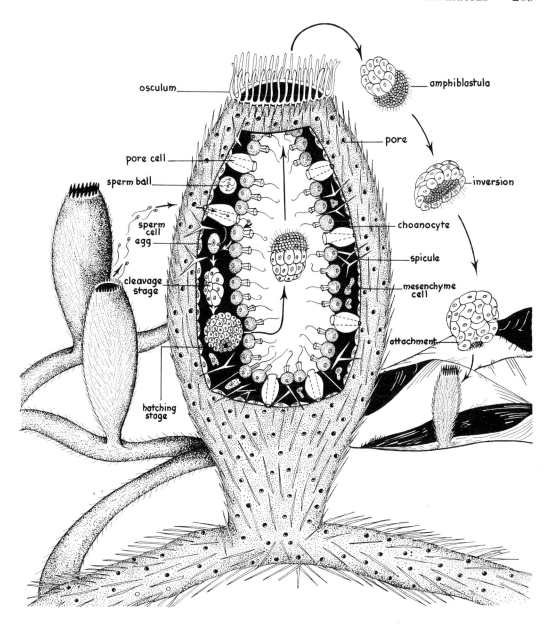

osculum

amphiblastula

pore cell

pore

sperm ball

inversion

sperm cell

choanocyte

egg

spicule

cleavage stage

mesenchyme cell

attachment

hatching stage

FIG. 8-4. Anatomy and life history of a simple sponge.

worms, and mollusks. Many animals make the channels of the sponges their home; even fish as long as 5 inches have been found swimming about inside of sponges. Certain species of crabs enlist the aid of the sponge in camouflage by placing small pieces of the sponge on their backs until they become attached. Thus the crab is amply hidden from its enemies. Sponges can become a hindrance in oyster beds where they cover the oysters and compete for the food supply.

Sponges have canal systems which vary in complexity (Fig. 8-5). The simplest, the

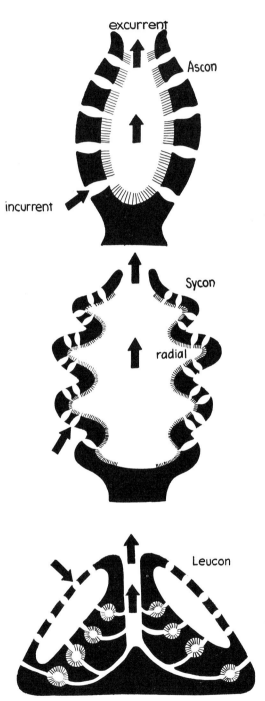

FIG. 8-5. Various types of canal systems among sponges.

Ascon type found in *Leucosolenia,* is merely a thin-walled sac. The first step in increasing complexity occurs in the **Sycon** type, which has two kinds of canals, **incurrent** and **radial,** the latter being lined with choanocytes. The most complicated of all is the **Leucon** type, which possesses a vast array of multiple tubes and chambers, with choanocytes lining only certain restricted chambers. Leucon sponges may reach more than a meter in diameter.

Sponges have been used by man for cleaning purposes from earliest times. The part used in the bath sponge is the skeleton, composed largely of **spongin,** a protein. It has many fine fibers which, through capillarity, have remarkable water-holding properties. Sponges for commercial use are found most frequently in the warm seas such as the Mediterranean, the Gulf of Mexico, and the Gulf of Florida. In preparation for market, sponges are pried loose from rocks by divers or dredges, and the living portion is allowed to dry and decay. They are then beaten, washed, and finally bleached. Needless to say, the bath sponge has considerable commercial value. In recent years it has even become necessary to cultivate it in order to prevent its extinction. Two million pounds of sponges are taken annually, even though the sponge must compete with its rubber and plastic imitations.

In review, we may think of the sponges as "blind alley" animals that came to their present state millions of years ago and have "stood still," failing to evolve any higher on the animal scale. They are sufficiently well adapted to their environment to carry on in their primitive way and they probably will continue to exist for millions of years to come. Since they are not on the direct line of ascent to higher forms, we must leave them in their isolated position without further reference to them and pass on to the next group which has much more significance in our story of the rise of animal life.

PHYLUM COELENTERATA

These sac-like radially symmetrical, diploblastic animals are the first metazoans to have their somatic cells organized into definite **tissues,** hence have reached the **tissue grade of organization.** Actually they have about the same number of tissues as higher animals (p. 100) and they function much in the same way. Special epithelial cells, called **cnidoblasts,** produce the **nematocysts** used for offense and defense. In many coelenterates there are two types of individuals, the **polyp** representing the asexual phase of the life cycle, and the **medusa,** the sexual phase. In their life histories each generation successively gives rise to the alternate type, a phenomenon called **metagenesis.** The asexual polyp is tubular in shape, with a mouth at one end, surrounded by tentacles richly supplied with nematocysts. The other end of the tube is closed and forms an attachment organ, the foot. These animals are usually sessile or nearly so. The free-swimming sexual medusa is a delicate transparent animal, shaped like an umbrella. Around the periphery or edge of the umbrella are tentacles, which are also heavily fortified with nematocysts. Both the polyp and the medusa have primitive muscle fibers which make movement possible.

The coelenterates are water-inhabiting animals, most of them marine. One form, **hydra,** has invaded fresh water and is very successful. The large marine **jellyfishes** and the **sea anemones** are members of this group (Fig. 8-1). In both the sea anemones and their close relatives, the corals, the medusae have been completely lost.

With the exception of some jellyfish, which may annoy bathers by the stings of their nematocysts, and the coral animals, which are used for jewelry, the group as a whole has little direct significance to man.

There are three classes of coelenterates (**Hydrozoa, Scyphomedusae, Anthozoa**) whose characteristics can best be under- stood by studying two representatives, *Hydra* and *Obelia,* of the class Hydrozoa. Members of the other two classes are discussed briefly later in the chapter.

Hydra

This tiny animal may be found clinging to underwater vegetation in nearly any fresh-water pond, lake, or stream (Fig. 8-6). It moves about very little, hence seeks its food by means of its long tentacles which may reach a length of 10–12 inches. The entire body extends and contracts remarkably so that it may be very long and thin or so short that it resembles a ball with the contracted tentacles as tiny stumps. The hollow tentacles surround a raised conical **hypostome,** in the center of which is the **mouth.** The mouth opens into the digestive cavity, the **coelenteron** or **gastrovascular cavity,** which continues into the tentacles. The outer layer, the **ectoderm,** sometimes called the **epidermis,** is made up of cells which form a protective covering. Some of these cells have an inner contractile portion which enables them to serve as muscle cells. Finally, scattered among the epidermal cells are specialized sensory cells. The inner layer of cells, the **endoderm** or **gastrodermis,** provides all other cells with nourishment. These tall, glandular cells secrete the **enzymes** which digest food that is brought into the coelenteron (Fig. 8-6). These cells also possess muscle fibers at their bases which run at right angles to those in the epidermis. It is by the combined action of these muscle cells with those of the ectoderm that hydra is able to contract and extend itself. Lying between these two layers, the ectoderm and the endoderm, is a thin, noncellular layer, the **mesogloea,** which lends support and holds all the cells together. Lying embedded in both the ectoderm and endoderm are the nerve cells, which are connected by minute fibrils to the sensory and muscular cells. They function in coordinating the activity of all the cells. The nerve cells form a network, called the

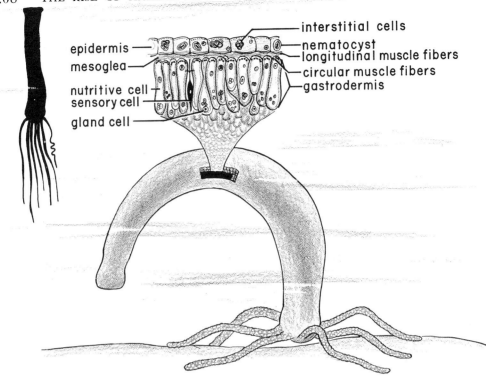

interstitial cells
epidermis
nematocyst
longitudinal muscle fibers
mesoglea
circular muscle fibers
gastrodermis
nutritive cell
sensory cell
gland cell

FIG. 8-6. Hydra often "hangs" from the water surface. A portion of the body wall is magnified here in order to distinguish its cellular structure. Note the variety of cells in both the epidermis and gastrodermis.

nerve net, which connects all parts of the animal, although there is no centrally located mass which could in any way be compared to the brain of higher forms. External **stimuli** initiate impulses in the **sensory cells** which are conveyed to the nerve net and through it to the **contractile fibrils.** This is the simplest form of a metazoan nervous system, but it contains the fundamental elements of which all higher nervous systems are built.

An interesting and intricate part of hydra's response mechanism is the **cnidoblast,** with its contained **nematocyst.** Cnidoblasts are located in nests or "batteries" along the tentacles, for the most part, although they may occur over the entire body with the exception of the foot, or basal disc, on which the hydra "walks." Nematocysts are derived from the interstitial cells and are usually arranged with one large and several small ones in each battery. There are several different kinds of nematocysts, each having a different use. The largest and most conspicuous type is the penetrating or stinging nematocyst, which upon discharge pierces the body of small crustacea or other aquatic animals that happen to touch the tentacles (Fig. 8-7). This nematocyst contains a hollow, coiled thread which everts through the trigger-like action of the **cnidocil,** a slight projecting bristle, when it is touched or stimulated in some other way. It is ejected with such force that it penetrates the soft and even some hard parts of the prey, injecting a small amount of poison which has a paralyzing effect on the victim. Once paralysis sets in, the tentacles move in a manner that draws the prey into the mouth and thence into the coelenteron. Other types of nematocysts function in a mechanical rather than chemical manner. When

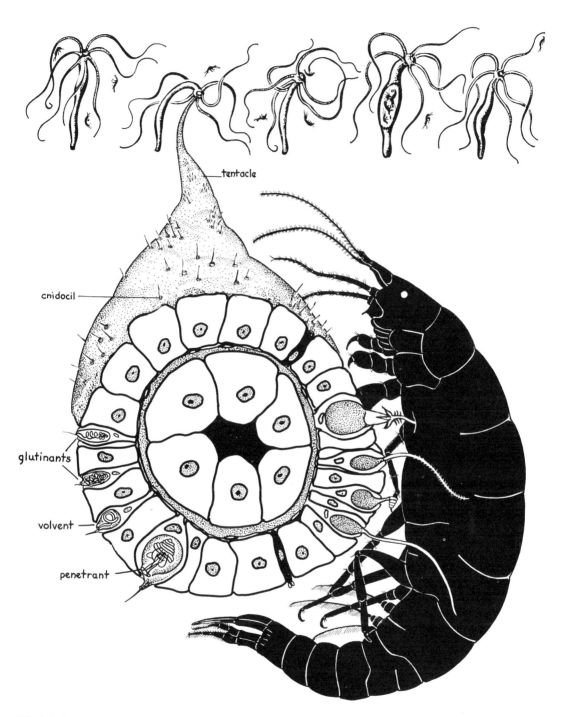

tentacle

cnidocil

glutinants

volvent

penetrant

FIG. 8-7. One tentacle of this feeding hydra is enlarged to show both discharged and undischarged nematocysts in detail. The largest type (penetrant) discharges its thread with such force as to penetrate the body of small animals such as the crustacean shown here. The volvent type coils about the appendages of the prey. The glutinants (two types) secrete a sticky substance used in locomotion as well as in feeding.

discharged, some wrap their threads about a portion of the attacked animal and hold it securely. Others fasten themselves to a portion of the substratum and by contractions of the tentacles make possible a slow, somersaulting type of locomotion (Fig. 8-8). A second method by which hydra moves from place to place in search of food is to "shuffle" along on its basal disc by means of special cells located in this region. Some species are able to secrete a bubble of air at the basal disc, which carries them to the surface where they float upside down.

Most of the actions of hydra are related to food-getting. A hungry hydra responds readily when a small crustacean or worm

higher forms, for it has been observed that many of the endoderm cells take in particles of food by an amoeboid process. Food vacuoles are formed and intracellular digestion proceeds, the same as in the protozoa. This might be expected, since this animal is not so far removed from its protozoan ancestors.

Hydra is sensitive to light and seeks out a suitable illumination. The intensity sought is usually that in which food is most likely to be found. The colorless hydra seeks a lower intensity of light than its green relative (*Hydra viridis*). The latter has tiny green algae in its endodermal cells, which require more light for photosynthesis (Fig. 5-15). Hydra prefers cool, clear water and

FIG. 8-8. Hydra somersaulting.

comes within reach of its tentacles. If meat juices are placed in the surrounding water, it responds by increased extension and contraction of its entire body. On the other hand, a well-fed hydra responds very little, if at all, to the presence of food.

The presence of food in the coelenteron stimulates the gland cells to secrete digestive enzymes into the cavity where the soft parts of the ingested animal are partially digested (extracellular digestion). The hard outer coverings are indigestible and are eventually regurgitated through the mouth. Thus a single opening functions both as a mouth for the entrance of food and as an anus for the exit of undigested food. The breakdown of food molecules in the coelenteron is probably not as thorough as in

seeks it out. If exposed to various concentrations of injurious chemicals, it avoids each with regularity. If unfavorable conditions are forced upon it, such as desiccation, it undergoes a series of regressive changes called "depression." The tentacles and body begin to disintegrate and this continues until the animal is destroyed. Under favorable conditions, however, it may recover at almost any stage in its disintegration.

In a suitable environment, hydra reproduces asexually by forming one or more buds. Sometimes several buds form simultaneously; indeed, buds may have buds upon themselves. This is very close to a colonial form, such as obelia, another hydrozoan, which will be considered a little later.

Since buds form so readily from almost any part of its body wall, it should follow that hydra could perhaps be made to reproduce itself experimentally by simply·cutting off small pieces of the body (Fig. 8-9). This idea apparently occurred to a Swiss naturalist, Abraham Trembley, around the middle of the eighteenth century (1744). He did just that and gave us our first experiments on **regeneration** in animals. By splitting the hypostome region Trembley was able to obtain a double-headed animal. He also found that by passing a needle with a knotted thread through the mouth and

ture mammary glands, including "nipples" (Fig. 8-11). An opening appears in the "nipple" end of the gland and the mature sperm cells swim out into the surrounding water in search of a mature egg on another individual. The eggs develop from interstitial cells also, the difference being that only one egg is formed in an ovary, whereas thousands of sperm cells are produced in a single testis. The eggs at first resemble large amoeboid bodies. As they mature they become spherical in shape, resting on the outer wall of the hydra attached to a cuplike depression in the epidermis (Fig. 8-12).

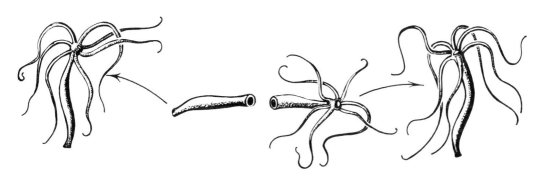

FIG. 8-9. Regeneration in hydra.

the basal disc, he could completely invert the two layers; in other words, he turned the hydra inside out. Then, instead of inverting back to its original condition, the animal simply moved its epidermal cells in between the endodermal cells so that both layers of cells found their original location.

Hydra also reproduces sexually by the production of eggs and sperm (Fig. 8-10). Usually both ovaries and testes are formed on the same animal, although as a rule not at the same time. In formation of the sperm, interstitial cells (undifferentiated cells) lying in the ectoderm undergo a series of divisions, forming a protuberance which gradually grows large as the sperm matures. A sexually mature hydra may have several "ripe" testes along its walls which resemble minia-

After fertilization, cleavage starts and continues until a hollow **blastula** forms. An outer resistant shell then develops and simultaneously the cavity (**blastocoel**) is filled with cells from the lining. The young embryo then drops off and lies quietly until favorable conditions eventually arise, when it emerges as a very small hydra with blunt tentacles. Sexual reproduction usually occurs in the fall of the year and seems to be a safeguard for passing the winter months because the young embryo resides in a capsule which resists adverse temperatures.

It has recently been claimed by Loomis that the differentiation (Fig. 8-10) of sexual organs is controlled by the pressure of CO_2 in the surrounding water. He showed that as hydra became crowded in a small amount

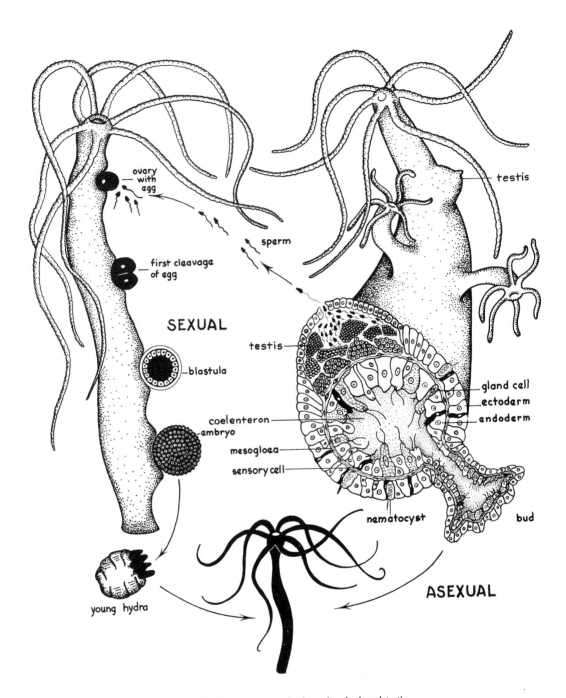

ovary with egg

sperm

first cleavage of egg

SEXUAL

blastula

coelenteron
embryo

testis

testis

gland cell
ectoderm
endoderm

mesogloea

sensory cell

nematocyst

bud

young hydra

ASEXUAL

FIG. 8-10. Life cycle of hydra. One hydra is cut transversely through a bud and testis.

of water the sex organs appeared, whereas if a single hydra was placed in a large volume of water it never developed ovaries or testes. Water normally contains about 0.03 per cent CO_2 and the sex organs appeared when it reached 1.2 per cent. Moreover, he was able to completely suppress the development of buds and tentacles by increasing the CO_2 pressure to 10 per cent. Obviously the level of CO_2 in the vicinity of cells has a pronounced effect on differentiation in hydra and probably does in other animals. Such information gained from the study of simple animals often has far-reaching implications which direct studies on high animals, including man.

Hydra possesses no medusa stage and hence does not exhibit metagenesis, which is common among most Hydrozoa. The next representative is a more typical example of this class and is discussed primarily for that reason.

Obelia

This tiny colonial coelenterate may be found attached to seaweed and other objects lying in the clear water of tide pools and below low tide level to a depth of several fathoms. It is attached to the substratum by means of a horizontal branching basal portion.

An obelia colony begins as a **single polyp** which by budding and the subsequent clinging together of the buds forms a colony (Fig. 8-13). The process is reminiscent of the bud-upon-a-bud condition observed in hydra. The tissues and gastrovascular cavity are thus continuous throughout the colony. There are two types of polyps in an obelia colony, the feeding polyp, or **hydranth,** and the less common reproductive polyp, or **gonangium.** The hydranth is not greatly different from hydra except that it possesses solid instead of hollow tentacles and it is surrounded by a tough, horny outer covering called the **perisarc,** which invests the entire colony. The transparent vase-like portion of the

FIG. 8-11. A hydra with many testes. The fourth testis from the anterior end is nearly mature. Note the nipple-like tip from which the sperm will be discharged. This is a stained specimen.

perisarc surrounding a hydranth is called the **hydrotheca.** The cellular portion just

213

FIG. 8-12. Only the middle portion is shown of this hydra bearing ovaries, one of which has produced an egg. Later this egg would have fallen to the bottom of the pond where it would over-winter. It would then hatch into a tiny hydra the following spring.

beneath the perisarc is known as the **coenosarc.** After food has been captured and partly digested by an individual hydranth, it is carried through the gastrovascular cavity by the beating flagella which line the cavity. Thus all polyps share in the good fortune of any one. Digestion is finally completed intracellularly in the lining cells.

Obelia reproduces asexually by forming buds either on the horizontal parent stalk or on the upright stalk. Asexual reproduction also occurs in a second type of individual, the **gonangia** (singular, *gonangium*), which have no tentacles and no mouth. This cylindrical polyp is covered by the transparent **gonotheca,** a continuation of the perisarc. Each gonangium contains a central stalk, the **blastostyle,** upon which are borne small **medusa buds.** As the buds mature they approach the distal end of the blastostyle, finally leaving the gonotheca through a terminal opening and swimming away. These free-living medusae

are the familiar jellyfish, which, since they are able to move about, spread the species to new areas.

Medusae develop gonads which produce eggs and sperm that unite in the sea water. The resulting embryo, the **planula,** swims about for a time but eventually settles to the bottom, becomes attached to the substratum, and grows into an asexual colony, the polyp, thus completing the cycle. This species is an excellent illustration of **metagenesis.**

The medusa of obelia appears to be quite different from the polyp, but basically they resemble each other closely. The former has a central hanging **manubrium,** located on the concave side. At the center of the manubrium is the mouth, which opens into four **radial canals,** continuing into the circular **ring canal** in the margin of the bell. This constitutes the coelenteron and is equivalent to the same organ in hydra or the polyp of obelia. The space between the epidermis and the coelenteron is filled with the rather extensive gelatinous mesogloea. The medusa of obelia is microscopic and these structures can best be seen in larger jellyfish such as *Gonionemus,* which is commonly used for laboratory studies (Fig. 8-14).

Obelia illustrates the beginning of division of labor among the polyps, but this is carried to a greater degree of efficiency among some of the other Hydrozoa. For example, in *Hydractinia* (Fig. 8-22), a colonial form that is often found on the shells of hermit crabs, some of the polyps gather food, others reproduce the species, and still others protect the colony by use of large batteries of nematocysts. This is one step higher than obelia. **Polymorphism** (many shapes), the name applied to this type of division of labor, is carried even farther in *Physalia,* the **Portuguese man-of-war** (Fig. 8-15), which comprises at least four types of individuals. In addition to the various types of individuals found in the

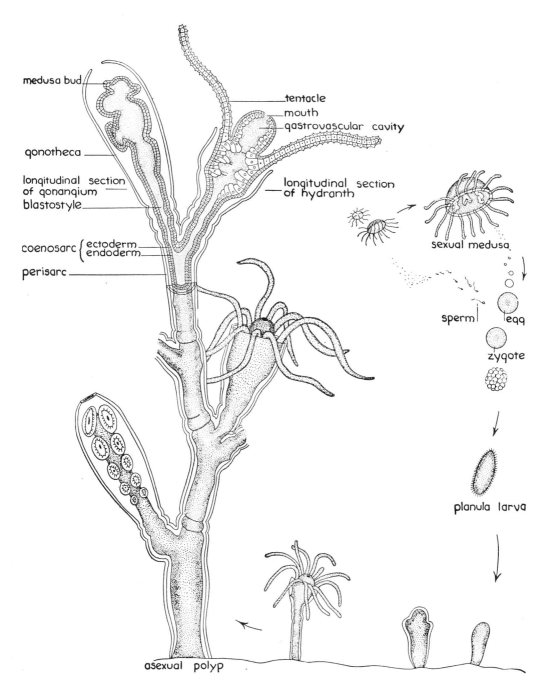

medusa bud

tentacle
mouth
gastrovascular cavity

gonotheca

longitudinal section
of gonangium
blastostyle

longitudinal section
of hydranth

coenosarc { ectoderm
endoderm

perisarc

sexual medusa

sperm

egg

zygote

planula larva

asexual polyp

FIG. 8-13. Life cycle of *Obelia*.

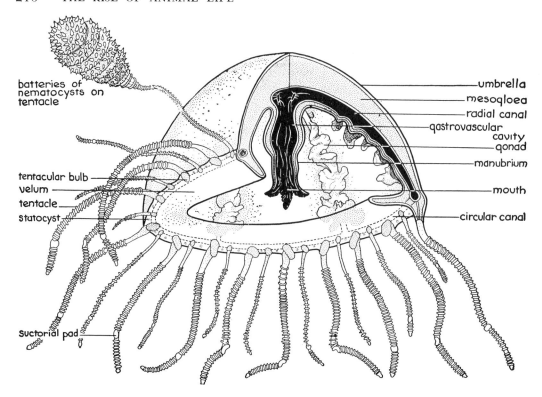

FIG. 8-14. *Gonionemus* sectioned to show internal structure. The tip of one tentacle is enlarged.

Hydractinia colony, Physalia also has a type that forms a gas-filled float which supports the colony on the surface of the sea as it is borne here and there by the wind and currents in a never-ending search for food. The tentacles bear unusually large nematocysts which are occasionally a menace to bathers if they happen to become entangled in them. This can easily happen in some species of Physalia, since the tentacles trail as much as 50 feet beneath and behind the float. Physalia has little difficulty in paralyzing a fish several inches in length and eventually consuming it. The many types of individuals in this colony illustrate polymorphism in its most advanced form among the coelenterates.

Other Coelenterates

The second class of coelenterates, the **Scyphozoa,** includes most of the larger jellyfishes (Fig. 8-16) which either have a reduced polyp stage or lack it altogether. *Aurelia* (Fig. 8-17), one of the most common examples, is found in great numbers up and down the coasts of the United States. Its rather flattened umbrella is fringed with small tentacles that are interrupted at eight equally spaced spots where a **sense organ** is located. The rhythmic contractions of the circular muscle in the bell are responsible for the graceful movement of this beautiful creature. Four long **oral lobes,** which are located on the short manubrium, are heavily armed with nematocysts and function like tentacles in capturing food and directing it into the mouth. The coelenteron is divided into four large **gastric pouches** from which radiate smaller canals that connect with the **ring canal** at the periphery of the **bell.** The gonads, lying in the gastric pouches, form four horse-

FIG. 8-15. Portuguese man-of-war (*Physalia*) stinging a fish. Note the large gas bag which functions as a float and sail combined. The numerous tentacles perform all of the functions of the animal. Some are heavily armed with nematocysts which are effective weapons against other animals, as this photograph shows. Note dead fish.

FIG. 8-16. A giant jellyfish (*Cyanea capillata*) common on our eastern seaboard. The dome is flattened during relaxation; during its power stroke it becomes more oval in shape.

shoe-shaped bodies when viewed from the aboral (opposite the mouth) side, and constitute a ready mark of identification.

The sense organs, consisting of **eyespots** (sensitive to light) and **statocysts** (sensitive to gravity), are located at the edge of the bell where the nerve net is somewhat centralized. The statocysts are hollow spheres containing small calcareous granules which, as they tumble about in the cyst, stimulate nerve endings and indicate to the animal its relation to the rest of the world. In other words, it functions as an organ of equilibrium, much the same as the semicircular canals in our ears. This is the first appearance of such an organ among the metazoa.

The sexes are separate, but resemble one another closely. Sperm, released by the male, pass into the mouth and then into the coelenteron of the female where the eggs are fertilized. The resulting zygotes move to the oral lobes where they develop into small ciliated larvae, the **planulae.** These soon swim free of the parent and settle to the bottom where they become attached. They then develop into polyps **(scyphistoma)** which are able to feed. These grow and may produce other polyps from lateral buds. However, in the fall the polyps transform into **strobila** which consist of a series of transverse sections that resemble miniature stacked plates. This process is called **strobilization.** These flat eight-lobed medusae **(ephyrae)** separate, invert, and swim free in the sea and eventually grow into the adult jellyfishes.

Sometimes, following a strong in-shore

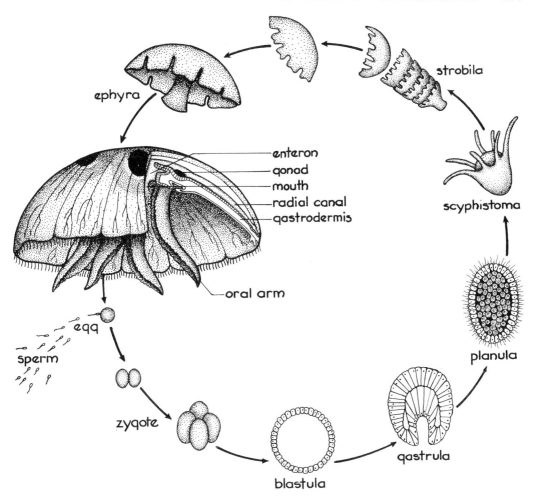

FIG. 8-17. Life cycle of *Aurelia*.

breeze, thousands of large jellyfish are swept up on the beaches to perish. Although they are thought to be very jelly-like, they do maintain their shape out of water and seem almost semisolid. They also retain some of their delicate beauty. When they are swimming in the open sea, they provide a sight that, once seen, is not easily forgotten.

Representatives of the next class, **Anthozoa,** are characterized by a heavy body, supported by numerous **septa,** transverse sheets of tough tissue. Members of this group possess no medusa stage, eggs and **sperm** being produced within the body and discharged into the surrounding sea. The most common representatives are the **sea anemones** and **corals;** others, less common, are the **horny, black,** and **soft corals,** the **sea pens,** and **sea pansies.** They compare favorably with the jellyfish in respect to beauty and number. Both the Atlantic and Pacific Coasts, extending from Alaska and Maine to Southern California and Florida, abound with anthozoans (Fig. 8-18). Some are found in the polar regions, some at great depths, but they are most numerous in shallow waters in the warmer seas.

The sea anemone usually remains in

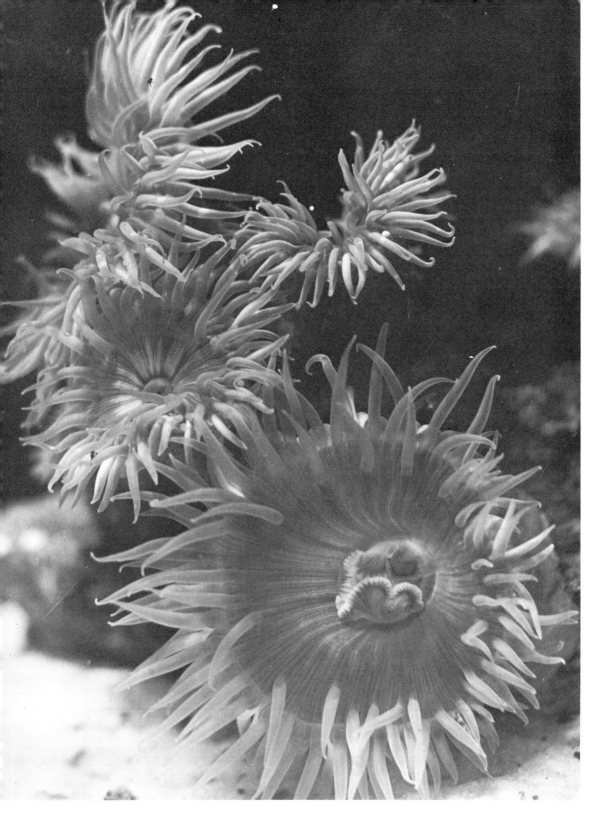

FIG. 8-18. A common Pacific Coast sea anemone (*Cribrina*). These feed on small fish which they capture with the aid of their powerful nematocysts.

FIG. 8-19. An underwater photograph of a typical coral reef (Great Barrier Reef). The fish are strikingly colored to match the background of corals, sponges, and other marine life. The corals are highly varied in size, shape, and color.

one place for a long period of time; some have been observed to live for years in a small depression in rock just below low tide level. It can move slowly on its pedal disk and some of the smaller ones are able to swim by beating their tentacles. It feeds on any unsuspecting crustacean, mollusk, or even fish that comes within reach of its tentacles. Once the prey is paralyzed by the nematocysts it is taken into the coelenteron, and digestion goes on much the same as in other coelenterates. The sea anemone, in spite of its tough outer covering, is preyed upon by a variety of animals such as fish, starfish, and crustacea. When in danger it can retract its tentacles, fold them inside

the body, and contract its entire body until it is nearly flat against the substratum. In this condition it is very difficult to remove; in fact, the body is often torn apart before its grasp is released. Although it usually reproduces sexually, occasionally an anemone is found undergoing fission, either longitudinally or transversely.

Other interesting anthozoans, resembling the sea anemones in many respects, are the corals (Fig. 8-19). These are usually very small and live in stony cups, of specific design, made by the limy secretions from the base. The colonies lie in close proximity and after thousands of generations produce the massive corals, bits of which are frequently seen reposing as mantelpiece ornaments in many homes. Corals live in warm waters for the most part, although there is one species, *Astrangia,* living as far north as Maine. They abound in many tropical seas of the world, particularly in the Coral Sea. Our overseas forces in the past war became familiar with the corals around the Philippines and Australia.

Perhaps the most interesting thing about coral is its ability to form reefs, some of which reach many miles in length, like the Great Barrier Reef of Australia, for example, which extends over 1,200 miles in length and has an area of over 80,000 square miles. There are three kinds of coral reefs, depending on how they were formed (Fig. 8-20). The **fringing reef** lies along the shoreline of an island or mainland and usually extends for a quarter of a mile into the sea. Boats approaching such shores are in great danger, particularly in rough weather. Sometimes, as the result of a shifting shoreline, a lagoon appears between the main reef and the shore; this type is called a **barrier reef** (Fig. 8-21). The **atoll** is perhaps the most unique of the three kinds of reefs. It is a rim of coral taking on varying shapes, usually a completely enclosed circle. These have always fascinated biologists. One of the greatest among them was Charles Darwin who gave an explanation of how they formed, a theory which is still considered fundamentally sound. He thought the peculiar formations started out as a fringing reef around an island, but due to shifts in

the earth's surface the island gradually began to sink. The rate at which it submerged was about as fast as the corals were able to secrete lime and keep themselves in the tidal zone. By keeping pace with the sinking island, the corals built the fringing reefs sufficiently high to catch vegetation and support growth of plants while the central portion gradually became submerged below the water's surface. This then produced a rim of coral, inscribing the outline of the old island and producing the strangely shaped atolls seen in tropical seas today.

RELATIONSHIP AMONG COELENTERATES

A possible explanation for the many different life cycles among the coelenterates might be that the original primitive coelenterate was much like the **planula larva,** which is found rather consistently in all of the groups, with the notable exception of hydra. The planula is a ball of cells that might be compared to *Volvox* except that the former is solid and the latter is hollow. It would not be difficult to understand how the early planula-like coelenterate might become temporarily attached to the bottom of the ocean and invaginate, to form the hydra-like polyp (Fig. 8-22: 1 to 5). The formation of the sex organs would be similar to those found in hydra (Fig. 8-22: 6), and the life history would also be the same, except that the zygote would develop into a planula which would eventu-

FIG. 8-20. Various types of coral reefs.

FIG. 8-21. An aerial view of a typical coral island—Green Island, located in the Great Barrier Reef. Note the vast expanse of the reef compared to the land that makes up the island itself.

ally settle down and grow into the polyp.

From the hydra-like type could be produced a form resembling *Hydractinia* (Fig. 8-22: 7), where the sex organs develop into separate bodies, although they are not detached from the polyp. The next logical step would be an obelia-like form in which the medusae detach themselves from the polyp and become the free-swimming sexual stage of the animal (Fig. 8-22: 8). This affords an opportunity for the species to spread by means of both the planula and the medusa stages. The next variation might be a continued emphasis of the medusa and a de-emphasis of the polyp stage, as is seen in *Aurelia* (Fig. 8-22: 9). This can be carried

still further until the polyp stage disappears altogether, which is the case with many of the large jellyfish (Fig. 8-22: 10). This is merely a possible explanation for the great variety of forms found in this phylum of animals.

In review, we have found the coelenterates a widely diverse group of animals that have explored many possibilities of form, structure, and habitat, remaining all the while within the limitations of two body layers, ectoderm and endoderm, and a simple third layer, or mesogloea. Animals could have gone no further in complexity had they remained within these limitations.

223

RELATIONSHIP
AMONG THE
COELENTERATES

Hydra

6

Hydractinia

7

Obelia

8

5

1

volvox-like
ancestor

4

9

Jelly Fish

3

2
Planula

Attached
Planula

10

FIG. 8-22. A hypothetical representation of how the various relationships among the coelenterates might have come about.

The next group surmounted this difficulty by the elaboration of the third body layer already present in the coelenterates, though primitive. This resulted in a modification in the entire body plan of the group. Let us see how this was accomplished.

PHYLUM CTENOPHORA

These animals are commonly known as comb jellies or sea walnuts and are found floating near the surface of the sea. They resemble the coelenterates in having radial symmetry, an epidermis, and a gastrodermis; but in addition they have a true **mesoderm** which gives rise to definite muscular elements. They are also characterized by the possession of eight rows of swimming **combs** or **plates** which are formed from fused cilia. The ctenophora occur in great abundance in the oceans and some are luminescent, adding beauty to the ocean at night by the rhythmic beating of their combs which send off a feeble blue-green light. This light is sufficiently intense to expose a photographic plate (Fig. 3-16).

In this chapter we have seen how animals with two layers of cells have been able to organize their simple bodies into divergent forms which have been so successful as to invade nearly all waters of the globe. The rudiments of a third body layer appear with the mesogloea in the coelenterates and a true mesoderm is present in the ctenophores, though very primitive. Let us continue to the next chapter where we will follow the further development of this layer.

SUGGESTED SUPPLEMENTARY READINGS

BUCHSBAUM, R., *Animals without Backbones* (Chicago, University of Chicago Press, 1948).

GILLETT, K., and McNEILL, F., *The Great Barrier Reef and Adjacent Isles* (Sidney, Australia, The Coral Press Pty. Ltd., 1959).

HYMAN, L., *The Invertebrates,* Vol. I, *Protozoa through Ctenophora* (New York, McGraw-Hill Book Co., 1940).

LENHOFF, H. M., and LOOMIS, W. F., eds., *The Biology of Hydra and some other Coelenterates* (Coral Gables, Florida, University of Miami Press, 1961).

LOOMIS, W. F., "The Sex Gas of Hydra," *Scientific American,* 200 (4) (April, 1959), 145.

PENNAK, R. W., *Fresh-water Invertebrates of the United States* (New York, The Ronald Press, 1953).

RAMSAY, J. A., *Physiological Approach to the Lower Animals* (Cambridge, Cambridge University Press, 1962).

YONGE, C. A., *The Seashore* (London, Wm. Collins & Sons, 1949).

9

Primitive Bilateral Animals – Flatworms

QUITE DIFFERENT from the symmetrical beauty of the jellyfishes and sea anemones are the representatives of this group of animals, the flatworms. Their flattened, elongated, and bilaterally symmetrical bodies account for the name of the phylum, **Platyhelminthes** (from the Greek, **platy**—flat). The primitive mesoderm seen in the ctenophores assumed much more importance in this phylum giving rise to rather elaborate organs; hence we consider these animals as having reached the **organ-system grade of organization** which we see throughout all subsequent higher animal groups.

It is also noteworthy that they possess no body cavity, hence are called **acoelomate** animals (see p. 153). The mesoderm has given rise to a good muscular system making possible other modifications. The worm can move on a flat surface, a feat which was probably instrumental in bringing about a change from radial to bilateral symmetry. This means that it acquired head and tail ends, dorsal and ventral sides, and left and right sides. Localization of the sensory system in the head region was initiated in these forms, signifying a definite step toward centralization of the nervous system.

Moreover, the animal now moved in one direction to seek food rather than acquiring its meal in a passive manner. All of these changes resulted in a much more complex animal, one that was well on its way toward higher forms.

Of the three classes of the phylum Platyhelminthes, only the class **Turbellaria** includes free-living animals. Members of this group may be found among the rocks in cool streams or ponds, or upon the shady side of submerged plants. Turbellarians are carnivorous, feeding on small animals, either living or dead. There are also marine forms in this group some of which live in the intestines of sea urchins and other forms of ocean life.

The other two classes of the phylum are the **Trematoda,** or flukes, and the **Cestoda,** or tapeworms. All members of these two classes are parasitic and will be described further in a later section, but first let us examine the free-living turbellarians.

PLANARIA

The study of **triploblastic,** or three-layered, animals may well begin with planaria, a common inhabitant of North American streams. It seeks shelter in darkened, secluded spots and comes out at night to move around in the cool waters in search of food. Planaria is flattened dorsal-ventrally and is darkly pigmented. It is covered with **cilia,** which enable it to glide along the substratum over a mucous path (Fig. 9-1) secreted by glands on the ventral surface of the body. By use of a muscle layer developed in the **mesoderm,** planaria can crawl in true worm-like fashion. Certain muscle groups produce a twisting motion so that it sometimes appears to raise its head and look about. Although it may appear that planaria can see when this occurs, actually its two large **eye-spots** form no image and are only sensitive to varying intensities of light.

Unlike most heads, that of planaria has no mouth, for the mouth is located on the ventral side of the body near the middle. It opens into a muscular **pharynx,** which lies in a sheath extending anteriorly, and when planaria is hungry and in search of food, it often protrudes its pharynx and moves about with it thus extended. When a small piece of meat is tossed into the water, hungry planarians attach themselves to it. A digestive fluid pours out from the pharynx to aid in the disintegration of the meat. The partially digested food is then taken into the digestive tract where digestion is completed. Planaria's chief food consists of small crustacea. When these are its prey the epidermal slime glands secrete a sticky substance which is sprayed over the victim, rendering it helpless. It is usual for planaria to grip its prey with the head region first and then attach its muscular pharynx to the food, bits of which are drawn into the mouth by a sucking action.

The digestive system of planaria is sac-like, similar to hydra, with but a single opening for the entrance of food and the exit of waste materials (Fig. 9-2). In some of the platyhelminthes, particularly the parasitic members, the sac is merely a straight and unbranched tube, but in planaria it branches into three distinct parts to form a **tri-clad intestine.** Each part, in turn, ramifies into many smaller branches which supply food directly to the various regions of the body (Fig. 9-3). Large thin-walled, unciliated cells line the gut and secrete digestive juices which carry on extracellular digestion. In addition, the cells lining the intestine are able to ingest solid food by means of pseudopods and digest it intracellularly, as in the case of hydra.

Between the ectoderm and the endoderm is a mass of large star-shaped mesodermal cells, the **parenchyma.** It is possible for food substances to pass not only from the gut into the lining cells, but also from the parenchyma into the lining cells. Thus, when planaria cannot find food, it may consume certain organs in the parenchyma by

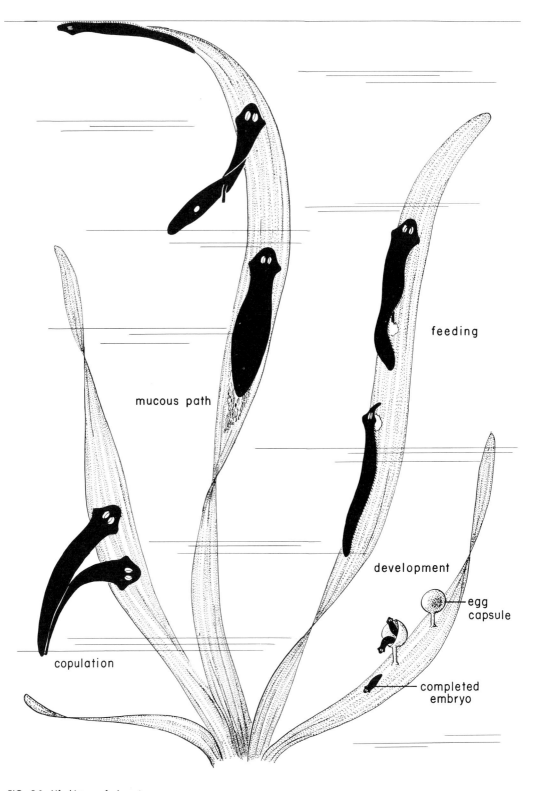

feeding

mucous path

development

egg
capsule

copulation

completed
embryo

FIG. 9-1. Life history of planaria.

passing them into the intestinal cells where they are digested. This enables planaria to go without food for quite a long time, through gradual reduction in size. In one species of planaria it was found that during starvation the absorption and digestion of its internal organs occurred in regular order. First the reproductive organs disappeared, leaving the animal reduced to sexual immaturity; next the parenchyma, the gut, and the muscles were consumed in that order. The nervous system remained essentially intact so that the animal appeared as a weird form with the bulk of its remaining body in the head region. On feeding these starved forms, all the lost parts regenerated to normal size.

Special excretory organs appear for the first time in a metazoan among the flatworms. In planaria the excretory system consists of a pair of branching tubes running down each side of the body. The main tubes or canals divide into small branches, each of which finally ends blindly in a single **flame cell** (Fig. 9-4). These cells have long cilia which extend into the lumen of the canal, and it is their flickering motion that suggests the name. The movement of the beating cilia carries some of the nitrogenous wastes into the tube and to the exterior through a number of **excretory pores.** Probably the chief function of this system is regulating the water balance, because most of the nitrogenous wastes are lost through the endodermal cells. Because the tubes of this system are a primitive type of **nephridium** (kidney), they are called **protonephridia.**

The **nervous system** of the planarian is simple (Fig. 9-4), yet it is strikingly more advanced than the primitive nerve net of the coelenterates. Perhaps most unique is the concentration of the nervous tissue in the head region below the eyes. The nerve cell bodies are contained in two masses of nervous tissue, the **cerebral ganglion,** commonly referred to as the **brain.** From this concentrated point two longitudinal **nerve**

FIG. 9-2. Planaria stained so as to differentiate the digestive tract. Note its ramifications into every part of the animal. The protrusible pharynx is clearly shown in this photo.

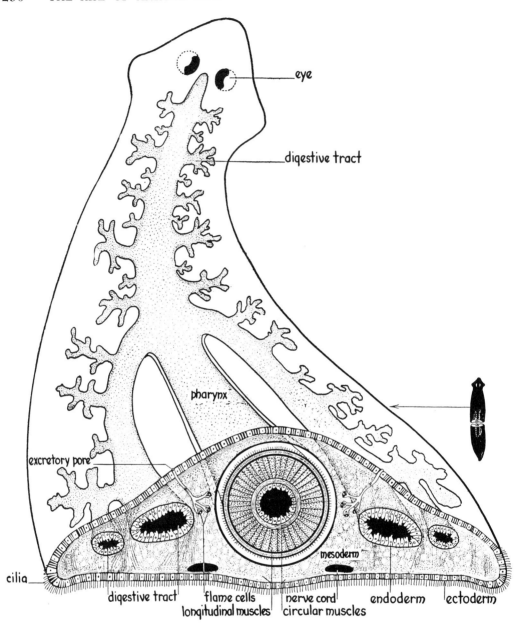

FIG. 9-3. A dorsal and sectional view of planaria to demonstrate the systems, particularly the digestive.

cords past posteriorly and two short nerves extend anteriorly to connect with the eyes. Along the two longitudinal cords are many transverse nerves, which are distributed to the various internal structures of the planarian body.

The eyes of planaria are found on the dorsal surface where they appear as two dark spots (Fig. 9-5). There is no lens, as such, although the ectoderm over the eye is without pigment so that light can pass through to reach the **sensory** cells below, which connect with the brain. Without a lens no image is possible, but the eye is sensitive to varying intensities of light and the animal characteristically withdraws from bright light and seeks out moderate illumination. Other sensory cells protrude from the surface of the body and act as receptors for registering changes in the flow of the water or other variations in the surroundings.

Although it is evident that the nervous system of the Turbellaria is still very simple, the increase of special sensory cells, their grouping into such an organ as the simple eye-spot, and the aggregation of

FIG. 9-5. Head of planaria (*Euplanaria* or *Dugesia*) highly magnified. Note the "crossed" eyes and the two ear-like extensions of the head region in which tactile sense organs are located.

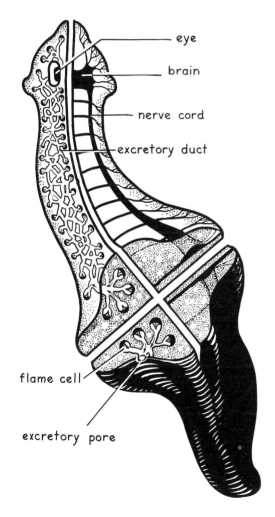

FIG. 9-4. A planarian in dorsal view and cross-section, showing the excretory system on the left and the nervous system on the right.

nerve cells into the cerebral ganglion are the beginnings of a definite central nervous system.

Of the various systems, the planarian reproductive system shows the greatest advancement over that of the coelenterates (Fig. 9-6). In the sexually mature worm, male and female reproductive systems are present in each individual, hence it is said to be monoecious (hermaphroditic). Both ovaries and testes develop from the cells of the parenchyma. The numerous testes are rounded bodies which lie along both sides of the body. They give rise to the **spermatozoa,** or **sperm cells,** which are conveyed through small ducts, the **vasa efferentia,** to a larger tube, the **vas deferens,** or sperm duct, running the length of the body on each side. The two seminal vesicles terminate in a pear-shaped **copulatory organ** or **penis**. At rest the copulatory organ opens into the **genital atrium,** which leads into the **genital pore,** the external opening through which the penis is thrust during **copulation.**

The two **ovaries** of the female reproductive system are found near the anterior end of the body; these produce the **ova.** The **yolk glands,** which give rise to the yolk and shell of the egg, are found along the

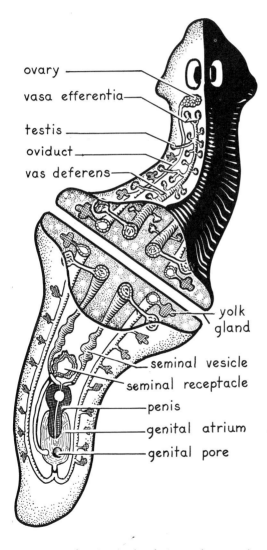

ovary
vasa efferentia
testis
oviduct
vas deferens

yolk gland

seminal vesicle
seminal receptacle
penis
genital atrium
genital pore

FIG. 9-6. A planarian in dorsal view and cross-section showing the reproductive system.

oviducts. The two oviducts lie parallel to the nerve cords and join before entering the atrium. The **seminal receptacle,** a sac for storing sperm, also opens into the atrium, very near the external opening. The genital atrium, therefore, receives the openings of both the female and the male organs.

At the start of copulation the ventral surfaces of the two animals come together, so that the openings of the genital atria are opposite one another. The penis of each is extended into the genital opening of the other and the sperm cells are exchanged. At the time of copulation the ova are also ripe. To prevent self-fertilization, the genital area has been elaborated. The penis, when extruded and dilated, completely fills the atrium and thus blocks the openings into the oviducts, so that neither can the ova escape nor sperm cells enter the oviduct, but sperm can be deposited into the seminal receptacles. At the completion of copulation the penes are withdrawn and the sperm cells then are able to enter the oviduct. The ova are fertilized in the oviduct and, as they move down toward the atrium, the products of the yolk glands are discharged. The mature fertilized egg is released from the atrium through the genital pore, and the capsule-like shell becomes attached by a stalk to submerged objects. The egg cases may undergo a rest period before growing into young planaria.

Planaria also reproduces asexually by means of transverse fission. Indeed, this is much the more common method of reproduction. The worm constricts itself in two and the parts which are missing after the fission has taken place are then regenerated. Planaria is an excellent animal for regeneration experiments. For example, if the head of planaria is split and if the parts are kept separated for a short period of time, a double-headed monster is formed. Should the animal be cut transversely into two separate pieces, two little planaria will result (Fig. 9-7). An animal can be cut

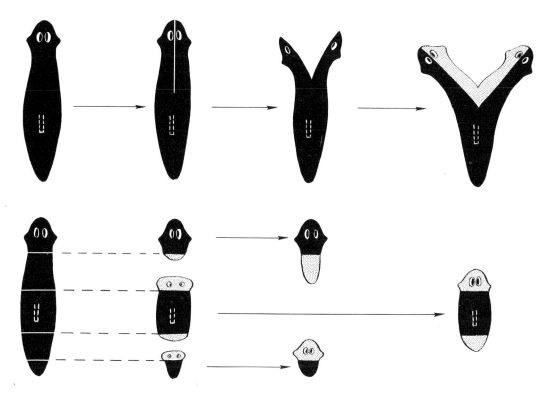

FIG. 9-7. Regeneration in planaria.

into as many as six pieces and each will give rise to a miniature worm one-sixth the size of the original. The significance of regeneration was pointed out in an earlier section.

OTHER TURBELLARIA

Members of the class Turbellaria are, for the most part, free-living, some live on the exterior of other animals and others are true parasites living in the intestines of mollusks and various echinoderms, such as the sea cucumber. Economically, they are of little importance.

The small primitive marine forms of the order **Acoela** have a mouth but no digestive system, the food being digested by the endodermal cells (Fig. 4-1). *Convoluta,* an animal that lives on sandy ocean shores, is a good example of this order. As it ma-

tures, algae enter and inhabit its parenchymous tissue, giving it a green color. Another member of this group is *Ectocotyla,* an ectocommensal on hermit crabs.

Members of the order **Rhabdocoelida** are turbellarians with a straight tubular gut. In certain forms the gut has lateral pouches, but not as highly branched as that of planaria. These turbellarians are commonly found in fresh water, but because of their small size are not as easily studied as planaria. The largest of these forms is *Mesostoma,* which, like members of the order Tricladida, has its mouth on the ventral surface. The smaller rhabdocoeles have their mouth in the anterior region, ventral to the brain. Some of these animals have such remarkable powers of reproduction by fission that individuals form long chains which remain together for some time before separating.

Members of the order **Polycladida** are marine forms, usually small, although some attain a length of 6 inches. This order includes a few rare species found only in isolated places, such as the Gulf of Naples. The digestive system is well branched and the body is unusually flattened. In some of the simpler forms, the mouth is centrally located and the pharynx, which is funnel-like in structure, can be extended from the mouth to enclose food. One difference between this order and the others is that development is not direct, but must pass through a rounded, ciliated larval form which possesses projecting arms. As the animal grows, it loses the cilia and the arms, develops a crawling movement, and becomes considerably lengthened and flattened.

CLASS TREMATODA

The trematodes, commonly called **flukes**, are characteristically flat like all platyhelminthes, but their gut is reduced in complexity. Because of their parasitic life they have lost their cilia and have developed hold-fast organs called **suckers.** They have no apparent sense organs, but the reproductive and excretory systems are well developed. In general, the entire anatomy is adapted to a parasitic mode of life.

All grades of parasitism are found in this group, from those that live on the outside of their hosts to those that inhabit the internal cavities. The life history of parasites that cling to the outside of animals such as fast-moving fish is relatively simple, its main characteristic being the development of hold-fast organs or suckers. The case of the internal parasite is an entirely different one. There is no great problem of staying put, hence the suckers are small, but in order to complete its life cycle an enormously prolific reproductive system has been developed. Not only is the production of large numbers of potential offspring necessary, but also various kinds of larval stages that are able to pass through several hosts, all of which are instrumental in spreading the parasite far and wide. Let us consider two examples of flukes that infect man, one that lives in the liver (*Opisthorchis sinensis*) and another that lives in the blood (*Schistosoma mansoni*).

The life cycle of the human liver fluke can serve as a typical example of most related flukes that are so prevalent in wild and domestic animals (Fig. 9-8). It involves two **intermediate hosts** which harbor the larval stages of the parasite, and, of course, one **final host** in which the adult lives. The human liver fluke infects 75–100 per cent of the people in certain parts of China, Japan, and Korea, constituting a real health problem in these regions. This situation should be alleviated with the advent of improved sanitation and a better educational program.

The adult fluke (Fig. 9-9) lives in the small bile ducts of the liver, where toxic products excreted by the flukes and the subsequent mechanical occlusions of the ducts may cause serious damage. For a heavily infected individual, this condition may eventually cause cirrhosis, which together with complicating infectious disease usually terminates in death. The adult fluke is about three-fourths of an inch in length and has two suckers, one at the anterior end, another about one-third of the way from the anterior end. It feeds on blood which is drawn in through the anterior mouth.

Eggs laid by the adult pass through the bile duct into the gut and eventually pass out of the body in the feces. Because of the oriental habit of using human excrement as fertilizer in the rice paddies, the eggs usually get into water. Unlike most flukes, this fluke does not hatch into the larval stage known as the **miracidium** until it is eaten by a certain species of snail of the genus *Bythinia*. Inside the snail the egg hatches, releasing the miracidium which makes its way into the tissues of the

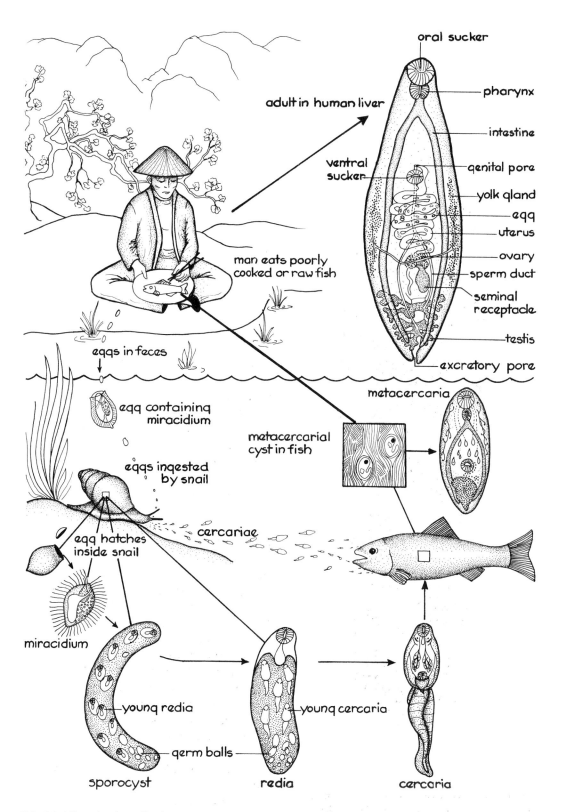

oral sucker

pharynx

intestine

adult in human liver

ventral sucker

genital pore

yolk gland

egg

uterus

ovary

sperm duct

seminal receptacle

testis

excretory pore

man eats poorly cooked or raw fish

eggs in feces

egg containing miracidium

metacercaria

metacercarial cyst in fish

eggs ingested by snail

cercariae

egg hatches inside snail

miracidium

young redia

young cercaria

germ balls

sporocyst

redia

cercaria

FIG. 9-8. Life cycle of *Opisthorchis sinensis,* the human liver fluke.

snail and develops into a **sporocyst.** The next stage, the **redia,** develops inside the sporocyst. Both the sporocyst and the redia stages make possible a tremendous increase in numbers by asexual reproduction. The redia finally develops **cercariae** within its walls, which make their way out of the snail into the surrounding water where they swim about by means of their large vibratile tails. The cercaria then becomes attached to the next host, one of several different fish and, after losing its tail, bores its way into the flesh of the fish. It rounds itself into a ball and produces a cyst wall; in response to the parasite, the fish secretes another wall around the invader. Here it lies until the raw fish is eaten by man in whose gut the cyst wall is digested away, releasing the young worm which makes its way up the bile duct and finally into the smaller tubes of the liver where it grows to maturity.

The control of the disease is obviously very simple, destroy the snails or cook the fish, either of which interrupts the cycle and kills the parasite.

Some of the most important flukes are the blood-inhabiting **schistosomes** such as *Schistosoma mansoni* (Fig. 9-11). Unlike *Opisthorchis,* these worms are **dioecious,** that is, there are two separate sexes. They are long slender worms, beautifully adapted for living in the small blood vessels. A strange relationship exists between the males and females; the male holds the extremely slender female in a groove on his ventral side, from which she ventures forth during the business of laying eggs. Her slender thread-like body is ideally adapted to fit in the tiny blood vessels of the intestinal wall or over the bladder where she lays her eggs. The eggs have a single sharp spine by which passively they work their way through the wall into the cavity of the intestine or bladder where they are voided with the urine or feces.

Again through the use of human excrement for fertilizer, the eggs usually find

FIG. 9-9. A stained adult human liver fluke (*Opisthorchis sinensis*). Compare this photograph with the drawing in Fig. 9-8 in order to make out the parts.

their way into water. They hatch into **miracidia** which penetrate the tissues of snails, and follow stages of development similar to those of *Opisthorchis* with minor variations. Instead of encysting on a fish, the cercaria burrows through the skin of a person who is unfortunate enough to be in the vicinity and makes its way into the vascular system. It passes through the heart, lungs, and liver, eventually maturing in the blood vessels (veins) that drain the intestines and bladder. Here it grows rapidly, feeding on blood, and when sexually mature lays its eggs, thus completing the cycle.

The several species of blood flukes infect people of tropical America, many parts of Africa, and the Orient, particularly China. In some irrigated regions the infection runs as high as 90 per cent among the adult males who are constantly in contact with the water, hence exposed to the cercariae. Treatment consists of giving large doses of antimony compounds and, if the patient can stand the treatment, he can be cured. Like all of the complex parasites, blood flukes can be controlled by removing the intermediate host.

Water birds such as ducks, terns, and gulls, have their own varieties of blood flukes which apparently cause them no particular harm. However, if this type of cercaria cannot find its proper final host, it does penetrate the skin of any person who happens to be near, causing a severe itching which has been called **schistosome dermatitis,** or just "swimmer's itch" (Fig. 9-10). The cercariae apparently are not able to penetrate the tough thick mammalian skin, but in their attempts to do so enter it and cause intense irritation. There are several different species of cercariae that follow this pattern. Some are found on the sandy bathing beaches in the lake regions of the North Central states, especially Michigan and Minnesota, where they sometimes become such a nuisance that bathing is actually prevented, much to the disgust and economic loss of resort owners. Elaborate

FIG. 9-10. A blood fluke normally infecting water birds occasionally enters human skin, causing "swimmer's itch" (schistosome dermatitis).

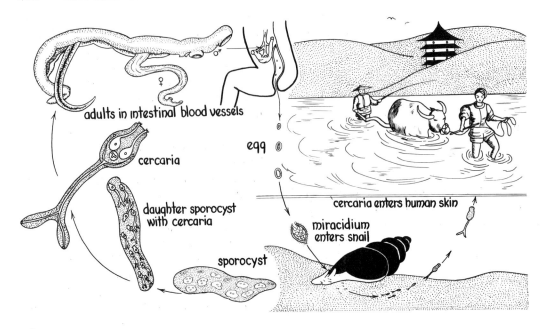

FIG. 9-11. Life history of a typical human blood fluke.

methods of treating the beaches with copper sulfate in order to destroy the snails have been developed and have had reasonable success.

CLASS CESTODA

These are the **tapeworms,** a group of parasites that the layman has long erroneously associated with lean hungry adolescents. The worm gets its name from its long ribbon-like appearance, a feature that is common to this large and varied group, members of which infect almost all, if not all, vertebrate animals.

The tapeworm is, perhaps, the most degenerate of all animals, a condition indicating that the association with its host is one of long standing. At the same time it is beautifully adapted to its specialized environment, the vertebrate gut. It is indeed the supreme parasite among parasites. It is provided with excellent hold-fast organs to keep it in place in the gut of the host (Fig. 9-12). All nourishment is received from the contents of the gut or from the gut wall directly, so the animal has not bothered to retain even a semblance of a digestive tract. Its nervous and excretory systems are very rudimentary, and its ability to move has been reduced to very feeble contractions. However, it has evolved an extremely elaborate and prolific reproductive system, an essential feature in its survival since the possibility for any individual egg to reach maturity is very small. Although it has degenerated in other respects, it has gone all out in this one phase of its life, and measured in terms of biological success, the shift in emphasis has apparently been satisfactory.

The common beef tapeworm (*Taenia saginata*) of man is a typical example of this group (Fig. 9-13). It consists of two principal parts, the head or **scolex,** and the **proglottids,** sectional pieces attached to one another, and growing larger as they proceed posteriorly. The scolex possesses hold-fast organs which make it possible for the worm to maintain its position in the gut. The proglottids, which are budded off from the region just back of the head called the **neck,** mature as they move progressively posteriorly. The younger proglottids are therefore anterior to the older. The mature proglottids, gorged with eggs containing young embryo worms, break away from the worm and pass out of the body in the feces. Because of the close association of cattle and their keepers in certain parts of the country, it is not unusual for the eggs to be picked up by grazing cattle. Once in the gut of this host the egg membranes and shell are digested away and the young **six-hooked embryo (hexacanth)** emerges. It soon bores its way through the gut wall into a blood vessel where it floats to the muscles, particularly heart and jaw muscles. Here it develops into a **bladder** and a tiny inverted tapeworm scolex grows from the wall of the bladder. Beef so infected is said to contain "bladder worms" and is usually unmarketable. If such beef is poorly cooked and then eaten by humans, the bladder worms "hatch." The tiny scolices evert and become attached to the soft intestinal wall where they immediately begin budding off proglottids.

An examination of the proglottid demonstrates the fact that it is almost a complete individual itself. Indeed, the tapeworm is sometimes considered a colony in which each proglottid is an individual, much like the buds in hydra or the polyps in obelia. Besides rudimentary nervous and excretory systems it possesses male and female sex organs, which are capable of producing prodigious numbers of sperm and eggs. The **testes,** numerous and scattered throughout the proglottid, are connected through fine tubules to the **sperm duct** which opens to the outside through the **genital pore.** The paired **ovaries** produce eggs which pass through a small duct (oviduct) where they receive sperm from another proglottid, or another worm, via the **vagina.** Here they also obtain the food material called **yolk** from the **yolk gland,** while the **shell gland** secretes material for forming the shell. The fertile eggs then are deposited into the **uterus** which eventually becomes greatly distended as the eggs begin to develop crowding all other structures out of place. Such a **gravid** proglottid (full of developing embryos) breaks off and follows the cycle indicated above.

Meat inspections in this country, together with sanitation among cattle raisers, have greatly reduced the incidence of this parasite. In fact, it has become so difficult to obtain this human parasite that biological supply houses usually have standing orders for them. Control of tapeworms is very simple: merely cook the suspected meat. There is a similar tapeworm in pork (*Taenia solium*) which is also becoming rare.

A few decades ago during the lumber-

FIG. 9-12. The scolex of the dog tapeworm (*Taenia pisiformis*). Note the sharp hooks and sucking discs used as attachment organs.

young tapeworm

bladderworm

adult tapeworm

MAN

eats poorly cooked beef

intestine

sperm duct

excretory tube

testis

genital pore

uterus

zygote

ovary

shell gland

yolk gland

nerve

mature proglattid
discharged with
human feces

striated muscle

encysted bladderworm

eggs

proglottid broken down

six-hooked
embryo in egg

blood vessel
carries embryo
to muscle

intestine

COW

FIG. 9-13. Life history of the beef tapeworm (*Taenia saginata*) of man.

jack days in this country, particularly in Minnesota and Michigan, the fish were heavily infected with a tapeworm larva that was transmitted to man through his habit of eating raw fish. The worm, *Diphyllobothrium latum,* was apparently introduced by emigrants from the Baltic region of Europe where the infection was known for centuries. The life history involves two intermediate hosts, a small crustacean and a fish. The crustacean receives the infection by eating tapeworm larvae, the fish (pickerel or pike) eats the crustacean, and finally man gets the worm by eating the uncooked fish. This is a giant among tapeworms, having been known to reach a length of 60 feet.

In review, we have seen that with the advent of the mesoderm and with it several important organ systems, the flatworms far outstripped the coelenterates in complexity. They are, however, still small creatures and relatively simple when compared to a mammal; in other words, still further important changes must have taken place in subsequent groups of animals. We shall see what additions are made in the next group, the group of tubular worms.

PHYLUM NEMERTINEA

The Nemertines

The development of a circulatory system first appears in this phylum, representatives of which are sometimes called "band worms" because of their long ciliated flat bodies. The nemertines live primarily in the ocean where they crawl among the rocks. They are highly colored and greatly elongated, sometimes measuring as much as 80 feet in length. If captured, their bodies stretch so that they often break into two parts under their own weight, but regeneration occurs as readily as it does in planaria. They are also able to break their bodies into many parts, a process called

autotomy (self-cutting), which is not an uncommon characteristic among invertebrates.

In addition to a complete digestive tract, the nemertine possesses a very primitive circulatory system (Fig. 9-14). It consists of three blood vessels that extend throughout the length of the body, but which do not break up into tiny capillaries as in higher animals. In these forms, oxygen and food still diffuse some distance through fluid before arriving at the cells. Although still inefficient, this method is a considerable improvement over that found in lower forms, where diffusion of digested material and oxygen from sources of intake to cell must pass a greater distance. The circulating fluid (blood) contains red cells in some species. The red color is due to **hemoglobin,** which makes up the major portion of the material found in these cells.

Another deficiency of the nemertine circulatory system is the lack of a pumping station. The only propulsive force for the blood is furnished by the contractions of the animal as it swims.

With the nemertines we have seen the introduction of a transport system which was not present in the metazoa studied earlier. Although very primitive it served the purpose for these simple animals. For more complex animals it would need to be greatly improved; which it was as we shall see.

The nemertines have retained the pocketed gut of planaria which in many ways is an unsatisfactory digestive tract. All of the food is taken in through the mouth and all undigested material comes out the same way. This is a rather awkward way of handling such an important function. A distinct improvement would be a tube extending throughout the body with a mouth at one end and a corresponding opening at the opposite end to permit undigested food to pass out of the body. This would mean the "invention" of a "tube-within-a-tube" body plan. Such a

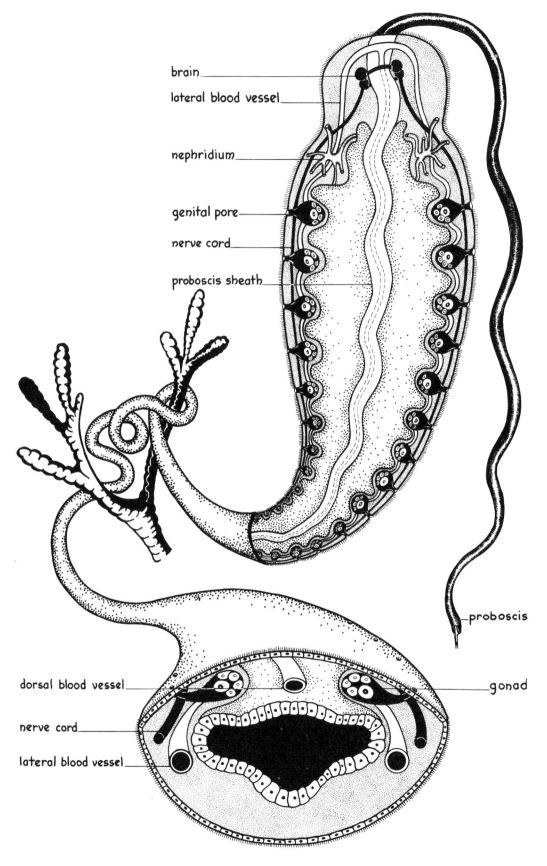

brain

lateral blood vessel

nephridium

genital pore

nerve cord

proboscis sheath

proboscis

dorsal blood vessel

nerve cord

lateral blood vessel

gonad

FIG. 9-14. A longitudinal and cross-section of a nemertine showing the tube-within-a-tube body plan and also the beginnings of a circulatory system.

plan appeared in the next phylum, the **Aschelminthes** which includes the roundworms.

It is interesting to note that not all improvements appeared in any one group of animals. For example, the nemertines produced the circulatory system but they retain the primitive digestive system of the flatworms. The roundworms, on the other hand, evolved the complete digestive tract but they are without a circulatory system. Both of these advances are consolidated in the annelids where we observe the evolution of far more complicated and larger animals.

SUGGESTED SUPPLEMENTARY READINGS

BROWN, F. A., *Selected Invertebrate Types* (New York, John Wiley & Sons, Inc., 1950).

CHANDLER, A. C., and READ, C. P., *Introduction to Parasitology* (New York, John Wiley & Sons, Inc., 1961).

HYMAN, L., *The Invertebrates,* Vol. II, *Platyhelminthes and Rhynchocoela* (New York, McGraw-Hill Book Co., 1951).

NOBLE, E. R., and NOBLE, G. A., *Parasitology, the Biology of Animal Parasites* (Philadelphia, Lea and Febiger, 1961).

PENNAK, R. W., *Fresh-water Invertebrates of the United States* (New York, The Ronald Press, 1953).

WARD, H. B., and WHIPPLE, G. C., EDMONDSON, W. T., ed., *Fresh-water Biology* (New York, John Wiley & Sons, Inc., 1959).

10

The Tube-Within-a-Tube Body Plan

A MIXTURE of widely diverse animals, of which the most important are the nematodes (roundworms) and the rotifers, are placed in the phylum **Aschelminthes.** They all have two characteristics in common: a complete digestive tract, mouth to anus, and they are **pseudocoelmates** (p. 154). Since there is much confusion among taxonomists about the lesser members of the phylum, we shall consider only the classes **Rotifera** and **Nematoda.**

Class Rotifera. These tiny animals are often called "wheelbearers" because their two tufts of cilia on the anterior end, when active, move in such a manner as to appear as two wheels turning in opposite directions (Fig. 10-1). Actually the cilia beat in this manner to propel microorganisms into the mouth during feeding. Rotifers are highly variable in body form, all microscopic in size, and they are abundant both in salt and fresh water. They are, of course, bilaterally symmetrical, and possess a complete digestive tract, although in some forms the anus apparently does not function. A characteristic organ in the gut is the **mastax,** a grinding organ which can be easily observed when in action through the body wall. They also possess a pseudocoelom but no circulatory system.

Class Nematoda. These are the "round-worms," a name which well describes their anatomy (Fig. 10-2). In numbers they exceed all others with the exception of the arthropods and the protozoa. The most notorious members are parasites but the greatest numbers exist as free-living forms in soil and water. Their characteristic whipping movement readily identifies them. Most of them are very small, almost microscopic, although there are a few—the "horsehair worms," for example—that may reach a length of 1 yard. Some of the ascarid parasites of horses may reach a length of 10 to 12 inches.

Their complete digestive tract consists of a slender tube, without pockets, extending from one end of the body to the other. Digested food is absorbed directly through the gut wall and diffuses into the fluid which fills the pseudocoelom, thence to the body cells. This is an inefficient system since it relies to a large extent on diffusion, although the fluid-filled pseudocoelom does permit a much more rapid dispersion of the food and oxygen than was possible without this cavity.

A pair of tubes extend internally along each side of the body, forming **excretory canals,** but they lack any cells comparable to the flame cells found in planaria. The two tubes unite into a single one, which opens ventrally to the outside through a minute **excretory pore.** Another feature of the nematodes is a complex **nervous system** which consists of several nerves extending the length of the body and terminating anteriorly in numerous ganglia.

The body wall contains a thick muscular component, separated into four banks of **muscle cells** extending lengthwise, and so attached that the animal can flex its body only in a dorsal-ventral manner, a rather ineffective method of locomotion in water.

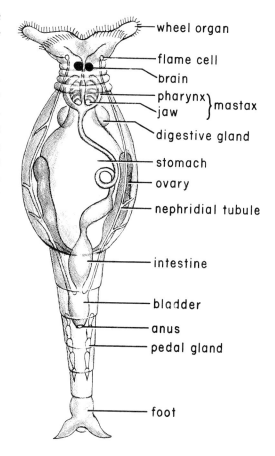

FIG. 10-1. A rotifer.

wheel organ
flame cell
brain
pharynx
jaw   } mastax
digestive gland
stomach
ovary
nephridial tubule
intestine
bladder
anus
pedal gland
foot

In fluids of high viscosity or in soil, however, it is more effective.

The rather elaborate reproductive system lies free in the pseudocoel. Since the sexes are separate, only one set of organs is found in each animal. Females, which are usually larger than the males, possess two ovaries in the shape of long coiled tubes. The two ovaries continue into two **oviducts,** which enlarge to form two **uteri** (singular, **uterus**). These join to form a single short **vagina,** which opens externally on the ventral side in the anterior portion of the body. The mature eggs are stored in the uteri. In the male, sperms are produced in a long coiled tube, the single **testis,** which joins the **vas deferens** and then becomes the **seminal vesicle,** the storage place for the sperm. A pair of bristles at the posterior end aid in conducting the sperm from the male to the female during copulation. The opening of the male reproductive system is close to the posterior end of the animal near the base of the bristles.

Parasitic Nematodes. Because of the economic significance of the parasitic nematodes we will discuss representative forms, particularly those that attack man. Although over 50 different species are human parasites, a still greater number affect man indirectly by their ruthless destruction of his domestic plants and animals. They invade almost every organ of the body, their damage depending on the kind and number of individuals. Like most parasites, the

nematodes tend to remain with a specific host, although they are a little more careless in this regard than some. Occasionally they attack a variety of hosts and may produce a serious disease when they enter a new one. For example, a hog may be riddled with *Trichinella* with no apparent damage, whereas a man with a similar infection is apt to die because he is the "accidental host" while the hog is the normal host. The hog has had trichinella in its tissues so long that it has built up some resistance to the parasite. Since man gets the parasite only occasionally, he has developed little or no resistance. Let us consider several common roundworm parasites.

Ascaris lumbricoides (Fig. 10-3) is a common intestinal parasite of many domestic animals as well as man himself. It is an

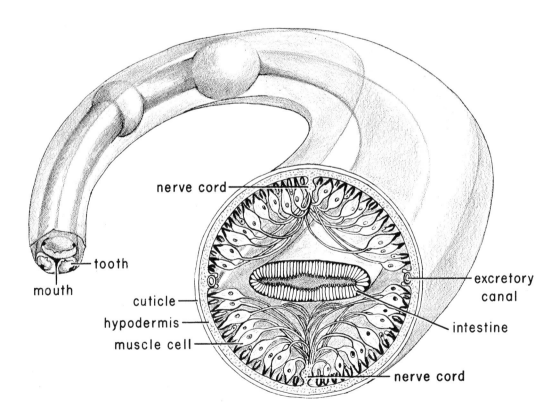

FIG. 10-2. The body plan of the roundworms includes two tubes: one, the gut, within the other, the body wall. This figure shows the anterior end of the worm with its three teeth surrounding the mouth, and a cross-section taken anterior to the gonads.

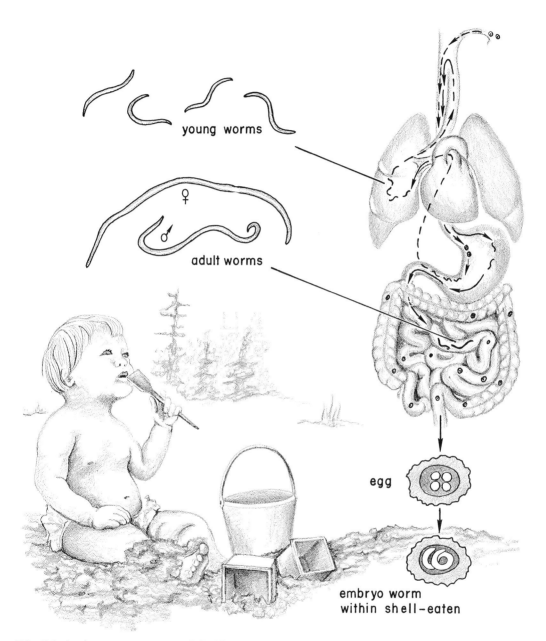

young worms

adult worms

♀

♂

egg

embryo worm
within shell-eaten

FIG. 10-3. A schematic representation of the life cycle of *Ascaris lumbricoides* as it occurs in humans.

excellent example of the usual life cycle of parasitic roundworms, although there are wide modifications. It is not infrequently found in the digestive tract of children, since they are apt to get ascaris eggs on their hands from the soil and transfer them to the mouth. The embryonated eggs pass through the stomach to the intestine where they hatch into tiny worms (0.2–0.3 mm. long). These bore through the intestinal wall into the lymph, then the capillaries, and finally the general circulation. They are carried through the heart to the lungs where they grow somewhat in size. Eventually the larvae break through into the air sacs, migrate up the trachea, and are swallowed, arriving in the intestine for the second time. Here they mature, copulate, and lay eggs which pass out of the host with the feces. The eggs may be picked up directly by another host, or they may become desiccated and blow around in the dust to be engulfed at some later time.

The adult ascaris probably maintains its place in the intestine by active movements, since it does not possess an attachment organ such as the flukes and tape-

worms do. It feeds on the food in the gut by a pumping action of its bulb-like pharynx. To keep from being digested by the enzymes secreted by the host, ascaris, like all intestinal parasites, is protected by a tough **cuticle,** through which probably is secreted substances that counteract the hydrolizing power of the enzymes. Metabolism is primarily anaerobic (without oxygen), since there is very little oxygen in the gut. The only hope for survival is to produce a great many eggs, which it does most effectively. A large female has been known to contain 27,000,000 eggs, 200,000 of which she lays every day. As in all parasites, the chance for any one egg to produce a mature

FIG. 10-4. Life cycle of the common hookworm (*Necator americanus*). The adult worms are shown attached to the lining of the intestine. The fertilized eggs begin development while still in the digestive tract. They pass out with the feces and eventually hatch in the soil where they lie in wait for their next host.

**Normal Host:
Pig and Rat**

GARBAGE

infected pork scraps
and dead rodents

cyst in
muscle
of host

**Accidental Host:
Man**

man becomes ill

host eaten by
man

female burrows
into mucosa where
larvae are deposited

cyst in poorly
cooked pork

adult

intestine

larva

encysted larva

blood vessel carries
larvae to muscle

FIG. 10-5. Life cycle of trichina (*Trichinella spiralis*).

FIG. 10-6. Larval *Trichinella* cysts in the muscles of a rat.

worm is extremely remote, but by this colossal effort to bring forth potential offspring ascaris has been very successful in the world, as attested by its universal occurrence.

A notorious relative of ascaris is the hookworm (*Necator americanus*), which is directly responsible for untold misery and indirectly for the death of millions of people throughout tropical and subtropical regions of the world. People in certain parts of the world are heavily infested which, in part, is responsible for their station in life. It is little wonder that they are lazy and shiftless when their intestinal walls are teeming with hookworms sapping their strength. Children tend to be retarded both physically and mentally which, coupled with extreme poverty and ignorance, dooms them to a life filled with misery, frustration, and servitude.

The adult hookworm differs from ascaris in that the mouth is provided with teeth so it can cling to the soft mucosal lining of the intestine from which it withdraws its food, blood (Fig. 10-4). Fertile eggs pass out with the feces of the host and are deposited on the ground where they hatch into larval worms. After a brief growth period the larvae are ready for their next host. They gain entrance by holding on to the foot or any other part of the body of the host, boring in, and finally getting into the blood stream. They then follow the same path described for ascaris, eventually reaching the intestine.

Preventive measures are so simple that one wonders why there are any cases of hookworm at all. Wearing shoes prevents the worms from getting into the host; proper methods of disposing of human excreta would also stop the infection very swiftly. Both of these methods have been tried with reasonable success but the incidence of hookworm disease is still much too high in this country. Perhaps the most important factor is poverty; if all people were gainfully employed and had an adequate education this disease would be completely eradicated. World-wide measures could stamp it out altogether, but such suggestions are only wishful thinking at the present time.

Another roundworm parasite that is of grave importance to man is **trichina** (*Trichinella spiralis*), a worm whose normal hosts are the pig and rat, although it has been found in other vertebrates as well. Man is an *accidental host* and is therefore perhaps even more severely affected by the parasite. The life cycle of trichinella varies somewhat from the two preceding examples of roundworm parasites (Fig. 10-5). The common source of human infection is through the muscle of the pig, which harbors trichina in its infective stage, small **cysts** containing **larvae** (Fig. 10-6). If these are eaten, uncooked, the tiny worms (1 mm. long) emerge in the intestine where they mature and copulate (Fig. 10-7). The very tiny worms deposited by the female bore through the intestinal wall into the blood stream and distribute themselves through the muscles of the body, attacking particularly those of the tongue, eyes, diaphragm, and ribs. It is this migratory period that is dangerous because, in addition to the mechanical injury that millions of worms can inflict, there is also the likelihood of bacterial infections. The disease at this stage is characterized by high fever, intense muscular pains, and frequently partial paralysis. The intake of a sufficient amount of infected meat can cause death at this time, but if the infection has been light enough not to cause permanent damage to nervous and muscular tissue, the symptoms will subside and the person recover. Infections are far more common than records indicate. For example, a large Midwestern hospital reported that 27 per cent of its autopsies showed positive trichinosis, although none of the deaths was directly caused by that disease.

Preventive measures are even simpler than for hookworm: merely cook pork. There is no treatment for the disease once an infection has gotten under way. It is also well to remember that meat sold on the market is not inspected for trichina, primarily because it is too difficult to detect light infections. One poorly cooked "pink" pork chop can contain thousands of worms, which are adequate to kill a person. It is true that there are fewer and fewer cases of trichinosis reported, probably because the practice of feeding meat scraps to hogs is less prevalent and also because a general war on rats has cut down the rat-hog cycle which normally keeps the worms going.

There are numerous parasitic nematodes that cause bizarre diseases in the tropics, diseases which are normally known only to parasitologists and medical men who are experts in the field of tropical medicine. However, during World War II the tropics became the battleground for many American men and consequently tropical diseases suddenly loomed as a significant health problem. Among the numerous roundworm parasites the one that causes **elephantiasis** (*Wüchereria bancrofti*) is perhaps the most important (Fig. 10-8). The life cycle of this worm differs from that of other nematodes in that it requires two hosts. The larvae, called **microfilariae,** circulate in the blood of the infected person (Fig. 10-9). An interesting adaptation is that these tiny worms come out in the peripheral blood vessels in the evening, a time when the mosquitoes which are the carriers (intermediate host) are active. The mosquito picks up the microfilaria with the blood as it feeds; inside the mosquito the worm grows and eventually makes its way out through the proboscis of the host. During the biting process the microfilaria slips off the proboscis onto the skin of the next host and immediately bores its way in.

FIG. 10-7. This is a photomicrograph of the sectioned digestive tract of a mouse, showing a female *Trichinella* (W) lying very near a venule (V) where she deposits her larvae.

FIG. 10-8. A case of elephantiasis. (From Smith and Gault, *Essentials of Pathology*, 1938, D. Appleton-Century Company.)

Once in the blood stream of the final host it moves into the lymph glands where it becomes mature. The worms become so numerous that they can effectively clog the lymph passages, which results in huge swellings, usually in the extremities. A leg may grow to weigh 100 pounds, hence the name *elephantiasis*.

Preventive measures consist of preventing oneself from being bitten by infected mosquitoes. Light infections are not serious because eventually the body forms new lymph channels so the swelling is re-

duced to normal. The danger lies in continual infection where the same individual is bitten again and again by infected mosquitoes.

Members of this phylum have acquired the rudiments of organ systems which we shall see greatly elaborated in subsequent phyla.

FIG. 10-9. The microfilariae that cause the disease elephantiasis live in the blood of man and can be seen in blood smears taken at certain times of the day. The tiny worm is clearly visible in this picture and its relative size can be determined by comparing it to the small irregular objects which are the white corpuscles.

SUGGESTED SUPPLEMENTARY READINGS

CHANDLER, A. C., and READ, C. P., *Introduction to Parasitology* (New York, John Wiley & Sons, Inc., 1961).

HYMAN, L., *The Invertebrates-Acanthocephala, Aschelminthes, and Entoprocta* (New York, McGraw-Hill Book Co., 1951).

NOBLE, E. R., and NOBLE, G. A., *Parasitology, The Biology of Animal Parasites* (Philadelphia, Lea and Febiger, 1961).

PENNAK, R. W., *Fresh-water Invertebrates of the United States* (New York, The Ronald Press, 1953).

11
Shelled Animals—Mollusks

FROM NOW ON we shall be dealing with **eucoelomate** animals which apparently split off into two divergent stocks, the difference between the two being the manner in which the coelom formed (p. 153). The **Schizocoela** stock gave rise to the mollusks, annelids, and the arthropods, whereas the **Enterocoela** stock gave rise to the echinoderms and the chordates. In both, large, swift-moving animals evolved. Each gave rise to great numbers of species and individuals which dominate the living world today; hence each stock was successful. Let us consider first the schizocoelomate stock

of which the phylum **Mollusca** is an important group.

This phylum includes a wide variety of animals which are well known to anyone. Most of them possess shells which greatly affect their mode of existence and which have been very important in giving us a more or less continuous story of their evolution, because shells produce excellent **fossils.** Fossils are imprints or traces of ancient animals or plants that have been preserved in the earth's crust. Ancestral mollusks appear in Cambrian rocks which were laid down 600 million years ago; throughout

oysters
squid
rockborer
chiton
scallop
mussels
razor clam
tooth-shell
shipworm
cuttlefish
quahog
abalone
conch
octopus
nautilus
whelk
nudibranch

FIG. 11-1. A few marine mollusks and where they live.

the ensuing ages they have prospered, giving rise to millions of species of which at least 80,000 exist on earth today. The phylum includes animals of wide diversity of form, such as the common slugs and snails, oysters and clams, slow moving chitons, swift darting squids, slithering octopuses, and the chambered nautilus of poetic fame. They have invaded most habitats, sea, fresh water, land, and even deserts. A few forms that live in the seas of the world are shown in Fig. 11-1. They constitute a significant part of the world fauna today and are important in our lives also as we shall observe later in this chapter.

The fossil records give us little evidence as to the origin of mollusks. It is generally believed that they were derived from "worm-like" ancestors, although these were not the familiar annelids of today. Larval studies indicate a close relationship with the annelids; but that relationship extends far back in time, since the larval stage of the mollusk, the *trochophore,* shows no segmentation in the mesoderm (Fig. 11-2). It seems rather strange that this group of animals failed to acquire a body arrangement that is so successful among the annelids, arthropods, and chordates. Since the trochophore larva is common to both the mollusks and annelids, the lack of segmentation in this larva may mean that these two great groups of animals split off and went their separate ways before segmentation was introduced.

The molluscan body plan has certain characteristic features that appear consistently in all of the species in the group. One of these is a muscular organ, the **foot,** an organ which serves for several types of locomotion. The snail and chiton (Fig. 11-3) crawl on it, the clam digs a wedge-shaped path with it and also walks on it, while the squid uses it to capture prey as well as to crawl over the ocean floor (Fig. 11-1). Another new character is the **mantle,** which is an envelope of tissue covering the entire animal. The mantle gives rise to the **shell,** common in so many members of this group. The original shell appears in the larva as a product of the mantle epithelium and gradually expands as the animal grows.

Those mollusks that possess shells use them as an abode which is readily available for a retreat in case of danger and, more important for land forms, to prevent desiccation. Although a clam is usually safe in its tightly closed shell, it is nevertheless preyed upon by the starfish, which has the ability to open the shell and devour the soft body parts (Fig. 14-6). Some members of the phylum have no shells, such as the slug and octopus. They are protected only by their coloration, their habits, or the ability of some to discharge a cloud of inky material into the water which totally obscures them. Still others secrete a mucus that is particularly distasteful to enemies of the mollusk.

The digestive tract is tubular and is coiled in various ways in the different groups of the mollusks (Fig. 11-4). Many of these animals are provided with a peculiar rasping tongue, the **radula,** which is found nowhere else in the animal kingdom. It is used in loosening algae from surfaces, and in tearing bits of plants loose as the animal feeds. Some are carnivorous with radulas constructed somewhat differently than for the herbivores but just as effective in tearing bits of animal tissue for food. The radula is a long ribbon of tough tissue, to which many sharp teeth are attached. Muscles are arranged so as to pull the radula back and forth over a projection which is thrust out through the mouth while feeding. It is an interesting and clever device to facilitate feeding.

The Clam

The fresh-water clam, although differing in some respects from other molluscan forms, is a familiar representative of the entire phylum. It is a bilaterally symmetrical, "headless" animal, enclosed in a double shell, usually found partly buried in the sand of lakes or streams. By means of its hatchet-shaped, muscular foot, which protrudes from the shell, it is able to plow slowly along, feeding on microscopic forms of life.

When the clam "walks" the foot is thrust forward between the two valves of the shell. This permits blood to flow into the many **sinuses** of the foot, causing it to swell and thus form an anchor. As the retractor muscles contract, the clam is drawn forward an inch or so. The blood then is

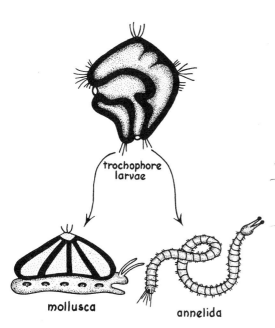

trochophore larvae

mollusca   annelida

FIG. 11-2. The ancestral trochophore larva from which both the mollusca and annelida are thought to have been derived.

forced out of the foot so that it thins down again and can be withdrawn from the sand. The process is repeated with each step (Fig. 11-5) and a wedge-shaped path is left behind.

If a clam is molested, its foot is hastily withdrawn into the shell by the **anterior** and **posterior retractor muscles,** and the valves are slowly and tightly shut by two powerful muscles, the **anterior** and **posterior adductors.** This is the only means the clam has of barring its door to intruders. To attempt to pull the valves of the shell open is a nearly hopeless task, unless a thin-bladed knife is first inserted through the edge of the shell to sever the large adductor muscles. The starfish, however, has a novel way of opening the valves. It circumvents the clam, attaches its tube feet to the two valves of the shell, and exerts a steady pull. The pull is resisted by the clam for some time, but finally the muscles are exhausted and begin to relax (Fig. 14-6).

The two valves of the clam are hinged dorsally by a ligament, which can be observed when the adductor muscles are cut. The shell itself is usually oval in shape, with a blunt anterior end. Along the dorsal surface is the **umbo,** a bulbous structure which is the oldest part of the shell. From it

FIG. 11-3. Chitons are primitive mollusks and probably resemble the ancient forms that gave rise to our modern mollusks. Note the eight overlapping shells on the dorsal side. Chitons live among the rocks on the seashore and are active at night.

appear the **concentric lines of growth,** which can be counted to determine the age of the clam.

The outer layer of the shell, the **periostracum,** is produced first, then the **prismatic** layer, and finally the innermost part,

FIG. 11-4. Modifications in the body plan of various kinds of mollusks.

the **nacreous** layer. The periostracum is rough and can resist the weak acids produced by the dissolved carbon dioxide in the water. The prismatic layer, which gives strength to the shell, is produced from crystals of calcium carbonate, lying perpendicular to the outer layer. The pearly layer, the portion that interests the shell collector, is also composed of calcium carbonate crystals that are arranged parallel with the shell, resulting in an extremely smooth iridescent layer. The mantle deposits this layer over any irregularities that occur, either in the shell or over loose particles that may lodge in the mantle itself. This is the origin of pearls. Foreign bodies, such as grains of sand or the larvae

of certain parasitic worms, sometimes become attached to the mantle or lodged between the mantle and the shell. In such a case, layer after layer of calcium carbonate (pearl) is secreted over the particle, eventually resulting in a pearl. The Japanese produce pearls artificially by inserting glass beads into the mantles of clams or oysters. After several years the pearls can be removed and sold on the market. These are true pearls artificially produced (Fig. 11-6).

Once the valves of the clam are opened, a soft body enveloped in a mantle is exposed. The mantle simply consists of two thin sheets of tissue, or **lobes.** The posterior free ends are muscular, and come together to form the **ventral incurrent** and the **dorsal excurrent** siphons, which permit water to move in and out by ciliary action of the inner mantle cavity (Fig. 11-7). Each side of the mantle adheres to the inner nacreous surface of the two valves. At these points of adhesion, the **pallial line** is formed on the shell. The heavy muscular foot lies directly beneath the mantle and extends anteriorly from the mid-portion of the body. Just posterior to the foot and beneath the mantle are two pairs of **gills.** The dorsal portion of the body, directly above the muscular foot, contains the internal organs of the animal and is called the **visceral mass.**

The four plate-like gills are attached from a point between the siphons to the region just opposite the umbo (Fig. 11-7). They hang freely between the mantle and the visceral mass. Each gill is made up of two plates, the **lamellae,** which are held together by bridges of tissue. The cavity between the lamellae is divided into separate **water tubes.** The lamellae are thrown into vertical folds called **gill bars** and are reinforced by chitinous rods. In addition horizontal rows of ciliated pores, or **ostia,** perforate the lamellae through which water enters the gill. The water tubes lead to a dorsally situated **supra-branchial chamber** that continues to the posterior portion of

FIG. 11-5. Locomotion of a clam.

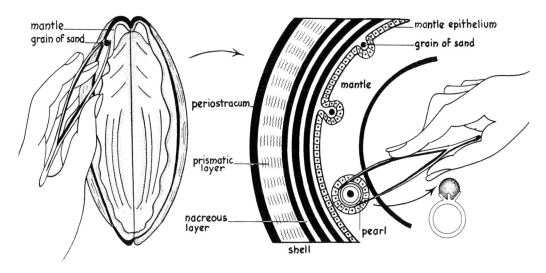

FIG. 11-6. Artificial production of pearls.

the gill and opens into the excurrent siphon. Blood from the veins circulates through tiny vessels within the gill to be aerated before returning to the heart. In this manner the constant stream of water flowing through the gills supplies the animal with oxygen.

The beating cilia of the gills and the mantle draw water and food into the mantle cavity through the incurrent siphon.

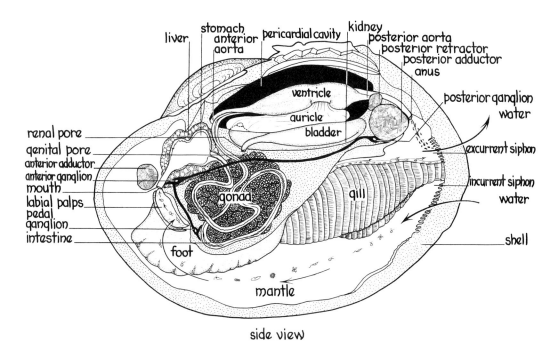

side view

FIG. 11-7. The internal anatomy of the clam, side view.

FIG. 11-8. Schematic drawing of the circulatory system of the clam.

The siphon opening serves to strain out all but very minute food particles such as algae, protozoa, and bits of debris. Mucus secreted by the gills catches these particles which are borne anteriorly by cilia to two pairs of triangular, ciliated **labial palps.** The surfaces of the upper part of the mantle cavity and the gills and those of the labial palps are covered with rapidly beating cilia which function in carrying food to the mouth (Fig. 11-7). The lower part of the mantle cavity, also lined with beating cilia, collects the heavier particles of debris that cannot be used as food. Material that has been rejected at the mouth as undesirable as food and the heavier fragments that have accumulated in the lower mantle chamber are massed together in clots of mucus. When these have reached consider-

able size, they are forcibly ejected from the animal by a rapid current of water set in motion by a quick contraction of the adductor muscles. In the buccal cavity more mucus is secreted and the food is carried through the short **esophagus** to the dorsally located, sac-like **stomach.** A pair of **digestive glands** joins the stomach through ducts. Digestion occurs both in the stomach and in the glands themselves. In some species of clams the **crystalline style,** a gelatinous rod resembling a pouch or caecum of the stomach, secretes a cellulose- and starch-digesting enzyme. The intestine, leading from the stomach, coils several times through the visceral mass, much of which is the yellow-colored, branched **gonad,** before it turns dorsally to pass through the **pericardial cavity** and the heart. Absorption takes place throughout the length of the intestine, particularly in the portion of the rectum which passes through the **ventricle** of the heart. The **typhlosole** is a longitudinal fold in the rectum. Posteriorly, the intestine opens through the **anus,** located within the excurrent siphon, where the feces are carried away with the outgoing current of water (Fig. 11-7).

The **heart,** lying in the dorsal pericardial cavity, forces the blood through the circulatory system of the clam (Figs. 11-7, 8). The **ventricle,** which is joined by two laterally situated **auricles,** pumps the blood forward into an **anterior aorta,** supplying the muscular foot and viscera, and posteriorly, through the **posterior aorta,** supplying the rectum and the mantle. Blood from those parts of the body supplied by the aortas, with the exception of the mantle, is returned through a vein to the **nephridia,** or **kidneys,** for the elimination of waste products. It then moves to the gills to pick up oxygen and eliminate carbon dioxide. Oxygenated blood is returned from the gills on each side of the clam to the corresponding auricle. The mantle also returns oxygenated blood to the auricles. Unlike the circulatory system of some other animals, some of the arteries and veins of the clam are not joined by capillaries, but end in **sinuses,** without cellular lining. Food and oxygen carried directly to these sinuses can pass into intercellular spaces and are not restricted to absorption through diffusion. This is particularly true in the region of the foot where blood sinuses are numerous.

Two U-shaped kidneys lie ventral to the pericardial cavity (Figs. 11-7, 8). These function in the removal of wastes from the blood and other fluid of the pericardial cavity. Each is a tubular organ, folded upon itself and divided into **glandular** and **bladder**-like parts. A ciliated opening from the pericardial chamber into the glandular portion drains this region, while the bladder region opens into the

path of the excurrent water, thus carrying wastes out of the body.

Three pairs of ganglia and their connecting nerve cords constitute the nervous system of the fresh-water clam (Fig. 11-9). Each pair of ganglia controls the body region in which it is located: the **anterior** or **cerebropleural ganglia** on either side of the mouth; the **pedal ganglia** in the foot; and the **posterior** or **visceral ganglia** ventral to the posterior adductor muscle. Each pair of ganglia is connected by a **commissure** and by two **connectives,** the **cerebrovisceral** and **cerebropedal,** to the other ganglionic pairs. Small nerves extend from the ganglia to the body surface and the muscles. Although the clam is a highly specialized animal in many respects, its nervous system is comparatively primitive. First of all, there is little evidence of a brain. The sensory apparatus is limited to sensory cells on the siphon margins, tactile organs on the mantle, and some areas which are believed to be sensitive to chemicals. Most of these structures resemble similar parts of lower type animals. Clams are slow, sluggish animals and the sensory system required is usually relatively simple.

Fresh-water clams, for the most part,

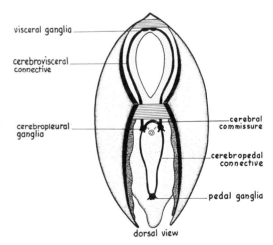

FIG. 11-9. Anterio-dorsal schematic drawing of the nervous system of the clam.

glochidia in gill

sperm

glochidia attach to
gills and fins of fish

young clams

FIG. 11-10. Life cycle of the clam.

are dioecious, but some are hermaphroditic. The **ovaries** and **testes,** yellow in color and surrounding the **intestine,** constitute much of the visceral mass (Fig. 11-7). The sperms of the male are liberated from the testes through the **genital pore,** just ventral to the aperture of the bladder portion of the kidney. From here they are carried through the body to be discharged through the excurrent siphon. As water is carried into the incurrent siphon of the female it may, purely by chance, carry sperm cells with it. These then enter the **suprabranchial chamber** of the gills where the **ova** discharged from the ovary await fertilization. After fertilization, the eggs are drawn into the water tubes of the gills and attached to them by mucus. While the tubes are carrying eggs they become enlarged and are called **brood chambers.** After a period of development, the zygotes become small larval **glochidia** (singular, *glochidium*), complete with two valves and a larval

thread (Fig. 11-10). Many species develop a hooked valve. At this stage they are discharged into the water through the excurrent siphon of the female where they may float in the currents or sink to the bottom. There is no free movement of the glochidium at this time, other than the opening and closing of its valves. Hooked forms try to attach themselves to any fish with which they may come in contact, whereas the hookless forms grasp the gills of fishes by means of their valves. In time, the epithelium of the fish encases the glochidium in a cyst-like case. During this period the young clam is entirely parasitic, receiving nourishment from its host through absorption. After the adult organs have developed, the glochidium bursts out of the cyst and sinks to the bottom as an independent free-living animal.

Most pelecypods (from the class name —Pelecypoda) are bottom dwellers. Some species of clams even burrow far down into the sand and push their siphons up into the water. Other forms, such as the **oyster,** are permanently attached to rocks or similar objects beneath the water.

There are many species of *shipworms* of which *Teredo navalis* is a common one (Fig. 11-1). It was not until the Dutch zoologist G. Snellius was appointed in 1733 to study the damage done to dykes that the true identity of the mollusk was discovered. The body is long and worm-like, and the small shell is confined to the tip where it functions as an effective cutting tool. Smooth and perfectly circular burrows are made in wood pilings and floating timbers. The animal passes all of the wood scrappings through its digestive tract, and owing to cellulases and other enzymes it is one of the few creatures that is able to obtain energy from this source. It therefore depends only to a very limited extent on food coming from the sea.

The reproductive powers of the shipworms are dramatic, and consequently even though their life span is no more than one year, they manage to infect practically all wood that remains in sea water for any length of time, thus doing untold damage to docks and wharfs. Millions have been spent in research for protecting wood against the invasion of these creatures.

Other Mollusks

Members of the class **Amphineura** are the most primitive forms among the mollusks. In this group are the chitons, which most nearly resemble the probable worm-like ancestors of the phylum (Fig. 11-3). Their dorsal covering of eight calcareous plates has led some biologists to believe that these plates may be the remnant of segmentation. The ocean-inhabiting chitons attach themselves so securely to rocks that it is almost impossible to pry them loose. If they are dislodged they promptly curl up into a ball. They are principally "vegetarians," feeding on various kinds of marine algae.

In most chitons the sexes are separate.

One investigator, Grave, found that the sexual activity of one species was influenced by moonlight. It is generally believed that periods of moonlight are preferred by this animal when the tides are low, a condition most favorable for successful spawning. Coloration in chitons varies, ranging from turquoise and slaty blue to gray and white. Most of the Amphineura are "shy" animals and tend to avoid daylight, although there are some species with "furry" mantles that do sally forth in the daytime.

The class **Scaphopoda** includes several "headless" species, the best known being *Dentalium*, the "elephant's tooth" (Fig. 11-1). It has a muscular foot which is modified for burrowing into the sand and is therefore quite sharply pointed. Its elongated body is encased in a tapering shell. Unlike most mollusks, this animal bears no gills and the mantle alone takes care of respiration.

Some of the most interesting and varied forms of the mollusks belong to the class **Gastropoda.** They range in size from microscopic forms to the large whelks and abalones (Fig. 11-11). Although most members of this class possess some kind of shell, forms that are entirely without a shell also appear. Some have adapted themselves to terrestrial life as well as the usual aquatic habitat. The most common form is the snail, an animal familiar to almost everyone. The snail is often observed wending its way slowly on the leaf of a water plant or along a sandy-bottomed pool. It moves by gliding over a secreted mucus path, using its flattened muscular foot which forms the ventral surface of its body. The movement of the snail closely resembles the gliding movement of planaria. In some species the foot is actually ciliated to aid the gliding motion; in others movement occurs by rhythmic muscular contraction of the foot. The land snail (Fig. 11-12) has a definite head which bears two pairs of tentacles, one short pair, supposedly the center of the

FIG. 11-11. (Top) The knobbed whelk (*Busycon carica*) laying its string of egg capsules. This large whelk inhabits the eastern coast of the United States.

(Bottom) This bright green abalone (*Haliotis*) is popular as a sea food on the western coast. It inhabits the Pacific Ocean; this one came from the Great Barrier Reef.

sense of smell, and a longer pair with a simple eye at the tip of each. In water forms the eyes are situated at the base of the tentacles.

Judging from its coiled shell, one would expect the snail to have an asymmetrical body. This is only partly true, however, for the head and the elongated flattened foot are bilaterally symmetrical, whereas the remainder of the body, which composes the visceral mass, is asymmetrical, parts of the digestive and circulatory systems being coiled. The shell of the gastropods is univalved, that is, one piece, but the single valve may vary in shape from tiny flattened spirals to long spindle shapes or even turban or slipper-like forms.

Originally snails were marine forms, but as some species migrated into fresh water and subsequently some of these took up life on land there was a gradual loss of the gills as well as other structures on the left side of the body. The more primitive marine forms that have retained the two gills are members of the order **Prosobranchiata,** while the fresh-water forms with the right gill remaining are in the order **Opisthobranchiata.** Those that invaded the land lost their gills and evolved a **lung,** hence are placed in the order **Pulmonata.** Members of the Prosobranchiata also possess a plate (**operculum**) to cover the aperture when they are completely withdrawn into their shell. Some of the land snails have returned to fresh water, but the lung is retained. Such forms must come to the surface of the water occasionally for a supply of oxygen, particularly during hot weather.

Snails occur in nearly all parts of the world, even in the Arctic and high snow-covered Alps. Some of the fresh-water snails, such as species of *Lymnaea* and *Heliosoma,* are able to survive for several weeks in cakes of ice, provided they are frozen gradually. Movements of these snails can be observed through the ice. Many snails pass the winter in an inactive state,

although some remain active throughout the year. Some aquatic snails are able to hibernate when the water dries up, and with the return of moisture they become active again. Land snails are active only during the warmer parts of the year in temperate zones and show greatest activity at night or immediately following a light rain. As cold weather approaches they seek a protected place for hibernation. During this quiescent period, a membrane is formed over the aperture of the shell, protecting the animal from desiccation.

FIG. 11-12. Land snails such as this one (*Helix aspersa*) have a part of their mantle modified into an air breathing organ so they are at home on land. The eyes appear at the tips of the two large tentacles.

With the exception of a very few snails, the West Coast abalone (Fig. 11-11) being one of them, snails are harmful to man. The herbivorous land snails, especially those that have been accidentally introduced into new regions, such as the giant African snail, cause considerable damage to vegetation. Some forms serve as intermediate hosts for parasitic flatworms, such as the human blood flukes causing schistosomiasis (see p. 236). It is difficult to calculate the damage done in this fashion by snails, but it must be tremendous. In for-

FIG. 11-13. A sea hare (*Tethys californica*) from the California coast. These large slugs secrete a purplish fluid when disturbed. This one had just completed laying its eggs when taken.

mer times snails were an important source of food for man, but this is negligible today.

The **slugs** are gastropods that do not bear shells. Some are large and drab such as the sea hare (Fig. 11-13). The nudibranch, sometimes called the sea slug, does have a shell during the larval stage but it is lacking in the adult. In other respects it resembles the snail (Fig. 11-14). The name *slug* was apparently given to the lifeless preserved laboratory specimen which takes on a drab, collapsed appearance after it has been exposed to light and preservative. When observed in its natural habitat on rocky coasts, however, these colorful animals are found to be most inappropriately named. Much of their beauty is due to their highly colored translucent gill-like filaments that extend some distance above their backs and are constantly waving in the ocean currents. Their exquisite beauty can only be appreciated when observed under natural conditions.

Other very interesting relatives of the snail are the **pteropods,** or sea butterflies. Their fleshy foot is modified into a pair of wings which make it possible for these tiny creatures to skip and sail over the surface of the sea. They travel in vast numbers, resembling butterflies in their flight, and some of them swim among the icebergs around Greenland where they serve as

the chief food for the whalebone whales.

While the gastropods were of economic significance to ancient man, the pelecypods are most important to modern man. Clam chowder, sautéed scallops, and oyster cocktails have become favorite forms of sea food all over the world. The so-called American oyster, *Crassostrea virginica,* is so commercially profitable that it is cultured and harvested in a very efficient manner. Millions of dollars are involved in this industry. The shells of bivalves were used by primitive man for household utensils and even today find their way into our lives. Bits of shell that are cut and polished into buttons are products of fresh-water clams, and in this day of "substitutes," men still fasten themselves in their shirts by means of these pearly gadgets. The most cherished product of bivalves are the rare jewels secreted by the mantle of fresh-water clams and pearl oysters.

Members of the class **Cephalopoda** are the most highly organized of the mollusks and include the largest species of the invertebrate animals. The head region, as the name implies, is large and well developed, unlike most of the preceding groups. Most forms of this class bear two large complex eyes, resembling the eyes of vertebrates. Some have continuous shells, such as the shell of the *Nautilus* (Fig. 11-15), a member of the group immortalized by Oliver Wendell Holmes in his poem, "The Chambered Nautilus." In others, such as the **cuttlefish** (*Sepia*) and the **squid,** the shell is located internally. In addition to a generally large, fleshy body, the cephalopods usually have long muscular **arms,** or **tentacles,** which are modified portions of the foot.

A very common cephalopod and one that has become an important animal in nerve physiological research is the squid, particularly *Loligo,* which inhabits our eastern seaboard (Fig. 11-16). In the oceans of the world other species abound varying in size from 1 inch long to giant forms 20 or more feet with tentacles 30 feet long. Fossil remains indicate that squids were one of the most numerous animals during prehistoric times.

The tapering body of the squid, which suggests an arrowhead or rocket, enables it to dart through water with lightning-like speed. This is accomplished by jet propulsion. In emergencies the water within the mantle cavity is forcibly ejected through the siphon which propels the squid in the opposite direction with considerable speed (Figs. 11-17 and 11-18). For ordinary swimming the squid employs its lateral muscular fins which are sufficiently strong to permit forward and backward movement at slow speeds. In spite of the fact that the squid is a rapid swimmer, it is often caught by large fish and some whales. When it is hard pressed by its enemy, it will discharge an inky fluid into the siphon, thus spreading a cloud of murky water which obscures the vision, and perhaps numbs the olfactory organs of the enemy. Thus the squid possesses a defensive device which man has only recently used in warfare.

Squids have still another protective device which, though present in many other animals, is developed to a high degree. This is its capacity to change color. Below their thin epidermis are complex **chromatophores** which are color-bearing structures. It can change from pale white to a deep purple in a matter of seconds. When frightened the squid puts on a most remarkable demonstration of color change. By examining a young squid under the low power of a microscope one can observe how this color change is accomplished.

The chromatophores are multicellular bodies made up of numerous muscles attached to the walls of an elastic sac which is filled with pigment. The color change is brought about by the relative tension of the muscles which enlarge or diminish the size of the sac. Whereas the effect is somewhat the same as that produced by the melanophores in vertebrates (p. 481),

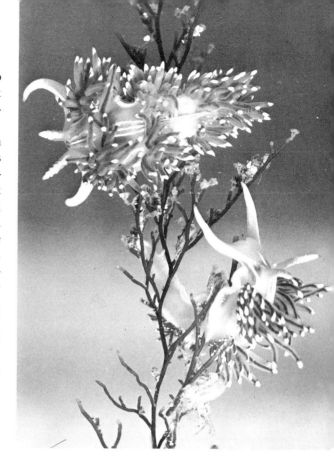

FIG. 11-14. The nudibranchs are without gills and breathe through their skin, which is often thrown up into papilla-like structures that function somewhat like gills do. (Top). These (*Hermissenda crassicornis*) are yellow-green in color and are about an inch long.

(Bottom). This nudibranch (*Hexabranchus imperialis*) inhabits the corals on the Great Barrier Reef. It is brilliant red.

FIG. 11-15. The chambered nautilus, a cephalopod mollusk, lives in the deep waters (1,800 ft.) of the South Pacific. Its shell shown here as it appears from the outside (left) and inside (right) is composed of many chambers, the last and most spacious being occupied by the animal. The picture on the right is an X-ray photograph.

FIG. 11-16. Members of the class Cephalopoda are conspicuous by their many tentacles or arms and their large complex eyes. The squid (*Loligo*) is a common member of the class. This one is resting on the bottom of an aquarium. Note the siphon just below the eye which controls the squid's direction of movement. Also note the contracted chromatophores which cause the animal to appear light in color.

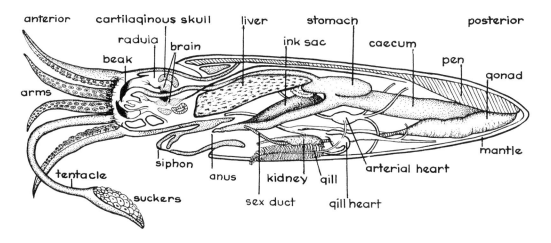

FIG. 11-17. The internal anatomy of the squid.

the anatomy of the chromatophores is quite different.

The squid is supported internally by two kinds of skeletons. One consists of the so-called **pen** which, in *Loligo,* is composed of chitin and lies in the mantle. The other is composed of cartilage and makes up a skull enclosing the brain. The cartilage is remarkably similar to that found in vertebrates which is another case of convergent evolution.

Another highly modified structure in the squid is the foot which is composed of ten muscular **arms** each of which possesses sucking disks. These are modified for different functions. One pair (sometimes specified as the tentacles) is longer than the others and is used in capturing prey (Fig. 11-18). The victim is held by the shorter arms while it is being crushed by the **mandibles** and torn into fine bits by the **radula.** The lowest left arm in males is modified for the transfer of sperm capsules to the female during the breeding season. During swimming the arms are clustered tightly lending a fusiform shape to the entire animal, the shape which resists movement in the water least.

Internally the organs resemble those of other mollusks. The digestive system begins with the long esophagus which terminates in the sac-like stomach. A large blind sac, the **caecum,** extends posteriorly (actually dorsally) to the end of the animal. The digestive tract continues as the intestine terminating in the mantle cavity, a handy arrangement for getting rid of wastes, much like in the clam. The large liver lies near the esophagus. The paired kidneys also have their excretory exit in the region of the siphon.

The circulatory system is quite unique in that it has two types of hearts. One (arterial heart) pumps arterial blood throughout the body, and the second type consists of two hearts (branchial hearts), one located at the base of each of the two gills. These hearts receive the venous blood from all over the body and pump it through the gills to the arterial heart.

The nervous system is composed of several large ganglia (brain) arranged in a ring around the esophagus. Under the mantle near the head there is a pair of star-shaped ganglia from which radiate a number of giant nerve fibers. These innervate the mantle and are responsible for the rapid contraction of the muscle in this organ when jet propulsion is required. These huge single nerve fibers have become popular with nerve physiologists because they are several hundred times larger than vertebrate nerve fibers. Because of their size they are much easier to use when it is necessary to insert tiny electrodes in determining the characteristics of the nerve impulse.

The squid is aware of its external world through the usual sense organs. It has a pair of **statocysts** located in cavities in the skull which serve as organs of equilibrium. Light stimuli are received by a rather remarkable eye, one that resembles in many respects that of vertebrates. The eye is made up of a transparent cornea, a pigmented iris, a more or less spherical lens located in a vitreous chamber, and a retina. The arrangement of the rods is the opposite of that in the vertebrate eye (Fig.

27-6). Its evolutionary significance is discussed in a later chapter (p. 766).

During the breeding season the mature single gonad practically fills the posterior end of the squid. In the male a complicated system of glands package the sperm cells into **spermatophores.** These are "handed over" to the female during courtship, and the sperms are released from them and then fertilize the eggs. The females possess **nidomental glands** which produce the jelly in which the eggs are embedded. Fertilized eggs develop directly into tiny squids which resemble the adults. They swim about in "schools" for some time, feeding on minute marine organisms.

Rather interesting behavior patterns are associated with mating in the squid, some of which were known and described

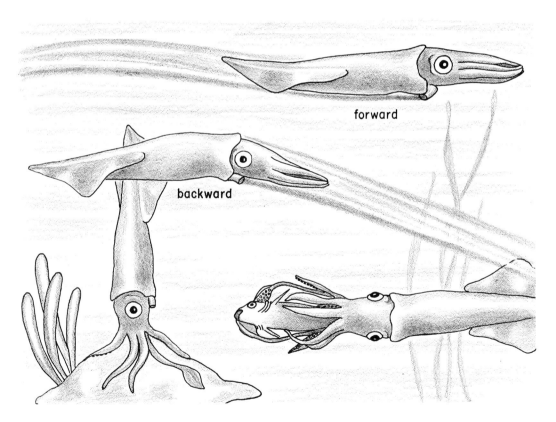

forward

backward

FIG. 11-18. During locomotion the squid forces water through its siphon which results in its rapid forward and backward movements. The direction it moves is controlled by the siphon. When laying eggs the female assumes the position shown at the lower left. The egg cases are shown attached to a rock.

FIG. 11-19. Cephalopoda. The octopus or devilfish (*Octopus*) is completely naked and has eight very long powerful arms, well provided with suckers, which aid the animal in crawling over rocks in search of crabs which are its main source of food. Its heavy horny jaws are used in cracking the shells of crabs and the radula tears the flesh in tiny bits that are eaten. Most octopuses are small and relatively harmless, although they continue to maintain their diabolical reputation.

In the top picture the animal is resting. Note the large siphon which is effective in swimming.

The same specimen is swimming in the bottom picture. Note that it is only slightly more awake than when completely at rest.

by Aristotle over 2,000 years ago. A sexually active male is conspicuous by the presence of a spot at the base of the third arm which alternately comes and goes and undoubtedly stimulates the female to approach him. This she does by swimming in an erratic manner at the same time vibrating her arms. The male then swims alongside of the female occasionally embracing her with his arms. He then places his spermatophores, which he retrieves from his siphon with his left fourth arm, into or near her mantle cavity. This entire process requires only a few seconds. Sometime later the female squeezes out a long tube of jelly-like material containing eggs. These are fertilized by the sperm cells which are in the immediate vicinity. The female then attaches the egg mass to a rock while she is in a vertical position. Owing to the shape of the egg masses they have been known for centuries as "dead man's fingers" (Fig. 11-18), easily observed by anyone interested in marine life.

The octopus (Fig. 11-19), famed in legend as a killer, is actually a very shy animal. Its food does not usually include humans although some reaching a length of 28 feet cause trouble, if provoked. The bulbous and flexible body of the octopus possesses muscular arms that are fortified with powerful suckers. It usually lurks in shady underwater caverns awaiting its prey, which it seizes with quick movements of the arms. A siphon, similar to that of the squid, enables the octopus to swim, but it more commonly crawls over rocks. Since it is so ambulatory underwater one wonders why it has not moved onto land during its long evolution.

In the mollusks we have seen a very successful group of animals with highly diverse body structure and a high degree of complexity. The coelom is small and rudimentary, although the organ systems have evolved to a point to permit the development of a large body, indeed one of the largest. Their circulatory system is sufficiently good to permit rapid movement. However, their nervous system is primitive in that it has no well-defined brain, the brain being clearly present in all subsequent higher forms. In the next phylum we shall see this system more centralized, the coelom expanded, and the introduction of a new type of body organization, segmentation.

SUGGESTED SUPPLEMENTARY READINGS

BUCHSBAUM, R., *Animals without Backbones* (Chicago, University of Chicago Press, 1948).

GILLETTE, K., and McNEILL, F., *The Great Barrier Reef and Adjacent Isles* (Sydney, Australia, The Coral Press Pty. Ltd., 1959).

KEYNES, R. D., "The Nerve Impulses and the Squid," *Scientific American,* 199(2) (December, 1958), 83.

LANE, C. E., "The Teredo," *Scientific American,* 204(2) (February, 1961), 132.

MACGINITIE, G. E., *Natural History of Marine Animals* (New York, McGraw-Hill Book Co., 1949).

RICKETTS, E. F., and CALVIN, J., *Between Pacific Tides* (Stanford, Stanford University Press, 1939).

WILSON, D. P., *They Live in the Sea* (London, Wm. Collins & Sons, 1947).

YONGE, C. M., *The Seashore* (London, Wm. Collins & Sons, 1949).

12
Segmented Animals—Annelids

THE FEATURES initiated in earlier phyla are further developed in the phylum **Annelida,** and a new one is added. This is **segmentation,** or **metamerism,** which is one of the most obvious differences noted in these animals from the ones previously studied. These are serially similar parts, conspicuous on both the outside and the inside of the body. Internal organs are repeated in every segment, each part resembling all others in most respects. There are modifications, however, in certain body regions, as we shall see. There is an intricate connection between the segments, so that the animal is a coordinated whole. Segmentation is retained in higher forms such as the arthropods and the chordates, and is therefore a feature that has contributed toward the greater complexity of animal bodies.

The members of the phylum Annelida are mostly marine worms (Fig. 12-1). They abound in the oceans and live near the shore and hide in the sand in burrows. Since they form the basis for further development, it is necessary to examine this group of animals carefully, which we shall do by studying two representatives, the sandworm (*Nereis*), and the common earthworm

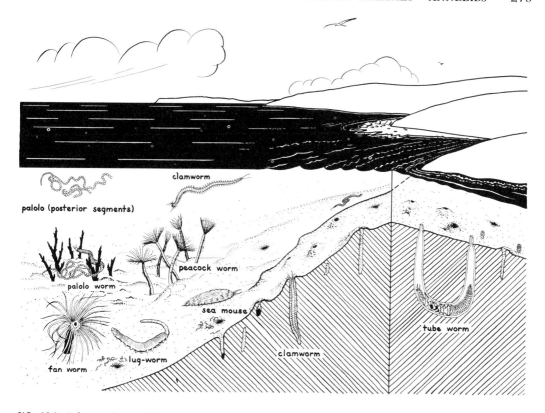

FIG. 12-1. A few marine annelids in their natural habitats.

(*Lumbricus*). Of these, *Nereis* is more typical because it is aquatic and possesses more of the characteristics of the phylum. The earthworm, on the other hand, is terrestrial and in many respects is quite unlike most annelids.

Nereis

Nereis, the common "sandworm" or "clamworm" (Fig. 12-2), lives in shallow water on the sandy shores of most oceans of the world, where it is found in burrows with its head and tentacles protruding slightly. When small animals venture too close, the worm suddenly everts its heavily armed proboscis, seizes its prey, and drags it into the burrow to be devoured. The worm leaves its burrow during the breeding season, but only rarely does it leave otherwise.

The segments of *Nereis* are conspicuous externally, especially because each one possesses a pair of laterally placed paddles, called **parapods,** which function like oars on a boat to propel the animal through the water. In addition, snakelike undulations of the body aid in swimming. Paired bunches of bristles (**setae**), located in the parapodia, hold the animal in its burrow, should an outside force attempt to remove it. The head is a distinct structure well provided with sense organs in the form of four eyes, and two pairs of tentacles which appear to be tactile in function (Fig. 12-3). There is a protrusible pharynx which terminates in a pair of fierce looking jaws. The sturdy muscular body is covered with a cuticle which takes on an iridescent sheen in the sunlight.

The tube-within-a-tube body plan is conspicuously evident when one studies *Nereis* internally (Fig. 12-4). The organs are serially repeated in each segment with the exception of the first and the last. The gut, a straight tube passing from mouth to anus, is surrounded by a sheet of tissue, the **peritoneum,** which forms the walls of the **coelom,** a very important cavity. The coelom functions in nutrition. A large portion of the food and waste products diffuse into the coelomic fluid and through it reach their ultimate destination.

The circulatory system consists of tubes to which the blood is confined throughout its circuit, quite different from the **open** system of the mollusks. However, contraction of the large blood vessels serves the function of the heart. Tiny capillaries allow rapid exchange of oxygen and carbon dioxide, as well as food and waste products. This type of **closed** system is present in most higher forms. The blood contains hemoglobin which is free in the plasma.

Nereis receives its oxygen and elim-inates its carbon dioxide through the thin walls of the parapods. The constant waving movement of these organs facilitates rapid gas exchange. The excretory system consists of tiny tubular "kidneys" called **nephridia,** a pair in each segment. The internal opening, the **nephrostome,** is a ciliated funnel into which coelomic fluid bearing waste products enters. As it passes through the long tubule, the wastes are concentrated and excreted through the outside opening, the **nephridiopore.** The glandular portion of the tubule is a special type of tissue that has the unique properties of accumulating and excreting nitrogenous wastes.

Nereis shows more varied and specific responses to the external world than are found in lower forms. Its four eyes and sensitive tentacles aid the worm in getting around in dim light. The centralization of

FIG. 12-2. The "sandworm" (*Nereis*) is a common inhabitant of our Atlantic Coastal waters. It lives in a burrow in mud or sand from which its head and tentacles protrude. Small animals passing near enough are snatched and devoured. During the breeding season worms leave their burrows and congregate in great numbers near the surface of the sea.

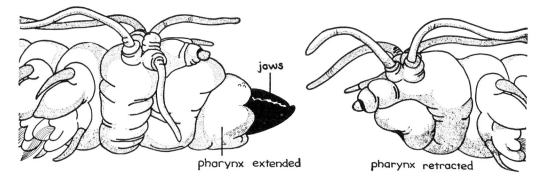

jaws

pharynx extended

pharynx retracted

FIG. 12-3. Side views of the head of Nereis showing the pharynx extended and retracted.

the nervous system, initiated in planaria, is carried much further in *Nereis*. Not only has the nervous tissue concentrated into two large masses, but also each segment has a similar enlarged **ganglion.** With this organization, the animal has a well-developed means of coordination, a far cry from the nerve net of hydra.

If *Nereis* is placed in a dish of sea water, it keeps up violent swimming movements, but if a test tube is placed in the container the worm backs into it almost

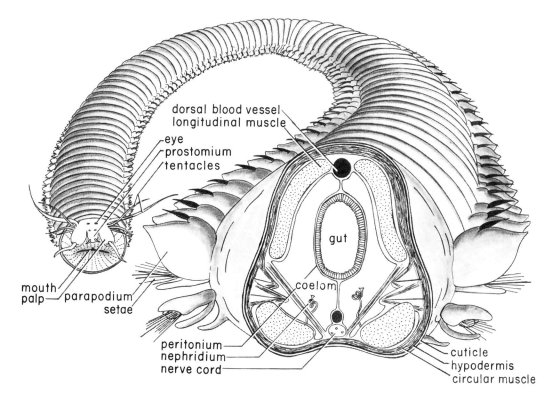

dorsal blood vessel
longitudinal muscle
eye
prostomium
tentacles

gut

mouth
palp
parapodium
setae

coelom

peritonium
nephridium
nerve cord

cuticle
hypodermis
circular muscle

FIG. 12-4. *Nereis* in cross-section to show the internal body plan of an annelid. A "head on" view demonstrates how well this animal is equipped with sense organs.

FIG. 12-5. Aphrodite (*Aphrodita hastata*), the sea mouse, from ventral view which definitely establishes it as an annelid. From the dorsal side it resembles a furry animal, hence its name. It is about 12 cm. long.

instantly and quiets down. This is presumably due to the tactile stimulation from the tube wall, reminiscent of the burrow. Movements during the breeding period also indicate a highly developed neuromotor mechanism.

During the nights of late July and August, *Nereis* gather in great numbers along the eastern coast of the United States for the purpose of shedding their eggs and sperm. By illuminating a small area of an appropriate ocean surface, thousands of worms may be seen at this time churning the water by swimming at a rapid, erratic rate, and swirling in apparent frenzy. Suddenly the females discharge their eggs into the sea water like a white cloud. The males, which are smaller than the females, shed their sperm in a similar manner. By dipping up some of this water it is possible to observe the early stages in the embryology of this animal. The eggs undergo segmentation and develop into free-swimming ciliated larvae, called **trochophores,** which promptly settle to the bottom and metamorphose into young *Nereis.*

Relatives of Nereis

There are many close relatives of *Nereis* living along the ocean shores, although some are found at great depths. They range from microscopic forms to those that reach 10 feet in length. Some are active swimmers and live in the open ocean catching their prey in flight, whereas others such as the sea mouse (Fig. 12-5) crawl over the ocean floor. Many construct burrows out of mucus, such as *Chaetopterus* (Fig. 12-6); others bore into rocks to provide a home for themselves. Some are highly colored, such as the peacock worm (Fig. 12-7), which could easily be mistaken for a flower.

Many of these worms have spectacular breeding habits. One, the **palolo worm** (*Eunice viridis*) of Samoa and Fiji, spawns in a most remarkably regular and peculiar manner (Fig. 12-1). On the first day of the last quarter of the October-November moon, the posterior portion of the worm, heavily laden with eggs or sperm, breaks off from the parent worm and swims to the surface where the gonadal products are discharged. The surface of the sea is milky white with the great numbers of these cells. Natives, who are familiar with the exact time of spawning, collect these worms when they are about to spawn and feast on them.

Many animals that have external fertilization must depend on rhythms in their environment to be able to synchronize the discharge of eggs and sperm in order to assure fertilization. In the oceans such rhythms as variation in temperature, length of day, and food control the sexual behavior of many marine animals. Also, the tides, which produce currents and changes in depth of coastal waters, and lunar and solar light are pronounced environmental changes to which organisms are sensitive. They seem to possess "clocks" which are set to synchronize with these environmental rhythms.

The Earthworm

No discussion of the phylum Annelida is complete without a study of the lowly earthworm, spurned by the squeamish and cherished by the fisherman and robin. It seems striking that this creature, which is so helpless when removed from its burrow, has been able to spread its kind over nearly the entire surface of the earth. This is even more surprising when it is known that most of its relatives are aquatic forms. It apparently deserted its ancestral watery environment and moved into a terrestrial habitat of semisolid soils. In this transition it lost certain of its ancestral parts and acquired others. There are relatively few species of earthworms compared to many species of aquatic forms.

The industrious robin searching for earthworms is a common sight, but other animals, such as moles, amphibians, small snakes, and fish, also feed upon this form. Some species of earthworms have been found to be intermediate hosts for such parasites as gapeworm and tapeworm of fowls, and lungworms of pigs. Hog influenza is caused by the mutual action of a virus and a bacterium contracted when lungworms borne by the earthworm invade the respiratory tract. Earthworms are highly beneficial to man by constantly tunneling the soil, thus permitting a greater circula-

tion of water and air. Charles **Darwin** noted that their castings on fertile soil amounted to as much as 18 tons per acre per year. This constant elevation of subsoils to the surface tends to cover rocks and gravel, thus making the topsoil more tillable. In this sense, too, the earthworms benefit man.

External Anatomy. The large species, *Lumbricus terrestris* (Fig. 12-8), is a good example of an earthworm. Its most conspicuous external characteristic is its segmenta-

FIG. 12-6. This annelid (*Chaetopterus*) lives in a tube secreted by its own body. The appendages are used as paddles to keep the water circulating through its tube, thus bringing in oxygen and small animals upon which it feeds. It is luminescent, which seems strange since there is no opportunity for any other animal to appreciate its beauty. This female specimen, which is removed from its burrow, is about 15 cm. long.

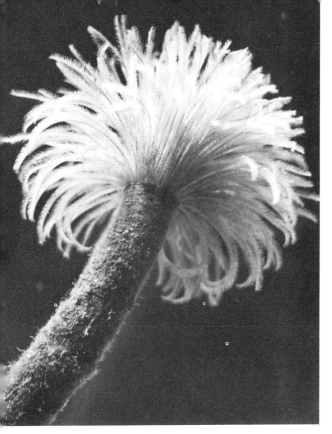

FIG. 12-7. This annelid, called the peacock worm (*Eudistylia*), builds its long tube in sand among the rocks. The miniature head, along with many brilliantly colored gills, protrudes from the end of the tube. The gills function in breathing and food gathering, since they are covered with a sticky mucus in which minute sea animals become enmeshed and are then drawn to the mouth by means of cilia. Peacock worms in clusters resemble flowers; their real identity becomes apparent when they suddenly withdraw the tentacles into the tube.

tion. Mere vestiges of the parapods remain in the form of four pairs of very short **setae** located on each segment. These are used for traction in locomotion. There are no conspicuous sense organs on the head end, like the eyes or tentacles of *Nereis*. Indeed, the animal seems to lack a head, though it does have a protruding "lip," the **prostomium,** which covers the mouth.

The saddle-shaped **clitellum,** which functions in reproduction, rests on the dorsal side about one-third of the way from the anterior end (Fig. 12-12). There are also several openings, the most noticeable of which are those of the **sperm ducts,** which

open on the fifteenth segment. The fourteenth segment bears the smaller openings of the **oviducts,** and each segment except the first three and the last bears a pair of **nephridiopores.** Finally, the four openings which lead into the **seminal receptacles** are located in the grooves between segments 9 and 10, and 10 and 11.

Internal Structures. A section of the body wall (Fig. 12-9) shows the outer thin, tough **cuticle,** which serves as a protective layer for the tall **columnar epithelial** cells composing the bulk of the epidermis. Among these are scattered sensory cells, sensitive to light, touch, and chemical stimulation. Other cells dispersed among the epithelial cells are the mucus-secreting cells responsible for the slimy condition of the skin, which is essential both for respiration and locomotion. Beneath the epidermis lie two layers of muscle, the outer **circular** and the inner **longitudinal.** Lying beneath the muscle layers and lining the coelom is the **peritoneum.** The digestive tract is a tube, making the tube-within-a-tube plan conspicuous. The segmentation which is so striking externally is just as conspicuous from the inside. Membranous partitions, **septa,** which wall off each segment, are perforated by the **gut, nerve cord, blood vessels,** and **nephridia.**

The **digestive system** starts with the **mouth** which opens into the large muscular **pharynx;** this latter organ functions as a pump to draw food into the mouth. Following the pharynx is the **esophagus,** which opens into the **crop,** a storage sac. This in turn leads into the **gizzard,** which functions in the grinding of food. The remainder of the gut is a long tube, the **intestine.** This organ bears a fold along its dorsal side, the **typhlosole,** which increases the surface of the gut without increasing the volume of the animal.

Various gland cells are located throughout the digestive epithelium. Some produce digestive enzymes, while the secre-

FIG. 12-8. Earthworms sometimes aggregate in great numbers under certain environmental conditions. These were found in a small stream.

tion of others also lubricates and thus facilitates the movement of food. Lateral to the esophagus and attached to it are three pairs of **calciferous glands,** which function in secreting calcium carbonate for neutralizing any acid soil that may be taken in with the food. The epithelial lining of the gut secretes fat-splitting, carbohydrate-splitting, and protein-splitting enzymes. The gut is surrounded by **chloragogen cells** which are derived from the peritoneum and probably function in the elimination of wastes from the blood.

Food for the earthworm consists of leaves and any other available organic matter, even bits of meat. Much soil is taken in with the food and used later in the gizzard for grinding the food in preparation for digestion. Food is temporarily stored in the crop before it passes into the gizzard, where it is ground to a fine mass. It then passes on to the intestine where digestion and absorption are carried on. Undigested mate-

rial passes out through the anus. Earthworms deposit their castings on the surface of the ground near their burrows. When millions of worms continue this process for centuries in the same areas, the result is a constant inverting of the soil reminiscent of plowing in agriculture. The castings of the worms also greatly enrich the soil.

The **circulatory system** (Fig. 12-10) of the earthworm is similar to that of *Nereis*. However, there is an improvement in the pumping system in the form of five pairs of "hearts" which surround the esophagus and connect the **dorsal** with the **ventral blood vessel.** In addition to the peristaltic waves that move the blood forward in the dorsal blood vessel, the "hearts" send it by a rhythmic contraction of their walls to the ventral blood vessel with considerable force. The **ventral vessel** is the main arterial trunk which conducts blood throughout the body. The paired **segmentals,** given off in each

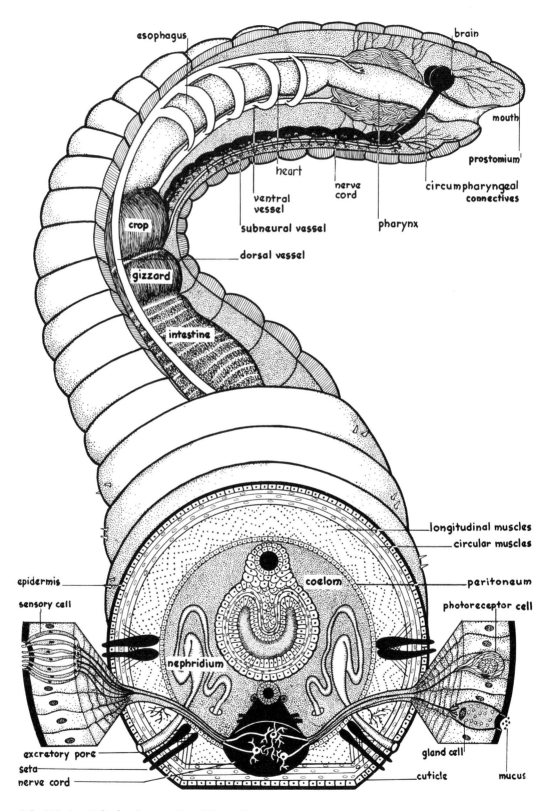

FIG. 12-9. Longitudinal and cross-section of the earthworm.

esophagus

brain

mouth

prostomium

heart

nerve cord

circumpharyngeal connectives

ventral vessel

pharynx

crop

subneural vessel

dorsal vessel

gizzard

intestine

longitudinal muscles

circular muscles

epidermis

coelom

peritoneum

sensory cell

photoreceptor cell

nephridium

excretory pore

gland cell

seta

mucus

nerve cord

cuticle

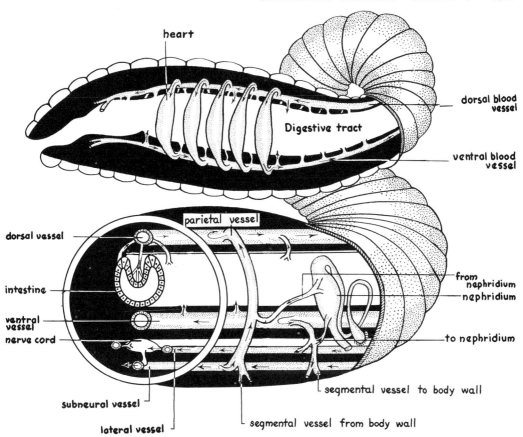

heart

dorsal blood vessel

Digestive tract

ventral blood vessel

parietal vessel

dorsal vessel

intestine

ventral vessel

nerve cord

from nephridium

nephridium

to nephridium

segmental vessel to body wall

subneural vessel

lateral vessel

segmental vessel from body wall

FIG. 12-10. A schematic view of the circulatory system of the earthworm. In the lower portion, one segment has been greatly enlarged in order to show the course of the blood.

segment, break up into branches to the nephridia, to the body wall and skin where external respiration occurs, and to the **lateral vessels** on each side of the nerve cord. These organs are drained by separate vessels which empty into the **parietals** which then return the blood to the **dorsal vessel.** The nerve cord is drained ventrally via the **subneural vessel.** Short blood vessels extend from the dorsal vessel and convey blood to and from the intestine; blood also enters the intestine from the ventral vessel. A careful study of Fig. 12-10 shows the plan of the system, namely, five principal vessels running the length of the worm, with numerous cross-connections and branches supplying blood to all parts of the body. These

animals possess a remarkably complete and complex circulatory system.

The blood of the earthworm contains many white blood cells (**leucocytes**) suspended in the fluid **plasma.** The respiratory pigment is hemoglobin, which is carried free in the plasma, not in corpuscles. The gas exchange takes place where the capillaries come close to the surface of the epidermis. For this reason the surface of the animal must be moist at all times, for a dry membrane will not allow the gaseous exchange to take place.

The arrangement of the nephridia is similar to that in *Nereis.* The nephridium consists of a small ciliated funnel, the **nephrostome,** which opens into a tiny coiled tubule (Fig. 12-11). This penetrates the septum of the next segment, where it coils, gradually becoming larger and finally expanding into a bladder-like sac before opening to the outside through the **ne-phridiopore.** Nephridia are found in all of the segments except the first three and the last. The actual excretory process is carried on by the beating of the cilia of the nephrostome and the lining of the tubule, which causes waste products from the coelom to enter the tubule and be discharged from the body. Waste materials in the blood are picked up by the glandular portion of the tubule and excreted directly. The chlorogogen cells may also aid in this process.

Behavior. The center of the nervous system is a bilobed "brain," located in the anterior region dorsal to the digestive tract (Fig. 12-9). The **circumpharyngeal connectives** connect to the **ventral nerve cord**

which consists of a series of **ganglia** much the same as in *Nereis*. There are a few nerve fibers extending into the prostomium, suggesting that this organ is probably sensitive to touch. The nervous system of the earthworm possesses the components of reflex arcs very similar to those of man. Impulses come in from the external world through the sense organs on **afferent,** or **sensory,** fibers, pass to **association neurons,** and from these to **efferent,** or **motor,** fibers, which extend to muscles or glands. Thus, in a form as low as the earthworm, there is an intricate nervous mechanism which enables the animal to carry out complex operations. The nervous systems of these animals become sufficiently complex to store response patterns which we call memory. One experimentalist (Swartz, 1929) found that an earthworm which at first would enter either branch of a Y-shaped tube could learn, after several hundred trials, to

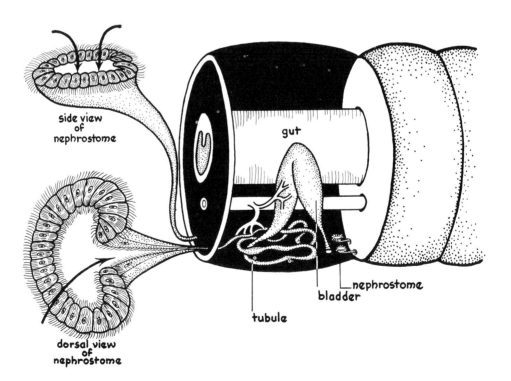

FIG. 12-11. A schematic side view of one segment of the earthworm showing the details of the nephridium. The nephrostomes have been greatly enlarged.

avoid one branch of the tube if an electrode were placed in it and the worm received a shock each time it entered that branch. Hence, this animal can profit by past experience.

There are no obvious sense organs present on the earthworm's body, but several kinds of sensory cells located among the epithelial cells connect directly to the nervous system and function as sense organs (Fig. 12-9). Such cells are located in the parts of the body that are most likely to come in contact with the environment: the prostomium, the portion of largest diameter in each segment, and the mouth cavity. Some of these cells are specialized for light reception, while others respond to chemical and tactile stimulation.

The earthworm responds readily to light. If removed from the burrow, the worm becomes very active and immediately attempts to get away from the bright light and crawl into a crevice or burrow. If sought for at night with a flashlight, as is the habit of those who search for the so-called night crawlers, the moment the light strikes, the worm retracts into its burrow with almost lightning-like speed, so fast that one must be very agile to catch it. It appears, then, that light is readily perceived and interpreted.

If an earthworm is experimentally placed near any volatile chemical, such as acetic acid, it responds violently and moves in the opposite direction. Likewise, it moves toward bits of meat or decaying vegetation, which, of course, are its food. In this case the sense organs appear to be located in the mouth cavity.

Since the earthworm is dependent on being able to find its way around underground in completely dark passages, it must rely on the sense of touch perhaps more than any other. The tactile end organs (Fig. 12-9) are bundles of modified epithelial cells with tiny protruding hair-like bodies that are in contact with anything that touches the body wall. They probably

also function as a sort of hearing device, since any vibration on the earth near the burrow, as in the case of footsteps, causes the worm to respond readily. They do not respond to air-borne vibrations which affect our ears.

The earthworm is sensitive to temperature; it avoids cold and hot areas and seeks out moderate temperatures. In its natural environment it lies near the surface in its vertical burrow with the "head" uppermost when the temperature is moderate, receding if it is too cold or too hot. In winter it burrows down below the frost line and remains inactive throughout the cold season; it does likewise when the soil becomes dry during a drought. It cannot tolerate desiccation and therefore responds positively toward moisture, but only to a certain point, since it cannot withstand immersion in water for a long period of time. After a rain it is common to see on sidewalks earthworms which have been "drowned" out of their burrows. The apparently fantastic stories of earthworms falling from the skies during storms are perhaps founded on the same basis as the stories of frogs and other animals having "rained." This usually follows a tornado where masses of water have been carried into the air, resembling a water spout in the ocean, and these animals are taken along in the water and released many miles away.

The bristle-like setae are the earthworm's chief organs of locomotion. While the animal is in its burrow the setae in the posterior end project out and are embedded in the wall of the burrow. This is done by contraction of the muscles at the base of the setae. Those at the anterior end then relax and the circular muscles contract, thus elongating the worm. The anterior setae then secure their end of the animal and the longitudinal muscles contract, bringing the posterior end forward. In such fashion the animal moves through its burrow. Since the setae are located on the ventral sides as well as the lateral walls, the animal

FIG. 12-12. Copulating earthworms, showing the various steps in the fertilization of the eggs and subsequent cocoon formation.

is able to crawl slowly over a surface when removed from the burrow. If the anterior segments containing the brain are removed, the worm seems to move in a normal fashion, which means that the nerve centers for crawling movements are located in the ganglia and not centered in the brain.

Reproduction. In order to survive in its terrestrial habitat, the earthworm has been forced to undergo some drastic adaptations in its reproductive system. It will be recalled that most annelids discharge their sex products into water where union of the eggs and sperm is purely fortuitous. On land, obviously, some other means must be provided to bring about this union and to insure adequate conditions for the developing embryo. In the first place, the sexes, which are separate in other annelids, are united in the earthworm, that is, it is **monoecious,** or **hermaphroditic.** This has the advantage of making it unnecessary for worms of different sexes to unite; any two worms can exchange sperm.

The **ovaries** and **testes** are located in the anterior end of the worm where ducts provide the proper exit for eggs and sperm (Fig. 12-12). There are two pairs of tiny testes located in the tenth and eleventh segments, surrounded by large sac-like bodies, the **seminal vesicles,** which are storehouses for the sperm cells. Funnels direct the sperm into the sperm ducts which open to the outside on the fifteenth segment. A pair of ovaries cling to the posterior wall of the septum in segment 13, and small funnels catch the eggs and direct them into a sac where they are temporarily stored. Eventually the eggs pass to the outside through the oviduct in segment 14.

The process of exchanging sperm occurs at night, usually following a rain. Two worms become attached along their ventral sides, as shown in Figs. 12-12, 12-13. A slimy material is then secreted mutually by the worms which, as it hardens, encases both animals together in a temporary sheath.

Small tubular passageways form between the sheath and the body walls, thus providing a pathway for the sperms, which are forced from each worm along these channels until they reach the **seminal receptacles** of the other worm. After this exchange of sperm cells the animals separate. Later, when the eggs are mature, the clitellum secretes a mucous sheath which slips forward over its "head." In the fourteenth segment eggs are forced into the mucous ring, and as it slips over the ninth and tenth segments, sperms pass out of the seminal receptacles and unite with the eggs. After the mucous ring slips over the anterior end, the ends contract, forming a closed capsule, or **cocoon,** full of fertilized eggs, which is left behind in the burrow. There is no larval stage and the eggs hatch into small earthworms which penetrate the wall of the mucous capsule and begin to shift for themselves.

Relatives of the Earthworm

Earthworms have many relatives which range in size from microscopic forms to species which may reach 10 feet in length. There are well over 2,000 species, and most of them are smaller in size than the common earthworm. Although nearly all live in damp soil, some are found in fresh or polluted waters. One form, *Tubifex,* is encouraged to grow in filter beds of sewage disposal plants in order to keep the filter

FIG. 12-13. Earthworms usually copulate during damp periods. These were photographed in the early morning during a drizzling rain.

open. The common blood worm, which is a species of *Tubifex*, is found in tubes at the bottom of fresh-water ponds where it feeds on the muck and perhaps aids in the purification of such waters when they are polluted. Another small white, almost microscopic, form, called *Enchytraeus*, is frequently sold in pet shops as a source of food for small fish.

Certain of the small forms, such as *Chaetogaster*, reproduce asexually by transverse fission and sometimes several cling together, resulting in a chain of individuals. In some species this method has apparently replaced the sexual method altogether.

Leeches

After a swim in the old swimming hole, boys often find small black leeches that cling tenaciously to the skin. When removed, they leave a stream of blood flowing from the wound. It is also common for the fisherman to see a large (12 inches long) leech, *Haemopis grandis*, swimming in beautiful undulating movements near the surface of the water. Another leech, *Hirudo medicinalis*, was once cultured in Europe for the specific purpose of blood-letting when that practice was in vogue. It is interesting to note that during the last century, and before, it was considered beneficial to remove blood in certain illnesses. Today the procedure is the reverse, as is indicated by the many blood banks over the country.

In some regions, particularly the tropics, leeches live in watering places where large vertebrates come to drink. They attach themselves to the buccal cavity, sometimes in such numbers as to cause serious injury to horses as well as other animals, including man. Some leeches live on land and are occasionally so numerous that they are a serious hazard to human beings. Army commanders have been known to provide their men with leech-proof stockings in order to get through such infested areas.

The leech has many of the annelid characteristics, but it lacks setae, and it possesses copulatory organs, which other annelids lack. What appears to be segmentation externally does not correspond with the actual segments, for there are fewer segments internally than appear from the outside. The body has remarkable powers of extensibility and contractibility, enabling it to move like the measuring worm. The hold-fast organs are two suckers, one on each end, which are used both in locomotion and in feeding. In the center of the anterior sucker is the mouth, which is usually provided with three small cutting teeth that inflict a wound when the leech is feeding upon its victim. The anus is located in the center of the posterior sucker. The digestive tract is sacculated so that it can retain a large meal of blood. Apparently this is provided because meals are usually few and far between, some leeches being able to live a year between feedings.

When securing a blood meal the leech becomes attached to the skin, which it pierces with its teeth. An enzyme (hirudin) is secreted by the salivary glands, which prevents the blood from clotting. Blood is sucked by the pumping action of the pharynx and stored in the large sacculated crop to be passed on into the intestine for digestion a little at a time.

We have seen in this chapter the advent of characteristics of key importance to the development of more complex animal bodies. The acquisition of a well-developed coelom, segmentation, and a centralized nervous system have laid the foundation for higher forms. Perhaps the features that have appeared so far in the animal kingdom are more important than any that follow, because later groups, while adding some new characteristics, actually become complex by elaborating features that are already established in these lower animals.

PHYLUM ONYCHOPHORA

Before going on to the next very important phylum, Arthropoda, perhaps we should consider a small group of animals that have puzzled taxonomists for a long time. They are represented by only a dozen genera, of which *Peripatus* is the best known (Fig. 12-14). They are often called "walking worms" and their anatomy would lead

remain in the adult, and the main body cavity is the hemocoel. It appears to be segmented, but this is not actually so. The tracheal system resembles that of arthropods but is sufficiently different to be thought of as having arisen independently.

Obviously, *Peripatus* possesses both arthropod and annelid characteristics, which fact has led many zoologists to consider it a connecting link between these two phyla.

FIG. 12-14. *Peripatus* is rare and of considerable interest to biologists because it shows both annelid and arthropod characteristics. This one came from Panama.

one to think of them as closely related to the annelids. However, on close examination one finds that they possess characteristics which resemble both the arthropods and the annelids. Like annelids, they possess a pair of fleshy appendages for nearly every segment. These have clawed feet but they lack joints, which is one of the principal characteristics of the arthropods. The exoskeleton resembles the cuticle of annelids; nothing like the covering seen in all arthropods. The excretory system is annelid-like, as well as the tubules of the reproductive system, which are ciliated, a characteristic found among the annelids, but not the arthropods. Only remnants of the coelom

Rather, the onychophores probably are very ancient animals that evolved from the annelid-arthropod stem and have no close affinities with either modern annelids or arthropods.

Peripatus is a small animal found only in widely separated places—Africa, Australia, Central and South America. Because they are limited to widely scattered, isolated places, it is believed that they were very common all over at one time, but eventually died out in the areas where they do not presently exist. Today they live in the dense, tropical forests, in damp places under logs and other objects found on the forest floor.

SUGGESTED SUPPLEMENTARY READINGS

BORRADAILE, L. A., POTTS, F. A., EASTMAN, L. E. S., and SAUNDERS, J. T., *The Invertebrata* (Cambridge, Cambridge University Press, 1958).

BUCHSBAUM, R., *Animals without Backbones* (Chicago, University of Chicago Press, 1948).

GALLOWAY, T. W., "The Common Fresh-water Oligochaeta of the United States," *Trans. Amer. Micro. Soc.*, 30 (1911), 285.

PENNAK, R. W., *Fresh-water Invertebrates of the United States* (New York, The Ronald Press, 1953).

WARD, H. B., and WHIPPLE, G. C., EDMONDSON, W. T., ed., *Fresh-water Biology* (New York, John Wiley & Sons, Inc., 1959).

13
Animals With Jointed Feet—
Arthropods

ALTHOUGH the arthropods resemble the annelids in many respects, they show important innovations. One of these is the hard outer skeleton, the **exoskeleton,** which functions as a rigid coat of armor. This means that the muscles can be attached to the inside of this material and function more efficiently in moving the body. The exoskeleton supports the entire animal, much like the framework of an airplane or automobile. It is composed of a nitrogenous polysaccharide, **chitin.** Some arthropods, such as the lobster, have a high percentage of lime in the exoskeleton, whereas the insects have smaller amounts. The greater the lime content, the harder the skeleton. For the land dweller, exposed to rapid desiccation, a waterproof outer covering becomes essential. Since the exoskeleton of these air breathers is practically waterproof, one may assume that this condition made it possible for the animal to invade land.

In order to increase in size, arthropods must periodically shed their exoskeletons by a complex process called **molting.** A new skeleton forms under the old one, and the actual process of shedding the old one and hardening of the new one requires

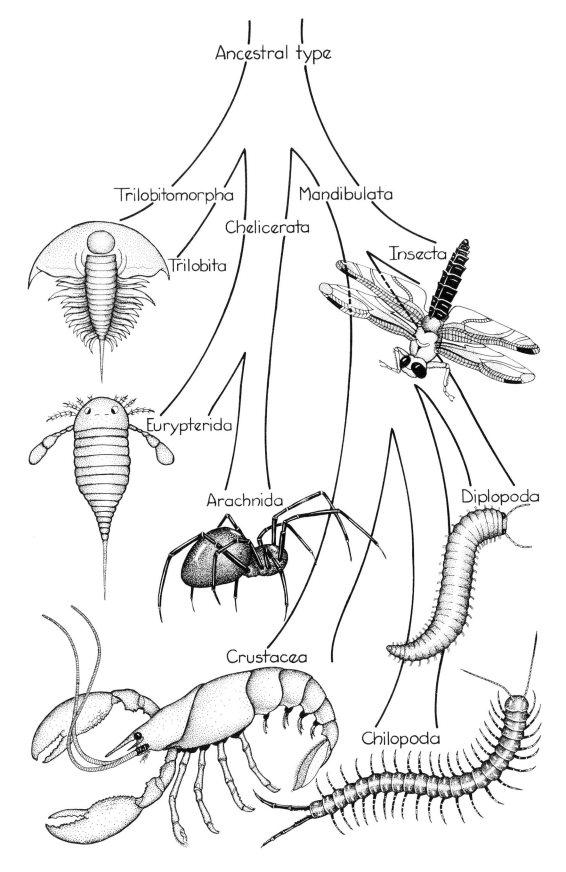

FIG. 13-1. A scheme to show relationships among the various groups of arthropods.

several hours in the larger arthropods, during which time they are vulnerable to predators. They seem to be aware of their precarious situation and take special precautions to hide during this period. A single layer of epidermal cells gives rise to the new skeleton, and just prior to shedding, a molting fluid is secreted which digests away parts of the old skeleton, the products of which are absorbed by the body. The animal then swells its body by swallowing air or water which splits the old skeleton open. The arthropod then crawls out, leaving behind the old skeleton which includes not only the covering of the body and legs, but also the lining of the foregut, hindgut, and sometimes the tracheal system. The animal then grows, again by swallowing air or water, thus stretching its new skeleton which hardens by oxidation of the products in the outer layer. In the hard-shelled forms, calcium carbonate is deposited which greatly stiffens the exoskeleton.

Another important difference between the annelids and the arthropods is the presence in the latter of appendages with **joints.** This conspicuous character gives the phylum its name. The feet and legs of animals with hard skeletons need joints for the purpose of movement. In the arthropods many appendages have lost their original locomotor function and have become radically modified into organs of defense, offense, and even sense organs. The exoskeleton and the jointed appendages thus have distinct advantages and have contributed much to the success of this group.

The nervous system, while similar in plan to that of annelids, is more centralized. There are fewer ganglia, and less independence of all parts of the body. This increased integration has resulted in an animal that is swifter, more agile, and better able to cope with its environment.

The coelom is much reduced in size, being replaced to a large extent by a system of blood spaces called the **hemocoel.** There are certain modifications in other systems also, but these will be discussed in the various groups, as they occur.

In recent years an elaborate system of hormones has been discovered in arthropods; indeed, they seem to be as numerous and as complex as in vertebrates, although they probably arose independently. Such processes as molting, color change, reproduction, and metabolism are under endocrine control. As in vertebrates, the hormones are related to the central nervous system, and they exist in pairs, each one being antagonistic to the other. One of the most interesting and important discoveries in hormone research was made with arthropod nerves. It was found that the nerve cell body produces the hormone, which passes along the nerve fiber to be secreted at its tip. For example, the so-called **x-organ** in crustacea, which lies one on each side of the optic ganglia, produces a variety of hormones affecting reproduction, metabolism, molting, and body color. The hormones travel through individual nerve fibers to the **sinus gland,** where they are stored until used. All of the hormones were once thought to be produced by the sinus gland itself. A similar situation exists in the vertebrate pituitary gland (p. 499).

Among insects a hormone is produced in the **intercerebral gland,** located in the brain, which initiates molting. The hormone passes through axons to a pair of small bodies posterior to the brain called the **corpus cardiacum.** When released, this hormone stimulates another hormone to be released from the **prothoracic glands,** located in the thoracic region, which actually sets the machinery going that brings about the molt. This hormone is also responsible for metamorphosis. Another pair of small bodies, located posteriorly to the corpora cardiaca, called the **corpus allatum,** found only in larval insects, is responsible for the juvenile state, and thus is antagonistic to the hormone that brings about metamorphosis. Here we see duplicate hormones that function in an antagonistic manner, much the same as we find in vertebrates (p. 483).

The arthropods include more species than are found in all other phyla put together; in fact, the species of all other phyla number about 130,000, whereas the arthropods alone add up to 870,000, of which over 800,000 are insects. They literally encompass the earth; they invade the soil, the water, the air, the frigid polar zones, and

FIG. 13-2. Trilobites were abundant in Cambrian times but later all died. They exist today only as fossils. This one (*Phacops rana crassituberculatus*) shows their arthropod characteristics. Note the broad head bearing compound eyes and the segmented trunk with attached appendages.

the torrid equatorial latitudes. Since they feed on the same foods as man, they have become his most serious competitor; indeed, it has been said that the main struggle for survival today is between the arthropods, particularly the insects, and man. Insects are carriers of some of the most serious diseases, and although some species are beneficial, it is doubtful that the benefit to man of some outweighs the damage done by others.

The phylum arthropoda is divided into three subphyla, based on the structure of the appendages of the first six segments. They are **Trilobitomorpha, Chelicerata,** and **Mandibulata** (Fig. 13-1). The first includes only extinct arthropods, a common representative being the trilobites (Fig. 13-2). The second subphylum includes those arthropods without antennae and with the first pair of ventral appendages modified into **chelicerae** which are pincer-like structures at the tip of the appendage. This subphylum is divided into four classes: **Xiphosurida,** which includes the famous "living fossil," *Limulus* (Fig. 13-43); **Eurypterida,** extinct sea scorpions; **Pycnogonida,** the sea spiders; and **Arachnida,** the spiders and scorpions. The subphylum Mandibulata includes those arthropods which possess a pair of **jaws,** or **mandibles,** from which the group gets its name. This subphylum includes the most important and numerous of all arthropods. There are a number of classes, of which we shall mention only four. They are **Crustacea** (lobsters, crayfish, and crabs), **Chilopoda** (centipedes), **Diplopoda** (millipedes), and **Insecta** (insects). Of this large and complex phylum, we shall spend most of our time with representatives of only two classes, the Crustacea and the Insecta, because they are by far the most important. Less important groups will be discussed at the end of the chapter.

CLASS CRUSTACEA

The Crustacea live on land, in fresh water (Fig. 13-3), and in the ocean (Fig. 13-4). They include such common forms as freshwater fairy shrimps and crayfish, seashore crabs (Fig. 13-5), lobsters, and barnacles (Fig. 13-6). The group is of considerable economic significance to man. It is a valuable source of food, as demonstrated by the fact that around $20 million worth of shrimp, crab, and lobster are marketed annually in this country alone. In addition, the Crustacea play an important role in the food chain of fishes (see p. 123). There is a stage in the development of all fish when they must feed on some form of Crustacea; this may be the larval stage of some larger form such as the crayfish, or it may be a minute adult crustacean, such as **cyclops** or **daphnia** (Fig. 13-3). Some Crustacea, on the other hand, act as intermediate hosts for certain dangerous parasites of man, such as the human lung fluke, *Paragonimus westermani*. On the whole, the group is important both economically and biologically.

Let us consider a representative member of the Crustacea in some detail. The lobster and crayfish are excellent examples and, because of their universal distribution, are readily available for study.

The Lobster and the Crayfish

These two closely related animals live in different environments, the lobster in the sea and the crayfish in fresh water (Fig. 13-7), yet their bodies have much the same appearance. In fact, a description of one also fits the other fairly well. This discussion is confined largely to the lobster, although frequent references will be made to the crayfish.

The lobster is a bottom dweller, spending its life seeking food, which consists of other Crustacea, small fish, and mollusks. It hides by day and sallies forth at night, crawling forward along the sea bottom. If in danger of attack by other predators, it can swim backward with darting speed by powerful strokes of its abdomen. The crayfish employs the same methods in defending itself, and it seeks the same type of food in much the same manner.

Structure. The animal is enclosed in a **chitinous exoskeleton,** containing considerable quantities of lime and sclerotin which make the skeleton heavy and bulky, but a very excellent armor plate (Fig. 13-7). The chitin thins out at the joints, allowing maximum flexibility. The anterior portion of the body is covered by the **carapace,** and

each posterior abdominal segment by an arched dorsal **tergum,** two lateral **pleura,** and a ventral **sternum.** Tiny holes perforate the entire skeleton, being particularly numerous in the appendages and tail region. Set into these are bristles, which make the animal extremely sensitive to its surrounding world through tactile stimulation.

The appendages of the lobster or crayfish demonstrate a very interesting series of adaptations and modifications for a particular mode of life (Fig. 13-8). There are nineteen pairs of appendages in all, one pair on each segment. The **antennules** and **antennae** are modified for tactile and chemical stimulation; the **mandibles,** or **jaws,** for chewing; the next five, **maxillae** and **maxillipeds,** chiefly for food manipulation; the next pair, the enormous **chelipeds,** for grasping food and for defense; the next four for walking; and the last six for swimming and various other functions. All of these appendages, with their variety of form and function, come originally from a simple appendage with a single function (locomotion) (Fig. 13-9).

The primitive appendage, one which appears in the early embryology of all Crustacea, is said to be **biramous,** because it branches into two parts. It persists in its primitive condition in the **swimmerets,** located on the underside of the abdomen. The single basal portion, the **protopod,** is attached to the body and two branches extend from it, the **endopod** toward the median line and the **exopod** away from it. The original function of such an appendage was locomotion (swimming), and all of the primitive Arthropods, such as the fossil trilobites, possessed just this type and nothing more. Through the ages it became modified in a most versatile manner in all of the appendages except the swimmerets. For example, the antennules and antennae are receptors for tactile and chemical stimuli and resemble the swimmerets very little. One of the most radical departures is the mandible, or jaw, where there is almost no

FIG. 13-3. Fresh-water and terrestrial crustacea. Although primarily aquatic, the pillbug lives on land.

hint of its progenitor. Among the walking legs, as well as other appendages, the exopod has been greatly reduced or lost entirely.

Structures that have a common origin, such as in the case of these appendages, are said to be **homologous,** and when they are on the same animal they are said to be **serially homologous.** This introduces the principle of **homology** which is illustrated throughout the animal kingdom and is very important in determining animal relationships. Homologous structures have a common embryological origin, therefore when two animals show such structures, even though they may not have the same function in the adult form, the animals are known to be closely related. The more nearly the structures are alike the closer the

relationship, which means that they came from a common ancestor. We shall discuss this topic again in the last chapter of this book.

Upon cutting through the body wall, among the first and most obvious structures noted are the muscles, particularly in the abdominal region. The muscles are attached to the internal side of the exoskeleton, where they are always in pairs, and oppose one another in action. One muscle pulls an appendage or any other part of the body in one direction, whereas the other pulls it back again. The principle is followed by all higher animals with skeletons, including man.

Digestive System. The **chelipeds** catch and crush the food, then pass it to the **mouth**

FIG. 13-4. [Upper] Marine crustacea: These vary widely from the sessile barnacle to the burrowing fiddler crab. [Middle] The hermit crab (*Pagurus*) lives in an abandoned snail shell. This habit has resulted in the loss of the heavy exoskeleton characteristic of other crabs. [Lower] The mantis shrimp (*Gonodactylus*) lives among corals and is a very agile swimmer.

FIG. 13-5. This is the Ghost Crab, *Ocypode ceratoph-thalma*, which inhabits the Pacific coral islands. It is a swift marauder that is normally a scavenger but during the hatching season of the large sea turtle eggs, it feeds on the emerging young.

with the aid of the **maxillae** and **maxillipeds** (Fig. 13-10). The **mandibles** break the food up still further, before it is swallowed through the short **esophagus** and taken into the large **cardiac stomach,** which functions more as a storehouse for food than as a digestive organ (Fig. 13-10). At the posterior end of this organ is the **gastric mill,** which is composed of three small tooth-like bodies called **ossicles,** two in a lateral position and one in the mid-dorsal line. These fit tightly together and the grinding movement is brought about by muscles attached to the outside of the stomach. Before food can pass on into the second stomach, called the **pyloric stomach,** it must pass

FIG. 13-6. A rock-encrusting acorn barnacle (*Balanus tintinnabulum*). Its arthropod characteristic is indicated only by the jointed appendages which protrude between the valves of its shell. These are used to strain the water for tiny sea animals that make up the diet of this strange arthropod.

through the gastric mill, which grinds all the food fine and renders it digestible. In addition, the two stomachs are separated by filtering "hairs" which act as strainers, allowing only fine particles to pass through. Foods that cannot pass through, such as parts of skeletons, are regurgitated through the mouth. Once the food is in the pyloric stomach some of it passes into the two large multi-lobed **digestive glands.** The enzymes necessary for the complete digestion of the food are secreted by these glands. Digestion occurs for the most part in the upper end of the **intestine,** although some apparently goes on in the digestive glands themselves. Absorption also takes place here, and in the intestine. All undigested food in the intestine passes out through the **anus** as feces.

Circulatory System. The circulatory system of the lobster varies markedly from that of the annelids. Instead of several pairs of hearts, the lobster possesses a single pulsating vesicle that lies on the dorsal part of the body, surrounded by a thin membrane and cavity, the **pericardium** and **pericardial cavity,** respectively (Fig. 13-11). The **heart** has three pairs of tiny valved openings, called **ostia,** which allow the blood to enter from the pericardial cavity. Seven arteries lead away from the heart and convey the blood to all parts of the body.

From this point on, the system differs even more radically from that of the earthworm. The blood leaves the tiny arterioles and passes out into spaces, called **sinuses,** where it bathes the tissues. This type of system is called an **open blood system,** in contrast to the closed system of the earthworm. Once the blood leaves the tissues, it seeps into the ventral portion of the **cephalothorax,** then through a set of **afferent vessels** (to the gills) where gas exchange takes place. It then makes its way to the pericardial chamber of the heart, through **efferent vessels** (away from the gills), thence through the ostia, and out into the body again. Valves located in the walls of the ostia permit the blood to pass through the ostia in one direction only, namely, into the heart.

The blood contains colorless leucocytes as well as a respiratory pigment, **hemocyanin,** which has a slight bluish color when oxygenated and serves the same oxygen-carrying function as the hemoglobin does in other forms. The blood has remarkable clotting properties. If an appendage is removed forcibly, there is hardly any noticeable loss of blood, the clot forming almost at once and filling the large opening.

Breathing System. When the lateral walls of the carapace are cut away, large feather-like delicate gills are exposed. These are the breathing organs of the animal. While the crayfish lies quietly in running water, the water moves over the gills without any help from the animal. However, when the demand for oxygen is greater or when the oxygen content of the water is low, a special modification of the second maxilla, the **gill bailer** (scaphognathite), waves up and down, like a gondolier sculling a boat, causing the water to flow over the gills in a posterior-anterior direction. This can easily be demonstrated by placing a crayfish in a shallow white pan and allowing a small amount of India ink to be placed near the posterior end. Great clouds of the carbon particles will issue from the anterior end, indicating a flow of water. Since the openings of the excretory organs, which lie at the base of the antennae, are in the path of this outgoing water current, the waste products from these organs are also carried away.

Excretory System. Nitrogenous wastes are withdrawn from the blood and body fluids by a pair of **kidneys,** called the **green glands** because of their color. They are located beneath the antennae in the body and consist

FIG. 13-7. The common crayfish (*Cambarus*) found over most of the United States. They live in ponds and streams where they feed on small fish or any other animal, dead or alive. Note the great area of the expanded tail (uropods and telson). This is very effective in locomotion. When disturbed, the animal contracts its tail powerfully, thus sending it darting backwards. The crayfish is much like its marine cousin, the lobster.

of a **glandular** portion and a **bladder** (Fig. 13-10). The bladder stores waste material until it is released through the opening at the base of the antennae, already referred to.

Reproductive System. The gonads differ slightly in shape in the lobster and the crayfish; they are longer and thinner in the former (Fig. 13-10) and fused into a three-lobed gland in the latter. Sperm cells are produced in a tubular **testis** and pass though the **vas deferens** to an opening at the base of the fifth (considering the chelipeds as the first walking legs) walking legs. An ejaculatory duct toward the end of the tube aids in removing sperm during mating. The first pair of swimmerets is modified in the male to form a **copulatory organ** for transfer of the sperm to the **seminal receptacle** on the ventral side of the female. The ovaries of the female produce eggs which pass through a straight oviduct to the opening at the base of the third walking legs (Fig. 13-10). Her first pair of swimmerets is rudimentary.

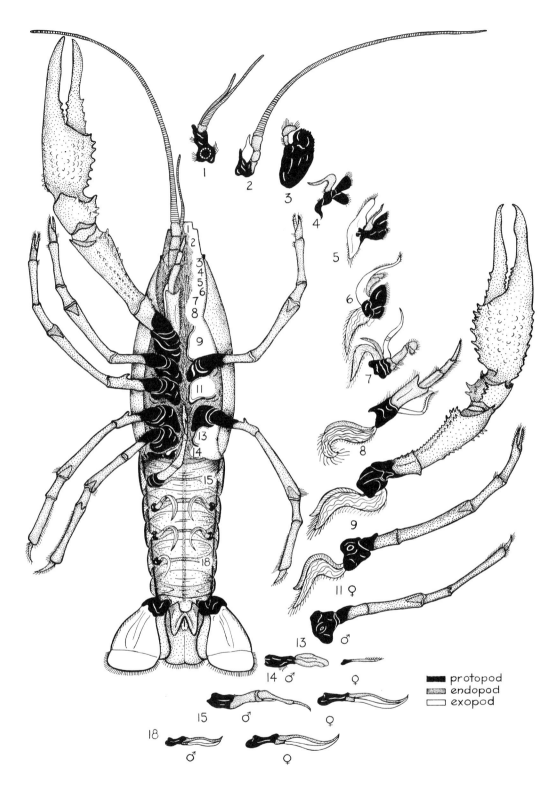

FIG. 13-8. Crayfish appendages. Most of the right appendages have been removed for comparative purposes. Each retains parts of the original larval appendage, but here it is drastically modified to perform specific functions. This is an illustration of serial homologies among the invertebrates.

protopod
endopod
exopod

At the start of copulation the male lobster grasps the chelipeds of the female with his pincer-like appendages and turns her over on her dorsal side (Fig. 13-12). The two ventral sides then come together. The first pair of swimmerets of the male is placed near the opening of the seminal receptacle of the female and the sperm are discharged. The female receives the sperm in packets or **spermatophores.**

The female lobster lays eggs only once in two years, usually at the time when the water has reached its summer temperatures (from about mid-June to September 1). The male, however, is unable to discern the sexual condition of the female and copulation often occurs long before the maturation of eggs in the ovary. In such cases the sperm cells, which are stored in the seminal receptacle of the female, must maintain their vitality for a long time, very often for several months. Eggs are fertilized after their ejection from the oviducts. As the eggs are extruded, a mucous material is produced by glands in the swimmerets which glues the eggs to the many bristles on these appendages. The eggs are thus carried by the female from ten to eleven months (see Fig. 13-13 where a crayfish is carrying her nearly hatched eggs) and usually do not hatch until the summer following that in which they were laid. This condition has resulted in much confusion concerning the laying of eggs by the lobster.

When the lobster hatches as a free-swimming larva, the period of fosterage is over for the female lobster. By fanning movements of the swimmerets the young are driven away from the body of the

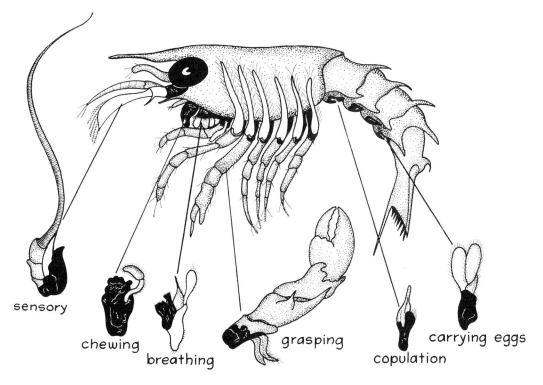

sensory

chewing

breathing

grasping

copulation

carrying eggs

FIG. 13-9. Young lobster, showing the undifferentiated appendages, together with the appendages as they will appear in the adult animal. Note how they are modified for specific functions. In the young form the appendages are designed primarily for locomotion, in the adult they take on a variety of functions.

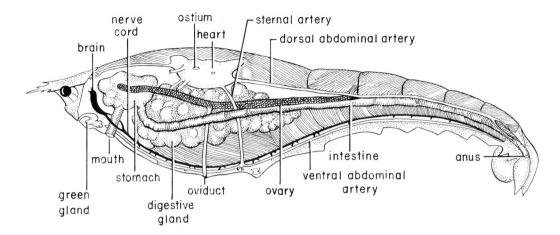

FIG. 13-10. Internal anatomy of the lobster.

mother. Young lobsters, however, tend to keep together in a cluster.

Growth. Molting is an important process for the crayfish and lobster, as it is for all of the arthropods. The manner in which this occurs was referred to earlier (p. 291). This is necessary in order to provide for increase in the animal's size, although a small amount of growth can occur under the rigid exoskeleton. Molting is so thorough that even the facets of the eyes and the lining of a part of the gut are included. Once the old skeleton is cast off, the animal grows rapidly for a period of time as a result of taking in a great deal of water. For several days during the hardening period the animal remains in hiding, and it becomes aggressive again only after its skeleton is well hardened.

Another interesting characteristic of many crustaceans, associated with growth and reproduction, is **autotomy,** the power to sever appendages. The fiddler crab affords a most striking example of this phenomenon. If one of its posterior legs is held with a forceps, it will drop off readily (Fig. 13-14). As other legs are pinched, they too are dropped but with increasing resistance,

until but three remain. Then the crab must be stimulated rather drastically before it will leave these behind. It seems to sense the danger of being legless, even though it will later acquire a new set through **regeneration.** The value of autotomy is obvious; it enables the animal to escape with the loss of a single appendage, whereas without this ability it might not escape at all. The break always occurs at a certain place near the base of the leg. There is a constriction of the wall at this point so that the loss of the appendage is followed by only a minor loss of blood.

The lost parts are replaced by the slow regeneration of a new appendage. This occurs more readily in young animals than in older ones, although the ability to regenerate seems to remain throughout life. Perhaps due to the greater specialization of these animals, regeneration is limited to the appendages and to the eyes, and thus is much less pronounced than in the lower forms of animals. This is as might be expected, since the greater the integration of parts, the more dependent each one is on the other, and the less possibility there is for any part to replace the whole animal. The ability to regenerate is reduced still further in the vertebrates.

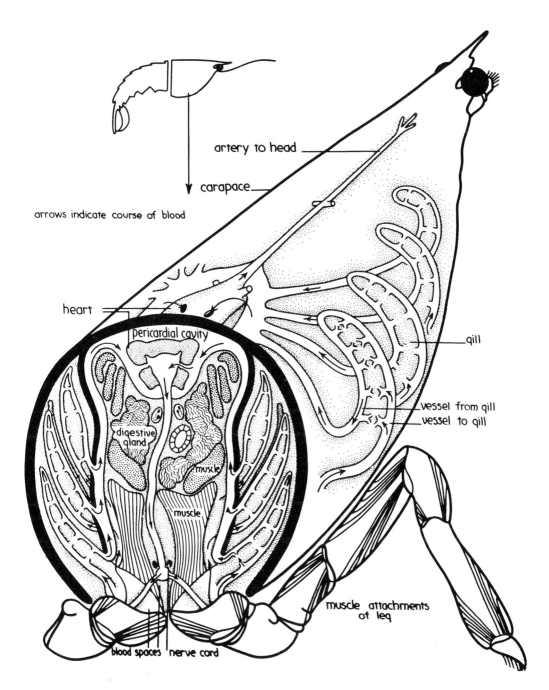

artery to head

carapace

arrows indicate course of blood

heart

pericardial cavity

gill

digestive gland

muscle

vessel from gill
vessel to gill

muscle

muscle attachments of leg

blood spaces   nerve cord

FIG. 13-11. Cross-section and partial side view of the lobster to show the internal organs, circulatory system in particular.

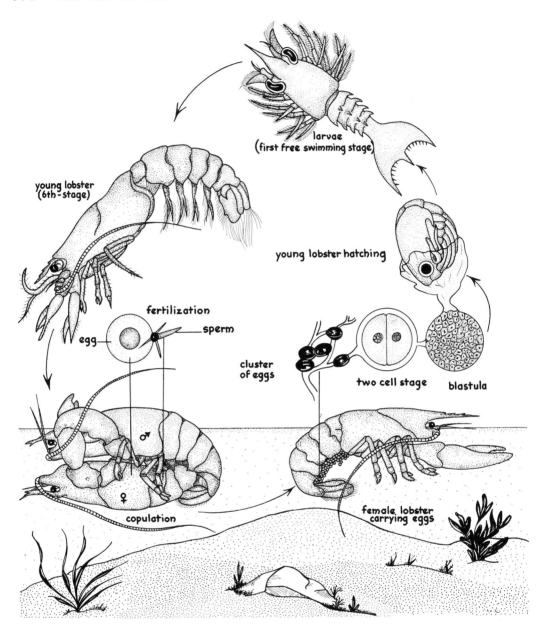

FIG. 13-12. Life history of the lobster.

The Nervous System. In contrast to the rather meager sensory equipment of flatworms and annelids, the lobster and crayfish are well supplied with sense organs. If a small bit of liver is dropped in one end of an aquarium containing a crayfish, very shortly the animal will orient itself in the proper direction and move directly toward the food. The soluble parts of meat diffuse through the water and touch tiny hairs on the chelipeds, antennules, antennae, and mouth parts, causing impulses to pass to the central nervous system. This sensitivity to chemicals is equivalent to man's senses of taste and smell.

The animal's ability to move about satisfactorily in total darkness indicates that it must have senses that guide it under such conditions. The sensory structures involved here are the tactile hairs which are stimulated whenever any part of the body comes in contact with an object. Tactile hairs are particularly abundant on the chelipeds, at the end of the telson, on mouth parts, and underneath the body. They may also be sensitive to vibrations in the water, thus providing the animal with a "hearing" mechanism which functions somewhat like the ears of vertebrates.

The animal is continually responsive to gravity, even when swimming freely, which means that it must have organs of equilibrium. These organs are the **statocysts,** located at the base of the antennules. They consist of small cuticular sacs, containing tiny grains of sand, which are glued to small sensory hairs (Fig. 13-15). The nerve fibers from these sensory hairs join to form a large nerve leading to the brain. The proof of the function of these statocysts can be determined experimentally. During the molt the cuticular lining of the statocysts, together with their grains of sand, are lost, so that the crayfish must replace its sand grains (**statoliths**) after each molt. Shortly after molting, the crayfish buries its head in the sand and thus fills the statocysts through its opening on the dorsal side of the antennule. A biologist working with a marine shrimp, *Paleomonetes,* allowed the animal to molt in a clean aquarium, then supplied iron filings which it promptly added to its statocysts. When the animal was placed in a magnetic field, it oriented itself with respect to the pull of gravity and the pull of the magnet. The special function of the statoliths is their ability to respond more promptly to the pull of gravity than would be the case if only the tiny hairs were present.

The visual mechanism has become very complex in the arthropods. While arthropod eyes vary considerably, a description for the crayfish eye will convey a general

FIG. 13-13. A female crayfish carrying her eggs attached to the swimmerets. The eggs are about ready to hatch because close observation will reveal the embryos just under the shell of the egg. As a matter of fact, these did hatch the following day.

FIG. 13-14. The fiddler crab (*Uca*) shows remarkable sexual dimorphism. One of the claws of the male (above) is very large, whereas in the female (below) the claws are the same size. The male brandishes his large claw in the presence of a female. These animals live in burrows near the seashore.

Uca also shows autotomy to a marked degree. Some of the appendages of the female were grasped with a pair of forceps and squeezed until the crab threw them off. It released the appendages shown here readily. But no amount of pinching would force it to throw off the others. The lost appendages will soon regenerate.

idea for the entire phylum. The eyes are located on long movable stalks and can be protruded or retracted in order to improve the vantage point of the observer. The eye itself differs markedly from any vertebrate eye (Fig. 13-15). It has an outer rounded transparent surface called the **cornea**, which is divided into at least 2,000 tiny sections, or **facets.** The facets merely indicate the outer limits of the units, or **ommatidia,** which make up the eye of the crayfish. Each ommatidium is composed of the outer facet, which functions as a **lens,** a series of cells below, which make up a sensitive portion, the **retinula,** and heavily pigmented regions at the outer and inner ends of this cylinder (Fig. 13-15). The sensory cells of each retinula terminate in nerve fibers, which lead directly to the brain, and the

fibers from all the retinulae form a nerve equivalent to the **optic nerve** in vertebrates.

The eye functions as a very efficient organ for photoreception. Light falling upon the lens of a given ommatidium at the proper angle is focused on the sensitive region below and stimulates the sensory cells. Since the ommatidia are long cylinders, the animal sees tiny points (one for each ommatidium stimulated) which are parts of objects that come within its vision. The image is thus a **mosaic** in which the slightest movement is readily detected. This is true, however, only in bright light when the pigmented walls of each ommatidium are spread over the entire cylinder. In dim light the pigment recedes toward the two ends of the cylinders, so that the rays of light pass readily from one ommatidium to another. The animal then sees the image superimposed, so that movement is not easily discerned. The image may be more distinct in reduced light, however, than when seen as a mosaic pattern (Fig. 13-15). Thus the animal has a means of seeing under varying light conditions.

It is obvious that the Crustacea are well supplied with sense organs that make the animals aware of the outside world. How they interpret the incoming sensations

and respond to them depends on the development of the nervous system.

The crayfish and lobster possess a bilobed **brain,** relatively large when compared to that found in lower forms. The brain lies between the eyes and is connected with the **ventral nerve cord** by means of a pair of **circumesophageal connectives,** very similar to the arrangement found in the earthworm (Fig. 13-10). There is a large **subesophageal ganglion,** made up

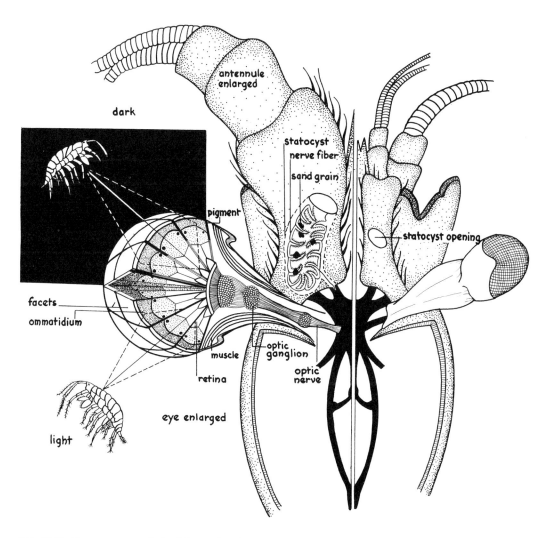

FIG. 13-15. Nervous system of the lobster, dorsal view. The eye and statocyst have been greatly enlarged and simplified in order to show their manner of function. The eye is further divided into two parts: the upper portion shows how it functions in the dark; the lower portion, how it functions in the light.

of six fused ganglia, followed by a series of ganglia, one for each segment. Large nerves extend out from the ganglia to the appendages and to other parts of the segment. Nervous coordination is supplemented by hormones which control color change, molting, and perhaps other activities (p. 292).

CLASS INSECTA

Insects are so widespread and numerous and touch upon man's life in so many ways that no one is entirely free from their influence, from the housewife who fights the ubiquitous fly and cockroach to the flea- and louse-bitten beggar who is constantly struggling to rid himself of these pests. Perhaps the most benefit derived from insects is from their work as pollinators of flowers. Many trees would bear no fruit if it were not for insects, and the same is true of such crops as clover and figs. Shellac is made from a secretion produced by certain lac insects in India; others produce a dye called cochineal. The cocoon of the silkworm is unwound and spun into silk thread used to make the fine silk cloth familiar to everyone.

On the debit side are those insects which carry disease, such as the mosquito (malaria, yellow fever, filariasis), the body louse (typhus), and the flea (bubonic plague). Even today these diseases are the cause of a vast amount of human misery. Bubonic plague alone wiped out from one-half to three-fourths of the population in vast areas of the world several centuries ago. Today approximately one-ninth of the population of the world is made wretched by malaria. With the eradication of the mosquito alone, much suffering would cease.

In addition to transmitting important human diseases, insects attack man's food and either destroy or actually consume it. Cereal grains both in the storage bins and in the fields are injured or destroyed by various types of insects. Clothes, furs, and upholstered furniture are eaten by the clothes moth. Not only the furniture, but the house itself can be tunneled and destroyed by termites.

Domestic animals are also harassed throughout their lives by numerous insects. The botfly causes most serious damage to the stomachs of horses, while the ox warble fly larvae bore holes in the skins of cattle causing them distress, and making the hide valueless for leather. Finally, there are the millions of gnats, flies, mosquitoes, and bugs that have a high-grade nuisance value, but do no special harm.

How is it that these small animals have so outstripped all other forms of life? First of all, their rigid exoskeleton has enabled them to invade the air and support themselves outside of water. This wax-coated cover prevents desiccation, an essential feature for an animal that divorces itself completely from an aquatic existence. They are the only invertebrates that have taken to the air. The wings of the insects have made it possible for them to travel long distances, thus not only increasing their ability to find food but also to spread themselves to new areas where they might thrive more successfully. Fortunately, present-day insects have never attained any great size. They range from microscopic dimensions to several inches in length.

Entomologists have grouped this vast array of insects into over 20 orders based on the following characteristics: (1) type of metamorphosis (p. 326), (2) presence or absence of wings, (3) character of the mouth parts, (4) the structure of the external genitalia. Many other characters are used to identify species, but these are the large general characters that separate the orders. Some of the orders are shown in Fig. 13-16. The best way to obtain an idea of the insect body plan is to study in some detail a generalized form with gradual metamorphosis, the grasshopper.

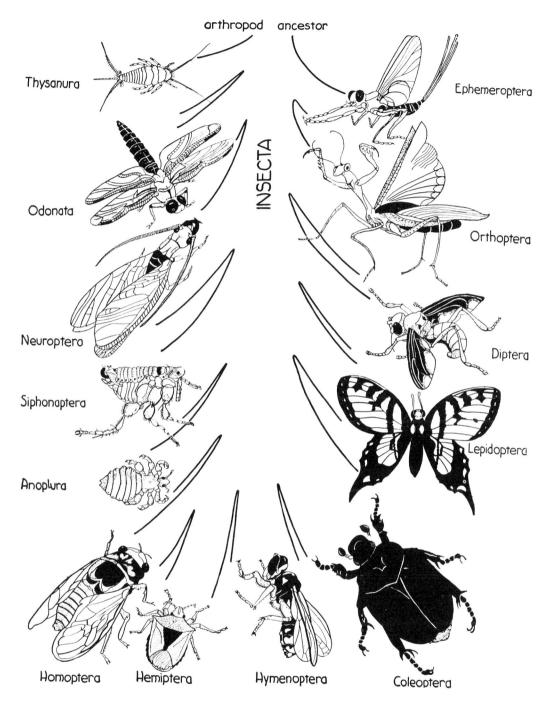

arthropod ancestor

Thysanura

Ephemeroptera

INSECTA

Odonata

Orthoptera

Neuroptera

Diptera

Siphonaptera

Lepidoptera

Anoplura

Coleoptera

Homoptera   Hemiptera   Hymenoptera

FIG. 13-16. The common orders of insects.

309

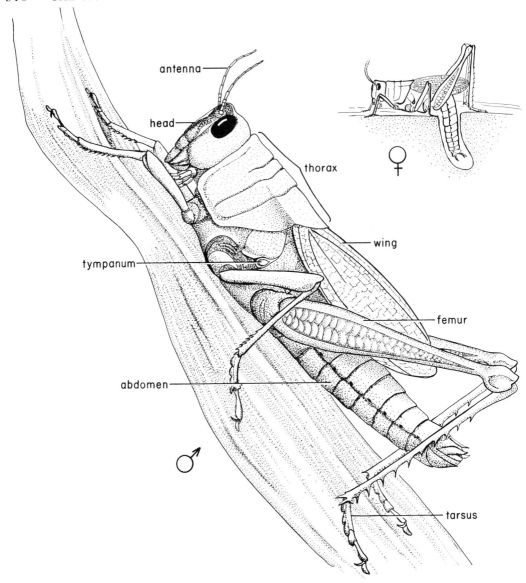

FIG. 13-17. External view of the grasshopper. Also female laying her eggs (upper right).

The Grasshopper

The grasshopper is selected because of its relatively large size and because it is well known to everyone. Furthermore, it shows certain primitive insect characteristics that make it easier to understand than other members of the group. Its many species are world-wide in distribution, living in and feeding on grass or any other available leafy vegetation. Sometimes certain species increase in such numbers that they become serious pests, great hordes devouring almost everything of plant origin, except wood, that lies in their path.

Structure. Externally, the grasshopper is divided into three parts, the movable **head,**

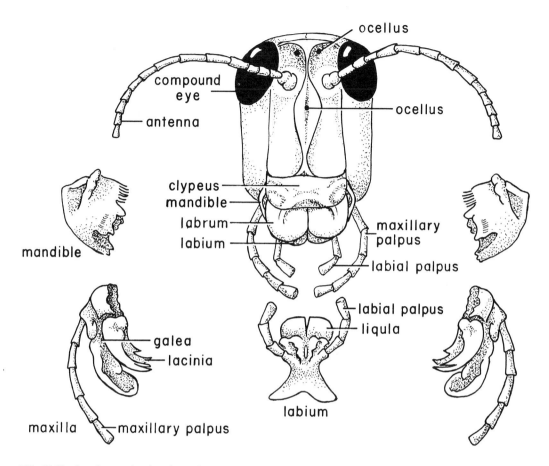

FIG. 13-18. Grasshopper head and mouth parts.

the **thorax,** and the **abdomen** (Fig. 13-17). There is a considerable amount of fusion of segments when compared to the crayfish. For example, the head appears as a single structure, but it is made up of six segments. Likewise, the thorax is composed of three segments, and there is a variable number of segments in the abdominal region, usually eleven. A pair of legs is attached to each of the three thoracic segments, and a pair of wings to each of the last two. The legs have several parts which, named from the body outward, are the **coxa, trochanter, femur, tibia,** and **tarsus.** The hind legs are long and well developed for jumping, whereas the other four are used in walking. The outer wings are leathery and rigid, serving as protective covers for the more membranous underwings. When the insect is at rest, the underwings, which are the propelling wings during flight, are neatly folded under the outer ones.

The **compound** eyes of the grasshopper are securely integrated into the head skeleton, but in other respects resemble those of the crayfish (Fig. 13-15). In addition, three small simple eyes, or **ocelli,** are located between the compound eyes (Fig. 13-18). The function of the ocelli is not understood. The single pair of antennae varies in length in different species of grasshoppers and functions as tactile as well as olfactory organs. Although most of the head is encased in a solid **epicranium,** the several mouth parts can be traced back to modifications in the crayfish appendage plan. There is a broad upper lip, the **labrum,** which is attached beneath the **clypeus.** A pair of lateral, dark-colored **mandibles** oppose one another in chewing in such a way as to make it convenient for the animal to bite the edge of a leaf without turning its head. Lying outside the mandibles are the paired **maxillae** (each composed of the **galea,** the **lacinia,** and the **palpus**), which are used in manipulating the food as it enters the mouth. The lower lip, the **labium,** possesses two small **palpi,** resembling the larger ones attached to the maxillae. Lying in the center of all these parts is the **tongue,** or **hypopharynx.** Together, these make an efficient chewing mechanism.

Digestive System. As food is taken in, it is copiously mixed with colorless saliva, secreted by several **salivary glands.** The food moves through the **esophagus** to the **crop** where it is stored, until it passes into and through the gizzard where it is ground to a fine consistency. The food then enters the **stomach** (Fig. 13-19) where digestion occurs by the action of **enzymes,** which are

secreted by eight double **digestive glands** or **caeca.** Finally the digested food passes into a large and then a small **intestine.** Small excretory tubules, the **Malpighian tubules,** empty into the anterior end of the large intestine. The gut opens into the **rectum,** and then to the outside through the **anus.**

Circulatory System. The body cavity of the grasshopper is the **hemocoel,** or blood cavity, not the coelom, as was the case in the earthworm. This is formed by a continued expansion of the vascular system until the entire coelom is obliterated, with the exception of the cavities of the gonads. The cavity is filled with a colorless blood which contains only leucocytes. Since the blood does not function as a conveyor of oxygen, it has no oxygen-carrying pigment as the blood of most other animals has. The blood is kept in motion by the action of the dorsal tube-like **heart,** composed of a number of chambers into which small **ostia** open (Fig. 13-19). The heart is surrounded by a **pericardial sinus,** which holds the blood before it enters the heart, much the same as in the crayfish. As the heart beats, blood moves forward and out into the hemocoel again. The heart has no oc-

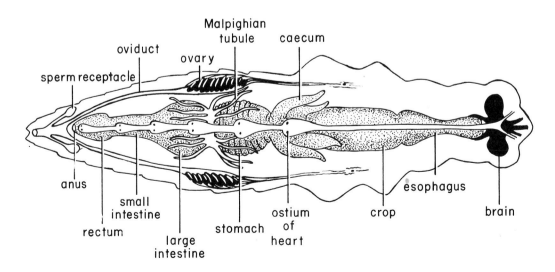

FIG. 13-19. Internal anatomy of the female grasshopper, dorsal view.

casion to be so active an organ as it is in many other animals, since respiration is carried on in another fashion.

Breathing System. The breathing system of insects and arachnids is unique in the animal world. Air, with its oxygen, is carried directly to the cells through a system of tubules called **tracheae** (Fig. 13-20). This very complex system consists of tiny tubes which must remain distended so that the air can pass freely in and out of them. Small chitinous **spiral threads** give support to the larger tubules and control their diameter. The smaller ones are filled with fluid in which gaseous exchange actually takes place (by diffusion). There are several openings into the tracheae along the thoracic and abdominal walls; these are called **spiracles.** A valve covers the opening so that the spiracle can be opened and closed during the breathing process. Leading in from the spiracles, the tubules become smaller and smaller until they are as small as capillaries and lie directly against the cells, supplying them with oxygen and carrying away the excreted carbon dioxide. The grasshopper also possesses several large air sacs which may be contracted to aid the movement of air through the many small tubules. The grasshopper contracts and enlarges its body, particularly the abdominal region, to facilitate the air flow; and the anterior spiracles open and close alternately with the posterior spiracles so that the air flows only one way.

Nervous System. While the grasshopper has many of the sense organs that the crayfish possesses, it lives in an air environment and therefore needs somewhat different methods of maintaining contact with its outside world. For example, the eyes and the tactile hairs which cover the various parts of its body resemble those of the crayfish, and it has organs of chemical sense on its antennae and mouth parts. However, the grasshopper and many other insects

have the means of making and receiving sound vibrations. In the grasshopper the organ for hearing is on the first segment of the abdomen (Fig. 13-20). In several respects this resembles the ears of higher vertebrates, in that it is composed of a stretched membrane, the **tympanum,** to which is attached a slender process that is connected to a nerve. The animal makes its characteristic clacking sound by rubbing its roughened hind femur against a wing vein.

As a result of the fusion of three head segments, the grasshopper possesses a rather large head with a highly developed brain consisting of three fused double ganglia. Nerves extend directly from the brain to the eyes, the antennae, and to a ganglionated cord running through the body. The first ganglion in the cord, the **subesophageal ganglion,** formed by two great nerves or connectives proceeding from the brain around the esophagus, is followed by three large ganglia in the thorax and five in the abdomen, where some fusion has gone on. Nerves go out to all parts of each segment and to the legs and wings, and there is also a fine network of nerves beneath the epidermis. The nervous system is somewhat better developed than that of the crayfish, as is indicated by both its structure and function.

Excretory System. The excretory organs, the **Malpighian tubules,** have already been mentioned in connection with the digestive tract. Insects are among the very few animals whose **excretory glands** (kidneys) open directly into the intestine (Fig. 13-19). The long, coiled tubules lying in the hemocoel are bathed in blood so that suspended nitrogenous wastes are easily removed. Uric acid has been found to be the end product of nitrogen metabolism in insects.

Reproductive System. On late August days it is common to see grasshoppers copulating. Some days after fertilization the fe-

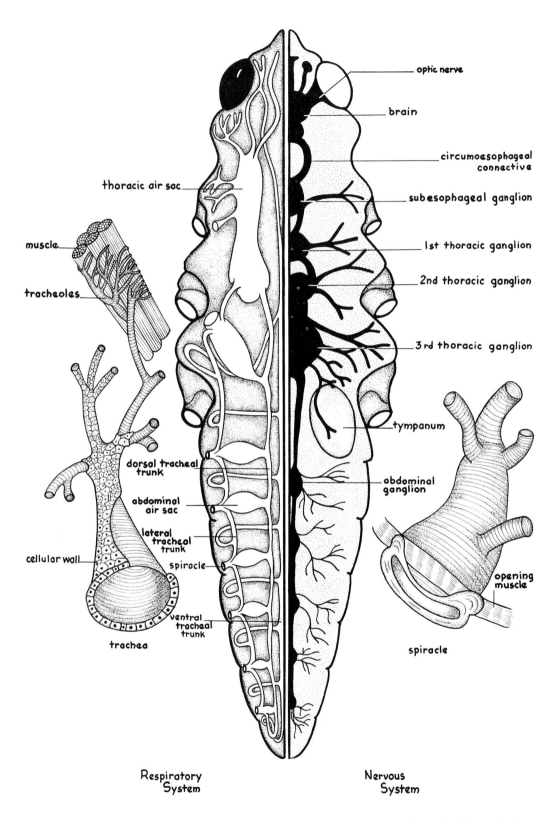

optic nerve

brain

circumoesophageal connective

subesophageal ganglion

1st thoracic ganglion

2nd thoracic ganglion

3rd thoracic ganglion

tympanum

abdominal ganglion

opening muscle

spiracle

thoracic air sac

muscle

tracheoles

dorsal tracheal trunk

abdominal air sac

lateral tracheal trunk

cellular wall

spiracle

ventral tracheal trunk

trachea

Respiratory System

Nervous System

FIG. 13-20. Dorsal view of the breathing and nervous systems of the grasshopper. Trachea and a few muscle fibers are drawn in detail at the left; the spiracle and end of the trachea to the right.

314

male grasshopper lays her eggs. She uses her powerful pointed **ovipositor** for digging a hole in the soil where the eggs are deposited, together with a mucous substance which cements them into a packet, known as a **pod.** She lays about 20 eggs at a time, and may deposit as many as 10 pods before death overtakes her some days after the egg laying is accomplished. The eggs begin to develop as soon as they are laid and become well-formed embryos before cold weather sets in. The embryos then undergo a rest period, the **diapause,** in which they pass the winter. In the warm spring days, development is resumed and the embryos hatch in early summer as **nymphs** (Fig.

13-40), which resemble the adult grasshopper without wings. Nymphs undergo several molts during their subsequent rapid growth, the wings appearing and becoming longer at each shedding period. It is during this period of rapid growth, when their bodies demand so much food, that the animals are so destructive to crops. The summer is spent leisurely, feeding and growing, until the breeding season begins.

The sex organs of the male and female grasshopper consist of a pair of **testes** and **ovaries** respectively. The testes are made up of several small tubules or follicles, which are joined to the **seminal vesicle** by means of the **vas deferens;** the seminal vesicle then

FIG. 13-21. The dragonfly (*Aeschna*) is noted for its excellent powers of flight and its enormous eyes. It captures mosquitoes and other insects while in full flight. Its two large eyes may possess as many as 30,000 ommatidia, and for that reason are probably excellent photoreceptors. Its antennae are rudimentary and are probably of little importance to the animal.

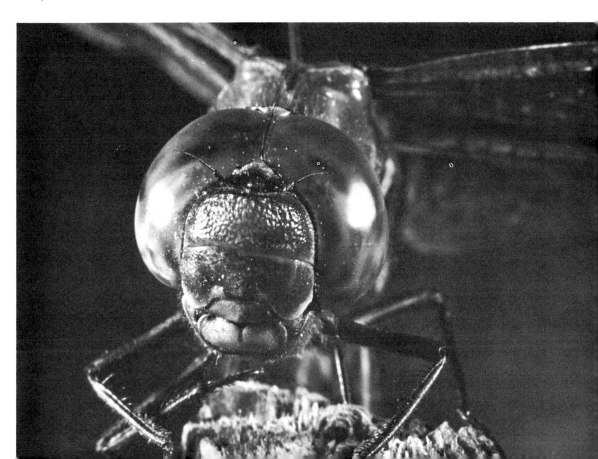

joins the ejaculatory duct and copulatory organ, the **penis.** A pair of accessory glands secrete a fluid in which the sperms are suspended. The large ovaries are composed of several egg tubes in which the eggs develop; two oviducts extend from the ovaries and join to form the **vagina** (Fig. 13-19). A pair of accessory glands is also present in the female, which contributes to the eggs during their formation.

Modifications in Form and Function

Although all insects, with few exceptions, have body parts similar to those of the grasshopper, there are wide modifications in these parts in different species. Starting at the anterior end of the insect and working posteriorly, some of the modifications are as follows: The antennae may be very short, as in the dragonfly (Fig. 13-21), or they may be very long, as in the long-horned grasshoppers, in each case performing a specific function that requires the particular type of antennae in question.

FIG. 13-22. The larval dragonfly is equipped with mouth parts that are adapted for catching other insects in the water, where it lives until it becomes an adult. The upper picture shows the parts thrust out in the striking position; in the lower picture they are retracted where they are held except when in use.

The eyes may be extremely large, as in the dragonfly, where they detect the flying mosquitoes which the airplane-like insect pursues. Or they may be absent, as in some termites, which work in the dark.

The mouth parts vary widely in form and function. The larval dragonfly has a formidable weapon for catching its prey (Fig. 13-22). The butterfly has a long tube which is carried in a coil under its "chin" when not in use, but, when stretched out during the process of taking nectar from a flower, it may be as long as the animal itself. The cicada possesses a stiff beak which is used in penetrating plant tissues to obtain the juices on which it feeds (Fig. 13-23). There are also the thin dart-like mouth parts of the mosquito which can pierce the skin very delicately and withdraw its meal of blood, at the same time injecting a small amount of saliva to prevent the blood from clotting. The mouth parts of all insects are homologous; yet, witness the variety of functions they perform.

The thorax of most insects bears two pairs of wings and three pairs of legs, all of which are variously modified in different insects. The appendages of the honeybee are an excellent example. They are modified for pollen gathering and other functions associated with its mode of life (Fig. 13-24). During a visit to a flower, the bee gathers some pollen with its mandibles and moistens it with honey. Pollen is also obtained from the action of the **pollen brushes** on the front two pairs of legs which clean the anterior portion of the body. The pollen is then carried to the **pollen packer** (on the third pair of legs) which is composed of two parts, the **auricle** and the **pecten.** Once the pollen has reached this position, the tarsus is flexed on the tibia, packing the pollen from the bottom into the **pollen basket.** Large quantities of pollen may be collected in this manner so that when the bees fly home, the huge balls of pollen cause the hind legs to dangle much lower than when they are not so loaded.

FIG. 13-23. The mouth parts of the cicada (*Tibicen*) are modified to form a stiff beak, which it uses in piercing twigs in order to obtain the sap, its chief source of food.

The anterior pair of legs has two cleaning mechanisms, an **eye brush** and an **antenna cleaner,** which the bee uses to remove pollen from these organs. The antenna cleaner is composed of a **velum,** a small flexible projection from the tibia, and a crescent-shaped depression on the proximal end of the tarsus, lined with short bristles. The antenna is brought into this depression and pulled through several times to clean it. In addition to the pollen brush on the middle pair of legs, there is also a **spur,** which is used in picking and transferring wax in the process of comb-building.

Insect legs may all be the same size and used for walking or running, or they may be modified for jumping, as in the case of the grasshopper. Other modifications include the paddle-like feet for swimming, the digging legs for excavating, as in the mole cricket (**Fig. 13-25**), and the pincer-like legs for grasping prey, as in the praying mantis (**Fig. 13-26**).

Wings of insects are formed as thin sacs, by evaginations from the thoracic wall, through which tracheae make their way. Eventually the sacs collapse and the walls unite and harden, the "veins" being formed by the trachea. Some insects, such as the wasp (**Fig. 13-27**), have membranous wings, while others, like the beetle (**Fig. 13-28**), have hard anterior wings (**elytra**) that fold over and protect the soft posterior membranous wings. Some wings are modified for making a sound, as in the case of the cricket (**Fig. 13-29**), in which the wings are

rubbed together to make the characteristic chirp of this insect.

The bee has two pairs of delicate membranous wings which can operate either separately or locked together by means of a row of hooks that fasten into a groove in the posterior margin of the forewing (**Fig. 13-24**). During a straight flight, where speed is essential, the wings are locked together and the bee flies as if it had only two wings. The question of flight in insects has been a puzzling one, not only to biologists but to engineers as well. Flight in insects is brought about in a peculiar manner, namely, not by wing muscles, as in the case of birds, but by powerful muscles which cause the thorax to vibrate and this in turn forces the wings to flap up and down. In Figure 13-30 this is illustrated. As the anterior-posterior thoracic muscles contract, the dorsal wall of the thorax (**tergum**) is forced upward. This pulls the dorsal basal edge of the wing upward, causing the wing as a whole to be forced downward with considerable force; the body wall acts as a fulcrum. The upstroke is accomplished by the sudden contraction of the dorsal-ventral muscles in a similar manner. Thus the wings move up and down by the throbbing of the thorax and not by any effort on the part of the wing itself. Its pitch can be altered so that the bee can hover, fly forward, or fly backward with ease. Bees are capable of long flights, sometimes as long as 10 miles.

The chief modification in the abdominal region of insects is the ovipositor of the

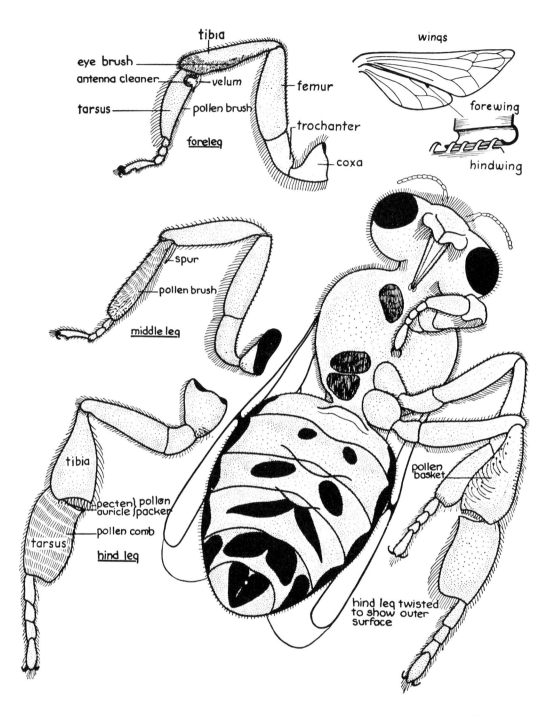

tibia

eye brush

antenna cleaner

velum

tarsus

pollen brush

foreleg

femur

trochanter

coxa

wings

forewing

hindwing

spur

pollen brush

middle leg

tibia

pecten) pollen
auricle) packer

pollen comb

tarsus

hind leg

pollen
basket

hind leg twisted
to show outer
surface

FIG. 13-24. Ventral view of the worker honeybee to show modification of the legs for carrying pollen. In the upper right corner a small portion of the fore and hind wings are drawn to show how the wings may be hooked together during flight.

FIG. 13-25. The mole cricket, *Gryllotalpa hexadactyla*, has highly modified anterior appendages which are efficient burrowing feet.

female. This has been described for the grasshopper. In the honeybee it has been modified into a **sting**. This organ has become a complicated apparatus, retaining the muscles which made it possible for the grasshopper to deposit its eggs in hard soil. In the sting these muscles enable the bee to force sharp-grooved **darts** into the tough skin of an intruder. A pair of **feelers** on either side of the darts "selects" the spot where the sting is to be released. Lying between the upper ends of the darts is the **poison sac** which is in contact by means of ducts with an **alkaline** and an **acid gland**. During the stinging procedure the poison sac is squeezed, and its product is forced into the wound made by the darts. This substance causes much of the pain and swelling associated with the sting of the bee. Once a worker stings, its darts become firmly fixed in the skin of the recipient so that the entire apparatus and sometimes other internal organs are torn out when the bee leaves. A day or two later this results in the death of the bee. Queens use their sting in battle with other queens, but are able to use it over and over again without the injury which results to workers.

In some insects, however, the ovipositor is developed in a most extraordinary fashion. Thus in the Ichneumon fly, it is several times as long as the body and can drill a hole in wood an inch or more deep. Since

this insect lays its eggs in the body of the larval wood beetle, such an apparatus is essential.

The overall color of insects varies as much as it does in birds, from the brilliant iridescent green Japanese beetle and highly colored butterflies to the inconspicuous

FIG. 13-26. The praying mantis (*Tenodera sinensis*) has its anterior legs modified into grasping appendages. It gets its name from its posture while waiting for some unwary insect to approach within striking distance. It is one of the larger insects, reaching 4 inches in length. Recently hatched young are shown in the lower photograph.

FIG. 13-27. The four wings of the mud-dauber wasp (*Chalybian californicum*) are membranous, but sturdy. Note the threadlike nature of the anterior part of the abdomen which is the source of the term "wasp waist." These insects often locate their mud homes under the eaves of houses. They lay their eggs in specially constructed chambers, each of which is supplied with spiders upon which the newly hatched larva feeds.

drab color of the housefly and the camouflaged walking stick. The colors are either in the exoskeleton or they are produced by differential interference of light impinging on regular minute depressions and elevations in the cuticula. Some insects resemble other insects or parts of their environment. One species of fly, for example, resembles and even acts like a bee, thereby taking advantage of the protection of the bee's sting, even though it has none itself. This is called **mimicry**. The mimic takes advantage of the weapon carried by other

FIG. 13-28. The forewings of beetles are hard and without veins, and the hindwings are membranous. This is clearly demonstrated in the familiar potato beetle (*Leptinotarsa decemlineata*) which is destructive to potatoes as well as other crops throughout the United States and Europe.

insects, simply by resembling it in both coloration and action, and is thus able to discourage its normal enemies. Some even mimic sticks or twigs (Fig. 13-31).

There are numerous modifications in the breathing systems. Although most of the insects breathe air, some, such as caddis fly larvae, receive their oxygen by means of thin gills and can get along perfectly well under water. These gills are not, however, in any way homologous to the gills of Crustacea. It is clear that the insects became air-breathing arthropods and that only a few have secondarily gone back into the water during their larval life. It is also interesting to note that they have taken only to fresh water and not to salt water. This would be expected, since the osmotic pressure of the tissues of insects is quite different from that of the sea today, although it may have been the same when the insects, or their progenitors, left their marine life long ago. It must be mentioned, however, that some vertebrates, such as turtles, seals, and whales were able to overcome this difficulty and returned to the sea. Finally, some insect larvae can survive in the mud at the bottom of bodies of water where oxygen is absent. They receive their oxygen by breaking down organic matter there, just as many anaerobic forms of life do.

The digestive systems of insects vary considerably, depending on their type of diet. Furthermore, the diet may differ widely during the larval and adult stages: the butterfly, for instance, feeds on leafy vegetation as a larva, and on nectar as an adult. Feeding may be confined to certain stages of the life cycle and absent in others. Such insects as the May flies and fishflies feed only as larval forms, the adults living but a few days during which time food is unnecessary. The adult stage is devoted to mating and egg-laying. Among mosquitoes, the male mates and dies, never feeding at any time on blood, whereas the female of some species must obtain a blood meal before her eggs will mature. She has a

FIG. 13-29. In some insects the appendages are used in making sounds. Here the male (left) cricket (*Acheta pennsylvanica*) chirps by rubbing its front wings together during courtship. Note the long ovipositor in the female, which is used for depositing the eggs in soil.

voracious appetite and is able to take a meal of blood equal to several times her body weight. Some insects, like the praying mantis (Fig. 13-26), are carnivores (meat eaters), others, like the grasshopper, are herbivores (vegetable eaters), and still others, like the cockroach, are omnivores (both meat and vegetable eaters). However, almost any one of them can be forced to change its usual dietary habits when it is confronted with starvation.

The sense organs and nervous systems have become greatly modified among the insects. The central nervous system of some of the lower insects does not differ greatly from that found in the earthworm, while in others, like the honeybee, there has been a great deal of fusion of ganglia and an apparently higher or more closely knit coordination of parts (Fig. 13-32). They are equipped with elaborate sense organs which are responsible for their complicated behavior (Fig. 13-33). Their compound eyes are generally similar to those of the crayfish. Since a great many experiments have been performed with honeybees, a considerable amount is known about their powers of discrimination. **Von Frisch,** a brilliant Austrian zoologist, discovered that whereas they could not discriminate among variousshaped solid objects, they could detect open figures such as circles, rectangles, squares, or two closely placed lines (Fig. 13-34). He discovered this by placing a food source over cards with various figures and designs on them and observing the association made by the bees between the kind of figures and the food. He concluded that the bee

is able to discern only discontinuity in a pattern and not its shape. Its eye records interruptions which the bee counts as it moves past the pattern in flight. Von Frisch also demonstrated that bees see color, but not as we do. They recognize four colors,

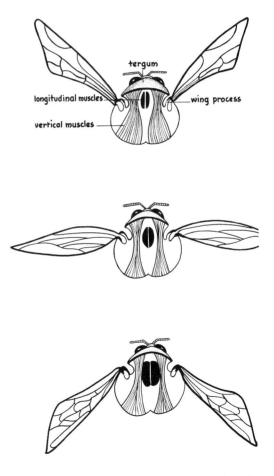

FIG. 13-30. Cross-section of the bee showing how the wings function during flight.

321

FIG. 13-31. A Panamanian orthopteran (*Pseudoceroys* sp.) which resembles the twigs of its environment. When disturbed, it becomes rigid and takes a pose that resembles a twig. Even its eggs (bottom) resemble the debris on the forest floor.

one of which is ultraviolet, a color we cannot see. The others are violet, blue-green, and yellow-orange. Bees have an excellent sense of smell which is made possible by sense organs located on the antennae.

Von Frisch also studied the bees' communication system which has been referred to as the "language of the bees." By carefully controlled experiments he found that when bees return to the hive after finding a source of nectar or pollen, they go through a kind of dance in which they walk forward, wagging their abdomens rapidly, then circling and repeating the process. At other times they simply walk in circles (Fig. 13-35). These he called the "wagging" dance and the "circling" dance respectively. Other bees in the hive follow the dance closely with their antennae (the hives are dark) and pick up information which guides them to the source of food. By moving the artificial food source, carefully tagging the bees, and following their course, Von Frisch discovered that the circling dance meant that the source was less than 100 meters away, whereas the wagging dance meant that it was beyond that distance. During the wagging dance the bee also indicates the direction in which the source lies as well as the approximate distance (indicated by the number of turns per minute). The information is given so effectively that they can find the source even if a large obstacle, such as a small hill, lies between the hive and the source. In this case the information is given in the proper direction, but the distance is indicated as that required to go around the obstacle. This ability of the bees to communicate in such an intricate manner is remarkable. Certainly other lower animals possess equally remarkable behavior.

Another means of communication is illustrated by the firefly, which is able to produce a light that seems to bring the sexes together at the mating season. Most insects are remarkably sensitive to chemicals, especially in the air, greatly exceeding man in this respect. Some leave a faint scent which

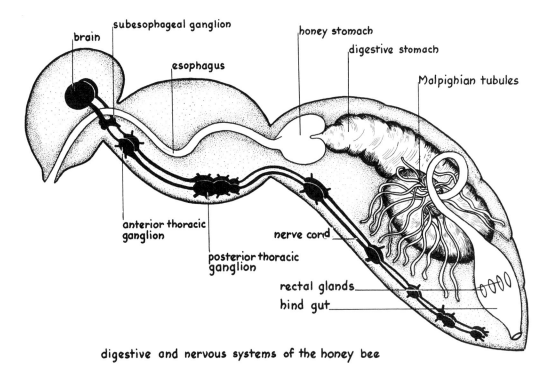

brain
subesophageal ganglion
esophagus
honey stomach
digestive stomach
Malpighian tubules
anterior thoracic ganglion
nerve cord
posterior thoracic ganglion
rectal glands
hind gut

digestive and nervous systems of the honey bee

FIG. 13-32. Side view showing some of the internal anatomy of the bee.

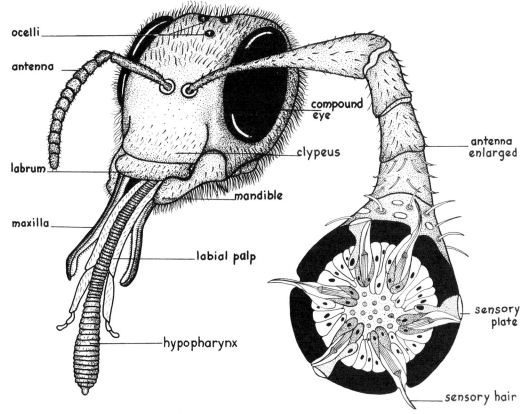

ocelli
antenna
labrum
maxilla
compound eye
clypeus
mandible
labial palp
hypopharynx
antenna enlarged
sensory plate
sensory hair

FIG. 13-33. The head of the bee, showing the mouth parts. An antenna has been enlarged in cross-section to show the details of the sensory end-organs.

323

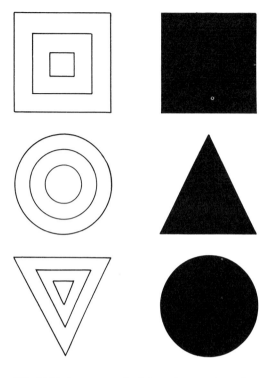

FIG. 13-34. Bees cannot discriminate between the various shaped objects indicated in this sketch but they can distinguish between any pair of objects, open and solid.

on the inside of a window screen. Very shortly a great many males, detecting her presence either by odors or by the production of sound, will collect on the outside of the screen. The male mosquito has a very large feathery antenna with which he can detect aerial vibrations coming from the female as much as a quarter of a mile away.

The social insects represent a very high development of the nervous system, perhaps the highest in the invertebrates. There is a long series of gradations from the solitary insects to those which aggregate during hibernation or migration, like some grasshoppers and the monarch butterfly. From such species have come the true social forms which live together in large numbers and have developed various castes, as in the honeybee (Fig. 13-36). The change in the various castes has been fundamental because it involves hormonal changes which in turn alter the anatomy of the caste, as, for example, the development of the large mandibles of certain of the soldiers among some species of termites. In this group, in addition to the soldiers which protect the colony, there are the workers, the males, and the queen. In some ant colonies there are as many as 27 different types of individuals, not all present at once but occurring at some time during the history of the col-

is detected by other members of the species, usually of the opposite sex. It is a common schoolroom experiment to place a female *Cecropia* moth, as she emerges in the spring,

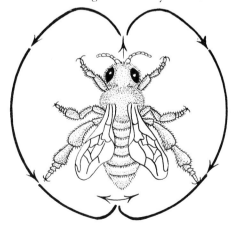

Circle dance   Wagging dance

FIG. 13-35. Behavior of the bee during its circle and wagging dance.

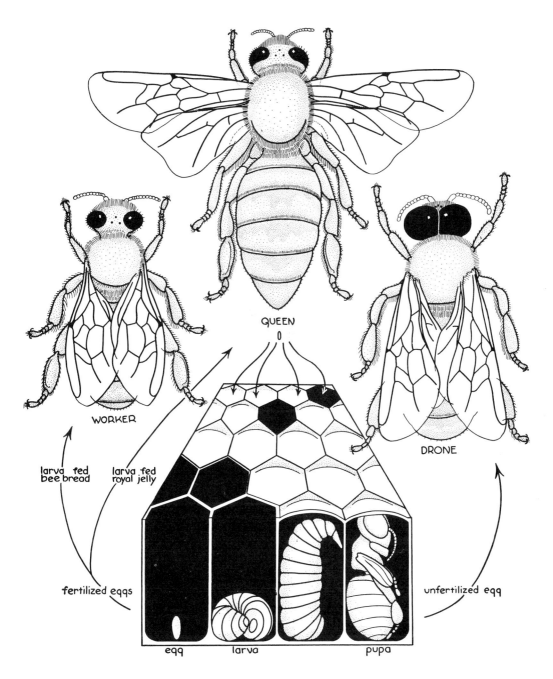

QUEEN

WORKER

DRONE

larva fed
bee bread

larva fed
royal jelly

fertilized eggs

unfertilized egg

egg   larva   pupa

FIG. 13-36. Life history of the honeybee.

FIG. 13-37. The leaf cutting ants (*Atta* sp.) possess complex patterns of social behavior. They cut uniformly sized pieces of a leaf, usually from tall trees, and carry them to their nest. The leaves serve as food for fungi, which serve as food for the ant. These ants inhabit Barro Colorado, an island in Gatun Lake, Canal Zone. Note the "hitchhiker" on one of the leaves.

ony. Each type performs certain duties and fits into the harmonious operation of this complex society.

Ants seem to have followed the food habits of man, at least in their methods of providing a food supply. The more primitive ants merely feed as carnivores, but pastoral ants take aphids into their nests and feed them, gathering the honeydew (an excretory product) from them in repayment for their efforts. The harvester ants show further development by carrying cereal grains into their burrow to supply them with food during the winter. Finally, the most advanced are those ants which gather a certain species of fungus and plant it in underground gardens, tending it even to the point of adding humus as fertilizer (Fig. 13-37). Such behavior represents a very complex interrelationship of instincts.

The termites also have reached a high level of colonial organization. One of the most striking aspects is the size of the colonies as indicated by the tremendous homes or "hills" that they build (Fig. 13-38). The most spectacular are found in Africa and Australia.

In the reproduction of insects, fertilization is internal. Most insects lay eggs (oviparous) and deposit them in a place where development of the larvae is most apt to succeed. This may be in the body of another insect, the tissues of a plant, the ground, the water or even on the body of the male (Fig. 13-39). In some species as in the housefly, the eggs hatch very soon, while in others many weeks or even months are required. Certain flies and all of the aphids bring forth active young (ovoviviparous). The eggs of some insects develop without fertilization by a sperm, that is, by **parthenogenesis.** The drone bee develops from an unfertilized egg (Fig. 13-36). Parthenogenesis is commonly found among the aphids, where the females lay eggs all through the summer months which hatch only into females. As fall approaches, the eggs produce both males and females. Fertilization then occurs and the resulting eggs remain over winter and hatch into females again in the spring. The number of offspring produced by one individual varies widely among different insect species. Some of the viviparous flies, for example, produce only a few offspring, whereas the queen bee may lay a million eggs in her lifetime. Under optimum conditions the housefly, if unchecked, could increase in one summer to such proportions as to cover the earth completely, for it goes through its entire life cycle in eight days if the temperature is high enough (80–90°F).

The manner of development from egg to adult varies among many animals and is particularly striking among the insects. The term **metamorphosis,** which means change in form, is applied to any animal that undergoes more or less marked changes of form between the time of hatching and of reaching the adult state (Fig. 13-40). A few primitive insects merely increase in size after hatching, showing no metamorphosis. Others, such as the grasshopper, hatch into a **nymph,** which resembles the adult fairly closely except for the wings which are acquired much later. Such change is known as **gradual metamorphosis.** Some, such as the dragonfly, hatch into a larva (Fig. 13-22), which resembles the adult to some extent, but not as much as the nymph resembles the adult grasshopper. This type of change is called **incomplete metamorphosis.** In the case of the bee (Fig. 13-36), housefly, and June beetle, the larval stage does not resemble the adult in any way (Figs. 13-41, 13-42); the larva is wormlike and usually its diet varies radically from that of the adult. Moreover, between the larval and the adult stage there is a "resting" stage, known as the **pupa,** during which time the larval body is transformed into the adult body. This type of change is known as **complete metamorphosis.** As we have already seen, hormones play an important part in metamorphosis. Other aspects of metamorphosis as it appears in other animals will be discussed in later chapters.

OTHER ARTHROPODS

There are several other classes of less important arthropods that need to be men-

FIG. 13-38. Some species of termites build tremendous homes, called "ant hills," as indicated in the top photograph. These reach as much as 15 feet in height. Others, such as the "magnetic ants," orient their hill north and south, hence their name. Both species occur in northern Australia.

tioned. Of the chelicerate arthropods, the classes **Xiphosurida** and **Arachnida** will be briefly considered.

The horseshoe or king crab, *Limulus* (Fig. 13-43), belongs to the class Xiphosurida and is of interest because it is a member of a very ancient group of animals. Since it is the only member left of a once very successful group of animals, it is called a "living fossil." It was dominant in the Cambrian period and has somehow been able to continue to the present, whereas millions of its relatives have become extinct. It is found in great numbers along our Atlantic coast, from Maine to Central America.

The class Arachnida includes the scorpions, ticks, and spiders. The scorpions are elongated with large, fierce-looking pincers held out in front when they are on the move (Fig. 13-44). The long, thin abdomen terminates in a sharp-pointed sting which inflicts an irritating, and sometimes fatal, wound on man as well as insects and spiders which make up its diet. It is active at night and hides by day under logs and rocks. Of much greater importance are the ticks and mites, many of which parasitize

FIG. 13-39. (top) Some insects, such as certain braconid flies (not a fly but a relative of the honeybee), lay their eggs inside the body of other insect larvae as shown here. The large sphinx-moth caterpillar in this case supplies the food for the developing fly larvae, which finally break through the skin and spin their white cocoons. The attack usually means death to the caterpillar. (bottom) The female water bug lays her eggs on the back of her spouse who carries them about until they hatch.

FIG. 13-41. Insects such as beetles undergo complete metamorphosis during their development. The larva shows no resemblance to the adult and frequently lives in quite a different environment. This is a larva, "grub worm," of the June beetle which matures in the soil, feeding on underground vegetation. Note the nine dark spiracles.

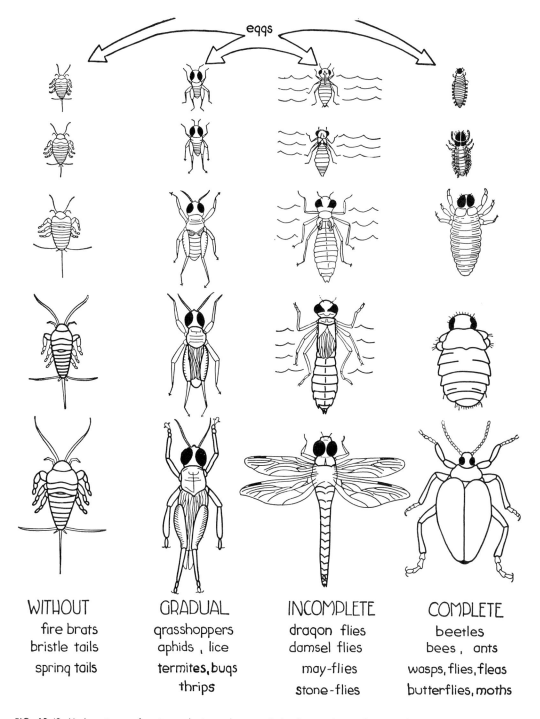

eggs

WITHOUT	GRADUAL	INCOMPLETE	COMPLETE
fire brats	grasshoppers	dragon flies	beetles
bristle tails	aphids, lice	damsel flies	bees, ants
spring tails	termites, bugs	may-flies	wasps, flies, fleas
	thrips	stone-flies	butterflies, moths

FIG. 13-40. Various types of metamorphosis, and some of the insects that undergo each type.

329

FIG. 13-42. Butterflies and moths undergo complete metamorphosis from egg to adult. These are photographs of the stages of development of the *Cecropia* moth. (Top) Recently hatched eggs. (Second) larva a few days old. (Third) Pupa lying within its cocoon. Note the impressions made by the developing antenna and wings. (Bottom) The adult.

FIG. 13-43. The king crab (*Limulus*), or horseshoe crab, is a distant relative of the spiders and scorpions and is not a crustacean at all. It is a "living fossil" whose close relatives have all become extinct many millions of years ago.

Note the leaf-like flaps just back of the legs. These are the book gills, so called because when in use the flaps wave in the water like the pages of a book. The snails (*Crepidula*) find it advantageous to "hitch hike" on the crab, thus affording them a much more extensive feeding area than they could ever attain under their own power. Note the track it makes in the sand when out of water. While clumsy on land *Limulus* moves effectively along the ocean floor where it shovels in the mud searching for worms of various kinds that make up its diet.

man and his domestic animals (Fig. 13-45). Some of these are intermediate hosts for certain microbes which cause serious diseases such as spotted fever, undulant fever, and tularemia.

The most common members of this class are the spiders, which are feared and destroyed by man, yet almost all of them are beneficial because they feed upon insects, many of which are pests. Spiders build delicate webs in which flying insects are trapped and sucked dry by the owner of the web. The thread of the spider web is made by forcing a fluid containing long protein molecules through a tiny orifice which causes the molecules to align themselves in one direction. The fact that they are so arranged causes them to become semisolid, hence a thread. Other spiders chase and catch their prey; still others leap upon it and kill it by piercing the body with their sharp fangs (Fig. 13-46) and injecting a small quantity of poison that simply paralyzes the insect until it is consumed by the spider. Such a paralyzed insect may stay in a fresh condition for a long time—a kind of room-temperature refrigeration. Some of the tarantulas may feed voraciously when food is available, but when it is scarce they may go for months without food and remain in good health. Although most spiders live only a year or so, tarantulas have been kept in captivity for as long as 28 years.

The bite of most spiders is harmless, even the bite of the large tarantula being no more serious than a bee sting. There is one species, however, which is very common in the United States, which can cause serious illness and death. This is the black widow, *Lactrodectus mactans* (Fig. 13-47), the female of which is three-fourths of an inch long, and glistening black. On the ventral side is a bright red hour-glass-shaped figure, which is a positive means of identification. It lives normally in piles of rocks, lumber, and more recently around buildings, particularly garages. It has been known to

FIG. 13-44. The common scorpion (*Vejovis*) of the Southwest is an arachnid like the spider. It hides by day and hunts spiders and insects at night. The sting at the tip of the tail is an effective weapon against predators and is useful in capturing prey. It sucks the body fluids from its prey. Its sting is sometimes fatal to humans.

cling to the underside of automobiles, thus being transported to all parts of the country.

The life history of the spider is rather unique in some respects. The male is always smaller than the female and in some cases, such as the black widow, he is hardly recognizable because of his proportionately minute size. He spins a web upon which he deposits his sperm in a mass, which is then picked up by specially formed front appendages and carried while searching

FIG. 13-45. The anatomical characteristics of the tick are well illustrated by this photograph of the Gulf Coast tick (*Amblyomma maculatum*) which bites cattle. Note the eight legs terminating with sharp hooks for clinging to the host and the mouth parts well suited for piercing the skin.

FIG. 13-46. American tarantula (*Euryplema*), one of the largest of all spiders. They are harmless if properly handled and live to a ripe old age in captivity. This specimen was 28 years old (estimated) when it died.

The dorsal view is shown. Note the four pairs of legs and the "hairy" body. The food of this spider is other arthropods, usually insects, although it will kill a small bird and feed on it. Its bite is relatively harmless to man.

for a female. Once he has found a mate, he usually performs a rather weird kind of dance and then deposits the sperm bundle into her genital pore. Sometimes the female proceeds to devour her unsuspecting mate. She then spins a tiny ball in which the eggs

FIG. 13-47. A female black widow spider (*Lactrodectus mactans*) with her egg case.

are laid and often carries it around with her until the young hatch (Fig. 13-47).

The class Crustacea (Mandibulata) includes a variety of forms which are divided into two subclasses. The **Entomostraca** are small simple forms to which the "fairy shrimps" and barnacles belong. The fairy shrimps are commonly found, for a brief period, in temporary fresh water ponds in the early spring. They swim on their backs by a rhythmic beating of their paddle-like appendages. They are beautiful creatures, often collected by children who are exploring small ponds made by melting snow. Another interesting relative is the "brine shrimp" which lives in water of high salinity, such as the Great Salt Lake. The dried "eggs" are collected in great quantities and sold as food for tropical fish. When placed in a strong salt solution they hatch into larvae which serve as an excellent source of food. Very unusual members of this subclass are the barnacles (Cirripedia) which are highly modified crustaceans. The larval stages are free-living, but the adults are attached to rocks and shells in the ocean. The rock barnacle, *Balanus* (Fig. 13-6), encrusts rocks between the high and low tides, making climbing over such objects hazardous owing to their sharp cutting shells. The free-swimming larval barnacle becomes attached by the anterior end and metamorphoses into the adult, whose appendages have become modified for sweeping small organisms into the mouth. The second subclass, the **Malacostraca**, includes the large crustacea such as shrimps, crayfishes, lobsters, and crabs.

Two other small classes of the Mandibulata should be mentioned. The many-legged centipedes (Fig. 13-48), class **Chilopoda**, are commonly found under stones and logs where they remain inactive during the day. At night, however, they move swiftly about in search of their favorite food, earthworms and insects. They possess a pair of poison claws on the first segment which are effective instruments in

FIG. 13-48. Centipedes have numerous jointed legs. Some tropical forms are nearly a foot long and can inflict a painful wound to a man. This is a smaller form common in the U.S.

securing prey. Some of the tropical centipedes reach a length of 10 inches, whereas in temperate zones the common house centipede is much smaller. The millipedes (Fig. 13-49), class **Diplopoda,** occupy similar habitats and resemble the centipedes in some respects. They may have several hundred appendages which move in a wave-like fashion as the animal crawls. They are slow-moving creatures, not at all like the centipedes. They feed on plants and decaying organic matter. When in danger some roll into a ball, whereas others secrete an offensive fluid which serves them well as protection against enemies.

In summary, we have seen that the arthropods have acquired a body plan so well designed that it has permitted the group to penetrate almost every type of land and aquatic environment. They have reached the pinnacle of the schizocoelomate line and are the most diversified of all animals. We must now go back and trace the enterocoelomate line which terminates with the chordates, another very successful group of animals which is more important to us because we are one of its members.

FIG. 13-49. The millipede (*Spirobolus*) possesses two pairs of jointed appendages on most of its segments. These numerous legs move in a rhythmic manner as can be seen from this photograph. Millipedes live in decaying vegetation upon which they feed.

SUGGESTED SUPPLEMENTARY READINGS

BAERG, W. J., *Introduction to Applied Entomology* (Ann Arbor, Edwards, 1948).

COMSTOCK, J. H., *Introduction to Entomology* (Ithaca, N.Y., Comstock Publishing Co., 1940).

COMSTOCK, J. H., and GERTSCH, W. J., *The Spider Book* (New York, Doubleday and Co., Inc., 1940).

IMMS, A. D., *Social Behavior in Insects* (London, Methuen & Co., 1947).

TINBERGEN, N., *Social Behavior in Animals* (New York, John Wiley & Sons, Inc., 1953).

VON FRISCH, K., *Bees, Their Vision, Chemical Senses and Language* (Ithaca, N.Y., Cornell University Press, 1950).

————., "Dialects in the Language of the Bees," *Scientific American*, 207 (2) (August, 1962), 78.

WHEELER, W. M., *The Social Insects: Their Origin and Evolution* (New York, Harcourt, Brace & World, Inc., 1928).

ZINSSER, H., *Rats, Lice, and History* (Boston, Little, Brown & Co., 1935).

14

Spiny Animals—Echinoderms

THIS SUCCESSFUL GROUP of animals possesses remarkable and unique characteristics. The phylum is named **Echinodermata** (Gr. "spiny-skinned") because its members usually possess external spines. Their close affinities to the next phylum, **Chordata,** are indicated by their skeletons of mesodermal origin and by their similar larval forms (p. 348). They have acquired uniqueness in structure which sets them apart from all other animals. They possess radial symmetry in the adult stage, although as larvae they are bilaterally symmetrical. In addition they have evolved a unique method of locomotion made possible by the **water vascular system.** The coelom is well developed, whereas the blood-vascular system is so rudimentary as to be nonfunctional and nephridial excretory organs are nonexistent. This puzzling situation in the adult is understood when one considers the evolution of the echinoderms. It seems quite clear that ancestors of the echinoderms were bilaterally symmetrical, free-swimming animals with coelomic pouches arranged in segments. At some later time they became attached forms which resulted in radial symmetry with five parts, reminiscent of

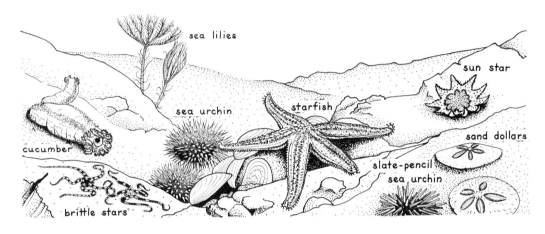

FIG. 14-1. All echinoderms are marine forms. A few of them are shown here in their habitat.

FIG. 14-2. The common starfish (*Asterias*), like most starfish, is found along rocky shores crawling over the hard surfaces in search of mollusks, particularly clams, which constitute its main food. This one is crawling over the shells of clams, many of which are empty because their soft bodies were sacrificed to satisfy the hunger of this and several other starfish.

coelenterates. The bilateral symmetry was completely obscured and can be seen today only in the larva. Echinoderms are all marine and usually slow-moving. Some are permanently attached forms living at the bottom of the sea whereas others are found along the seashore among the rocks or in the sand (Fig. 14-1).

The phylum is divided into two subphyla, the **Pelmatozoa** which includes mostly fossil forms, and the **Eleutherozoa** containing modern echinoderms. The only living Pelmatozoa are in the class **Crinoidea** (feather stars and sea lilies). The four classes of the subphylum Eleutherozoa are: **Asteroidea** (starfish and sea stars), **Ophiuroidea** (brittle stars, basket stars, serpent stars), **Echinoidea** (sea urchins and sand dollars), **Holothuroidea** (sea cucumbers). The starfish is a typical representative which we shall study in some detail.

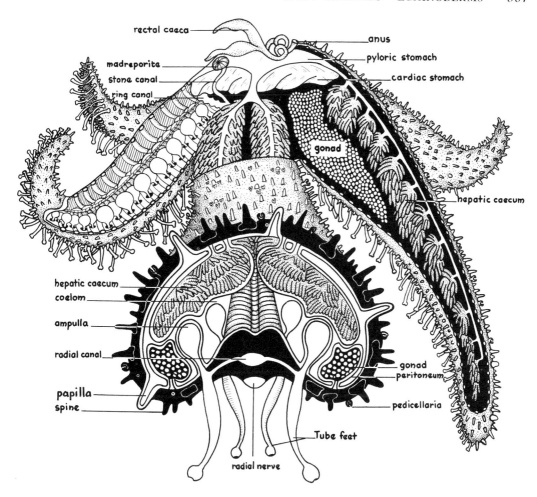

rectal caeca
anus
madreporite
pyloric stomach
stone canal
cardiac stomach
ring canal
gonad
hepatic caecum
hepatic caecum
coelom
ampulla
radial canal
gonad
peritoneum
papilla
spine
pedicellaria
Tube feet
radial nerve

FIG. 14-3. Starfish cut in such a manner as to show the internal anatomy.

The Starfish

Starfish, found in abundance along most seacoasts, vary greatly in size from tiny species about one-half inch in diameter to the giant starfish, which measures about 18 inches. The common starfish, *Asterias vulgaris* (Fig. 14-2), is found chiefly upon rocky seashores and bottoms where mollusks, its main food, are also most abundant. Starfish resemble the conventional five-pointed star pattern, the five radiating arms rising from a central disk (Fig. 14-3). It usually moves with the two arms adjacent to the **madreporite** (a sieve-like structure through which

water enters) pointing forward. The upper portion of the body, the **aboral** surface, is covered with **spines,** along the bases of which are small pincer-like structures, the **pedicellariae,** which serve to keep the body free from foreign material. Because the animal is so well armored with various types of sharp projections, it is little wonder that it is not chosen as food by other animals. The **oral** side, or undersurface, on which the mouth is centrally located, serves two main purposes, locomotion and food collection.

An outstanding feature of the echinoderms is the appearance of a unique device,

FIG. 14-4. A close-up of the tube feet of the deep sea red starfish (*Hippasteria phrygiana*) to show the nature of the sucking disc at the tip and the circular muscles in the tube that aid in its action.

the **water vascular system,** consisting of two rows of tube feet which extend from the mouth down the oral side of each of the five rays (Fig. 14-3). The tube feet enable the animal to move slowly over rocks or along the ocean floor, to twist and turn its body, and to capture food. If a single foot is examined, the portion that protrudes externally from the oral surface is found to be an elongated tube (Fig. 14-4). Internally, at the opposite end, a bulbous structure, the **ampulla,** joins a central tube, the **radial canal,** which extends up the ray of the animal to join a central circular tube, the **ring canal.** A short tube, the **stone canal,** is joined to the ring canal and runs up to the dorsal surface of the disk, opening externally into the madreporite plate.

Water enters through the madreporite plate, passes into the stone canal, then the ring canal, and to the ampullae. At the margin of the ring canal are located the **Tiedemann bodies** which produce the **amoebocytes** found in the fluid of the system. When the ampulla contracts, the fluid is forced into the tube foot, which is thus elongated. If the sucker-like tip of the foot touches and attaches to an object, the muscular wall of the foot contracts, forcing the fluid back into the ampulla, thus causing the foot to be shortened. Since the foot adheres to the object it has touched, the shortening of the

foot draws the body forward. In this manner the starfish is able to move. It also uses this mechanism to obtain food, but instead of the alternating "push-pull" system of locomotion, a steady contraction of the tube foot is exerted to produce a constant pull.

The endoskeleton, which is produced by the mesoderm, is a calcareous framework composed of many **ossicles,** most of which are arranged in a definite pattern. Even though the starfish has this strong endoskeleton, it is capable of autotomy. Thus it can break off an arm and readily regenerate the lost part, in a very short time (Fig. 14-5). Experiments have been tried in which all five arms were removed from the disk, and in some cases the disk was able to regenerate the five rays.

The **ossicles** of the endoskeleton are joined together by a network of connective tissue and muscle fibers. Lying within the skeleton and extending through all portions of the body is the **coelom.** It contains the internal organs and a lymph-like fluid which carries free amoebocytes. In certain regions the coelom comes close to the external epidermis which forms a tiny finger-like extension, and in these structures, called **branchiae,** the respiratory exchange of gases takes place. The amoebocytes gather waste materials and escape from the body through these same structures.

When feeding, the starfish holds the victim with its arms and secures its grasp by attaching the tube feet (Fig. 14-6). The sac-like **stomach,** which consists of a large lower portion, the **cardiac stomach,** and the smaller upper region, the **pyloric stomach,** is then everted through the mouth. If the captured animal is small enough, the stomach may completely surround it. Retractor muscles in the arms, just below the digestive glands, draw the everted stomach back into the body to complete digestion. If the animal is large it is digested in portions while the stomach remains everted. The digestive juices flow from the pyloric region of the stomach and the **hepatic caeca**

FIG. 14-5. Regeneration in a starfish. It required six weeks for this starfish to accomplish the regeneration of the two arms seen here.

(paired digestive glands of each ray) until the remaining food is small enough to be withdrawn into the pyloric stomach. Very often partially digested food enters the hepatic caeca, as well as other portions of the digestive system, and absorption takes place in these various organs. The digested food passes into the coelomic fluid where it is distributed. Attached to the dorsal portion of the pyloric stomach is a short intestine with rudimentary **rectal caeca** and a small **anal opening** on the aboral surface of the disk.

The circulatory system is reduced to such an extent that it can scarcely be called a circulatory system at all. There are vessels encircling the mouth and extending down into each ray, but they are too inadequate to transfer the digested material to all parts of the body. Instead, the fluid of the coelomic cavity transports the food to various parts of the body.

The nervous system of the starfish shows the same radial symmetry seen in the other parts of the body and is, in general, simple. It consists of a nerve ring surrounding the mouth, giving off five branches, one to each arm, called **radial nerves** (Fig. 14-3). Two other systems of nerves lie internally, one on the oral side and another near the aboral side. Each part of the nervous system seems to function independently. The starfish has only a few sense organs. An **eye** and a **tentacle** are located at the tip of each ray, and the **pedicellariae** function as dermal sense organs.

Experiments show that the nervous system of the starfish is sufficiently organized to exhibit definite responses. A hungry starfish, placed in a pan of sea water containing bits of pulverized mollusk, will move toward the food. Through its eyes the starfish reacts positively to light. This response is best shown by removing the eyes of four

339

the adult form appears, radial symmetry becomes evident. Larval forms are partially ciliated and free-swimming. After a period of swimming near the surface of the water, sometimes for several weeks, the larva finally drops to the bottom of the sea, where it undergoes metamorphosis into the adult starfish.

Other Echinoderms

While the starfish gives us a good idea of the echinoderm body plan, there are many modifications of this plan within the phylum (Fig. 14-8). The most primitive forms are the stalked **crinoids,** commonly called **sea lilies** and **feather stars.** They are the only living representatives of a large successful group of animals. They have five greatly branched arms and are attached by means of a stalk to the bottom of deep seas. Food is carried down to the mouth by cilia in the ambulacral grooves. The tube feet resemble tentacles and are probably sensory in function. Their general appearance resembles a flower, hence the name.

The class **Ophiuroidea** includes the **brittle stars** (Fig. 14-8) and the **basket stars** (Fig. 14-9). Both forms possess small disks and long, slender, motile arms, the arms of the basket star being branched to form a kind of basket. The brittle stars, characterized by five long, serpentine arms, can move more rapidly than any other echinoderm. Their tube feet are few in number and are used primarily as touch receptors rather than for locomotion. Mild stimulation can cause an arm to be snapped off immediately; the rapid regeneration of a new member makes this a valuable means of escape for these animals.

The sea urchin and sand dollar (Fig. 14-10) are also seashore oddities and belong to the class **Echinoidea.** A common species of sea urchin is usually purple in color and often found lying in the small pockets of rocks, homes that may be occupied for many years. It has remarkably long spines that are used in locomo-

FIG. 14-6. Starfish frequently feed on clams. In the top picture the starfish is huddled over the clam. In the bottom picture the starfish has been turned up on one side. Note the long tube feet attached to the two valves of the clam. Their continued pull eventually weakens the clam so that it gapes open, allowing the starfish to consume its soft body.

rays, allowing one to remain. With but one eye, the starfish will continue to react positively to light, but if the remaining eye is removed, orientation to light is lost.

Sexes of the starfish are separate. The reproductive system consists of five paired gonads, lying close to the hepatic caeca and attached in the angles between the arms where their external openings are located (Fig. 14-3). Ova and sperm cells are discharged into the sea water, where fertilization occurs (Fig. 14-7). The larva, or **bipinnaria,** is at first bilaterally symmetrical; later, as the pentagonal shape of

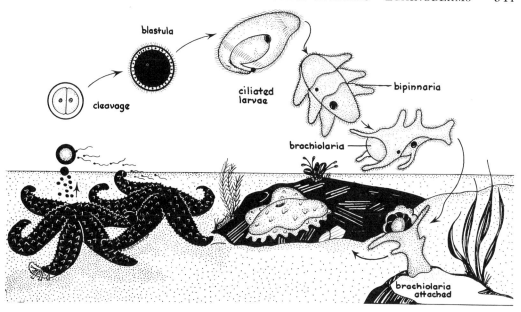

FIG. 14-7. Life cycle of the starfish.

tion as well as in securing prey. The tube feet which cover the rounded body are also used in locomotion. An interesting organ, characteristic of this animal, is **Aristotle's lantern,** a complicated arrangement of teeth in the mouth that is used for picking food apart. Even small fish are captured and torn to pieces by this effective instrument.

In most other details the sea urchin resembles the starfish. The sand dollar is extremely flattened dorsal-ventrally, so that it resembles a flat disk. Otherwise, it possesses the organs common to other forms already described.

The **sea cucumber** (Fig. 14-8), a bizarre type, belongs to the class **Holothuroidea.** It

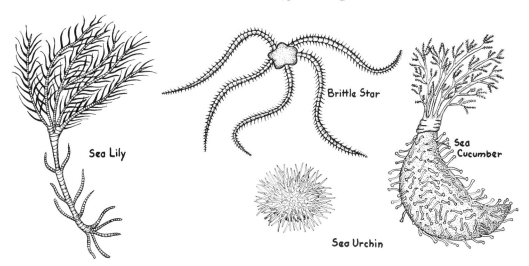

FIG. 14-8. Various kinds of echinoderms.

FIG. 14-9. A basket star (*Georgonacephalus articus*) taken in 420 feet of water. The five principal arms are subdivided into a great many smaller branches. This is a ventral view.

is quite unlike the starfish in its general appearance, although its fundamental structure is similar. These animals resemble cucumbers with a fringe of tentacles on one end. The surface of the body seems to be devoid of calcareous plates, but microscopic examination reveals tiny plates embedded in the soft tissue of the body wall. The branched tentacles are located at the anterior end, surrounding the mouth; the anus is at the opposite end of the animal. There are five rows of tube feet, the two dorsal ones functioning as respiratory and tactile organs, while the three remaining rows on the ventral side aid in locomotion, much the same as those of the starfish. The animal is able to crawl in worm-like fashion, by contracting the rather heavy muscles which make up the body wall. It feeds by allowing the tentacles to become covered with detritus from the muddy ocean bottom and then pushing them, one at a time, into the mouth. Organic material is separated from the mud and carried into the digestive tract where it is digested.

Breathing is carried on by means of a pair of **respiratory trees** which extend from the lower end of the digestive tract anteriorly in the body cavity. Water is taken into the cloaca through the anus and circulated through these ramifying tubes. It is likely that excretory wastes find their way to the outside through these organs as well.

This animal possesses remarkable powers of autotomy and regeneration of lost parts and, in fact, even employs this behavior as a mechanism of defense. If disturbed by an intruder, the sea cucumber suddenly contracts its muscular walls until considerable pressure is built up within. Then it splits open, almost explosively, near the anus, everting the respiratory trees which secrete a mucous fluid that becomes stringy and tough when it contacts sea water. The unfortunate enemy, usually a lobster, thus becomes hopelessly enmeshed in this mass of threads so that it is no longer concerned with the sea cucumber as a prospective meal. The sea cucumber is able to break the trees loose at their base and regenerate a complete set within a short time.

Before going on to the last phylum we need to discuss a small controversial group of animals which have characteristics that closely approach those of the chordates, hence are often regarded as primitive members of the phylum Chordata. Since they do not measure up in all respects, they may well be discussed following the echinoderms with which they also have affinities.

PHYLUM HEMICHORDATA

These are small, sedentary or burrowing, worm-like animals that live exclusively in the sea. Their body is divided into the **proboscis, collar,** and **trunk.** A "half chord" supporting structure, from which the phylum gets its name, is present in the proboscis and the collar contains a dorsal **nerve** component. The pharynx wall is perforated by numerous **gill slits** which permit water

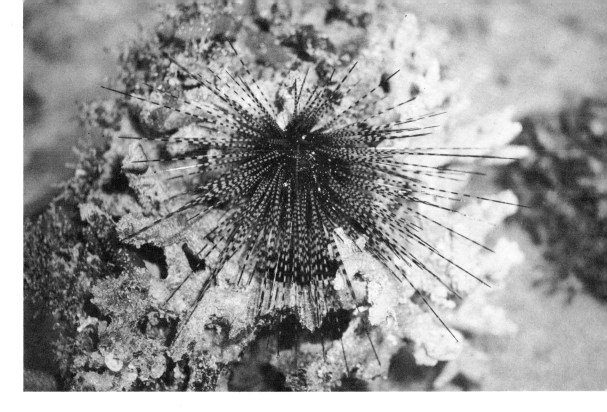

entering the mouth to pass out of the body. These characters have been used to place them with the chordates but only the gill slit is a true chordate characteristic, the others are hardly comparable to similar structures in chordates. A common example is the **acorn worm** (*Saccoglossus*) (Fig. 14-11).

FIG. 14-10. (Top) Sea urchins are covered with long spines which aid the slender tube feet in moving slowly over the ocean floor. By means of a set of five sharp teeth, they are able to tear vegetative and decaying matter to tiny bits which they consume. This one from a coral reef has particularly long spines. (Bottom) Sand dollars are close relatives of the sea urchins but are flattened and the spines are much smaller. Both the tube feet and spines make movement possible in the sand where they live. They feed on the organic matter that is present in the sand.

FIG. 14-11. Acorn worms (*Saccoglossus kowalevskyi*) from the sand flats of Cape Cod. Note the long proboscis for burrowing in the sand and mud.

SUGGESTED SUPPLEMENTARY READINGS

BROWN, F. A., *Selected Invertebrate Types* (New York, John Wiley & Sons, Inc., 1950).

BUCHSBAUM, R., *Animals without Backbones* (Chicago, University of Chicago Press, 1948).

GILLETTE, K., and McNEILL, F., *The Great Barrier Reef and Adjacent Isles* (Sidney, Australia, The Coral Press Pty. Ltd., 1959).

MACGINITIE, G. E., *Natural History of Marine Animals* (New York, McGraw-Hill Book Co., 1949).

RICKETTS, E. F., and CALVIN, J., *Between Pacific Tides* (Stanford, Stanford University Press, 1939).

15

The Animal Climax—Chordates

THE LAST and most diversified group of animals is the phylum Chordata, to which man himself belongs (Fig. 15-1). Not only are the chordates the largest animals in existence today, but they have adapted themselves to more modes of existence than any other group, including the arthropods. They are found in the sea, in fresh water, in the air, and on all parts of the land from the poles to the equator. They range in size from the tiniest fish to the great whales, which reach a length of nearly 100 feet and a weight of 150 tons and more (Fig. 15-44). Birds and mammals have been able to pene-

trate cold climates because they have a constant body temperature, something no other animals have.

All chordates possess at some time in their life cycle three characteristics which are not found among the animals studied so far (Fig. 15-2). The first is a **dorsal tubular nerve cord,** which varies from a more or less undifferentiated tube extending throughout the entire length of the body of the lower chordates, to a shorter, highly differentiated tube, with a greatly enlarged anterior portion, the **brain,** in the higher forms. In lower forms the nerve cord is

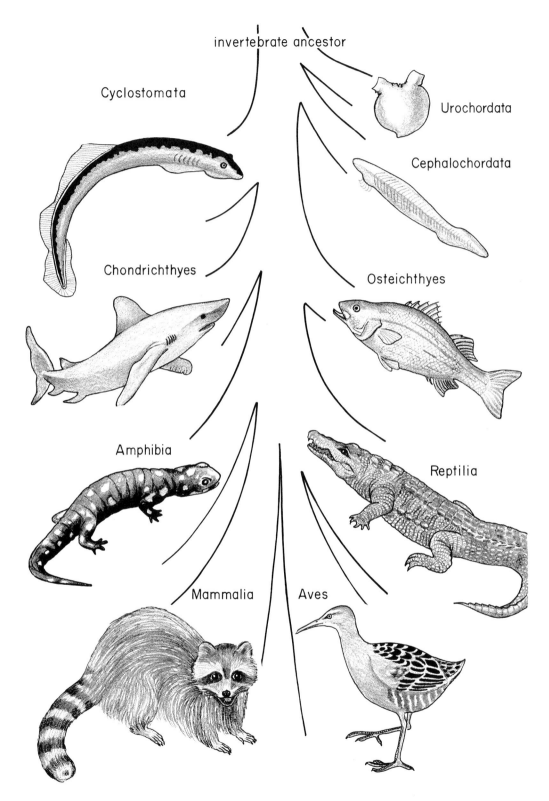

invertebrate ancestor

Cyclostomata

Urochordata

Cephalochordata

Chondrichthyes

Osteichthyes

Amphibia

Reptilia

Mammalia

Aves

FIG. 15-1. The phylum Chordata is composed of widely diverse animals as indicated by representatives from each of the major groups.

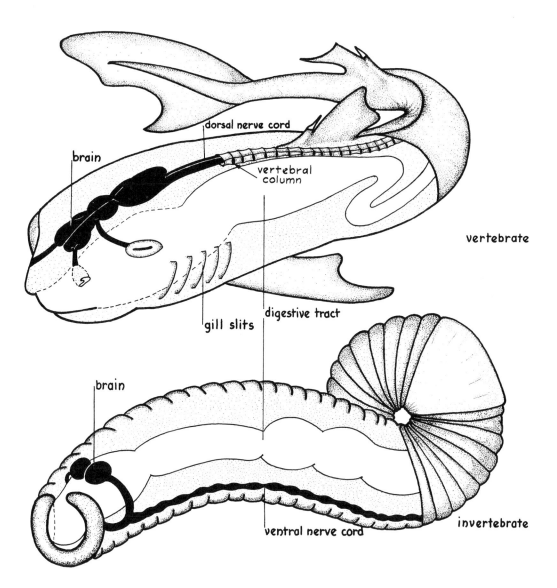

Fig. 15-2. Comparative study of the vertebrate and invertebrate.

solid, but in all chordates it is tubular or hollow.

A second characteristic of the chordates is the presence of an internal supporting rod, or skeleton, the **notochord.** This may be thought of as a precursor to the vertebral column in vertebrates, but it must not be considered identical. Although the notochord is found in the embryos of all vertebrates, it persists only in the adults of the most primitive. The notochord is made up of a gelatinous matrix, surrounded by a tough, outer sheath, which is inadequate to support a large animal in water, much less on land. In all higher forms, therefore, it is replaced by the more rigid **vertebral column.**

The third characteristic is the presence of pharyngeal **gill slits.** It is obvious that adult land animals have no gill slits, but during embryological development gill slits do appear at some stage. The structures which originally produced functional gill arches in fish produced other structures in higher forms, such as the sound-making apparatus (middle ear bones). These fitted the animal better for a terrestrial existence and gave it a greater chance for success. As already noted, the arthropods have also been able to divorce themselves from water and have likewise developed a new means of communication by employing old structures to perform new duties. Legs and wings are employed for making sound; antennae and legs for receiving sound.

CHORDATE BEGINNINGS

Scientists have been perplexed about the origin of the chordates and have been unable to determine which lower forms gave rise to this last and perhaps most specialized group. Fossil remains have provided us with a great deal of information about other animals, but man's digging into the earth has failed thus far to reveal any substantial remnants of the early chordates. The reason for this is that these soft-bodied animals did not remain intact sufficiently long to become fossilized. In spite of the lack of evidence concerning the early progenitors of the chordates, there has been a great deal of speculation as to their origin.

The phyla Echinodermata, Hemichordata, and Chordata show common ancestry by the embryonic origin of the coelom: all are enterocoelomates (p. 153). In all the anus forms from the blastopore (p. 155),

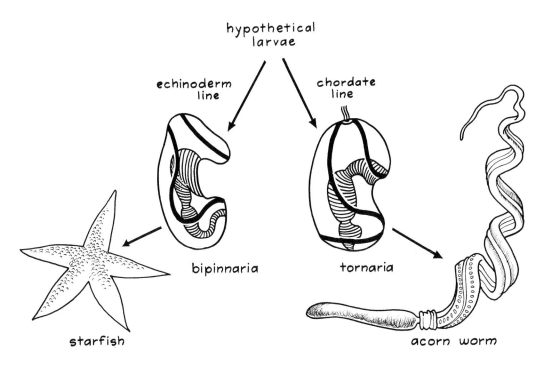

FIG. 15-3. A study of the larval stages of the acorn worm and echinoderms has lent support to the idea that both came from a common ancestor.

and for that reason they are sometimes spoken of as **deuterostomes,** in contrast to the schizocoelomates in which the mouth is clearly a part of the blastopore and hence are called **protostomes.** Serological studies (p. 573) demonstrate that the proteins of these three phyla are more closely related to one another than to those of any other phyla. Moreover, the remarkable similarities between the echinoderm (bipinnaria) and hemichordate (tornaria) larvae (Fig. 15-3) is taken as good evidence for common ancestry. The close relationship between the hemichordates and the chordates has already been mentioned (p. 342). There is little doubt that the chordates arose from the same stock that gave rise to the echinoderms and that the two lines separated in very early geologic time.

PHYLUM CHORDATA

We usually think of the chordates as synonymous with vertebrates and while certainly the vertebrates do make up the vast majority of the animals in the phylum, there are some inconspicuous and primitive chordates (prochordates) that share the three characteristics which define the phylum. The phylum is divided into three subphyla: **Urochordata, Cephalochordata,** and **Vertebrata.** We shall consider the first two briefly, but shall spend some time with the last.

The **tunicates,** or **sea squirts** (subphylum Urochordata) (Fig. 15-4), are commonly attached to rocks along the seashores where they live by forcing water in and out of their sac-like bodies through **siphons,** resembling the clam in this respect. The water passes into a large perforated pharynx which strains out the tiny food particles that are carried into the digestive tract. Gills line the many openings in the pharynx wall, but aside from this one chordate characteristic, the adult appears to have no claim to membership among the chordates. However, a careful look at the larval form demonstrates at once its true chordate re-

lationships, for the larva possesses a notochord and dorsal tubular nerve cord, in addition to the gill slits. As an embryo, the animal is tadpole-shaped and swims actively in the sea water (Fig. 15-4). Late in embryonic life, however, it settles on a rock and metamorphoses into the sessile adult, which is a degenerate form compared to the active, free-swimming, fish-like chordate from which it came. Tunicates are very numerous in the oceans of the world and range from microscopic size to more than 12 inches in diameter. They may live in shallow or deep water and are commonly found by the bather who is sufficiently curious to examine the rocks along the coast. The group as a whole has no economic significance.

There is another tiny animal (2 inches long) that cannot be mistaken for anything but a primitive chordate and, moreover, it possesses body structures that force us to believe that some such form might have given rise to the vertebrates. This animal is known as **lancelet** or **amphioxus** (subphylum Cephalochordata) (Fig. 15-5). It is an ocean dweller, found in relatively few though widely separated regions, and reaches such numbers along a part of the shore of China that it is utilized as a source of food. Not only does it possess the three chordate characteristics exhibited by the two preceding groups, but it also has a body plan that closely resembles that of the vertebrates.

Amphioxus has a general shape not unlike that of a slender fish, with two longitudinal folds of skin extending throughout most of its length, which may be forerunners of appendages (Fig. 15-6). Its notochord functions as a semirigid supporting internal skeleton, extending from one end of the animal to the other. The muscles are segmentally arranged and by their rhythmic contractions make possible lateral undulations of the body used in swimming. Above the notochord is the hollow nerve cord which terminates anteriorly in the eye-spot.

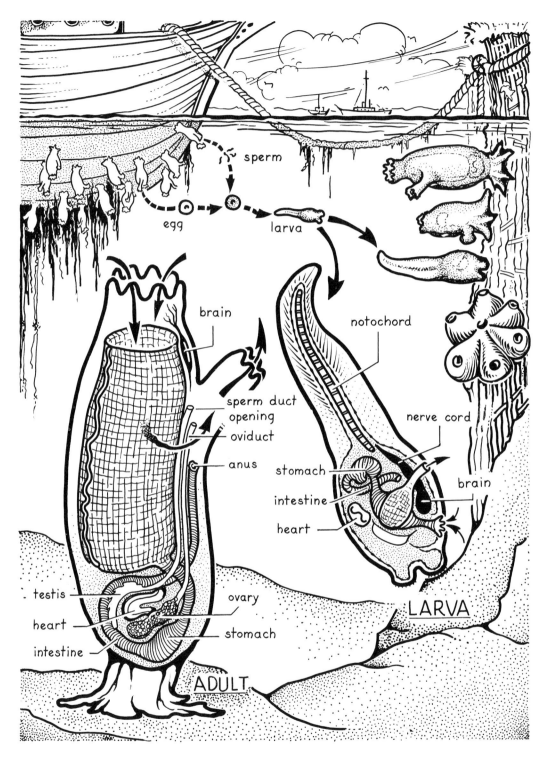

FIG. 15-4. Life cycle of a tunicate. Note the definite nerve cord and notochord in the larva, both of which are reduced or absent in the adult. Three stages in the metamorphosis of the larva into the adult are shown in the upper right. A colonial prochordate is also seen, attached to the piling.

Numerous gills function in breathing. Its digestive and circulatory systems are relatively simple and add nothing to what we have already seen among lower forms. In fundamental plan, however, these organ systems, like so many other features of this little animal, show great similarity to the vertebrates and thus point to the possibility that the vertebrates may well have come from a form not greatly unlike it.

THE FIRST ANIMALS WITH BACKBONES—VERTEBRATES

We now come to the large group of animals known as **vertebrates** (subphylum Vertebrata) because they possess backbones. All animals studied up to this point are called **invertebrates**. The characteristics of the vertebrates, in addition to the three which identify the chordates, are an internal skeleton of bone and cartilage; a vertebral column or backbone which replaces the notochord of the prochordates; usually two pairs of jointed appendages which may be fins or limbs; a closed circulatory system with a two-or-more-chambered heart; a large coelom containing vital organs. Of these, perhaps the most important is the possession of a rigid internal skeleton. It is quite certain that without this structure the group could not have become so diversified in body form. To invade the land and air required a substantial internal support upon which a body could be built that would succeed in these environments. This was accomplished by the development of the backbone to which appendages and other structures were attached. Let us examine representatives of the eight classes of vertebrates.

The class **Agnatha** includes only one group of living representatives, the **cyclostomes** or "round-mouthed" lampreys. They have no appendages and no jaws, only a circular mouth lined with denticles, small tooth-like structures that aid in clinging to prey. When the lamprey seizes a bony fish,

FIG. 15-5. Amphioxus (*Branchiostoma californiensis*), partly emerged from its burrow along the California coast.

351

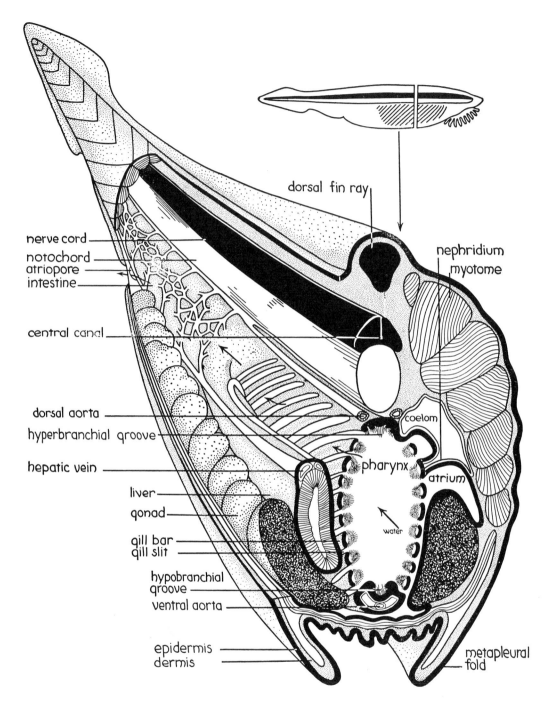

dorsal fin ray

nephridium
myotome

nerve cord
notochord
atriopore
intestine

central canal

dorsal aorta
hyperbranchial groove

hepatic vein

liver
gonad

gill bar
gill slit

hypobranchial
groove
ventral aorta

epidermis
dermis

coelom

pharynx

atrium

water

metapleural
fold

FIG. 15-6. Amphioxus in longitudinal and cross-sections.

FIG. 15-7. Sea lampreys (*Petromyzon marinus*), attacking a fresh-water fish. Note the scar from a previous injury on the dorsal side just above the fore-fins.

its usual prey, it first attaches itself with the sucking mouth and then removes small bits of tissue with its rasping tongue. If the point of attachment happens to be in the abdominal region, a perforation is made through the body wall and the internal organs are injured so severely that the fish usually dies. However, if the injury occurs on the dorsal side over the large muscles, the effect is usually not fatal. The common sea lamprey, *Petromyzon,* has invaded rivers and streams where it has become a formidable foe of fish populations (Fig. 15-7). These ravages have been particularly severe in the Great Lakes region where in many areas commercial fishing has all but ceased. Poisons are being employed with considerable success to kill the larval stages. Prospects are good that with continued effort this parasite will be controlled and commercial fishing may once again return to some of the Great Lakes.

Internally as well as externally the lamprey shows its lowly origin (Fig. 15-8). It retains a notochord similar to amphioxus, but also has the beginnings of a spinal column and other internal skeletal parts which are composed of cartilage. There is a well-developed brain, together with an olfactory organ, a pair of poorly developed

eyes, and a pair of simple semicircular canals on each side of the head, used in balancing. It has seven pairs of gills—fewer than amphioxus, but more than the bony fish. Internally, also, the complexity of its body structures far exceeds that of amphioxus.

A group of animals called **ostracoderms** (Fig. 15-9) that lived about 400 million years ago (Silurian Period) resembled the present-day cyclostomes in many respects. They developed heavy armor plates on their external surfaces, possessed a ventral mouth, and were without appendages. Their heavy exoskeletons were essential in order to survive the onslaughts of their invertebrate enemies, the water scorpions (eurypterids). It is agreed now that later descendants of the ostracoderms lost their plates as these enemies disappeared. With the development of jaws, it became possible for them to pursue and capture their prey more effectively. Under these circumstances a heavy exoskeleton only hindered rapid progress, and perhaps this was a factor in its disappearance.

At one time, the cartilage of the lamprey skeleton, as well as that of the sharks and skates, which came later, was considered a precursor to bone and therefore a more

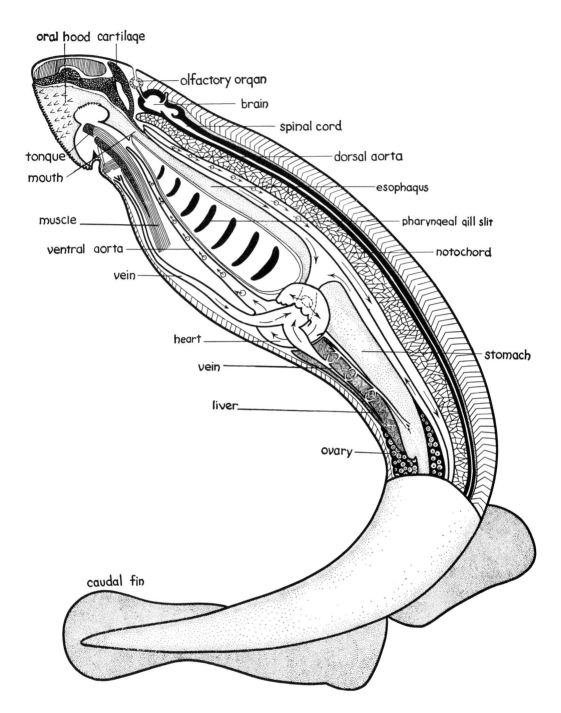

FIG. 15-8. Cyclostome in partial longitudinal section.

FIG. 15-9. The oldest vertebrates are the ostracoderms shown in the upper figure. They had many features of modern cyclostomes shown in the lower figure.

The prehensile jaws of the early primitive fish were another important acquisition, making it possible for them to become predators, searching out and capturing their prey. A clue to the development of the jaws can be found from a study of the shark's gill arches. These differ but little from the jaw itself and, in fact, they are so much alike in this animal, as well as in many fossil forms, that it is generally agreed that the jaws have developed from the first gill arch. As will be shown later, other important organs also developed from these same primitive gill arches.

The teeth found in the shark's jaw occur in never-ending rows and show a remarkable similarity to its scales. It is thus clear that the scales in the region of the mouth opening merely enlarged and became the teeth of the shark. These teeth simply grow over the edge of the mouth and are continuously shed as they wear out. Later it will be shown that all teeth are modified scales, including those of man.

The sharks and their close relatives, the rays, show diversification in body form (Fig. 15-12). The latter is greatly flattened, with enormously developed pectoral fins that look more like wings (hence the name, sea bat) as they undulate in the sea. The

primitive condition. More recently this has been interpreted as a degenerate condition. It is now thought that the cyclostomes and sharks probably descended from forms that possessed not only internal skeletons of bone but also heavy outside bony plates which degenerated into the cartilage found in these animals today. This appears to be true, since the early fossil remains present in so many forms of bone or a hardened bonelike substance.

THE FIRST APPENDAGES AND JAWS

The lower forms such as the cyclostomes do very little free swimming in the water and get along satisfactorily with a broad fin in the tail region and a dorsal fin to aid in locomotion. In order to be more maneuverable, vertebrates gradually developed more elaborate appendages. Shark-like fossil remains of forms possessing many paired fins (Fig. 15-10) seem to indicate that they originally had many and, according to Romer, only later settled down to the orthodox two pairs, the pectoral (chest region) and pelvic (hip region). From these two pairs of fins, which became so prominent in the early sharks and all later fishes, evolved the appendages of land forms (Fig. 15-11).

FIG. 15-10. Primitive sharks had many paired appendages extending throughout the length of the body, as shown in the above figure. The two conventional pairs (pelvic and pectoral) appeared in later forms and in all present-day vertebrates.

FIG. 15-11. Primitive vertebrates, according to some zoologists, had fin folds much like amphioxus (upper figure). Portions of these folds were retained in the pectoral and pelvic regions to become the paired appendages; other parts became the other fins (middle and lower fish figures). Coming out on land necessitated greater development of the appendages, as is seen among the amphibians, reptiles, and mammals. At first they dragged their bodies over the ground, later the appendages supported the body above the ground, which made it possible for the animal to move more swiftly. This reaches its peak in such cursorial animals as the horse.

FIG. 15-12. Cow-nosed rays (*Rhinoptera bonasus*). Note their huge pectoral fins that give them the appearance of flying when swimming.

tail is drawn out to a long whip-like structure which, in the sting rays, bears a spine at the tip. When annoyed, the ray can inflict a painful wound. Some rays produce electricity in considerable quantity and employ it as a mechanism of defense. Modified muscles are so constructed as to produce an electrical potential sufficiently high to stun lower forms and to cause a good deal of pain in larger animals. Shocking devices are also found among a few species of eels. The mechanism of this device is not thoroughly understood.

THE FISHES

The cartilaginous fishes, the sharks and rays (class **Chondrichthyes**), developed appendages and true jaws as important adjuncts to success in the water. Once these became established as a permanent part of the anatomy of acquatic vertebrates, a

FIG. 15-13. The long-nosed gar (*Lepidosteus osseus*), a vicious carnivore which feeds on other fishes. This fish inhabits the Great Lakes and most of the streams of the Mississippi Valley.

great deal of "experimentation" apparently ensued. The result was the modern bony fishes (class **Osteichthyes**) which have gone "all out" in exploring possible body shapes, sizes, and colors that best suit them for their particular aquatic niches. They range

FIG. 15-14. The sea horse (*Hippocampus kuda*) swims in a vertical position by means of its dorsal fin. Note its prehensile tail, used to cling to vegetation. The male has a pouch under the tail where the eggs are brooded until they hatch.

from ordinary fish such as the common perch to the vicious garpike (Fig. 15-13) and bizarre sea horse (Fig. 15-14). They are found in the oceans of the world—from the surface to great depths, where they have attained the most weird shapes and have developed extraordinary luminescent organs. In fresh water they are found in swift-moving streams as well as stagnant pools. Some, such as the salmon and eel, can survive satisfactorily in either fresh or salt water and migrate seasonally from one environment to the other, movements which are synchronized with their breeding cycle.

Structurally, the bony fish are similar to the sharks with a few minor exceptions. For example, the gills are reduced to four pairs and are covered with a thin bony structure, the **operculum.** Their bodies are covered with large overlapping scales arranged like the shingles on a house. The fins, while in general of the prototype, are highly variable both in position and in size among the different groups of fish. There is nothing strikingly different about their internal anatomy with the possible exception of the **swim,** or **air, bladder,** which functions in regulating the buoyancy of the body. As the fish moves to different depths, the gases (CO_2, N_2, and O_2) increase or decrease in the swim bladder automatically, adjusting the specific gravity of the fish to the corresponding depth, but if a fish is suddenly pulled from great depths to the surface the expanding bladder may force the stomach out of the mouth.

Most present-day fish possess bony skeletons which made it possible for them to begin their migration onto land, to a new type of life outside of water. Although this movement began with the fish, it was not completely accomplished until the advent of the land egg, many millions of years later. The hard bones made it possible for appendages to become sufficiently strong to support a body in the air, a feat which the degenerate cartilaginous skeleton of the sharks could never have accomplished.

FIG. 15-15. Ancient lobe-finned fish (*Latimeria*) found off the coast of Africa in 1938, supposedly extinct for millions of years.

Among the ancient fish there were some that had a fleshy portion, or "lobe," which extended some distance out into the fin. This contained certain skeletal elements that have been found to correspond directly with similar bony elements in the appendages of true land forms. Descendants of these fish undoubtedly were able to migrate onto land and at a later time to give rise to the great array of land vertebrates. "Lobe-finned" fish were long thought to be extinct until a fisherman off the coast of South Africa caught one (*Latimeria*) in 1938. Others that have been found since have been studied carefully and described in detail (Fig. 15-15). Relatives of the "lobe-finned" fish are not uncommon today. The **lungfish,** for example, inhabits certain tropical parts of the earth where frequent droughts occur (p. 118). Since this form followed a different path of evolution, it does not possess well-developed appendages and, in spite of the fact that it has lungs, probably did not give rise to the land forms.

One other absolute essential had to be achieved if fish were to live outside of water, and that was some means of utilizing the oxygen of the air. The "lobe-finned" fish of the past, as well as the lungfish of today, accomplished this rather satisfactorily. Apparently these fish lived in regions where nearly all the water dried up for extended periods during the year, and in order to survive they found it necessary to come to the surface of drying pools and take in air, since there was little oxygen in the water. These animals developed a pair of sac-like lungs from the ventral side of the pharynx which allowed them to gulp air during periods when their gills were useless. This, it must be remembered, is a primitive condition. Its counterpart is found in present-day fishes in the form of a swim bladder which functions as a hydrostatic organ rather than a lung, since these fish have no need for a lung-like structure at any time during their lives. It therefore appears that once this lung-like structure developed among the "lobe-finned" fish, it was utilized on land where it eventually became the complex organ that is found in such animals as birds and mammals of today (Fig. 15-16).

Thus two features, the bony appendage and the lung, made it possible for ani-

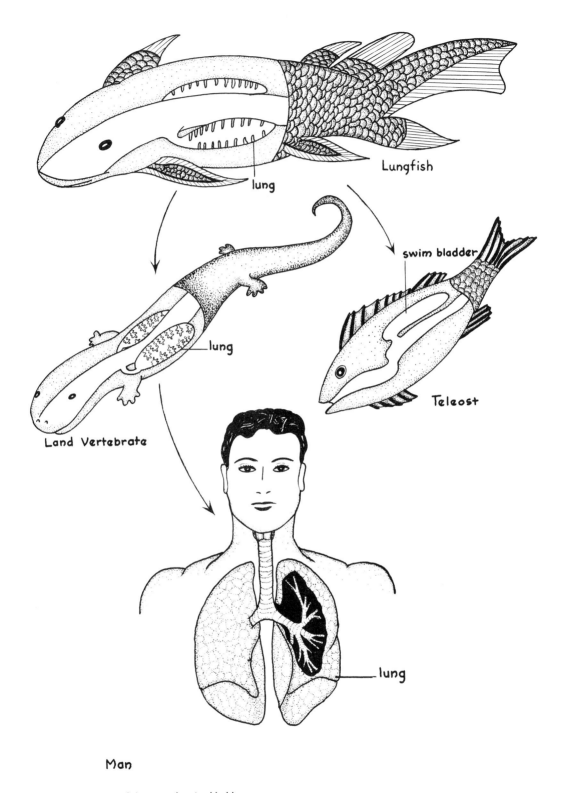

FIG. 15-16. History of lungs and swim bladder.

mals to attempt the greatest of all transitions—from the water onto land.

INVASION OF THE LAND

Of all the changes that have occurred in vertebrates during their long evolution to present-day forms, the most striking was the fishes' leaving their aquatic life for life on land. According to Romer, this was the "result of a happy accident." They would hardly have left the water in search of food, since during these times most animals were aquatic, and fish would hardly leave a food-laden world for one almost devoid of food. They had already supplied themselves with a means of breathing air, so this could not have been the cause. Romer reasons that if drought periods were too extensive, those fish which could breathe air and walk about on the land were able to move to other ponds and survive. Thus the appendages and lungs aided them in finding water rather than leaving it. However, during these excursions some may have found abundant food near the water's edge, whereas others which could not stand drought may have found it more profitable to wander from pond to pond in search of food. Again, some may have found other members of their own group to feed upon, while others may have changed to a herbivorous diet, since vegetation was abundant. From such beginnings the great variety of life among land vertebrates appears to have developed.

THE AMPHIBIANS

There were undoubtedly numerous unsuccessful attempts by many groups of fishes to make the transition onto land. The ancestors of the "lobe-finned" fish were apparently successful and gave rise to the amphibians which include our present-day frogs, toads, and salamanders. As the name *amphibian* implies, these animals live both in and out of the water. Their larval stages are always spent in water or some moist place, whereas the adult of most species are able to live on land, although they do not venture far from moist places. The degree to which amphibians are linked to water varies with different species. Some have divorced themselves completely from an aquatic environment, as for example, the South American toad, whose eggs brood in fluid-filled sacs upon its back. Other species, such as the mud-puppy, spend their entire life in the water and cannot leave it. A curious intermediate is a variety of tiger salamander (*Ambystoma tigrinum*) which normally spends its entire life in the larval form, but which if fed thyroid extract or high levels of iodine, can be made to lose its gills, develop lungs, and come out on land just as its relatives do (Fig. 15-17). This tiger salamander larva was thought to be a different species from the usual adult and was called the **axolotl**. It would seem that while the axolotl has descended from forms that attained the adult stage, it retained its larval body form, perhaps because of more abundant food or for some other reason. Among the amphibians, then, there are those which attempt to leave the water altogether and those which tend never to leave it. This is exactly what would be expected if their evolution occurred as described on these pages.

Other characteristics of the amphibia are moist glandular skin without scales; two pairs of appendages used in locomotion (except the legless caecilians); a pair of nostrils connecting with the mouth cavity; breathing by means of lungs, gills, or skin; a heart possessing two auricles and one ventricle; external fertilization of the eggs in toads and frogs, internal in salamanders.

The class is divided into three orders; the **Apoda** (limbless)—caecilians; the **Caudata** (tailed)—salamanders; and the **Salienta** (tailless)—frogs and toads. Of these we shall consider one, the frog, in some detail.

FIG. 15-17. The common tiger salamander (*Ambystoma tigrinum*) normally undergoes a typical amphibian metamorphosis resulting in the adult. One variety of this species living in western North America, particularly in the Southwest, becomes sexually mature while still a larva and never reaches the adult stage. The specimen on the extreme left is a young larva, while the one next to it is a sexually mature larva. This is as far as development proceeds in nature. Several specimens similar to this one were placed in water with a high level of iodine. During the next few weeks the "adult larvae" metamorphosed to typical adults as the next two pictures show.

The frog: the halfway vertebrate

If numbers be taken as a criterion for success, the amphibians were much more successful at an earlier time than now. At that time they did give rise to very successful groups of animals, the reptiles, birds, and mammals. The amphibians seem to have reached the halfway mark between the aquatic and the land forms and for that reason they show some very interesting intermediate structures. To study a bird or a mammal without reference to the frog would be like studying the present-day government of the United States without reference to the struggle for independence. Understanding of a mammal can only come from a historical approach to the whole problem, which means that it is essential to examine an intermediate type. There is no better form to use for such a study than a representative amphibian, and the frog lends itself especially well for several reasons (Fig. 15-18). First, aside from its well-developed, atypical, jumping legs, it possesses most of the typical ancestral amphibian characteristics. Secondly, it occurs universally, which makes it an inexpensive form for study. Lastly, it is of such a size that it is easily handled in the laboratory by students; a larger or smaller animal offers some difficult problems in this respect. A thorough knowledge of the "halfway" animal at this point provides the background for a better understanding of the mammal.

Life History (Fig. 15-19). One of the first harbingers of spring is the familiar croaking of the frogs (Fig. 15-20). While these sounds are pleasant to hear, they have more important meaning to the frogs. In temperate climates the male frogs usually emerge from hibernation first and begin croaking; the females follow some days later. At this time of the year, the eggs in the body of the female are fully mature. In most species the male mounts and clasps the female with his front legs, grasping her just back of her front legs and pressing the small swollen parts of each thumb (**nuptial pads**) against her chest. This process is called **amplexus** (Fig. 15-21), and is a kind

FIG. 15-18. The common leopard frog (*Rana pipiens*).

of copulation. As the female lays her eggs the male discharges a milky fluid containing sperm, thus fertilizing them. Very shortly thereafter, the gelatinous matrix surrounding the eggs swells, causing them

FIG. 15-19. Life history of the frog.

FIG. 15-20. A tree toad (*Hyla versicolor*) croaking. Note the greatly extended vocal sacs which aid in producing its shrill sound.

to adhere to twigs or any other underwater debris. In some species the eggs are at first black above and white below, a characteristic which may possibly offer some degree of protection during the early stages of development.

Under the microscope, one can see the egg divide, once, twice, three times, and so on, producing furrows along one side, then elongating, and finally developing a small tail. Some time later a tiny tadpole emerges from the jelly mass. By means of a pair of suckers under the mouth, the tadpole remains attached to the mass for a few hours while it is undergoing further develop-

FIG. 15-21. A pair of toads (*Bufo blombergi*) in amplexus.

ment. Presently, it begins to swim about and can be seen to feed by a scraping movement of its mouth as it moves along a leaf of a water plant. In this stage it breathes by means of gills just as fish do and as its ancestors did. It is a vegetarian, feeding exclusively on algae and other plant life.

After some months or years, depending on the species of frog, the tadpole rather suddenly begins to develop miniature legs while its tail becomes shorter. At the same time its mouth grows larger and wider, and its digestive tract shortens. It gradually seeks shallower water and occasionally comes to the surface for air as its lungs develop. These trips for air become more frequent until finally the frog hops away from the water, sans tail and strictly carnivorous. Thus, in a brief period it has re-enacted the entire history of this long and arduous migration out of the water onto land, a most remarkable feat!

The Frog Body Plan. Frogs range in size from the tiny chorus frog (*Pseudacris*), about an inch long, to the bullfrog which may be a foot over-all. In general, their features are so similar that, aside from coloration and habits, a description for one fits them all. During the following study refer to Figure 15-22 for general anatomical features.

When a study is made of a living frog, the moist, slippery skin is at once conspicuous even if the frog is kept away from water for some time. This is due to tiny **mucous glands** in the skin which constantly pour out their fluids to keep it wet. The frog receives considerable amounts of oxygen through its skin and must therefore have a moist skin.

Other distinctive features include the protruding **eyes** which permit the frog to come to the surface of the water and see without exposing the rest of its body. Lying just back of the eyes are the large **eardrums** which are a part of the hearing mechanism. Above the tip of the nose are

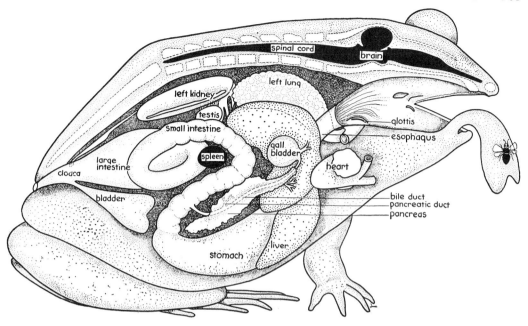

FIG. 15-22. Longitudinal section of the frog, showing internal organs.

the **nostrils** which have valves that can be opened and closed at will. These function in breathing. The **mouth** is a very large one, and is kept shut all of the time except when the frog feeds. At the posterior end is the **anus,** which is the terminal opening of the **cloaca.**

The front legs function in breaking the fall after a jump, as well as in supporting the anterior portion of the body. The long muscular hind legs are ideally adapted for jumping. When surprised on land, the frog suddenly straightens out its legs, throwing the body forward several feet. This process can be repeated in rapid succession, so that it requires an agile pursuer to overtake the little animal. These are the principal external features that are noted in a cursory examination.

Outer Covering. Like all vertebrates, the skin of the frog consists of an outer thin **epidermis** and a thicker under layer, the **dermis.** The outer layer, which is shed periodically, is made up of flat cells. The dermis contains many glands which pro-

vide the mucus for keeping the skin moist. Some species have, in addition, smaller glands in this region which secrete a substance that is offensive to animals that might feed upon it. The dermis is also heavily vascularized for its function in breathing.

The dermal scales of the fish are noticeably absent among the modern amphibians, although fossil remains indicate that their ancestors were well covered with scales. Scales offer excellent protection from attack and it seems strange that the amphibians have given up this apparently valuable aid in self-preservation. It must be remembered, however, that in present-day species the skin is an "accessory" lung and very important in respiration. Only because of this condition is it possible for the amphibian to spend its quiet periods in an environment where breathing with lungs is impossible.

Locomotion and Support. When the loose skin of the frog is removed, a set of muscles is exposed that far surpasses those of

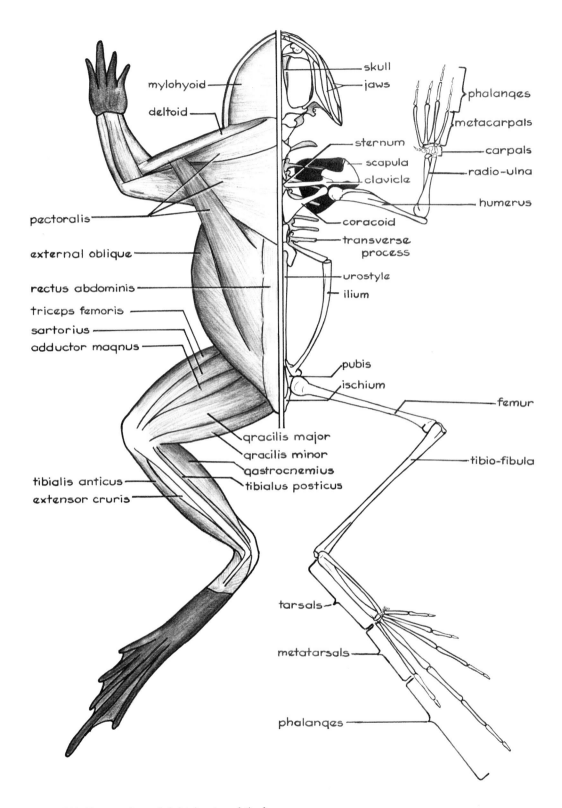

FIG. 15-23. The muscular and skeletal system of the frog.

skull
jaws
phalanges
metacarpals
sternum
scapula
carpals
clavicle
radio-ulna
humerus
coracoid
transverse process
urostyle
ilium
pubis
ischium
femur
gracilis major
gracilis minor
gastrocnemius
tibialus posticus
tibio-fibula
tarsals
metatarsals
phalanges

mylohyoid
deltoid
pectoralis
external oblique
rectus abdominis
triceps femoris
sartorius
adductor magnus
tibialis anticus
extensor cruris

the fish. The most conspicuous difference noted between the frog and fish is the remarkable development of the muscles that operate the appendages. Although many of the muscles approximate the position and seem to function much the same as similar muscles in man, most comparative anatomists agree that only a very few of them are identical. Some of the muscles of the frog are named in Figure 15-23 and should be studied in terms of their function in locomotion and not from a comparative point of view.

Although the internal skeleton of the frog is made of bone and in many respects resembles that of man, in other respects it must be considered as the skeleton of a "specialized" vertebrate rather than a "generalized" form because it differs so markedly from primitive vertebrates (Fig. 15-23). The appendages are attached to the vertebral column by means of girdles, the **pectoral** in front, the **pelvic** behind. These are quite generalized and hence much like those in most other vertebrates. The pectoral girdle consists of three principal pairs of bones attached to a series of midventral bones called the **sternum**. The **scapulae** are located on the dorsal side of the trunk (the flat extension is called the suprascapula), and this structure is similar to the human shoulder blade. It joins ventrally with the **clavicle** and **coracoid** which in turn fuse to the sternum. The clavicle (collar bone) is well developed in man but the coracoid is only a small "bump," fused to the scapula. The pelvic girdle is composed of three pairs of bones, which in the adult are fused into a single structure. The long, flat, anteriorly directed **ilium** joins posteriorly with the **ischium** and ventrally with the **pubis** (the latter remains as cartilage) to form each half of this girdle.

The front and hind legs of the frog are homologous, that is, they are very similar, possessing approximately the same bones although of somewhat different proportions. A single bone, the **humerus**, which fits into a cavity (**glenoid fossa**) of the pectoral girdle, forms the top of the front leg; this is followed by a pair of bones, the **radius** and **ulna**, which are fused together in the frog but separate in most other vertebrates. The wrist is composed of several bones called **carpals**; these are followed by the **metacarpals** and **phalanges** of the **digits.**

The posterior appendage likewise has a single bone, in this case called the **femur**, which fits into a socket (**acetabulum**) in the pelvic girdle; this bone is followed by a pair of bones, the **tibia** and **fibula**, which again are fused in the frog. The **tarsals** are next, and two of these are enlarged to add a joint in the hind legs, thus facilitating jumping. Following the tarsals are the **metatarsals** and finally the **phalanges**. The bones of these appendages have remarkably similar counterparts in the human skeleton (Fig. 16-9).

The anterior end of the spinal column articulates with the base of the skull which houses the brain. Other parts of the skull make up the food-getting and breathing mechanism. The jaws of the frog are made up of three bones and resemble the gill arches of the shark from which they were derived. Behind the jaws and lying between them is the **tongue**, which possesses a rather good support, the **hyoid apparatus**. The hyoid apparatus, like the jaw, has been derived from the gill arches. Other gill arches have been modified into supporting structures for the **larynx**, the sound-making apparatus. Here is seen a phenomenon constantly found in evolution, that is, the formation of new structures from old ones which no longer function in their original manner.

Nervous System. The nervous system of any animal begins with the end organs which receive stimulations from the outside world. The nostrils open into nasal passages which are lined with sensory cells that join the olfactory nerve (Fig. 15-24).

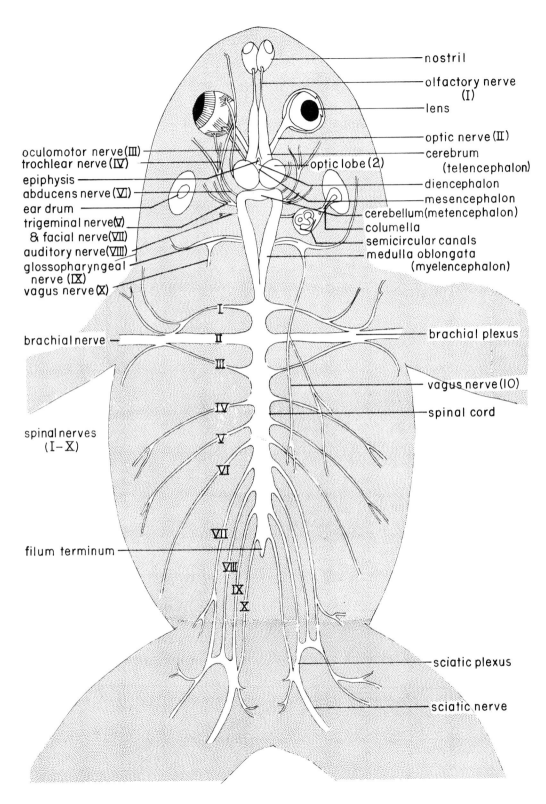

nostril

olfactory nerve
(I)

lens

optic nerve (II)

oculomotor nerve (III)
trochlear nerve (IV)

optic lobe (2)

cerebrum
(telencephalon)

epiphysis

diencephalon

abducens nerve (VI)

mesencephalon

ear drum

cerebellum (metencephalon)

trigeminal nerve (V)
& facial nerve (VII)

columella

semicircular canals

auditory nerve (VIII)

medulla oblongata

glossopharyngeal
nerve (IX)
vagus nerve (X)

(myelencephalon)

I

brachial nerve

II

brachial plexus

III

vagus nerve (10)

IV

spinal cord

V

spinal nerves
(I–X)

VI

VII

filum terminum

VIII

IX

X

sciatic plexus

sciatic nerve

FIG. 15-24. Frog nervous system, dorsal view.

The frog has a rather good sense of smell.

The frog's eye differs from the human eye in minor details only. For example, the lids will not cover the eye completely. The typical six muscles for moving the eye in all directions are present, just as in all higher vertebrates. The lens is fixed in place so that the focus cannot be changed as in man by altering its own shape, or as in the fish by moving back and forth. Therefore, the frog sees clearly only at one distance, and it is near-sighted in air and far-sighted under water. The **rods** and **cones** of the **retina,** which are the parts of the eye sensitive to light, are scattered, rather than concentrated in one spot as in man (p. 451). Consequently, the frog probably does not see as distinctly as higher forms do.

The conspicuous **eardrum** of the frog is exposed to the outside world, whereas in higher forms it is buried deep inside the head. Lying beneath the drum is a cavity in which a single bone, the **columella,** extends from the thin eardrum to a tiny bit of sensory tissue which is stimulated by the vibrations as they are passed to it. Because of the rather primitive nature of the auditory organ, the frog probably cannot discriminate between sounds that vary slightly in pitch. The organs of equilibrium (**semicircular canals**) are similar to those of both lower (shark) and higher (man) forms.

With the exception of a few major modifications, there is remarkable similarity between the brain of the frog and man. The brain is proportionately much larger in man and the spinal cord sends out three times as many nerves. The foreshortened trunk of the frog accounts for the fact that there are so few spinal nerves. When the brain and cord are dissected out and viewed as a unit, the brain seems to be no more than a slightly expanded anterior end of the cord (Fig. 15-24). Starting at the base of the brain and progressing forward, the five parts of the brain can be seen.

The first enlarged portion is the **me-**dulla oblongata (myelencephalon—5) which gives rise to most of the cranial nerves (Fig. 15-24). These have to do with most of the automatic functions of the body, just as they do in man. A slight projection which runs transversely across the medulla is the **cerebellum** (metencephalon—4) which is much smaller in the frog than in most other vertebrates. This may be owing to its function in muscular coordination, which is poorly developed in amphibians. The most conspicuous objects of the entire brain are the **optic lobes** (outgrowths of the mesencephalon—3) in which nerves from the eyes terminate. These lobes seem to function in inhibition of spinal cord reflexes, rather than as the centers for sight. The small projection just anterior to the optic lobes (diencephalon—2) is the **epiphysis,** an organ of doubtful function. On the ventral side of this same region is a tube-like stalk which terminates in an enlargement, the **pituitary** (hypophysis), a very important gland of internal secretion about which more will be learned later.

The anterior part of the brain (telencephalon—1) is only poorly developed in the frog. It is composed of a pair of lobes which are partly divided transversely. The two anterior parts are the **olfactory lobes** to which the **olfactory nerves** are attached. The posterior parts of these lobes make up the **cerebral hemispheres,** the function of which is not clear. In fact, when this portion is removed the animal responds in a near-normal fashion when various stimuli are applied (Fig. 17-22). This is one of the greatest differences between the frog and man, for in man many important sensations are recorded in the conspicuous cerebral hemispheres.

The frog has only ten cranial nerves, but reptiles, birds, and mammals possess well-developed eleventh and twelfth cranial nerves. There is some evidence that primitive amphibians, too, had these additional nerves, but strangely enough, the frog seems to have lost them somewhere along the way. The spinal nerves that pass to the legs are grouped together in two plexi, the anterior **brachial plexus** and the posterior **sciatic plexus.** From these regions the nerves spread out again and pass to all parts of the appendages.

Digestive System. This system starts with a disproportionately large mouth which when fully open can enclose a body one-fourth the size of the frog itself (Fig. 15-22). The jaws are feebly armed with a top row of teeth and a few on the front edge of the palate. The teeth function only in holding prey and are incapable of crushing or chewing. The large protrusible tongue lies on the floor of the mouth with the two pointed tips directed down the throat. It is attached in a peculiar manner, the anterior end being fastened just inside the lower jaw. When in use, the mouth is opened wide and the tongue is flipped out with lightning-like speed, so fast, in fact, that it has no difficulty in capturing agile insects, since the sticky mucus secreted by mouth glands makes a good adhesive agent. There are no digestive enzymes in the saliva and hence no digestion occurs in the mouth.

Openings into the mouth cavity are those of the **eustachian tubes** which connect with the cavity under the eardrums, the **internal nares,** which connect with the nostrils, and the **esophagus** which leads abruptly into the large U-shaped **stomach.** The back part of the mouth, the **pharynx,** is lined with cilia which beat continuously and help carry food down to the stomach. The stomach is merely a portion of the digestive tract which is enlarged for storage of food, and the frog has occasion, indeed, to use a sac of such ample proportions. Some digestion takes place in the stomach. The lower extremity is marked by a constriction, the **pyloric sphincter** (a band of circular muscles which, when contracted, closes the opening). The stomach is followed in turn by the **small intestine** which receives the pancreatic juice and bile from

a single duct. The **pancreas** is a long, light-colored, ribbon-like organ that lies between the stomach and the first part of the intestine. The **liver** is composed of three lobes, two large lateral lobes and one smaller median lobe. The **gallbladder** usually lies dorsal to the smaller lobe, and the **bile duct** passes from it through the substance of the pancreas on its way to the intestine, picking up the **pancreatic duct** along the way. The gall bladder is green in color due to the **bile** which it contains.

The small intestine of the herbivorous tadpole is very much longer than that of the carnivorous adult frog, a distinction that generally separates animals that feed on vegetation from those that feed on meat. Digestion takes place much faster where meat is the principal diet and therefore a shorter gut is sufficient. On the other hand, the cellulose found in plant tissue requires a longer period to digest; hence a longer gut is necessary in animals that are vegetarians. The small intestine of the frog opens directly into the short expanded **large intestine** which soon constricts down to the **rectum** and then opens into the **cloaca** (sewer). Here the **genital** and **urinary** ducts also empty. Undigested food deposited in this region is soon voided to the outside through the **anus.** The cloaca is found among reptiles, birds, and low mammals, but among all higher mammals the urogenital and digestive tubes have separate openings to the outside of the body.

Circulatory System. In fish, the heart is a simple pump in which all of the blood is carried through a single circuit. In the air-breathing vertebrates, however, a change occurs. There are two blood circuits. One circuit carries blood rich in oxygen to the tissues, then brings the "used" blood, poor in oxygen, back to the heart. The other circuit carries this depleted blood to the lungs and brings it back, after oxygenation, to the heart. Because the only source of oxygen is from the lungs, these two circuits

carotid arch
systemic arch
pulmocutaneous arch
to pulmocutaneous arch
right auricle
longitudinal valve
semilunar valve

to carotid arch
to systemic arch
from pulmonary veins
from sinus venosus
right auricle
left auricle
auriculo-ventricular valve
ventricle

FIG. 15-25. Ventral view of the frog's heart, sectioned to show chambers and valves.

must be kept separate in order to do an efficient job.

A study of the blood pathway through the frog heart will help us to understand the evolution of heart circulation in land vertebrates. Because both auricles (atria, singular-atrium) pour their contents into the single ventricle, it has long been a controversial question as to whether or not the blood was completely mixed when it left the heart. The position of the entrances of the blood into the ventricle (Fig. 15-25), together with the existence of the longitudinal valve, was thought to be sufficient evidence to prove that blood returning from the body to the right auricle and that coming from the lungs to the left auricle remained separated when it left the ventricle upon its contraction. Recent studies of the oxygen content of the blood in the heart and major blood vessels indicate that the carotid arteries receive highly oxygenated blood from the left auricle, whereas the

pulmocutaneous arteries receive blood low in oxygen from the right auricle. The aortas receive mixed blood. Apparently the amphibian heart separates the oxygenated and reduced blood much as is done in the bird and mammalian heart, although not as efficiently.

The extensive cutaneous circulation in the frog explains why lung breathing is only supplementary to the gaseous exchange that takes place in the skin. The frog spends much of its time underwater where only skin breathing is possible, and even on land the frog receives much of its oxygen through the buccal membranes. The lungs are brought into use only when the animal is hard pressed, the skin and buccal membranes being quite adequate for most activities.

Blood coming from all parts of the body first enters the sac-like **sinus venosus** and then the **right auricle**; simultaneously blood from the lungs enters the **left auricle**.

Blood in the right auricle contains considerable oxygen, because part of it has just returned from the skin and buccal region where it picks up oxygen. That in the left auricle, of course, is rich in oxygen. The auricles then contract, the right slightly before the left, forcing the blood into the single **ventricle** where a certain amount of mixing occurs. The ventricle then contracts, forcing the blood into the **truncus arteriosus** and to all parts of the body through the arteries. The **longitudinal valve** probably serves as a mechanical support for the truncus, making it possible to produce a higher blood pressure when the truncus contracts. The modern amphibian heart, while not as efficient as the bird or mammalian heart, certainly is quite adequate for amphibious life.

Arteries. There are three pairs of large arteries leaving the heart: the **pulmocutaneous** which goes to the lungs and skin, the **systemic arches** which join and become the **dorsal aorta,** and the **carotids** which go to the head and neck regions (Fig. 15-26). Each of these vessels divides many times until a network of capillaries is formed, and these networks supply all portions of the body with oxygen and food.

Capillaries. The arteries terminate when their walls become one cell layer in thickness. Through vessels of this diameter blood cells can only pass single file, and these tiny, thin-walled tubes are the **capillaries.** These are the most important tubes of the entire vascular system because it is through the capillary walls that food and oxygen can get to the cells. The passing of the corpuscles through the capillaries can be easily observed under the microscope. The larger vessels in such a preparation are the **arterioles** and **venules,** which can be distinguished from each other by the fact that the blood flows in spurts in the arterioles and only gently in the venules.

Veins. After leaving the capillaries, the vessels become **veins** which carry the blood back to the heart. These grow larger and fewer in number as they approach the heart (Fig. 15-26). The blood from the hind legs has an alternate course in getting back to the heart. It may pass via the kidneys through the **renal portal system,** or via the liver through the **hepatic portal system.** A portal system is a system of veins which starts and ends in capillaries. The frog, like other lower vertebrates, has two such systems, whereas man and the higher vertebrates have only the hepatic portal system. It can be seen that this system is most important in carrying the blood heavily laden with food to the liver where it can be stored and otherwise processed. The two **precavas** and the single **postcava** veins enter the sac-like sinus venosus through three openings before proceeding on to the **right auricle.** Blood coming from the lungs in the **pulmonary veins** empties into the **left auricle,** thence into the ventricle where it joins the blood from the sinus venosus.

Breathing System. The tadpole breathes by means of gills much the same as fish do. As it metamorphoses into the adult frog it gradually loses its gills and develops a pair of lungs. The **larynx** is located at the point of junction with the mouth cavity, and contains the vocal cords which, when vibrated, produce the characteristic sounds of the frog. The air passes into the mouth cavity through the nostrils and then is forced into the trachea and lungs through the **glottis,** a slit-like opening in the rigid circular larynx (Fig. 15-22). The trachea is short and immediately branches into the two thin-walled, sac-like **lungs.** The air is brought into the mouth through the nostrils by the sudden lowering of the floor of the mouth. The valves in the nostrils are then closed and the floor of the mouth raised causing the air to be forced into the lungs. However, much of the gas exchange takes

Arteries

Veins

external carotid

internal carotid

carotid arch

systemic arch

pulmocutaneous arch

truncus arteriosus

lung

liver

dorsal aorta

fat body

testis

urogenital

kidney

iliac

femoral

sciatic

anterior vena cava

sinus venosus

pulmonary

hepatic

posterior vena cava

hepatic portal

gastric

stomach

renal

renal portal

ventral abdominal

large intestine

pelvic

femoral

sciatic

FIG. 15-26. Ventral view of the frog circulatory system.

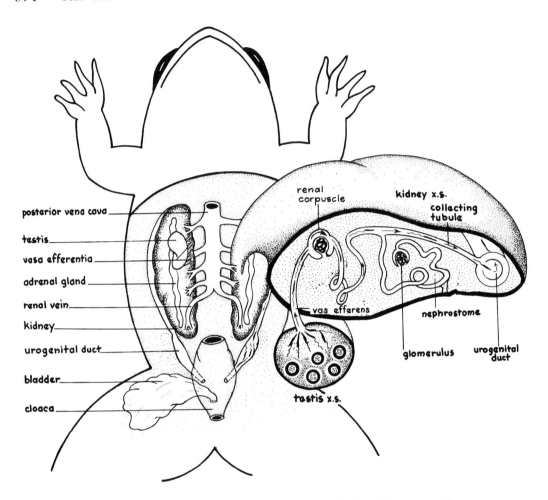

posterior vena cava

testis

vasa efferentia

adrenal gland

renal vein

kidney

urogenital duct

bladder

cloaca

renal corpuscle

kidney x.s.

collecting tubule

vas efferens

nephrostome

glomerulus

urogenital duct

testis x.s.

FIG. 15-27. Male frog urogenital system, showing the kidney and testis enlarged in a cross-section.

place in the mouth alone, for only now and then is the air taken into the lungs.

Excretory System. The excretory system of the frog is essentially the same as in invertebrates such as the earthworm or lobster, as far as the individual units are concerned. It is made up of a great many nephridia massed together into a pair of organs, the **kidneys.** Urinary wastes, urea, salts, and so forth, are withdrawn from the blood as it passes through the kidney. The blood coming forward from the posterior parts of the body passes to the kidney and as it

does the vessels break up into tiny masses **(glomeruli)** in the **renal corpusles** (Fig. 15-27). As the blood passes through the glomeruli the urinary products are removed (p. 595). They pass down a long coiled tubule and finally reach a larger duct, the **urogenital duct,** in the male **(Wolffian duct)** which also carries the reproductive (sperm) cells. The corresponding duct in the female carries urine only. The urine is deposited in the **urinary bladder** which in turn opens into the **cloaca.** Urinary wastes and feces, as well as the genital products, all pass to the outside through a single opening, the **anus.**

Reproductive System. The sex organs of the male are the yellowish **testes** located ventral and anterior to the kidneys (Fig. 15-27). They hang in a sheet-like bit of tissue, the mesorchium, through which tiny tubules, the **vasa efferentia,** pass on their way from the testes to the kidneys. Upon entering the kidney, the vasa efferentia connect with the uriniferous tubules which are connected to the **renal corpuscles.** Therefore, the tubules carry both sperm from the testes and urine from the renal corpuscles. The two products flow to the lateral edge of the kidney where they are poured into a larger tube, the **urogenital duct,** which eventually deposits its sperm load into the **sperm sac.**

In the female, the ovaries lie in the same position on the kidneys as the testes do in the male. Sometime in the summer months when the food is abundant, the residual eggs lying in the walls of the ovaries begin to grow and continue at a rapid pace until the ovaries are tremendous in size, almost filling the body cavity. The eggs develop in tiny pockets in the wall of the hollow ovary (Fig. 15-28) and when the breeding season approaches, the mature eggs burst out in the body cavity. Here they are swept along by the united effort of cilia

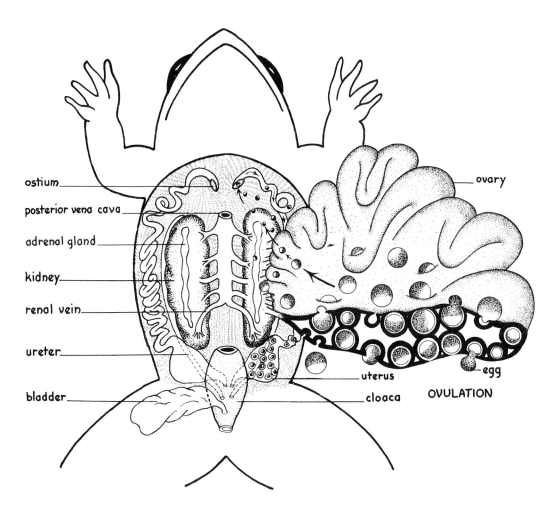

FIG. 15-28. Female frog urogenital system showing the ovary enlarged and in cross-section.

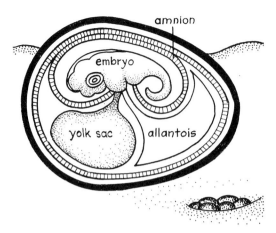

FIG. 15-29. In order for vertebrates to divorce themselves from water a method of caring for their young during early development was accomplished with the evolution of the land egg.

which line nearly all the walls. Their goal is the **ostium,** the tiny anterior opening of the long coiled **oviduct.** Once inside the opening, the eggs make their way single file through the long oviduct which is also lined with cilia. During their passage they accumulate a jelly-like substance on their exteriors which swells rapidly the moment the eggs become immersed in water. Just before the oviducts join the cloaca they enlarge into thin-walled sacs, the **uteri.** Here the eggs are stored until amplexus occurs, at which time they are laid.

This somewhat detailed study of the frog lays a foundation for an understanding of vertebrates in general, and particularly man which we shall consider at some length in Part VI. Let us now continue with the evolution of higher vertebrates.

LAND CONQUERORS: THE REPTILES

The reptiles (class **Reptilia**) moved one step farther in the long trek to complete terrestrial existence. They spend no part of their life in the water unless they choose to do so. Means developed whereby the early

embryos could exist in a fluid environment. A medium was supplied with sufficient nourishment to carry the embryo through the stages equivalent to the tadpole stage among amphibians. For this reason, reptilian eggs are large, with great quantities of stored food in the form of yolk and albumin (Fig. 15-29). A large, fluid-filled sac, called the **amnion,** develops around the embryo, which not only provides a fluid environment but also protects the developing embryo from injury and desiccation. Shortly after the formation of the amnion, the **allantois** develops from the posterior end of the embryo. This enveloping membrane receives discarded material, including carbon dioxide, from the embryo. It lies very close to the porous, rigid **outer shell** so that a gaseous exchange can readily take place. Therefore, in addition to being an organ of excretion, the allantois acts as a temporary breathing organ during embryonic life. The young reptile need not be immersed in water at any time during its life, and thus the first true land animal has been evolved. This was probably the greatest step forward in conquering the land.

Other changes also occurred that made the reptile better suited for terrestrial existence. Internal fertilization was accomplished by the development of efficient copulatory organs, insuring a direct transfer of the sperm into the genital tract of the female. In addition, reptilian legs became longer and were usually more ventrally located, making it possible for them to support the body completely off the ground. The heart also began to form a complete partition in the ventricle, producing the beginnings of two complete hearts, thereby separating the pulmonary and systemic blood to make a much more effective circulatory system.

Early Reptiles

Sometime in the distant past there were amphibians that gradually took on reptilian characteristics. Such animals have been

CENOZOIC

MESOZOIC

CRETACEOUS

OPOSSUM

JURASSIC

PRIMITIVE BIRD

TRIASSIC

MAMMAL-LIKE REPTILE

PALEOZOIC

PERMIAN

STEM REPTILE

FIG. 15-30. Primitive reptiles gave rise to all higher groups of animals. The reptiles as a group have been the most successful of all vertebrates, as indicated by their great numbers and variety of form in Mesozoic time and by the fact that they gave rise to the birds and mammals.

FIG. 15-31. A scene from the Mesozoic Period when the great dinosaurs were dominant. The flesh-eating *Tyranno-saurus* is shown attacking the well-armored *Triceratops* (left center) and two tremendous herbivorous *Brontosaurus* are feeding in the swamps (right center). Some reptiles took to the air and are shown flying over their land-dwelling relatives. A primitive bird (*Archaeopteryx*) was present during these early times (lower right).

found in fossil remains and are called the Stem Reptiles. Among these is *Seymouria*, which resembled both amphibians and reptiles. It, or forms like it, probably gave rise to the great variety of reptiles known to have lived during the Mesozoic Era and, indeed, to birds and mammals as well (Fig. 15-30). The Age of Reptiles lasted over 100 million years. By comparison, it is estimated that man is no older than two million years at most.

The Dinosaurs

Dinosaurs had their meager beginnings in the Triassic Period when they were small unimportant animals. Evolving in both size and numbers during the Jurassic and Cretaceous periods, they reached the pinnacle of walking land vertebrates near the close of the Mesozoic Era, finally disappearing from the earth never to appear again.

They ranged in size from the barnyard fowl to the largest of all land animals.

Many of the dinosaurs developed the bipedal method of locomotion, that is, they rose on their hind legs when in haste and propelled themselves entirely by these two appendages. This idea proved successful in some of the largest flesh-eaters, which had powerful hind legs but only short anterior appendages (Fig. 15-31). Bipedal locomotion in four-footed animals is, then, very ancient. Footprints left in various parts of the world by these ancient animals have given paleontologists some interesting evidence as to the nature of the reptiles that made them. For example, in the old mud flats of the Connecticut Valley there are some that resemble bird footprints of to-day, and hence were first thought to be footprints of giant birds (Fig. 15-32).

The flesh-eaters grew to enormous size

and the largest one unearthed, *Tyrannosaurus* (tyrant reptile), reached a height of 19 feet. It must have been an awesome creature in those prehistoric times, perhaps feared by all living animals. Its skull was over 4 feet in length and the jaws were armed with formidable teeth, which must have functioned well in rending and tearing other animals to bits. It possessed massive hind legs and small front ones. It is thought that its chief source of food was the giant amphibian forms which existed at the same time.

The great amphibious dinosaurs were vegetarians and grew to great lengths and heights. *Brontosaurus* and *Diplodocus* reached a length of 85 feet and a weight of 40 tons or more. They walked on all four feet and their powerful legs were placed in such a position as to carry the body evenly balanced. The head was much too small for the size of the animal, and it is difficult to see how it could house a brain sufficiently large to govern such a massive hulk. The dorsally placed nostrils have led scientists to conclude that the animal was amphibious and probably remained submerged most of the time with only the nostrils protruding above the surface of the water for breathing air.

In the hip region, the spinal column supported an enlargement several times the size of the brain. Apparently impulses received by the brain from the sense organs were sent down to the large posterior ganglion which operated the posterior legs and perhaps the rear portion of the body. The strange anatomy of this great beast inspired the late Bert L. Taylor of the *Chicago Tribune* to write long ago the following poem:

Behold the mighty dinosaur,
Famous in prehistoric lore,
Not only for his power and strength
But for his intellectual length.
You will observe by these remains
The creature had two sets of brains—
One in his head (the usual place),

FIG. 15-32. Dinosaurs often left footprints in soft mud that later became buried with fine sand, leaving almost perfect impressions of the feet of these ancient animals. The sedimentary rock in which this one was found separated, so that both the mold (right) and the cast can be seen.

The other at his spinal base.
Thus he could reason *a priori*
As well as *a posteriori*.
No problem bothered him a bit
He made both head and tail of it.
So wise was he, so wise and solemn,
Each thought filled just a spinal column.
If one brain found the pressure strong
It passed a few ideas along.
If something slipped his forward mind
'Twas rescued by the one behind.
And if in error he was caught
He had a saving afterthought.
As he thought twice before he spoke
He had no judgment to revoke.
Thus he could think without congestion
Upon both sides of every question.
Oh, gaze upon this model beast,
Defunct ten million years at least.

Horned dinosaurs such as *Triceratops* were the last of the large dinosaurs (Fig. 15-31). The body was relatively bare, but the head was heavily armed with bony organs of defense. Two great horns protruded anteriorly over the eyes and another over the ridge of the nose. An enormous flare of bone, extending out from the back of the neck, probably functioned admirably in preventing an injurious blow to this vulnerable region.

It has been a question why these great animals became extinct by the end of the Cretaceous Period. There are many answers, but possibly a combination of many factors was responsible for their extinction. Since the flesh-eaters depended on the plant feeders for food, a gradual extinction of the latter meant annihilation of the former as well. Geological changes going on at that time resulted in the gradual rising of the land, culminating in the formation of the Rocky Mountains in this country. This meant not only less water and consequently fewer swamps, the habitat of these animals, but also cooler climates and perhaps much less vegetation. With the declining food supply the great herbivores starved to death, taking the carnivores with them.

Modern Reptiles

At least sixteen orders of reptiles have lived on earth; today only four remain (Fig. 15-30). Of these the most common are the lizards, snakes, turtles, and the large alligators and crocodiles.

Perhaps the most despised of all animals are the lizards and snakes, not because they are particularly harmful to man or because he inherits a fear of them, but because he is taught to be afraid of them, particularly snakes. The group as a whole does little harm to man or his domestic animals, and what harm it does do is offset by its creditable deeds.

Lizards and snakes belong to the order **Squamata.** They are covered with scales which they shed periodically. Lizards are four-legged animals and exemplify the typical modern reptile, that is, they show the least amount of modification in body form of any of the reptiles. A good example of the group is the *Iguana* (Fig. 15-33). The only poisonous lizard is the Gila monster (Fig. 15-33), a highly colored, sluggish, plump creature found in drier regions of North and Middle America. It rarely uses

its venom in killing prey because its diet consists of bird and reptilian eggs as well as nestlings. Its bite is rarely, if ever, fatal to man.

With the exception of pythons and boas, snakes are without limbs. Many move in an undulating fashion much the same as fish swim. Their eyes are large and without lids. Because their sound-recording organs are degenerate, they are deaf. The snake possesses a long forked tongue which has sensory functions in tracking down prey. The snake's mouth is equipped with sharp teeth that curve inward and are well adapted for holding its victim (Fig. 15-34, 15-36); any struggling movement of the prey tends to force the creature further down the throat of the snake. Another convenient adaptation associated with food taking is the enormous potential size of the mouth, which can be stretched to accommodate an animal several times its own diameter (Fig. 15-35). Some snakes such as the boas kill their prey by squeezing it to death (Fig. 15-36). All of the snake's internal organs are stretched out so as to be accommodated within the slender body.

The snakes have received their bad reputation from the poisonous members of the group. Just how these creatures evolved this deadly offensive and defensive mechanism is hard to say. Many different kinds of tooth formations have been produced for inoculating the poison into the wound made by the sharp teeth. In some forms, such as the rattlesnake, the fangs possess a hollow tube through which the venom is injected, as with a hypodermic needle (Fig. 15-35). Others, such as the cobra, have deep-grooved fangs which allow the poison to enter at the base of the tooth and exit near the tip so that, upon striking, the poison will be deep within the wound. The poison glands are located above the angle of the jaw and empty their venom into a flap of skin at the base of the fangs. Once the venom has entered the blood stream, its effect is very rapid, causing a

FIG. 15-33. (Top) One of the largest lizards alive today, *Iguana iguana*, reaches a length of 6 feet. It inhabits tropical America. (Bottom) The Gila monster (*Heloderma suspectum*) lives in southwestern United States and is our only poisonous lizard.

FIG. 15-34. (Top) A rattlesnake (*Crotalus seutulatus*) in striking position. Note that the rattles at the tip of the tail seem blurred because of their rapid vibration. (Bottom) The position and size of the fangs are shown in this picture. Note the pit located anterior to the eye.

FIG. 15-35. The skull of a rattlesnake. Note how loosely the jaw bones are attached to the skull. This, together with the lack of fusion of the jaw bones in front, makes it possible for the snake to swallow an animal several times its own diameter. One of the fangs has been enlarged in the lower picture to show its hollow construction. It resembles an inoculating needle.

small rodent to become paralyzed in a matter of a few seconds. The venom acts by destroying the red bloods cells. Antivenoms have been prepared for all of the common poisonous snakes and have proved valuable in alleviating the effects of their bites. A person may die from the bite of a poisonous snake if he is not treated. Of the types of poisonous snakes in the United States, the most common are the rattlesnakes. The water moccasin and copperhead have fangs like the rattlesnakes. The coral snake, beautiful though poisonous, has erect fangs much smaller than those of the others.

The turtles, the most odd-looking of all reptiles (Fig. 15-37), belong to the order **Testudinata.** If they were extinct, man would regard them with wonder, but because they are so commonplace we think little about them. Turtles have existed a long time on the earth, since the earliest ones were contemporaries of the most primitive dinosaurs. The great reptiles came and passed on to extinction, but the turtles have persisted. Even with the advent of mammals, the turtle, concealed in its protective armor, has maintained itself and, who knows, may survive long after the mammals, including man, have passed out of existence.

Turtles live both on land (tortoises) and in the water. Like many other groups of land animals, they have returned to the water and have so modified their bodies that they are well adapted to an aquatic existence. The great sea turtles, such as the hawksbill and the green turtle (Fig. 15-37), have their appendages modified into flippers. They are never seen on land except during the egg-laying season. Others, such as the common painted turtle, are usually found in water but also frequently are seen on land near bodies of water. Still others, like the high-shelled tortoises, live in certain parts of the world where they have no enemies and grow to enormous sizes, often weighing 600 pounds. These desert forms feed on vegetation alone and rarely if ever take any water.

The surviving members of the great ruling reptiles, the dinosaurs, are the crocodiles, the caimans of the Amazon, the gavials of the Ganges and the alligators of Florida (Fig. 15-38). They belong to the order **Crocodilia.** They inhabit the large rivers of the world and are often hunted for their valuable hides. These animals show some anatomical features which place them among the highest reptiles. For example, they have a nearly completely divided ventricle in the heart, resulting in a four-chambered heart like that of birds and mammals. They also possess the mammalian characteristic of a nearly complete **diaphragm,** which is a muscular separation between the chest and abdominal cavities.

One very interesting reptile is *Sphenodon* (order **Rhynchocephalia**), more commonly known as Tuatara (Fig. 15-39), which carries in its body many anatomical features definitely identifying it with the earliest of reptiles. Tuatara has appropriately been called a "living fossil." Many of its characteristics show definite relationships to the stem reptiles as well as to modern reptiles. It is always interesting to speculate why such isolated members of a once flourishing group were able to survive down to the present day when all its relatives are long since extinct. In the case of Tuatara, its location is probably responsible; the reptile lives on islands off the coast of New Zealand where it has had few, if any, natural enemies. Tuatara living in other parts of the world were set upon and apparently destroyed by the aggressive, more agile mammals. Thus it can be said that isolation has saved one species of animal. Since its environment has remained unchanged, Tuatara, itself, has changed but little through the past 200 million years.

FIG. 15-36. A California boa (*Lichanura roseofusca*) constricting and swallowing a field mouse.

383

FIG. 15-37. A native Australian riding a large marine turtle (*Chelonia mydas*). Note how the anterior appendages are modified into flippers, which are efficient organs of locomotion in water.

AIR CONQUERORS: THE BIRDS

It is a far cry from the lowly turtle and slithering snake to the most decorated of all animals, the birds (class **Aves**). Yet they have many characteristics in common with reptiles (Fig. 15-40). An early biologist has called them "glorified reptiles," which describes them very well. In conquering the air, several body modifications have been necessary. The drastic need for a lighter body framework was met by lighter, hollow bones (Fig. 15-41), and a lessening of the weight of the outer covering.

The scales of the reptiles have probably given rise to the feathers of birds, and actually there is little difference between them except in weight and texture. The bird still carries scales on its legs and sometimes around the base of the beak. Because of their loose arrangement, feathers act as excellent insulating material, an extremely important need for birds who live in both tropic and arctic regions. The wings are the modified anterior legs of the reptiles in which the three fingers have fused at the tip and the space between has been spanned by a sheet of skin covered with feathers. The wing spread is due principally to the large quill feathers at the outer edges of the wings. The breastbone is greatly overdeveloped. It is known as a **keel** and functions as an anchor for the powerful breast muscles which are used to give the power stroke in flight.

Other structural modifications have been essential for the flying animal. The hearts of birds are large and very well developed, an essential factor in maintaining a rapid circulation when so much energy is consumed in flight. The body temperature of birds is constant and slightly higher than in man, enabling the birds to keep active during all times of the year in both temperate and arctic regions.

The swift movement of a bird in flight requires keen eyesight. Birds have eyesight that is several times better than man's. The **cerebellum,** the part of the brain which controls muscular coordination, is propor-

FIG. 15-38. American alligator (*Alligator mississippiensis*). These grow to 16 feet in length.

tionately larger in the brain of birds than it is in the reptilian brain (Fig. 17-21). This again is required for flight. The cerebral hemispheres, that portion which controls innate patterns of behavior, or instincts, are also large. Bird behavior is remarkable, particularly that concerned with nest building, care of the young, and migration. Biologists have always been mystified by the complex migration routes taken by many species of birds, often great distances over large bodies

the pituitary gland (a ductless gland which secretes a number of hormones), which then activates the ovary to produce eggs out of season.

The paths taken by some birds in their migrations are truly amazing and that of the American golden plover is especially so. It nests in June on the northwestern shores of Canada above the Arctic Circle; shortly after the young birds leave the nest, the adults desert them and start across Can-

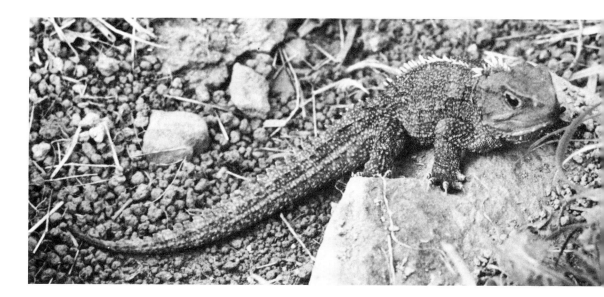

FIG. 15-39. Tuatara (*Sphenodon*) from New Zealand. A "living fossil."

of water, and in spite of a great deal of experimental work, exactly how they accomplish these feats remains a mystery.

Experiments have shown rather definitely that migrations start at remarkably regular periods which can be determined only by the amount of light received by the birds. It has been found, for example, that birds will start to lay eggs even in the wintertime if the length of daylight is increased artificially. The farmer has profited from this information by turning on lights in the chickenhouses, thus stimulating the hens to lay more eggs. Light shining on the retina of the chicken apparently stimulates

ada, flying eastward to Labrador where they arrive in early autumn. From there they take a direct course south, flying out over the Atlantic Ocean until they reach Venezuela; they then fly more leisurely on to the region of Paraguay where they overwinter. Another remarkable point is that the young birds follow a month later over approximately the same path, a total distance of over 6,000 miles, with no experienced birds to guide them.

The First Birds

As has already been mentioned, the birds apparently came from reptilian ancestors

FIG. 15-40. Birds resemble one another anatomically although they show wide modification of body parts which are used for special modes of life. For example, the beak of these four birds is modified for food-getting. The pelican's (top left) elaborate beak with its saclike attachment serves as a net in scooping up fish, its sole source of food. The sac is also used during the breeding season for storing fish for the young. The tropical toucan (lower left) possesses a colorful beak which seems overdeveloped for breaking open tree fruits upon which it feeds. Its light, though strong, structure and great length extends the bird's reach in securing fruits on the ends of branches. In addition, the bright color probably is secondarily used in social behavior. The kookaburra uses its powerful beak for killing and eating mice and snakes as this one is doing (upper right). It also has a characteristic throaty cry which has given it the name, "laughing jackass." The spoonbill uses its long broad beak to shovel through the mud in search of food (lower right). This is a rare picture of a mother and young. Both the kookaburra and the spoonbill are found in Australia.

(Fig. 15-30), a fact that should reveal fruitful intermediate types, animals that are neither reptile nor bird but a combination of both. *Archaeopteryx,* an ancient bird about the size of a crow, was found in limestone about 80 years ago in Germany. These remains were sufficiently intact to enable us to describe the bird rather well; even the feathers were preserved. Discounting the feathers, however, the animal appears very similar to a small dinosaur. The wings were weak and the finger tips bore claws. The beak was lined with teeth and the skeleton was made up of heavy bones, in contrast to the light, hollow bones of modern birds. The fact that the bones were heavy and that the keel was poorly developed indicates the bird was a poor flyer. In fact, if it could have been observed at that time it undoubtedly would have been seen gliding from branch to branch of trees much the same as the flying squirrel does today.

Some of the marine rocks of Kansas reveal later birds. One, the "fishbird" (*Ichthyornis*), shows considerable advances over *Archaeopteryx* in that it possessed a large keel bone, indicating excellent powers of flight. It did retain a toothed beak, however. Aside from this feature it probably was not greatly different from the modern tern.

Some Giant Wingless Birds

There are several species of wingless birds on earth today which have persisted over a long period of geologic time. These birds are all much alike; they are usually very large, some reaching as much as 12 feet in height, with powerful legs, small heads and rudimentary wings which are useless for flight. They depend on their fleetness for security. An interesting fact is that all modern flightless birds live in regions where there are no carnivores, that is, no members of the cat or wolf tribes. Examples are the ostrich of Africa, the cassowary and emu (Fig. 15-42) of Australia, the rhea of South

FIG. 15-41. Skeleton of the domestic fowl. The skeletal design is adapted to accommodate flight and bipedal locomotion. The large keel provides a secure point of attachment for the powerful wing muscles.

America, and the kiwi of New Zealand (Fig. 15-43). It has been suggested that these birds once were able to fly, but because there were no terrestrial predators they simply ceased flying and remained on the ground all of the time, thus conserving their energies for the important job of obtaining food. One reason that birds probably took to the air in the first place was to be better able to flee from their enemies. If the enemies are removed, then the need for flight is no longer present; hence, why fly?

THE CLIMAX ANIMALS: THE MAMMALS

The dominant and most complex animals on earth today are the mammals (class **Mammalia**). Let us consider the characteristics

FIG. 15-42. The Emu from Australia is one of the large flightless birds. Its powerful legs carry it swiftly over the ground, and they can be used as weapons of defense.

Fig. 15-43. A kiwi (*Apteryx mantelli*) probing for worms in leaf mould. These flightless birds are found only in New Zealand, where they are rigidly protected. The female lays very large eggs which are incubated by the male, who also cares for the young. The kiwi is related to the extinct giant moa, which was the largest of all flightless birds.

that have made it possible for this group of animals to be so successful. They possess a unique body covering, **hair,** which functions in conserving heat and as a protection against mechanical injury. Like the birds, mammals are warm-blooded. A new structure, the **diaphragm,** has been added to aid in breathing. This sheet of muscle and connective tissue separates the chest and abdominal cavities and operates like bellows during breathing. Their red blood cells have no nuclei when mature, which enhances their efficiency as carriers of oxygen. The cerebral hemispheres of the brain are more highly developed than in any other group of animals, which probably had much to do with their success. They produce tiny yolkless eggs which must be fertilized inside the body of the female. The young develop within the mother, receiving nourishment from the uterine wall through a special organ, the **placenta.** The young are born alive and receive a special food, **milk,** secreted by special glands, the **mammary glands,** for which the class is named. These are also the characteristics that set the mammals off from the rest of the vertebrates.

When measuring success of a group of animals, we usually think in terms of numbers of species, diversity of habitats occupied, and numbers of individuals. Aside from the arthropods, the mammals are more successful than most other groups of animals and certainly they outstrip all other vertebrates. They show marked variation in size, shape, and habitats (Fig. 15-44). They seem to have invaded every possible portion of the earth, water, and air and are reasonably successful in all environments. Just how long they can retain the zenith where they now find themselves is a problem for speculation.

The mammal arose from some primitive reptilian type and the first ones were more lizard-like than mammal-like (Fig. 15-30). Among the earliest groups to show definite mammalian characteristics were the **therapsids** whose skulls possess a tooth pat-

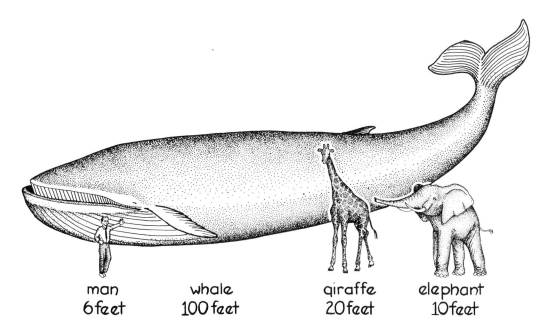

man   whale   giraffe   elephant
6 feet   100 feet   20 feet   10 feet

FIG. 15-44. Relative sizes of a few mammals.

tern similar to that of modern mammals. They had incisors, large canine teeth, and molars with cusps. This pattern is not found among reptiles. The limbs had also shifted to the far anterior and posterior positions, typical of mammals, and were much better developed than in reptiles. Indeed, if one saw one of these creatures, he would think it the result of a cross between a lizard and a cat or dog. Since the fossil remains of these animals include only the bones, we have no way of knowing whether other mammalian characteristics accompanied these skeletal changes. It is highly likely that they did.

These primitive mammals were present on the earth long before the coming of the great dinosaurs but they were small and inconspicuous, and probably kept in hiding throughout the reign of these great beasts. They remained small and insignificant until the dinosaurs met their end. The world was then left free for any animal that was capable of taking over. Even then, while the mammalian characteristics in general

persisted, many animals evolved that were not able to survive very long—the mammoth, saber-tooth tiger, and the giant sloth are examples. Some survived, however, and gave rise to the present mammalian population of the world.

The presence of hair in place of scales is an accessory structure necessary in a warm-blooded animal. Sweat glands aid in regulating body temperature, which is nearly constant. In addition, the heart is a double one, similar to that of birds.

One of the more important characteristics that has contributed to the success of mammals is their method of caring for their genital products and subsequent offspring. Most reptiles lay large, yolk-packed eggs, whereas mammals typically have very small eggs which are fertilized internally in the female and go through a great part of their early life inside the body of the mother. Although internal hatching of eggs is not uncommon in lower forms (reptiles and fish), receiving nourishment from the mother during the process of development

FIG. 15-45. Different ways mammals care for their young, from the duckbill to man.

egg

opossum

marsupium

nipples

FIG. 15-46. Platypus (*Ornithorhynchus anatinus*), an egg-laying mammal. It possesses both reptilian and mammalian characteristics.

is only rarely found (for example, placental shark) in the animal kingdom. Mammals have fewer offspring and retain them longer within the body in order to give them greater protection while allowing them, at the same time, to develop to a more advanced state. Furthermore, since mammals are so highly organized, more time is needed to develop the young to a stage where it can care for itself. The transition took place very slowly and over a long period of time. Even though fossil remains offer little real proof about such things, it is reasonably certain that this process of caring for the young within the mother started very early in the evolution of mammals.

The embryos receive nourishment from the fluids of the mother through a **placenta** which is a temporary attachment of the allantois and other membranes to the uterine wall of the mother. At first the placenta must have been a very primitive affair and only partially satisfactory in performing the important function of nourishing the young. Consequently, the young were born in a very immature state and needed extra-uterine care. This was furnished by the use of a belly pouch, called a **marsupium**, in which the young could not only be protected from the cold but also could receive

nourishment from the mammary glands through nipples located inside the marsupium (Fig. 15-45). Later in their evolution, more and more time was spent in the uterus and less in the marsupium until the latter was finally discarded. This is a possible explanation of how the present mammalian reproductive system came into being; it is recapitulated in the mammals of today from the duckbill to man.

In certain parts of the world such as Australia, which were isolated during the time the mammals were evolving (Eocene), there survive to this day two different types of primitive mammals which might help to bear out the narrative of the preceding paragraph. They belong to the subclass **Prototheria** and are known as monotremes, which means "one opening," so named because both the urogenital and intestinal tracts open into a common cavity, the **cloaca** (a reptilian character), with only one external opening. The spiny anteater (*Echidna*) and the well-known platypus or duckbill (*Ornithorhynchus*, Fig. 15-46) are the two examples that remind us of what must have happened many millions of years ago. These animals lay large yolked eggs like the reptiles and birds and they possess broad, flat bills. They are partially warm-blooded and the duckbill incubates

FIG. 15-47. Marsupials from Australia. (Top) Frightened kangaroos (*Macropus*) on the run. (Bottom) The tree-dwelling koala (*Phascolarctos einereus*) or "teddy bear" sleeping in the eucalyptus tree which provides its only diet. It feeds on the leaves.

its two eggs (Fig. 15-45). When the eggs hatch the young are nourished for a time from milk secreted by two rows of glands along the belly side of the mother. There are no teats and the young merely lap up the secreted milk. It is noteworthy to mention again that these archaic animals have survived up to the present time due to their isolation. Had they been forced to compete with modern mammals they would long since have vanished from the earth. It is indeed fortunate that such animals have been preserved for us to study, making possible more logical conjectures as to how present mammals came about.

Another interesting group of present-day mammals are the **marsupials** (infraclass **Metatheria**), including the kangaroo and koala of Australia (Fig. 15-47) and the opossum of North America (Fig. 26-19). These do not lay eggs like the monotremes but retain them in the uterus where a rudimentary placenta forms. Since this organ is inadequate to maintain the embryos for any great period of time, the young are born in a very immature state (Fig. 15-48). A 200-pound kangaroo, for example, may give birth to offspring no longer than 2 inches. Following birth, the embryos make their way to, or are placed in, the marsupium where they grasp and almost swallow the nipples of the mammary glands to which they cling during what is equivalent to later embryonic life of a more advanced mammal (Fig. 15-45). After a time they come out of the pouch to feed for themselves, retreating to it only in case of danger. Although the marsupials give us a clue to the past history of mammals, their direct line probably diverged from the reptilian mammal stock very early in geologic time.

The Placental Mammals

These animals all have a well-developed placenta. In addition, they show further refinement in ancestral systems. For example, the brain is an even more conspicuous part of the central nervous system and its func-

FIG. 15-48. The young of the opossum (top) are born in a very immature stage and must continue their development in the marsupium. Here they are shown clinging to the teats in the pouch. The young of higher mammals are well developed at birth. This calf (bottom) is able to stand and even run alongside its mother, though only a few minutes old.

tions are much more precise. The coordination and precision of operation of all the parts of the body are brought to an all-time high in these animals. This combination of improvement on systems inherited from their reptilian ancestors has been responsible for the success of mammals. Let us now discuss representatives of several important orders which are placed in the infraclass **Eutheria**.

The most primitive modern placental

mammals are the insect feeders (order **Insectivora**). While there are some fairly large, highly specialized forms such as the moles in this group, the most typical are the tiny shrews. These mouse-like creatures are probably similar to the stock that gave rise to higher mammals including man himself. Their mouths are armed with needle-like teeth which aid in securing their specialized diet of insects. They are extremely active animals, in fact, so active that it requires a volume of food equal to their body weight each day to satisfy their needs. Most of them live in burrows and are such secretive animals that they are seldom seen by the casual observer. Some, however, live in trees much the same as the ancient forms that gave rise to the tree-loving primates (Fig. 15-49).

The bats (order **Chiroptera**) have conquered the air. To be sure, other mammals such as the flying squirrel are able to soar from tree to tree, but they have not approached the bat in any sense as a flying creature. The bat competes very well with the birds; in fact, it can perform some feats that birds cannot. The wing is a modified hand with the fingers greatly extended and covered with skin. Many species of bats live in deep caves, such as the Carlsbad Caverns in this country, where they are forced to fly in complete darkness. Just how these animals can avoid objects has puzzled biologists for a long time. Recently, however, with the aid of delicate electronic equipment, it has been discovered that the bat, instead of being a silent animal as all had thought, does emit bursts of high frequency sound waves during flight. These have a frequency of about 50,000 vibrations per second and are therefore beyond the range of the human ear. When these high frequency sounds strike an object, they bounce back to its ears; this happens at such speed that the animal can respond soon enough to avoid obstacles without the use of its eyes. Man now uses this same principle in detecting distant objects, em-

ploying both sound and radio waves. Thus the bat has had in operation for ages the first sonar system.

The order **Primates** may seem the most important of all because we belong to it. Other members of the group are the great apes, the circus monkey, the fierce-looking baboon, the lemurs, and the wide-eyed tarsiers, all coming from an arboreal insectivore ancestor (Fig. 15-49). It is difficult to name any especially striking characteristics that set the primates off from all others, though there are several minor variations which distinguish them as a group. First of all, most of them possess a brain and central nervous system that is developed far and above that of all others. It must be said, however, that some of the lowest primates are probably not as intelligent as some of the brightest carnivores. The lower mammals have depended to a large extent on their sense of smell to orient themselves, for their vision at best is not very good. But the primates, as inhabitors of trees, need good vision to detect their enemies on the ground, this being of greater importance to them than a keen sense of smell. Arboreal life thus appears to correlate with the development of the excellent visual organ of primates. It also has had a profound effect on the skeleton.

As the appendages became well adapted for life in the trees, both the anterior and posterior digits became modified for grasping limbs. The great toes and thumbs opposed the other four digits and the digital tip flattened out into nails. The appendages became well developed for supporting the body weight and for carrying it with considerable speed from limb to limb through the tree tops. When at rest, the hands were free to handle objects and to bring them close to the keen eyes for closer observation. Freeing the front appendages from the burden of supporting the body weight and development of the prehensile hand have *probably* both been responsible to a

ARBOREAL INSECTIVORES

LEMURS

TARSIOIDS

NEW WORLD MONKEYS

OLD WORLD MONKEYS

GREAT APES

MAN

FIG. 15-49. The primates apparently rose from the arboreal insectivores. Some groups retained tree habitats, whereas others, among them man, descended to the ground where they became at home.

FIG. 15-50. Lemurs are primitive primates that are found only in isolated parts of the world. They are stupid, sluggish animals. This is the ring-tailed lemur, *Lemur catta*.

large extent for the advance in the primate brain.

Other minor characteristics of the primates are the tooth pattern and skull structure. The early primates were apparently omnivorous just as most primates are today, and a generalized mammalian tooth pattern is characteristic of all of them. Most of them possess two incisors, two premolars and four molars in each half jaw, making 32 in all, considerably less than that possessed by the primitive mammals. The jaw is short, so that a relatively short face results; this is obvious when the faces of a monkey and a dog are compared (Fig. 16-6). Furthermore, the large nasal chambers essential to lower animals which depend upon smell are much reduced in primates with a corresponding reduction in this sense. Since the brain has grown a great deal in size, it has risen over the face, bringing the latter into a more vertical position. Along with this change has come a gradual shifting of the eyes from the lateral position to a frontal position. This has resulted in overlapping images, producing **stereoscopic vision,** essential to tree-dwellers for judging distances accurately, and men for driving cars.

Various Primates

The Lemurs. The lethargic lemurs are not greatly removed from the insectivores (Fig. 15-49). They are slow-moving, sluggish, stupid animals quite unlike the other primates. Their primitive nature is indicated by the fact that their eyes still lie in such a lateral position that their vision does not overlap (Fig. 15-50). They live in the tree tops where they move about so conservatively and cautiously that they are rarely seen by enemies and consequently have been able to survive in Madagascar up to the present time.

Tarsier. The East Indies are the home of the only hopping primate, which is not much bigger than a rat (Fig. 15-51). Its mark of distinction lies in the fact that zoologists consider it intermediate between the lemurs and the monkeys. Its rat-like tail and long legs are well adapted for leaping, which it performs with great agility. The swollen tips of its digits are useful in catching limbs of trees as it forages for insects and lizards during its nocturnal sorties. The extremely large eyes are directed forward and probably permit stereoscopic vision.

Anthropoids. The highest group of all primates are the anthropoids, the man-like primates. These include the **monkeys,** the **great apes,** and **man.** While visiting the zoo many will resent the thought that these animals are our closest relatives, but after viewing them for any length of time, only the most doubting are unconvinced. It is important to point out, however, that man did not descend from monkeys, nor is the monkey a degenerate man. Both had separate beginnings a long time ago and have been and are traveling along separate paths in their evolution (Fig. 15-49).

The Monkeys. These creatures are man-like both in physical characteristics and in attitudes. They are primarily arboreal, although they are able to get along on the ground. They walk on all fours, but when at rest usually sit down on their haunches, thus freeing their hands for the job of manipulating food or any other object. Their large and forward-placed eyes are probably as keen as those of humans.

The monkeys are divided into two groups: New World forms of Central and South America and the Old World forms of Asia, Africa, and Europe (Fig. 15-49). Two members of the New World monkeys are of interest because of their specialization: the spider monkey, with its prehensile tail which functions as a fifth hand (Fig. 15-52), and the howler monkey, which has a remarkable voice made possible by modifications of the throat into large, bony resonating chambers. Each has specialized in its

FIG. 15-51. Tarsier (*Tarsius tarsier*) is a rat-sized hopping primate. Note its tremendous eyes and the padded finger tips which aid in grasping twigs.

own peculiar way and these variations set them off from all other members of the group.

The Old World monkeys exhibit a wide variety of form and habits, from the sacred langur of India to the highly colorful ground-dwelling mandrill (Fig. 15-53). Most of them are tree-dwelling, although the baboon lives on the ground most of the time. It is as firmly committed to life on the ground as the spider monkey is to life in the trees.

The Man-like Great Apes. These predominantly large primates, the gibbon, orangutan, chimpanzee, and gorilla, separated very early from the common stem that also produced the monkeys, probably about the same time a branch separated off on its long course toward man. This appears to have taken place at least 20 million years ago.

397

FIG. 15-52. This spider monkey (*Ateles paniscus*), a representative of the New World Monkeys, possesses a handy adaptation in its prehensile tail which functions as a fifth appendage.

FIG. 15-53. The mandrill (*Mandrillus sphinx*) is a colorful member of the Old World monkeys. It is noted for its dog-like face and its highly colored cheeks.

Among the great apes, the gibbon (Fig. 15-54) is best adapted to arboreal life. Its long arms permit it to brachiate (swing hand over hand) through the trees with great speed. This type of locomotion in arboreal primates probably had some bearing on the achievement of the upright position in man. Ancestral forms may have begun to assume this position at an early date but before specialization had gone as far as it has in the gibbon, they descended to the ground and started their terrestrial existence.

The closest relatives of man are probably the great African apes, the gorilla and chimpanzee. Although they are at home among the trees, particularly the chimpanzee which brachiates very well, they still spend a good deal of their time on the ground. The gorilla seems to prefer the ground, retreating to the trees only to sleep. The chimpanzee possesses a disposition more favorable to captivity and for that reason a great deal is known about its behavior. In size it matches man very well, being about 5 feet in height and weighing about 150 pounds when full grown. When young it is easily handled, and is a very affectionate, playful, and extremely curious animal. It seems to approach the human type of intelligence as illustrated by its ability to solve problems. Experiments, notably those by Yerkes, have shown that the "chimp" will solve simple problems much like a small child. For example, if food is placed just out of its reach and several boxes are placed near by, the chimp will pile the boxes in order to obtain the food. It has also been found that if given two bamboo poles which fit together, it will so place the two parts in order to reach a desired object. This requires a kind of intelligence far greater than that possessed by any other animal, except man.

The gorilla is perhaps more intelligent than the chimpanzee, but because of its sullen and individualistic disposition, it will not tolerate training or testing of any sort (Fig. 15-55). A two-year-old gorilla responds in a manner similar to a child of about the same age or a little older. Soon, however, it develops a morose disposition and cannot be trusted for close association with man. In size the gorilla exceeds all other primates, and an old male may reach a height of 6 feet and a weight of 500–600 pounds. Because of its herbivorous diet the gorilla is not a predator, and for that reason does not get into much trouble. The gorilla walks rather well on the ground but frequently reverts to all fours, especially when in a hurry. Its short sturdy legs and man-like feet support its weight well, although it is not a swift runner.

At this point we should discuss man because he is a primate, but a discussion of his evolution has been reserved for a later section of this chapter.

Some Other Mammals

One of the more successful groups of mammals are the flesh-eaters, the carnivores (order **Carnivora**). They include cats, dogs, weasels, bears, civets, and the marine seals and walruses. The carnivores have teeth well adapted to the rending and tearing of flesh (Fig. 15-56). The large canines readily tear through tough skin and the shearing molars cut the flesh into pieces sufficiently small to be swallowed. Furthermore, since meat is easily digested, the alimentary canals are short when compared to those of the plant feeders. In general, the carnivores are active and sometimes vicious animals, some hunting in packs like the wolves and others leading more or less solitary lives like the big cats and bears (Fig. 15-57).

Some very interesting and bizarre carnivores are those that inhabit the water, and have practically lost their ability to locomote on land. These are represented by the seals, sea lions, walruses, and others (Fig. 15-58). They are relatively helpless on land, but in the water they compare favorably with the best of the true aquatic forms, including fish. Having been on land

long enough to acquire the intelligence and cunning of the mammals before returning to their original environment, they offer considerable competition for the stupid fishes. Their appendages have become flippers which are effectively used in locomotion. They swim in a fish-like manner by undulating motions of the body. Curiously enough, the tail has dwindled to a useless structure and the two posterior legs function like a tail in locomotion.

In contrast to the carnivores are the herbivores (ungulates), of which the domestic horse and cow are examples. The horse possesses an odd number of toes (order **Perissodactyla**) and the cow an even number of toes (order **Artiodactyla**). In their evolution, the former came first and reached large sizes, as illustrated by the giant rhinoceroses that attained a shoulder height of 18 feet. Those alive today are doomed to

FIG. 15-54. The long-armed gibbon (*Hylobates lar*) is strictly an arboreal primate, being able to travel more rapidly through the tree tops than many animals can travel on the ground. This specimen has her nursing baby held securely between her legs.

FIG. 15-55. The gorilla (*Gorilla gorilla*) is the largest and probably the most intelligent of all the great apes. This is a young male that has just been enticed into new quarters which it is thoroughly investigating.

extinction in spite of the fact that man has been able to save the horse by domestication. Members of this group have their weight borne on three toes in the rhinoceroses or on one toe in the case of the horse. The even-toed herbivores usually have four toes, of which two bear the main weight of the animal; this is illustrated by cattle, sheep, giraffe (Fig. 15-59), and many others. Some, such as the hippopotamus (Fig. 15-60), bear their weight on four toes. These have dominated the previous group both in the past and present. Some of the present-day forms are **ruminants** or "cud-chewers." Their stomachs have several compartments, a condition that permits large amounts of hastily acquired food to be temporarily stored and then brought back into the mouth at a later period to be properly chewed at the animal's leisure. This is a most comfortable and effective adaptation since the animals may feed voraciously during certain periods of the day when grazing is less dangerous and then retire to secluded spots to finish the job of chewing. The teeth of both the odd- and even-toed animals are well adapted for cropping grass and grinding it to the proper consistency for digestion.

Perhaps the most curious of all mam-

FIG. 15-56. The teeth of mammals are adapted to different diets. The beaver (left) has huge incisor teeth for gnawing and flat molars for grinding, whereas a carnivore as the wolf (right) has small incisors but large spike-like canines which are efficient in rending flesh. Its molars have a shearing action for cutting its food.

FIG. 15-57. A few large carnivores.

FIG. 15-58. A young Atlantic walrus (*Odobenus rosmarus*). Note how well the appendages are adapted for aquatic life but very poorly for land locomotion.

mals is the slow moving, thick-skinned elephant (order **Proboscidea**) with its nose, in the form of a proboscis or trunk, touching the ground (Fig. 15-61). This handy organ makes possible an unusually short neck, because it performs the function of securing grass from the ground. It is also useful in obtaining water. Actually, it is a prolongation of the upper lip, including the nostrils. The teeth have undergone several changes, the most striking of which is the formation of the great tusks, which are overdeveloped incisor teeth. During the Miocene and Pliocene these great beasts spread over much of the northern land masses and survived in great numbers on our continent until ten or twenty thousand years ago when they became extinct.

Some distant relatives of the elephant went into the sea and became adapted for an aquatic existence. These are the sirenians (order **Sirenia**), which include such mammals as the dugong of the Indian Ocean, the sea cows formerly from Bering Straits but now practically extinct, and the man-

atee from the Atlantic Ocean in the tropics. These ugly, stupid beasts feed on the abundant marine vegetation along the shores but are unable to come ashore themselves because they lack posterior appendages and the front ones are adapted for swimming only. The sirenians are not related to the whales; fossil records indicate that their closest relatives seem to be the Proboscidea, in spite of the vast difference in their external appearance and way of life.

The whales and porpoises (Fig. 15-62) (order **Cetacea**) are probably the most specialized of all mammals. They are descendants of land carnivores which have returned to the sea and become so successful in this environment that they are found in all of the oceans of the world. They were probably flesh-eating mammals much like the present-day otters, fishers, and minks which, returning to the water in search of prey, gradually became better and better adapted to marine life.

Whales have few anatomical features remaining that are reminiscent of their land life. They have lost their posterior limbs, although they still have useless remnants left buried deep in their bodies, and their anterior appendages have modified into efficient flippers. The adult whale is generally completely lacking in hair; a few species have some around the mouth region, however. The whales' nostrils have moved back to the tops of their heads, which facilitates breathing at the water surface without exposing the head. A tremendous tail is the principal organ of locomotion; it undulates up and down rather than sideways as a fish.

Even though the first whales were probably all carnivorous, many subsequent species became herbivorous. All whales today are divided into two groups: the **whalebone whales** and the **toothed whales**. The latter have retained their teeth, which may be used in crushing fish and squids, their chief source of food. The more interesting whalebone whales have evolved a sieve-like structure called whalebone which hangs from the roof of the mouth and is used to strain small marine organisms. Whalebone, which is derived from ectoderm and is homologous to nails and claws, makes up the strainer. The blue whale, also a whalebone whale, has prospered on this diet of minute marine life, and some specimens reach a weight of 150 tons, which exceeds that of any other animal that has ever lived, dinosaurs not excepted. One problem that is difficult to understand is how this animal can dive to great depths and remain under water for 30–45 minutes without being crushed and without getting the "bends" (see p. 549). It apparently has oxygen reserves and other devices for satisfying its needs under these rigorous conditions.

A small group of mammals show remarkable reduction in teeth, jaw skeleton, and jaw muscles. These are the so-called toothless mammals (order **Edentata**), represented by the anteaters and sloths (Fig. 15-63).

The most abundant of all the mammals are the rodents (order **Rodentia**), the "gnawers." These include many small mammals commonly known to everyone: squirrels, chipmunks, beavers, porcupines, guinea pigs, and even the pestiferous rats and mice (Fig. 15-64). They are characterized by their large chisel-like incisor teeth which are self-sharpening and which are kept almost incessantly active (Fig. 15-56). The incisor teeth grow continuously and if not worn down could soon become so long that the animal would not be able to close its mouth. Most rodents are small today, although at one time there were giant beavers which grew to the size of a small bear (Fig. 26-2). Rodents have a high degree of intelligence and are usually secretive animals, many living in burrows. One, the beaver, is almost human in its ability to build dams. In some regions where conservation laws have made it possible for them to come back, they have become almost pests because of their habit of damming every small

FIG. 15-59. A large mammal from Africa.

stream in large areas, thus flooding fields and roads in the surrounding country.

The rabbits and hares are often thought to be rodents because of their chisel-like teeth. In other respects, however, they have few rodent characteristics, hence have been placed in a separate order (order **Lagomorpha**). Hares are larger than rabbits

403

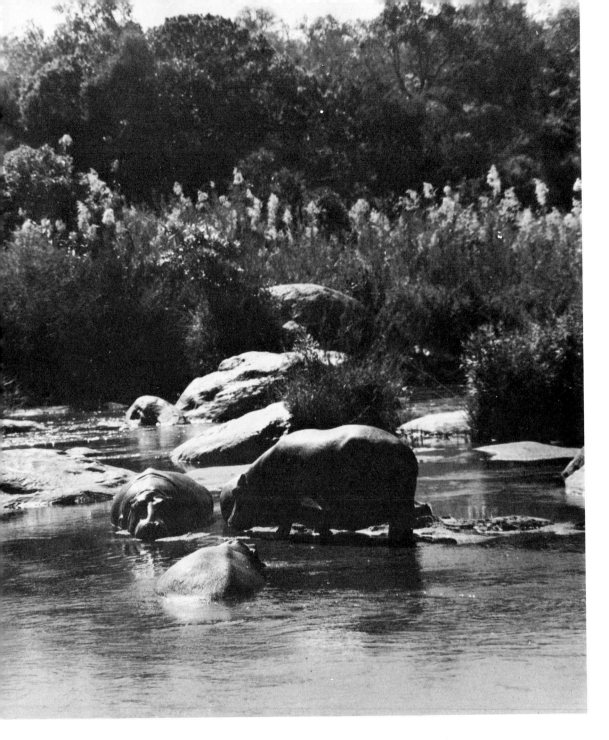

FIG. 15-60. Hippopotomuses (*Hippopotomus amphibius*) in their native African environment.

FIG. 15-61. The African elephant (*Loxodonta africana*) with its upper lip and nose drawn out into a trunk, a remarkable prehensile appendage.

and do not construct burrows. In other respects they are very similar. Both rabbits and hares are ubiquitous in distribution and have been very successful, particularly when they have been introduced in new areas. The scourge of rabbits in Australia is a familiar example.

We have now completed a synopsis of animal life, from protozoa through mammals. Before going on, let us consider the story of man's origin.

The Origin of Man

Fossil remains of early man have been few and only fragmentary to date, a fact which makes the reconstruction of man's evolution a very difficult task. However, certain important discoveries have been made which give some clue as to his origin. The most primitive skull of a man-ape is that found in South Africa, called **Australopithecus,** the "southern ape" (Fig. 15-65). The several skeletons or parts of skeletons that have been found were in Pleistocene deposits, the period in which man made his long slow evolution to present-day types. This fossil ape skull shows characteristics of both the great apes of today and of man, which is what would be expected in a "missing link." Its brain case has a capacity of over 700 cc., which is about the size of the largest gorilla's today, but smaller than that of the next higher fossil man's, *Pithecanthropus*, with a capacity of about 900 cc. Its teeth and brain development certainly could have belonged to a form that was heading toward modern man.

Pithecanthropus (Fig. 15-65) has stirred up more controversy since its discovery than any other fossil man. This is understandable, since its discoverer, Eugene Dubois, a Dutch Army officer, set out to find the missing link between man and the apes, probably because of the intense controversy that had been stirred up by Darwin's *Descent of Man*. It is most remarkable that a man should set out to accomplish such a difficult task and actually carry out his promise. Others searched furiously for the next few years, but it was not until 1936 that similar skeletons were found. The original material, which consisted of a skull cap, three teeth, and a femur bone, was discovered in the banks of the Solo River in Java in 1891. Dubois called these finds *Pithecanthropus erectus,* the "erect man." His claim that this was an intermediate form, half ape, half man, is probably not correct. Recent studies seem to indicate that it was a man and not an ape. The man had a very low brow and the size of his brain case was about 900 cc., a much greater capacity than that of the great apes though smaller than any modern man (average about 1,500 cc.). The tooth pattern is definitely human, and it is interesting to note that the wisdom teeth show no signs of disappearing, as is common in modern man.

FIG. 15-62. A group of porpoises, mother and month-old offspring in the foreground. Note the nostril on the top of the head, an adaptation that makes it possible for the animal to breathe at the surface without exposing its head.

He probably lived about 500,000 years ago.

A close relative of *Pithecanthropus* is **Sinanthropus** (Fig. 15-65), commonly known as the Peking man because the remains were found in a cave some 30 miles from Peking, China. These middle Pleistocene deposits stimulated Dr. Davidson Black in the 1920's to investigate them for the possibility of human remains. He found first only a tooth here, but during the next decade over 30 individuals were unearthed, so that the evidence is very complete concerning this primitive man. *Sinanthropus* is so similar to *Pithecanthropus* that they are now thought of as belonging to the same genus. However, the brain case of *Sinanthropus* is somewhat larger on the average (915–1,200 cc.). The leg bones indicate an upright posture. He apparently had a culture which was far above anything the apes would be likely to have. He used fire and made stone tools. There is evidence that he was cannibalistic, based on the fact that so many skulls are present in the deposits, each one crushed at the base. This might mean that the bodies were eaten and the brain removed for the same purpose, a horrible but probably not uncommon custom for early man.

The **Neanderthal** man (Fig. 15-65) was the first fossil man discovered (1856) and many of his remains since have been uncovered, indicating that he roamed over parts of Asia, Africa, and Europe about 100,000 years ago. Physically he was a rather short man, not exceeding 5 feet 4 inches (the females were several inches shorter), but very powerfully built. His upper arms and femurs were short and the latter were curved forward so that in posture he probably walked with his knees slightly bent forward. Furthermore, his massive head was set somewhat forward over his thick neck and barrel chest, so that he was probably quite gorilla-like in appearance. His brain case capacity was 1,550 cc., larger than the average for modern man, although it had different propor-

FIG. 15-63. South American toothless mammals: (Top) The Giant eater (*Myrmecophaga tridactyla*) possesses powerful claws for opening ant hills and a long sticky tongue for lapping up the ants which are its sole source of food. (Bottom) The sloth (*Bradypustridactylus*) is remarkably adapted for tree life. Its hooked claws make it possible to hang comfortably from branches.

tions. The forepart of the brain case, the seat of higher intelligence, was rather small, the larger portion being in the back of the head. His skull was heavy, with large protruding brows, and the massive jaws bore teeth much more substantially built than those of modern man. The mandible was chinless just as among the apes; a chin is a more recent development.

He had some type of culture which included religious rites, because he buried his dead—probably the important reason why so many remains have been found. He had learned to shape and use stone implements in the daily business of securing food, and these, together with bones of the animals he hunted, are found in Neanderthal deposits.

There is always great interest not only among anthropologists but also among laymen concerning the story of the origin of modern man. Which of these early men gave rise to modern man, *Homo sapiens?*

Was the Neanderthal man the immediate forerunner of *Homo sapiens?* There has been a great deal of discussion over this point and, like all problems under fire, there are several possible answers. It must be admitted certainly that Neanderthal showed considerable advance over *Sinanthropus* and *Pithecanthropus*. Whether or not he gave rise to *Homo sapiens* is questionable. There is evidence to indicate that he was wiped out rather suddenly by another race, probably *Homo sapiens*. If this was the case, then the latter must have been derived from another stock as yet not unearthed.

In order to portray the interest and enthusiasm that centered around the subject of man's origins, and the lengths some people will go to establish a point, even to fabricating evidence, let us examine a most remarkable scientific hoax that baffled anthropologists for over 40 years. It started

Fig. 15-64. Two rodents, the white rat (top), a domesticated variety of the Norway rat (*Rattus norvegicus*), and the guinea pig (middle), a domesticated variety of the South American cavy (*Cavia porcellus*), have become popular laboratory animals. Others, such as the flying squirrel (*Glaucomys volans*) (bottom), have adapted themselves as gliders. The webbed skin attached to fore and hind legs supports them as they glide from tree to tree.

FIG. 15-65. A comparative study of the reconstructed faces of early men together with their skulls from which the reconstructions were made. They are arranged top to bottom in the chronological order, although there may well have been some overlapping. *Australopithecus* appeared first, followed by *Pithecanthropus* and *Neanderthal*. Modern man is portrayed by the *Cro-Magnon*.

when Charles Dawson, a country solicitor and amateur archaeologist turned over to the Natural History Museum in London a collection of bones among which were skull and jawbone fragments of what seemed to be a very ancient man, at least a contemporary of *Pithecanthropus*. These were found near Piltdown, Sussex, England in 1912, hence the man became known as the *Piltdown man*. The skull resembled that of other ancient men, but the jaw was definitely ape-like, the only human characteristics being the flattened surfaces of the teeth. This, together with the fact that it was found in the same deposits with the skull, convinced many scientists of the period and for many years later that this certainly was one of the oldest remains in existence and may well have given rise to *Homo sapiens*. However, there were a few dissenters among the men who studied the fragments, scientists who were never convinced of the authenticity of the remains. As more human skeletons became available, the position of the Piltdown man became untenable, even ridiculous. In 1949 a chemical test, the fluorine test, came into use for dating fossil remains. Buried bones absorb fluorine, which increases with time. In spite of the fact that this is a rather crude test, it did prove conclusively that the Piltdown skull was no more than 50,000 years old, and that the jaw was even younger. In 1953 three scientists, Oakley, Weiner, and Legros-Clark, employed modern techniques in studying the fragments. They confirmed the earlier findings that the skull was no more than 50,000 years old and proved that the jaw was that of a modern great ape which had been skillfully tampered with. Iron salts and bichromate had been carefully worked into the fragments to make them look very old and the teeth had been ground down to resemble those of man. Since Dawson died long ago (1916) it is impossible to know whether he was the perpetrator of this hoax or if the fragments

were buried by someone else for him to "find." This episode has caused some embarrassment to scientists; the only value that might have resulted from it is that much greater care is taken now to establish the authenticity of all fossil remains. It must be remembered that scientific fakes are rare and that the scientists themselves discover them sooner or later.

Whenever *Homo sapiens* made his appearance, he split off into many races which spread over the entire world. One of the outstanding of these is the *Cro-Magnon*, who lived in Europe 15,000 to 40,000 years ago (Fig. 15-65). Most of the remains, about one hundred skeletons, have been found in France, and the records afford a rather complete story of the culture as well as the anatomy of this man. He was tall, many males reaching 6 feet in height, although the females were considerably shorter. His skull was long and massively built with the tremendous capacity of 1,700 cc., which is greater than that of any race today. Furthermore, the shape was definitely modern in that the forehead was high and the back part rounded as in modern man. None of the apelike characteristics observed in *Pithecanthropus* are evident in this man. The mandible terminated anteriorly in a pronounced chin, and the face was short and broad with the eyes set far apart. Undoubtedly, he was a handsome fellow.

In culture these men far surpassed their predecessors. They made their hunting weapons skillfully, producing the spear and axe, and they may have even devised the bow and arrow. They apparently were superior hunters, as judged by the contents of their caves, which are strewn with the bones of large animals they had killed and feasted upon. They probably clothed themselves with skins of animals to protect their hairless bodies from the elements. They evidently possessed great skill in making and mixing paints, and in depicting the life as it existed in their time, for they have left behind on the walls of many caves in Spain and southern France magnificent paintings showing many of the animals which they hunted. These are portrayed in a most realistic manner, even to the natural colors which have resisted the ravages of time. The remains of these men would indicate that they were superior both mentally and physically to any races alive today. What, then, has happened to them? Some think their descendants still live in Europe today. If so, are they degenerate types? Is *Homo sapiens* actually on the decline?

Knowledge of early *Homo sapiens* in other parts of the world is not as complete as in Europe. One might expect to find some early Negroid types in Africa, the home of the Negro. An early skull from the Sahara does show Negroid characteristics. As this part of the world becomes more modernized, the diggings of various sorts which always accompany the process will perhaps throw more light on this. Undoubtedly, rich deposits exist in parts of Asia which when unearthed will reveal an interesting story concerning the origin of the Mongoloids, about whom little or nothing is known today.

Apparently, *Homo sapiens* invaded America comparatively recently, because no remains of very early man have been found. The primates that were here in the early Tertiary times became extinct and no others appeared until modern man made his way from Asia across Bering Straits. It is highly probable that this is the path he took in populating the Americas, because geologists have shown that a drop in the sea level of 100 feet would leave a land connection between Asia and North America. Such rising and falling of the sea took place with each great glacial period. For many thousands of years it was possible for these people, filtering gradually over this narrow neck of land, to migrate southward to the semitropical and tropical regions of the Americas.

Races of Homo Sapiens

The criteria that have been used to distinguish the various races are such points as stature, hair, face proportions, skull shape, complexion, eye and skin color, and blood groups. Using these characters, it is possible to define four major groups: Australoids, Negroids, Caucasoids, and Mongoloids.

Even though there are many difficulties in attempting to separate *Homo sapiens* into races, most anthropologists agree that one is more primitive than others. The Australian aborigines are usually considered to be the most primitive and probably have a somewhat different line of descent from the others. They are referred to as the Australoids. The Negroids include the Negroes, pigmies, Bushmen, and Hottentots, all with heavy pigmentation in their skin and hair. This race is widespread today, occupying much of Africa as well as most of the Pacific islands, from New Guinea to Fiji.

The Caucasoids include a wide range of people, indeed all of those that are not Australoid, Negroid, or Mongoloid. They possess hair and skin color from light to dark brown, eye color from blue to dark brown. The hair, however, may be straight or wavy, but never kinky or wooly as is typical of Negroids. They include the most aggressive people of the world, representatives of which inhabit Europe, the Americas, and parts of Asia. The Mongoloids are characterized by coarse, black, straight hair, and skin that has varying shades of yellow and brown. Their heads are heavily covered with hair, but the face and the rest of the body is relatively naked. They are also widespread, occupying much of eastern Asia as well as the American continent. They include the Chinese, Japanese, Eskimos, and American Indians.

Man's Present Status. One might think that with all laws of evolution operative through these past 500,000 or more years, present-day man might be an animal physically perfect in all respects and geared beautifully to his environment. This, in fact, is far from the truth. The number of people with defective vision is a glaring example. The occasional inadequacies of the various organ systems is confirming evidence that they do not always function as they were intended, at least under present treatment which itself may be at fault. In spite of these apparent inadequacies, man has done rather well, biologically speaking. He has spread himself over a very large portion of the globe and has reached nearly three billion in numbers, not a large figure, to be sure, when one considers that there are more bacteria in a quart of sour milk! He has managed himself rather well in most respects; he plans for his own food and shelter as well as other comforts of life. He has, by concerted effort, been able to allow himself some leisure time from the endless task of providing the bare necessities of life. He has sometimes used this time creatively, thus improving not only his immediate environment but also his relation to it.

There has been little, if any, improvement in our brain since the Cro-Magnon man; and during the intervening 50,000 years, progress toward civilization as we know it has been extremely slow. Only during the last 5,000 years, and particularly the past 300 years, has outstanding progress taken place. Why was man so slow in rising as a social animal, and why, when he started, did he rise so rapidly? It was undoubtedly due to the fact that he acquired the ability to put down in writing what he had learned so that those who followed could profit by his experience. Once this took root it flourished and with it the progress of mankind. Information is accumulating today at a staggering rate. Most scientists, for example, have great difficulty reading the literature that has been and is accumulating even in their own restricted field, to say nothing of that in the cognate sciences. One of the big problems today is to condense this information so that any one person can have some understanding of it all.

It is well worthwhile, then, to study rather carefully this animal that has made such stellar progress in the past few hundred years, and whose primary mark of distinction is a huge brain.

SUGGESTED SUPPLEMENTARY READINGS

Barbour, T., *Reptiles and Amphibians* (Boston, Houghton Mifflin, 1926).

Bates, M., *Man in Nature* (Englewood Cliffs, N.J., Prentice-Hall Inc., 1961).

Berrill, N. J., *The Origin of Vertebrates* (London, Oxford University Press, 1955).

Clark, W. E. LeGros, *The History of Primates* (London, British Museum, 1949).

Colbert, E. H., *Evolution of the Vertebrates* (New York, John Wiley & Sons, Inc., 1955).

Gates, R. R., *Human Ancestry* (Cambridge, Harvard University Press, 1948).

HOOTON, E. A., *Up from the Ape* (New York, The Macmillan Co., 1945).

HOWELLS, W. W., "The Distribution of Man," *Scientific American*, 203(3), (September, 1960), 112.

LANHAM, U., *The Fishes* (New York, Columbia University Press, 1962).

LORENZ, Konrad, *King Solomon's Ring* (New York, Thomas Y. Crowell, 1952).

ROMER, A. S., *The Vertebrate Story* (Chicago, University of Chicago Press, 1959).

SCHULTZ, L. P., *The Ways of Fishes* (New York, D. Van Nostrand Co., 1948).

SHAW, E., "The Schooling of Fishes," *Scientific American*, 206(6) (June, 1962), 128.

TINBERGEN, N., "The Evolution of Behavior in Gulls," *Scientific American*, 203(6) (December, 1960), 118.

HOWELL, F. C. "Isimila: A Paleolithic Site in Africa," *Scientific American*, 205(4) (October, 1961), 118.

PART VI

Organ Systems of Man

16

Housing, Support, and Movement

THE GRADUAL EVOLUTION of animals has been discussed in the preceding chapters, and considerable time has been spent on each group so that you have a working knowledge of the anatomy and physiology of each one. In studying the last group of animals, we have selected man as a typical mammal. A study of the rat, cat, guinea pig, or dog would afford no more information than that of the human body and for the readers of this book certainly no more interest.

MAN: A TYPICAL MAMMAL

Man is a typical mammal, unusual only in the size of his brain. He is not the largest or the smallest mammal, nor is he highly specialized when compared to the whale, for example. In fact, he is a rather mediocre mammal, being poorly endowed with organs of offense and defense. His puny, flat finger nails and short canine teeth are no match for the claw and tooth of the tiger or lion. His hide is not thick, like that

417

of the elephant or whale, and it is completely unprotected by hair, the normal coat for most mammals. He has no horny outgrowths for defense, like the ungulates, and even his locomotor appendages are only fairly effective in getting him out of danger.

Man is no longer at home in the trees but lives on the ground and employs the bipedal method of locomotion, a method far from new, for the great carnivorous dinosaurs also employed it. Other present-day bipeds such as the ostrich can easily outstrip him in cursorial travel. He is poorly fitted for life in the water where his appendages are not well adapted for locomotion. He can submerge for only very short periods without coming up for air, and in cold water his survival time is very short.

He has, however, one crucial organ that accounts for most of his success, his well-developed brain. This organ, by its intricate disposition of nerve impulses, has made it possible for man to compensate for most of his physical deficiencies. With it he has been able, through the power of speech, to communicate with his fellows and later to put words down in writing. Over a long period of time this type of specialization has finally "paid off," because man today is the dominant species on the earth.

In order to understand man it has been necessary to study other forms of animal life. Man does not lend himself well to experimentation for obvious reasons and, furthermore, he grows too slowly to permit studying succeeding generations. He cannot be kept under the controlled conditions that are possible with rats in a cage. However, most of our information about his functioning has come through the careful study of lower animals. If it were not for these experiments our knowledge would be very meager. This brings up an interesting and important point concerning attitudes.

There are isolated groups of people who oppose any animal experimentation (primarily experiments on dogs, cats, and other pets), sincerely, perhaps, or stirred by some ulterior motive. In any case, these groups are small but usually active and are constantly stumping for legislation that would curtail present-day experimentation. It requires only a slight knowledge of the subject to realize that most of the information about the functioning of the human body can come only through such experiments. How would anyone suffering from appendicitis, for example, particularly an antivivisectionist (the self-styled name applied to these people), appreciate having a doctor who has had no experience whatever on lower animals attempt to remove the offending organ? If the antivivisectionist lived up to his code, he should rightly refuse any medication which stemmed from a study of lower animals. Such groups have been responsible for bills that have come before state legislatures and even the Congress. Fortunately, most of them have been voted down. Much more could be said on the topic, but perhaps at this point the student should draw from his own experiences and form his own conclusions about this matter.

We shall now turn to a discussion of the organ systems of man, as illustrative of vertebrate organ systems in general. Each system will be discussed at some length, together with a brief account of similar structures in other animals from the lowest to the highest. Although some attention has been paid to these topics in the discussion of each animal group, the information should be reviewed briefly before each system of man is studied. With this approach, perhaps the structures and their functions as found in the human body may be better understood.

OUTER COVERING—THE SKIN

As we have seen in the preceding chapters all animals are provided with an exterior covering that functions as a barrier against the outside world. This is extremely simple in the lower invertebrates but becomes much more complicated in higher forms as, for example, in the vertebrate skin with all of its derivatives.

In these animals the skin forms a continuous unbroken sheath which protects the internal structures from the environment. In addition to being tough itself, it is often fortified with scales, feathers, or hair for added protection against physical injury by predaceous enemies. Moreover, it is refractive to bacteria and other microorganisms that could be injurious if allowed to enter the internal environment. It is impervious to most harmful chemicals and is important in regulating the water content of the body, functioning differently in aquatic and terrestrial forms. Heat regulation is also controlled by the skin indirectly through water loss, as well as by various insulators such as hair and feathers. The penetrating effect of light is regulated by pigmentation of the skin. Among some vertebrates the skin takes part in respiration (for example, the frog). These many functions of the skin signify its importance.

It is necessary to examine the skin microscopically if one is to understand how it performs its many and sundry jobs, and we will take human skin as our example. It is usually divided into two parts, the outer, thinner **epidermis** and the inner, thicker **dermis** (Fig. 16-1). The epidermis is composed of an outermost nonliving covering, the **corneum,** which is the part in immediate contact with the outside world; lying beneath it is a layer of epithelial tissue called the **stratum germinativum** which is composed of actively growing cells. As the cells grow they move toward the outside, die, and eventually become the corneum. These dead cells are constantly being sloughed off in mammals and many of the lower vertebrates. Everyone is familiar with the loss of these cells in unexposed parts of

the body such as back of the ears and between the toes. They are particularly noticeable in the hair, where they resemble flaky "scales" and do not have an opportunity to escape readily. These dead cells are spoken of as dandruff and often erroneously considered a pathological condition. The corneum is perforated by many tiny holes through which **sweat** passes from **glands** that lie deep below. The corneum becomes very thick on the soles of the feet and the palms of the hands (callused), especially in people who perform heavy labor requiring the use of these appendages. Another interesting characteristic of the corneum of these areas is the formation of **friction ridges.** It is the presence of these in the hand and foot which causes fingerprints and footprints. These friction ridges apparently have come through a long evolutionary history, being originally digital pads of four-footed animals. When mammals took to the trees, the pads developed into transverse ridges which functioned in increasing the friction between the hand and the branch, thus preventing slipping. In man the ridges are generally arranged in whorls, although they are transverse to the long axis of the fingers for the most part. The designs appear to be infinite in number and never seem to be repeated on the tip of any digit, either on the hand of one individual or on any other individual. This has provided a convenient means of identification because it positively distinguishes one person from another.

The stratum germinativum produces many structures which, on the one side, are sunk deep into the dermis and, on the other side, are an important part of the external covering. The scales of fish and reptiles, the feathers of birds, and the hairs of mammals have such relationships. Although these all have similar origins, in the final adult stage they are quite different both in structure and function. Digital tips in various vertebrates, such as the carnivore claw,

hair development   gland development

hair shaft

hair follicle

sebaceous gland

erector muscle

bulb of hair

papilla

corneum

stratum   germinativum

corium

fat

EPIDERMIS

DERMIS

sweat gland

Fig. 16-1. Human skin in cross-section. Gland and hair development are shown in several stages (top left).

the ungulate hoof, and the primate nail, are likewise produced from this region of the epidermis (Fig. 16-2). They are all homologous, since each has the same origin although each performs a different function.

Derivatives of the Epidermis

Scales and Feathers. Reptilian scales and feathers of birds have a common origin (Fig. 16-3) and they are very much alike

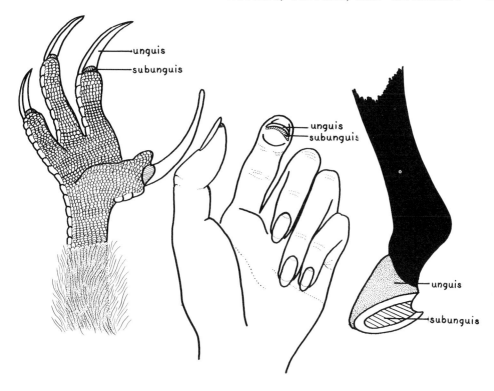

FIG. 16-2. Homologous digital tips: claws, nails, and hoof. Note that the unguis and subunguis are emphasized differently in all.

both anatomically and functionally. Scales of bony fish, however, are dermal in origin and hence are not homologous with reptilian scales or feathers. Epidermal scales similar to those of reptiles are found on the legs of birds and various parts of the anatomy of some mammals (for example, tail of rat and beaver). Structurally, they resemble overlapping or abutting plates that offer considerable resistance to outside mechanical injury. When overlapping like shingles, they are so arranged as to offer the least resistance to forward motion.

Feathers resemble scales in their overlapping arrangement, although otherwise the likeness is not so obvious. They are much lighter in construction, possessing numerous tiny filaments that offer resistance to the passage of air through them. The wing feathers of birds will allow air to pass one way but not the other—a beautiful example of adaptation to flight.

Teeth. Teeth are compound structures, the dentine developing from mesoderm and the enamel from ectoderm. Their development is similar to that of the placoid scales of cartilaginous fish (Fig. 16-4). Since the mouth is lined with ectoderm (the germ layer that gives rise to epidermis), we might expect that the mouth could be equipped with any structure that could arise from ectoderm. The scales in sharks enlarge and grow over the edge of the jaw, producing teeth. Human teeth develop in similar fashion except that the final structures are quite different in that they fit into deep cups or sockets in the jawbone.

Hair. These tiny projections from the skin of mammals perform a protective function

stratum corneum

stratum germinativum

papillae

corium

FIG. 16-3. Stages in the development of reptilian scales and feathers, showing their common origin.

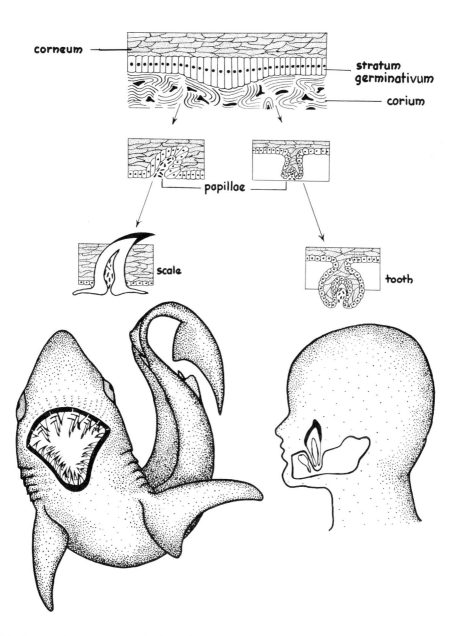

corneum

stratum germinativum

corium

papillae

scale

tooth

FIG. 16-4. Stages in the development of scales and teeth, showing their common origin (top). A photograph of shark's skin showing the tiny scales. Note their tooth-like nature (bottom).

against both physical injury and heat loss. The numerous hairs tend to provide a dead air space just above the skin which prevents heat loss much as insulation materials in a house. Feathers also act as heat insulators, a fact readily observed on cold days when birds ruffle up their feathers to improve the insulating properties of their integument. On a hot day, a bird keeps its feathers close to its body to allow as much heat to escape as possible.

Mammals, with few exceptions, are covered with a thick coat of hair. Man has lost most of his hair, probably because he evolved in a warm climate. Today it is present only in the pubic regions, under the arms, and on the face and head. The facial adornment is a male secondary sexual characteristic because it is not found in the female. The rest of the body is usually covered with very tiny hairs which are vestigial, for they perform no function in modern man. This loss of body covering carries with it the obvious disadvantage of rapid heat loss in a cold climate, and man has thus been forced to clothe himself with an artificial covering. The adornment feature of clothing cannot be overlooked, for even in hot climates aboriginals frequently cover themselves, particularly if the cloth is highly colored.

Hairs are arranged in definite patterns in the various regions of the body of man as well as on the body of other mammals. They are not perpendicular to the skin surface but slant, usually in a specific direction. For example, in a dog the hair slants away from the mid-dorsal line, usually in the direction of the pull of gravity, and this probably helps in shedding water. In man the direction of the hair slant in the back region is the same as in dogs. On the arms and legs it also follows a common pattern but on the top of the head it sometimes forms whorls or "cowlicks" which are inherited from generation to generation.

Attached to the base of each hair are tiny muscle fibers which, when contracted, cause the hair to stand on end, producing "goose flesh" (Fig. 16-1). These muscles are under the influence of the autonomic nervous system and are therefore beyond voluntary control. When one is frightened or sometimes under other emotional stress, the hair can be seen to stand on end, particularly along the spine. The common statement, "Chills run up my back," has a physiological foundation. A similar reaction can be observed in a dog and cat when in the presence of potential enemies.

Pigment granules lying in the lower epidermal layers of the human skin give it color ranging from no color at all, as in the abnormal albinos, to the dense pigmentation in black people. Sunlight has a decided effect, not only on increasing the amount of pigment (tanning), but also on increasing the thickness of the epidermis itself. The purpose of such a response is protection, because ultraviolet light damages unprotected skin, as most people know. Continual exposure to bright sunlight produces a dark, tough skin, even in white people—a far cry from the complexion recommended by beauty experts. It has become the fashion to expose the body to the damaging rays of the sun in order to obtain a "tan," which for some strange reason has been identified with good health. There is no relationship; indeed skin cancer occurs only in those people who have been exposed excessively to the sun.

Glands. Near the base of each hair is a tiny sebaceous gland which secretes an oily substance designed to keep both the hair and the skin in a soft, pliable condition. These glands, like other skin glands, come from the epidermis, although they are buried deep in the dermis (Fig. 16-1). The tiny, much coiled sweat glands are likewise found deep in the dermis where they function in extracting water from the blood and tissues and spreading it over the surface of the skin for the purpose of cooling the body (Fig. 16-1). The resulting evaporation reduces the temperature of the skin and thereby aids in the regulation of the temperature of the entire body. This is very important to a mammal, although in many species these glands are localized in small areas, which are quite different in different mammals. The cow, for instance, has them confined to its nose, whereas others such as the horse and man have them distributed rather generally over the body. In man they are concentrated in the palms of the hands, soles of the feet, and under the arms.

Another very interesting skin gland found only among mammals and fully developed only in females is the *milk* or *mammary* gland, a name that identifies the group. These are modified sweat glands and are confined to areas most convenient for suckling the young mammal, which they supply with a complete food during its early post-embryonic life in a sort of continuation of umbilical feeding.

The Dermis

This layer of the skin is much thicker than the epidermis and is composed of tough connective tissue (Fig. 16-1). The nature of this layer becomes apparent if one recalls the various kinds of leather that are employed by man for thousands of purposes. It is interesting to note that man uses the skins of other animals to supplement his own. Fat tends to store in the deeper parts of the dermis and becomes localized in characteristic regions of the body familiar to everyone. In unusual cases, the stored fat can weigh as much as the remainder of the body. The distribution of this layer of fat is characteristic of the sex. For example, in the female the layer is thicker, giving the skin a more velvety touch. The body contours are smoother and the underlying muscles are less pronounced than is the case in males. Women are therefore better insulated than men and seem to suffer less from the cold.

Many tiny bundles of blood vessels project up from below into the dermis where they function in bringing the blood close to the surface for cooling the body when it is too warm. They contract when the body is cold (**vasoconstriction**), preventing the blood from coming to the surface. They are under the influence of the autonomic nervous system and may be influenced in some people by emotions such as in blushing (**vasodilation**). Also, the dermis contains many nerve endings which are receptors for heat, cold, pressure, touch, and pain. With the exception of the pain nerve endings, they are specially designed end organs for special stimuli. Since the skin is in contact with the outer world all of the time, a great deal of information comes to the brain from it. Pain, for example, is a very uncomfortable sensation, ideally designed to make the animal do something about the situation, if possible. This sensation is responsible for preservation of the individual, for without it great areas of the body might be destroyed without the organism being aware of it. A few people have no sensory nerve endings in their skin and hence feel no pain; as a consequence, they can be seriously burned or injured in other ways before becoming conscious of the danger.

Thus we see that most animals possess some sort of protective covering. Animals also need some internal support, particularly the larger forms and those animals that live on land. This is provided by an **endoskeleton.**

THE SKELETAL SYSTEM

Animals have acquired many forms of support for their bodies. The various structures not only hold the body together but also, in many cases, have an important protective function. To be sure, such single-celled animals as amoeba exist completely naked, with no protective covering whatever. Their close relatives, however, such as *Difflugia* (Fig. 16-5), secrete a substance

Paramecium
pellicle

Difflugia
glass house

Sponge
spicules

Lobster
chitinous
exoskeleton

Rabbit
bony endoskeleton

FIG. 16-5. Representatives of some animal groups showing the way they have solved the problem of support.

426

which collects tiny siliceous particles (sand) and cements them together to provide an enclosure into which they may draw themselves when hard pressed. Paramecium possesses a semirigid **pellicle** which gives it some external support so that its body maintains a relatively constant shape. Sponges produce minute angular **spicules** which afford a rather rigid skeleton, and many coral animals secrete substantial external skeletons. Larger invertebrates, such as arthropods and mollusks, possess hard outer coverings which not only lend the body substantial support but are highly protective as well. Vertebrates, on the other hand, have an internal skeleton which functions primarily for support. It affords very little protection to the soft external parts of the animal, although it provides excellent protection for such vital organs as the brain, heart, and lungs.

Let us consider the human skeleton as an example of a vertebrate skeleton.

THE HUMAN SKELETON

The skeleton of man is similar to that of other mammals, almost bone for bone, but certain parts are emphasized more or less when compared with similar parts in other mammals. This is because of the upright position his body has taken. All animals that have adopted bipedal locomotion—dinosaurs, birds, and the kangaroo, for example—have shifted their body weight so that some parts of the skeleton must bear a greater portion of the burden than other parts. In quadrupeds the spinal column and legs resemble a suspension bridge where the column functions as the bridge itself and the legs as the supporting piers at either end. In man and other bipeds the body is elevated at one end until it is in a vertical position which requires more secure footing at the base. This is essentially how a tall building such as the Empire State Building in New York is constructed—merely a bridge stood on end with elaborate footings.

In the human skeleton, this shift in weight has also necessitated more rigid connection between the supporting vertebral column and the pelvic girdle to which posterior supporting appendages are attached. This appears to function in a fairly satisfactory manner, although if one may judge by the number of middle-aged people suffering from a "sacroiliac" (the development of a faulty union between the column and pelvic girdle), it is clear that the arrangement could be improved.

The skeleton is usually divided into two general parts: the **axial** region comprising the **skull**, the **column**, and the **ribs**, and the **appendicular** region which includes the **appendages** and their **girdles** (Fig. 16-9). All of the bones are so securely tied together with ligaments that they are torn apart only under great strain. In spite of this seemingly well-built frame, it is often badly mutilated in accidents.

The Axial Skeleton

The Skull. The skull shows considerable modification when compared to that of lower vertebrates. The greater emphasis on the cranial case compared to the mandible is obvious when the heads of the dog, monkey, and man, for example, are placed side by side (Fig. 16-6). As the brain has grown forward over the shortened jaws, it is easy to see how the facial angle (angle between a line drawn along the forehead and one from the base of the nose to the foramen magnum) has increased and how the human face has been formed.

The human skull is made up of 28 bones, 22 of which are joined by jagged-edged **sutures**. The other 6 are the tiny ossicles of the ears. The bone which supports the tongue and larynx, the **hyoid,** is loosely connected with the skull. Although most of the skull is heavy, solid bone, certain portions contain cavities. These are remnants of chambers that formerly had specific functions but which perform no known function today. For example, the

FIG. 16-6. Comparative profiles of the dog, monkey, and man to show the relative shift in the facial angle (see text). Because of the increasing size of man's brain, which has grown over his shortened jaws, his facial angle has increased over that of lower forms.

three sinuses in the anterior and middle portion of the skull once served the sense of smell but do not do so now. There is a pair of maxillary sinuses in the cheek region, a pair of frontal sinuses over the eyes, and a pair of sphenoid sinuses in the posterior part of the nasal chamber. They all have small ducts which drain into the nasal chambers, but the arrangement is such that drainage is not good, especially when the membranes are swollen with a cold. Under such conditions the large surface area of the sinus membranes becomes infected, causing the so-called **sinus trouble** which is often difficult to treat satisfactorily. Another spongy bone, the **mastoid,** lying behind the external ear may also become infected via the eustachian tube and the middle ear. Such an infection can reach the brain because the mastoid is separated from it only by a very thin bone. Surgery, the treatment of choice for mastoiditis some years ago, has largely been replaced by the use of antibiotics.

The brain is exposed to the outside world in only one place, and that is in the nasal chamber. The floor of the brain case, where the olfactory nerves leave the brain and pass down into the nasal chamber, is called the **cribriform plate.** It is a piece of bone perforated with many small openings through which the nerves pass and through which, unfortunately, nasal infections can reach the brain.

The cord enters the human brain case ventrally instead of posteriorly as is the case with most mammals. The large opening through which it passes is called the **foramen magnum.** Since the skull is precariously perched on the tip of the spinal column, it might be expected that the cord could be injured at this point rather easily, and such is indeed the case. A severe blow at the base of the neck will stretch the cord at the point where it enters the skull thus causing complete paralysis of all body functions. This vulnerable spot is taken advantage of by man in getting rid of his incorrigible fellows by hanging. Other openings into the brain case are the foramina for numerous small blood vessels and for the cranial nerves, including the optic nerves at the base of the orbits.

At birth, several bones from the brain case have not come together (sutured), so that five spaces are left without bony covering. These are called **fontanelles** (little fountains—so named because they rise and fall with each heart beat). This lack of suturing before birth plays a very important function in the birth process, for the head of the child undergoes severe squeezing while passing through the birth canal and needs to change its shape to fit the narrow passage. Were the skull hard the difficult process of being born might be even more difficult or impossible. The head of the newborn child is very plastic and can be molded into almost any shape. Flathead Indians took advantage of this fact by placing a board on the head of the newborn, thus causing the forehead to have a peculiar flat appearance in the adult. As the child grows, the fontanelles gradually close, leaving fine jagged lines at the junctures. The age of a skull can be told by the clearness of these lines. They are faint or absent in old skulls.

Injuries to the skull have been common throughout man's history. Early skulls often show evidences not only of natural injuries but also of apparent deliberate removal of small portions. Such drillings (called trephining) seemingly had some religious significance, but the remarkable thing about them is that the patients often recovered, as revealed by the smooth edges of the opening, indicating that the bone healed. Similar operations are performed today for entirely different reasons and with much more satisfactory results.

The Spinal Column. When a comparison is made between the spinal column of man and almost any of the other mammals, certain striking differences are noted (Fig.

FIG. 16-7. The spinal column is the axial support of vertebrates and is subject to considerable variation among the different groups, depending on the stress and strain put upon it. In the quadruped, such as the dog, the column functions like a bridge with the two supports at either end. When the support is shifted to the two posterior appendages, such as in the ape, a more secure attachment must be affected between the column and the pelvic girdle. This is carried further in man, where we see a huge pelvic girdle, since the posterior appendages must provide the only means of support and locomotion.

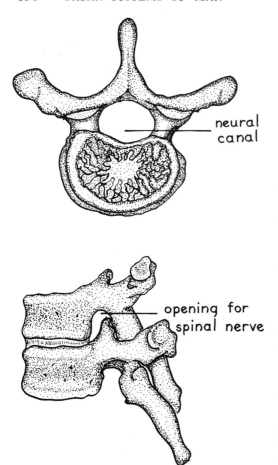

neural
canal

opening for
spinal nerve

FIG. 16-8. The spinal column is composed of interlocking vertebrae that, taken together, form a sturdy, flexible support for the entire body. The large openings in the vertebrae form a bony canal in which the delicate spinal cord is housed. Between the vertebrae are paired openings through which the spinal nerves pass.

16-7). These result from the upright posture man has assumed. In the dog, for example, the column forms a smooth arch between the two pairs of legs; in man, on the other hand, it forms a sigmoid or S-shaped curve. This serves an important function in an upright animal. With the head resting on the top end of the column, a rigid, straight rod would afford very little resilience, whereas a curved column would spring gently, thus cushioning the jolts that are conducted through the legs from the feet as they come in contact with the ground. The curved spine of man is admirably designed to give the head a smooth ride. If the pliable spine of a growing child is subject to undue stress, it may ultimately affect the development of the adult skeleton. Much of our posture is dependent on the spine and there is much emphasis today on the desirability of good posture. While this is highly desirable, it is not a guarantee of good health. Good health is due to a great many things and cannot be guaranteed by any such simple formula.

The spinal column is composed of 33 articulating **vertebrae** of rather irregular sizes from the neck to the pelvis fitted snugly together. They are securely laced together by many ligaments. This is essential because the column houses the very delicate spinal cord which, if injured even only slightly, may cause dire effects in the operation of the appendages as well as of other parts of the body. The column is more flexible in some regions than in others. For example, the vertebrae of the thoracic region are relatively immovable whereas those in the lower back and neck region have considerable amplitude of movement. This arrangement allows for a large variety of movements of the trunk, as evidenced by the ballet dancer in action.

Pairs of small openings between the vertebrae provide exits for the spinal nerves (Fig. 16-8). Each vertebra has a large cylindrical passageway, and these taken together form the **neural canal** which houses the nerve cord. Five of the lower **sacral** vertebrae are fused into a solid bone, the **sacrum**, which joins the **ilia** (singular—*ilium*) on the dorsal side, thus securely attaching the pelvic girdle to the spine. It needs to be a broad, secure attachment because the whole upper body pivots at this point and the stress is considerable. Unfortunately, the joint is not bone-to-bone but via ligaments, and when it partially gives way under unusual strain much distress is caused.

The spinal column terminates in several tiny, useless, fused vertebrae collectively known as the **coccyx.** In many vertebrates they give support to a functional **tail,** but in man they are mere vestiges of the past. Undoubtedly, far back in man's early history, long before he was man, he had a tail. It must be remembered that the presence or absence of a tail means nothing from an evolutionary point of view. The bear and guinea pig are without tails, yet they are no more related to each other than either is to man.

The Ribs. The 12 ribs are attached to the **transverse process** and the **centra** on the column side and 10 of them to the **sternum** directly or indirectly on the ventral side. These together form the **thoracic basket,** a convenient enclosure for the vital organs located in the chest region (Fig. 16-9). It is interesting to note that the number of ribs is not always 12. The millions of chest X-rays taken of soldiers in the last war brought to light the fact that there is considerable variation, ranging from 11 to 13, the latter number being the most common variation. Incidentally, the gorilla also possesses 13 ribs.

The Appendicular Skeleton

The remainder of the skeleton, consisting of the appendages and their supports or girdles, is called the appendicular skeleton (Fig. 16-9). The **pectoral girdle** to which the arms are attached is located in the anterior region. It consists of two **clavicles** (collar bones) and two **scapulas** (shoulder blades); taken together they form a triangular brace with the arm hanging at the apex. Clavicles are rudimentary or absent in most mammals, but in the primates they are large, functional bones. Life in the trees, where brachiation was responsible for the development of not only the clavicle but also the nerves and muscles of the arms which make them such useful appendages today, is responsible for this difference. While the clavicle is firmly attached to the sternum on the front, the scapula has no secure attachment and is loosely slung over the thoracic basket by means of muscles and ligaments. This arrangement permits a great deal of movement in which the shoulders can be freely rolled over the ribs. The anterior appendages have much more freedom of movement than the posterior appendages, whose primary function is locomotion.

The upper arm, the **humerus,** fits into a crude socket made by the union of the scapula and clavicle called the **glenoid cavity.** The humerus is held in place by ligaments at its upper end, but since the attachment is none too secure, under certain stresses it may be forced out of the socket, resulting in a dislocation. Such stretched ligaments allow dislocation more readily under similar subsequent stresses. The advantage of this junction lies in its loose arrangement that allows more freedom of movement for the arm. For example, the arm may be turned in a complete circle as well as rotated in the socket. A dog, on the other hand, could not possibly perform such a feat, for the arrangement of the bones in its pectoral girdle is much more rigid.

The two forearm bones, the **radius** and **ulna,** form a combination whereby hinge action as well as partial rotation can take place. This means that the forearm can be flexed (bent on the upper arm) in a straight pull or it can twist through 180 degrees. The number of times one performs these movements each day is almost unlimited. At the wrist another hinge is produced by the end of the radius and the **carpals,** the small wrist bones. Actually, this is as much a universal joint as it is a hinge, with the result that the hand can move in all directions with equal facility. The hand with its large, opposable thumb is a primitive but most useful instrument, and it is hard to imagine life as it is lived today without it.

The **pelvic** girdle is the most specialized part of the entire skeleton. A quadruped,

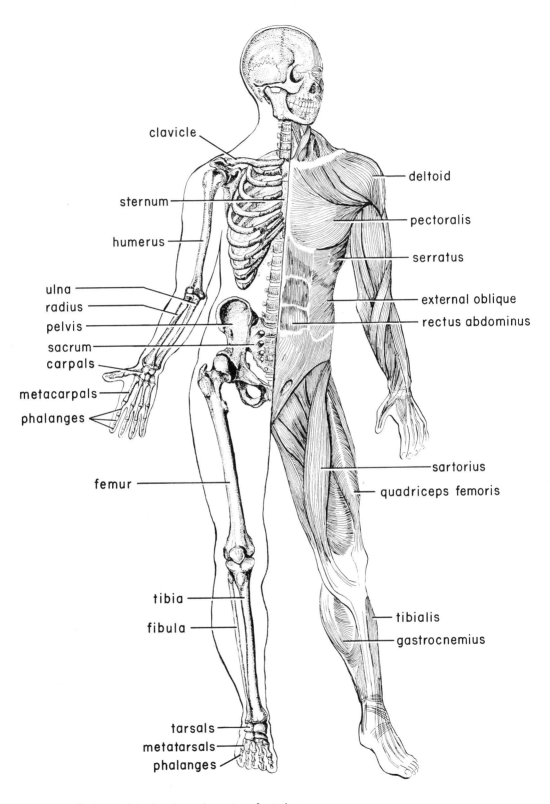

clavicle

sternum

humerus

ulna
radius
pelvis
sacrum
carpals

metacarpals

phalanges

femur

tibia

fibula

tarsals
metatarsals
phalanges

deltoid

pectoralis

serratus

external oblique

rectus abdominus

sartorius

quadriceps femoris

tibialis

gastrocnemius

FIG. 16-9. The human skeletal and muscular systems, front view.

running on all fours, does not require as secure an attachment to the column as does a biped, whose pelvis has become correspondingly modified. However, in man the pelvis not only has become an excellent support for the entire body but it has also broadened and flared out so that it functions as a support for the organs of the abdominal cavity. This again is a satisfactory method of handling the pendent viscera of the upright animal.

The pelvis is composed of three pairs of fused bones: the large, flat and cupped **ilia** (singular—*ilium*), the **ischia** (singular—*ischium,* the bones used in sitting), and the **pubic bones** which complete the girdle in front. The fused vertebrae of the sacrum form a complete circle at the back, leaving a large opening through which all mammal offspring must pass in the process of birth. The urinary and digestive tracts pass through here also. The dimensions of this opening are one of the clues used in determining the sex of a skeleton. Not only is the opening larger in females but, in addition, the attachment of the pubic bones is not so broad. Both features are essential to allow such a large object as a fetus to pass through. The ilia also flare outward more abruptly in the female than in the male; this changes the position of the legs somewhat so that the method of walking and running differs in the two sexes. The familiar female "waddle" is a result of this skeletal arrangement.

The **femur** is the longest bone in the skeleton. Its proximal end (end nearer the body) is a pronounced ball which lies at an angle to the rest of the bone and which fits into a deep socket in the pelvis called the **acetabulum.** This is a much more secure arrangement than the one in the shoulder region, although it does not have equivalent freedom of movement. For this reason the hip joint is not nearly so apt to dislocate as the shoulder joint. The leg can circumscribe a narrow cone but not a wide one like the arm. The leg is primarily concerned with the business of carrying the body forward in progression and consequently is constructed to function essentially in a forward and backward motion.

At the distal end (end farther from the body) the femur flattens out, forming a hinge with one of the two lower leg bones, the **tibia** or shin bone. The other lower leg bone is the **fibula,** which is smaller and lies on the outside of the leg. Together with the tibia it affords a point of contact, in turn, with one of the two large ankle bones. The other forms the heel. These two, together with the five other tarsal bones, the **metatarsals** and the **phalanges,** form the foot. This part of the skeleton is man's contact with the ground and is a very important part of his anatomy. When something goes wrong here he is practically helpless.

There are two arches in the foot, **longitudinal** and **transverse,** which are primarily supported by stretched tendons that come from muscles in the lower leg. Being always under tension, they possess a resilience that puts a "spring in one's step" and they also take away the shock from sudden contact with the substratum. Flat feet may be caused by undue stress such as comes from overweight or they may be inherited. Such dislocation of the bones of the feet may cause considerable pain and make normal walking difficult.

We have considered in some detail the arrangement of the structural units of the vertebrate skeleton. Let us now examine the composition of these units.

The Composition of Bone

If a long bone like a femur is cut in cross-section, it will be found to be hollow with a soft spongy material, the **marrow,** occupying the cavity (Fig. 4-5). The outer portion is very hard and resists breaking. The tubular nature of the bone makes it even stronger than a solid piece of equal weight; to understand this, one has only to compare solid and tubular rods of steel with respect to strength where bending and twisting is concerned. The hard part of bone is composed of calcium carbonate, or lime, and potassium phosphate, as well as an organic matrix which resembles cartilage. This can easily be demonstrated by placing the bone in an acid solution which dissolves out the minerals, leaving the matrix. Although the bone retains its original shape, it is very soft and pliable and as such could certainly be of no use to an animal. On the other hand, the organic matrix can be removed by heating the bone for some time so that only the minerals are left. Such a bone also retains its original shape but if disturbed crumbles into ashes. Again a bone of this composition would be of no use to an animal. Minerals and matrix taken together, then, are necessary to produce satisfactory material from which to construct skeletal units.

Bone Growth

It is obvious that the bones of a child, while fully formed and quite solid, must increase in both length and diameter as growth occurs. This is accomplished by a rather elaborate bone-destroying and bone-building process going on within the bone itself. The bone is covered on the outside by a thin cellular membrane, the **periosteum,** which has to do with the increase in the diameter of the bone. At the ends, called the **epiphyses** (singular—*epiphysis*), there is also active cellular growth which causes the increase in length. As bone is produced by both periosteum and epiphyseal cells, a simultaneous bone destruction is going on within the marrow cavity. In other words, as the bone cells produce bone on the outside and at the ends of the bone, similar cells are destroying bone on the inside. Thus the bone gradually becomes longer and increases in diameter.

Although bone may seem dead, it is far from it, as was pointed out earlier (p. 102). The **Haversian system** (Fig. 4-5) consists of a canal in the center containing blood vessels and a nerve, surrounded by concentric rings of bony matrix, and between them scattered tiny spaces, **lacunae,** filled with the bone cells. Very tiny tubes (canaliculi) connect the bone cells with one another and the central canal, and it is through these canals that the cells are nourished and kept alive. These bone cells secrete the bony matrix in which they are entombed. It is as if a mason were to surround himself with a concrete wall of his own building and thus be enclosed in a chamber which he could never leave, but in which he would be kept alive by small portals through which nourishment could be supplied.

Ability to Move

Nearly all animals from amoeba to man have the ability to locomote, and the few which lack this are still able to move some parts of their body (Fig. 16-10). Amoeba moves by a complex sol-gel reversal mechanism which causes the pseudopods to extend and retract (p. 161). In addition to being able to move its body in a wormlike manner, Euglena has a contractile flagellum which propels it through the water. Paramecium is provided with numerous cilia that beat in unison to bring about its erratic movements. Hydra is the first animal with cells that contain muscle fibers which contract along an axis. It is the combined action of the many **neuromuscular** cells that makes it possible for this animal to contract and to extend itself in its movements. Once this type of movement, that is, muscular contraction, had appeared in animals, it persisted through all subsequent forms. We shall, therefore, spend some time in studying muscles and their operation.

THE MUSCULAR SYSTEM

One of the most striking characteristics of animals is movement. Since they are voracious feeders they must be on the move most of the time in search of food. Among all but the protozoa and perhaps a few

FIG. 16-10. Various ways in which animals from representative groups have solved the problem of movement.

others contracting muscles are responsible for movement, not only of the body as a whole and its external appendages but of the internal organs as well, such as the organs of digestion and circulation. It is not surprising, therefore, that a man's body has more than 600 separate muscles.

Muscle Structure

Muscle is the principal part of the meat that is bought at the market and it usually makes up about 40–50 per cent of the body weight of large animals. Viewed with the naked eye, muscle is seen encased in a sheath of connective tissue which often glistens. The color of the muscle may vary with the nature of the fibers and with age; young mammals such as calves have lighter muscle tissue than older beef. Finally, muscles of the viscera possess a different texture than those of the skeleton.

The microanatomy of muscle tissue was described in an earlier section (p. 102). **Smooth** or **involuntary** muscle is located in the organs of digestion and in the skin, as well as in other places. They are concerned with those movements which are not directly under voluntary control, such as peristaltic movements of the digestive tract. These muscles are slow to respond to stimuli and the response that eventually occurs is of long duration. If one pricks the intestine of a frog with a sharp needle it requires from 1 to 10 seconds before any reaction is noted, but once the contraction starts it lasts for a minute or two, clearly demonstrating the character of smooth muscle action.

The **skeletal muscle** is composed of numerous fibrils (tiny fibers) suspended in the more fluid protoplasm, the **sarcoplasm** (p. 102). Differences in the relative amounts of sarcoplasm and fibrils make a difference in the appearance of voluntary muscle tissue. Muscle fibers that contain a great many fibrils and relatively little sarcoplasm are light in color, and when the proportion is reversed the muscles are dark. In birds

such as ducks, where sustained flight for long periods of time is essential, the breast muscle fibers contain more sarcoplasm and are therefore red, whereas the breast muscles of the domestic chicken which flies only short distances, if at all, are white. Bird muscles adapted for sustained activity are red, whereas those that contract for only short periods are white.

Cardiac muscle functions as a unit because of the nature of its cells (p. 105). As a result of its sustained action, it is dark in color, as one might expect.

Muscle Action

The muscle responds like a rubber band; it can do only one positive thing and that is **contract.** When it is not contracted it is said to be **relaxed.** The function of a muscle, then, is to pull two objects closer together. This means that there must be muscles which pull bones in one direction and those which pull the same bones back again (Fig. 16-11). Muscles working against one another are said to be **antagonists.** For example, by contraction of the large muscle in the front of the upper leg the bent leg straightens, as in kicking a ball (Fig. 16-9). Once the leg is straight it must be bent again before another step or kick can be executed, and several large muscles on the back side of the leg carry out this movement. To be sure, there is no complete relaxation of one set of muscles during the contraction of their antagonists. Both contract, the resultant action depending on how much each contracts. When bones are bent on one another the action is spoken of as **flexion;** when they are straightened out the action is described as **extension.** The example of kicking is a case of flexion and extension of the leg bones. Although there are many other types of muscle action, antagonistic action is the most common in the animal body. Antagonistic muscles are not equally matched in strength. For example, the muscle which raises the

FIG. 16-11. Muscle action in the human arm and leg. In the upper left figure, the triceps brachii muscle contracts in extending or straightening the arm while the biceps brachii relaxes. In the lower left figure, the opposite action occurs, that is, the triceps brachii relaxes and the biceps brachii contracts. This flexes or bends the arm as in lifting. To rise on the toes as in walking the large gastrocnemius contracts (right).

jaw is stronger than the one that lowers it. Hence, when both contract violently as they do in convulsions, the jaw is closed tightly (lockjaw).

Muscles vary considerably in size and shape, some being long and fusiform, whereas others are thin and flat (Fig. 16-9). Most of them have a fleshy middle or **belly** part and two tapering ends which terminate in round or flat cords called **tendons.** Tendons consist of tough, fibrous tissue which attaches the muscle to the bone. The two ends of the muscle are identified by the amount of movement that takes place in the bones to which the tendons are attached. The end which moves the bone the greater distance is called the **insertion;** the end which moves the bone the shorter distance is the **origin.** Thus the biceps brachii muscle (Fig. 16-11) has its origin on a point of the scapula and its insertion on the radius, because the latter bone moves the

greater distance when contraction occurs.

Tendons act like cables, attaching a muscle to a bone sometimes at a considerable distance from the muscle. This is a very convenient arrangement because it makes possible the location of muscles some distance from the point where action must occur. For example, the muscles that support and operate the foot are located in the lower leg. The large tendon at the heel, the tendon of Achilles (Fig. 16-11), is like a steel cable when one is standing, particularly if he is on his toes. If the large calf muscles that are necessary in operating the foot were located in the foot itself the latter appendage would reach astounding proportions. This trend to longer tendons and concentration of the muscle's action farther from the muscle is most handsomely illustrated in the leg of the deer. Its lower leg is little more than skin, bones, and tendons, yet all the power of the strong

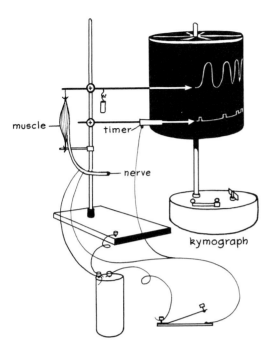

muscle

timer

nerve

kymograph

FIG. 16-12. Muscle action can be studied by attaching an isolated muscle, such as the gastrocnemius muscle of the frog, to a lever which can scratch a line of its path on a smoked moving drum (kymograph). When the muscle is electrically stimulated, the nature of the contraction can be recorded on the smoked drum.

during which time there is a chemical readjustment taking place in the muscle (discussed below). If successive stimuli are increased in their frequency, there will come a time when the contractions will be superimposed upon one another until there is a sustained contraction which is greater than any derived from single stimuli (Fig. 16-14). Such a condition is called **tetanus,** and is what usually occurs in most muscular contractions, however short.

If a stimulus is given to an isolated frog heart muscle, contraction occurs, provided the stimulus is sufficient to initiate a response. No matter how much the stimulus is increased, the resulting contraction remains the same. This fact has led to the establishment of the so-called **all or none principle,** which means simply that if the heart muscle contracts at all, it will do so to its greatest extent. The question arises as to whether or not this applies to skeletal muscle. Obviously such muscles contract in graded amounts, because one can contract any of his muscles as much or as little as he likes. Here the principle does not apply to whole muscle but to individual fibers or to **motor units** (about 100 fibers). Although there still seems to be some question about

leg muscles is transmitted efficiently to the tiny digits that contact the ground.

Muscles normally contract as a result of impulses coming to them through nerves. However, an isolated muscle can be made to contract if stimulated directly by an electrical current, even though all the nerves have been destroyed. The nature of the contraction can be studied by attaching the muscle to a recording device (Fig. 16-12) and noting its action following stimulation. When the muscle first receives a very brief stimulus there is no visible evidence of anything happening. This period is known as the **latent period** (Fig. 16-13), and lasts about 0.01 second in the frog muscle. Contraction then begins and continues for 0.04 second. This is immediately followed by a relaxation period that lasts 0.05 second,

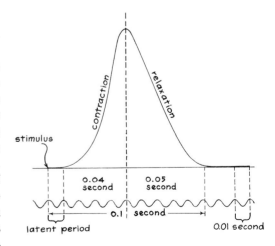

stimulus

contraction

relaxation

0.04 second   0.05 second

0.1 second

latent period   0.01 second

FIG. 16-13. This record was made when the frog gastrocnemius muscle contracted and relaxed, using a recording device as shown in Fig. 16-12. Note the time required for each event to occur.

it, the available evidence points to the fact that motor units do obey the "all or none" principle. Hence, the force with which a muscle contracts depends on how many motor units are stimulated. A mild contraction

FIG. 16-14. This record shows that by applying stimuli to a skeletal muscle with gradually increasing frequency, contractions merge until there is a sustained contraction called tetanus. The contraction is stronger in tetanus than in the single contractions.

would result when only a very few are stimulated; a maximal contraction, when all of the units receive a stimulus.

Chemistry of Muscle Action

The mystery of muscle contraction is gradually being solved although the entire story is still not clearly understood. As a result of the efforts of physiologists, biochemists, and cytologists, particularly those working with the electron microscope, we are obtaining a clearer picture of what happens when a skeletal muscle contracts and relaxes.

It was once thought that the chemistry involved in muscle contraction was rather simple, because when a frog leg muscle (usually the sartorius) was stimulated continuously lactic acid accumulated, which subsequently was oxidized to carbon dioxide and water. Since glycogen disappeared simultaneously from the muscle, it was thought to be the source of energy which brought about the contraction. Further experimentation, however, demonstrated that if glycogen was prevented from breaking

down into lactic acid (this can be done by using the specific poison, iodoacetic acid), the muscle continued to contract. In addition, it was discovered that the muscle would contract with the same force if denied oxygen as in the presence of the gas; in other words, it functioned **anaerobically.** What then, was the source of the energy?

By preventing the breakdown of glycogen to lactic acid there is none of the latter to burn to carbon dioxide and water from which energy could come. Obviously, this was not the reaction that supplied energy for contraction. It meant that the muscle must possess some other substances that released energy in a manner resembling oxidation. A diligent search revealed the presence of a phosphate-containing compound, **creatine phosphate** (CP), which turned out to be energy-rich very much like the phosphate in adenosine triphosphate (ATP), a compound with which we are already familiar (p. 83). Both compounds result from glycolysis and the Krebs citric acid cycle and both liberate a great deal of quick energy when their phosphate bonds are broken. This then turns out to be the source of energy for muscular contraction. It is now known, however, that CP acts as a reservoir of high energy phosphate and that the immediate source of energy for muscle contraction is ATP. During glycolysis ATP is generated and when it is in excess the high energy phosphate is transferred to creatine forming creatine phosphate, which is stored for use when ATP is exhausted following continued muscle contraction. The CP then comes into action in the following manner:

$$CP + ADP \rightleftarrows ATP + C$$

thus replenishing the supply of ATP. We see here, then, a very efficient system of chemical reactions which makes possible the sudden expenditure of large amounts of energy without going through the relatively slow process of oxidation. This remarkable achievement in chemical evolution accounts for the swift movement of animals.

In spite of our rather extensive knowledge of the chemical events that occur during muscle contraction we know very little about the mechanism involved in the conversion of the chemical energy in ATP to mechanical work. Obviously it is somehow tied up with the muscle proteins themselves. We do have considerable information about these proteins. Located in the muscle fibrils are two proteins, **myosin** and **actin,** which are involved in the actual shortening of the fiber. Both are essential; neither one nor the other can function alone. These have been isolated in test tubes and when they are mixed they form a complex, **actomyosin,** which can be made into "synthetic" fibers. When ATP is added to these fibers they contract the same as muscle, simultaneously decomposing the ATP to ADP. This experiment is one of the milestones in further understanding the chemistry of muscle contraction.

All evidence points to the fact that actin and myosin are the major proteins of the contractile muscle fiber. The mechanical arrangement of the muscle fibers and the part played by ATP in bringing about contraction is becoming more clear as we gain more knowledge about the morphology of the muscle fiber from electron microscopy. Whereas it was once thought that shortening of the muscle fiber was caused by the folding of the actomyosin filaments, recent fine structure studies seem to prove that this is not so. It has been observed that the myofibrils are composed of thick and thin filaments which slide past one another upon contraction. It is this action which accounts for the different positions of the bands (striations) in a relaxed and a contracted muscle, a fact that has been observed with the light as well as with the electron microscope. ATP supplies the driving force for this action and it is thought to bring about contraction by its capacity to dissociate actin and myosin. Therefore in the presence of ATP the two proteins are separated; with the arrival of the nerve impulse the enzymes which convert ATP to ADP (ATPase system) go into action and bring about the conversion. With the destruction of ATP, actin and myosin combine or re-associate which results in simultaneous contraction of the individual fibers. As was pointed out earlier we still do not know how the chemical energy in ATP is converted to mechanical work.

We may sum up the chemical steps that take place during muscular contraction and relaxation as follows:

Contraction Phase

$ATP \rightarrow ADP + \sim P$ (high energy phosphate)

Relaxation or *Recovery Phase*

Glycogen $\rightarrow$ lactic acid $+ \sim P$ (glycolysis)
Lactic acid $+ O_2 \rightarrow CO_2 + H_2O + \sim P$ (Krebs cycle)
$ADP + \sim P \rightarrow ATP$
$\sim P \rightarrow$ Body heat
Excess $\sim P$ stored as CP

From this review it becomes clear that during contraction the only reaction is the conversion of ATP to ADP, releasing energy in a sudden but controlled manner. This is an anaerobic reaction, which accounts for the fact that a man can run a hundred yards without taking a breath. When the ATP is exhausted CP comes into action converting ADP to ATP. With continued activity, naturally this reserve supply will also be depleted, and when that happens no further contraction can occur until time has elapsed for recovery, or partial recovery, to occur. A person exhausted in this manner must remain quiet while breathing rapidly and deeply to supply sufficient oxygen to permit the next reactions to occur. Actually the ATP and CP are never completely used up in the body; indeed, the moment contraction is initiated, the recovery process starts and these compounds are being restored all during contraction. During recovery glycolysis occurs during which glycogen is converted to lactic acid, releasing a small amount of $\sim$P. Lactic acid is then oxidized via the Krebs citric acid cycle to CO_2 and H_2O, yielding large quantities of $\sim$P. This step requires large quantities of oxygen, hence the deep breathing following severe exercise (or during, if prolonged). The energy released from this reaction is utilized in several ways; part of it is used to convert ADP to ATP, part to convert lactic acid back to glycogen, part is converted to heat to keep the body warm, and that which is left over is stored as creatine phosphate. The overall process results in the most economical method of obtaining the greatest possible amount of energy from glycogen. It means that the animal body is unusually efficient, about 40 per cent of the available energy being released in the form of mechanical work, 60 per cent as heat. This is a very satisfactory figure when compared with internal combustion engines which rarely exceed 25 per cent.

Referring once again to the runner, we know now that during the entire hundred-yard dash his muscles required very little oxygen because only ATP was required, the expenditure of energy being of short duration. Once the race ended he remained quiet and breathed deeply for some time to replenish his ATP. During the run he was building up an **oxygen debt,** which he "paid back" during the heavy breathing at the termination of the race. The obvious advantage of such an arrangement is that muscles are ready to contract with all of their force almost instantly. They contract until their store of ATP has been nearly exhausted; then they must stop until the blood brings sufficient oxygen to oxidize the accumulated lactic acid which releases the energy required to restore glycogen and ATP to their original levels.

Prolonged muscular activity results in **fatigue** which can be painful as anyone knows who has experienced it. From the foregoing discussion it would seem that fatigue results from the accumulation of lactic acid and the exhaustion of ATP and glycogen in the muscles. This is not quite so because in the intact animal fatigue sets in before there is an appreciable amount of lactic acid present in the muscles. Some of the lactic acid slowly diffuses into the blood, passes to the liver where it becomes liver glycogen, and then returns to the muscle and other tissues as blood glucose. The discomfort of fatigue probably is due to a combination of factors. Experimental evidence seems to demonstrate that the site most susceptible to fatigue is the junction between the muscle and nerve, and not the muscle or nerve itself.

The limitations for work are set by the ability of the body to restore exhausted organic compounds in the muscles; this depends indirectly on the functioning of the respiratory, circulatory, and excretory systems which, in turn, the muscles must depend on to receive their quota of burning material (sugar and oxygen) and to carry away their accumulated wastes (urea and CO_2). There are great individual differences among human beings for this capacity. Some get along well with very little sleep—Edison was such an example—whereas others require eight hours or more per day.

Muscles can be developed to considerable size and strength if they are constantly put to difficult tasks. By lifting heavy weights each day the muscles of the entire body will grow disproportionately large and will function very well in lifting heavy objects. If this is to be the life work of the individual it is wise to have such a set of muscles, just as it is wise for the man who handles a shovel all day long to have thick calluses on his palm. Modern living requires minimal development of one's muscles, hence recreational activities are helpful in compensating for this deficiency. Man evolved as an active animal and it follows that a certain amount of muscular activity is conducive to good health.

SUGGESTED SUPPLEMENTARY READINGS

CARLSON, A. J., and JOHNSON, V., *The Machinery of The Body* (Chicago, University of Chicago Press, 1962).

HAYASHI, T., "How Cells Move," *Scientific American,* 205(3) (September, 1961), 184.

HILL, A. V., *Muscular Movement in Man* (New York, McGraw-Hill Book Co., 1927).

HUXLEY, H. E., "The Contraction of Muscle," *Scientific American,* 199(55) (November, 1956), 66.

ROMER, A. S., *The Vertebrate Body* (Philadelphia, W. B. Saunders & Co., 1962).

SZENT-GYORG, A., *Chemical Physiology of Contraction in the Body and Heart Muscle* (New York, Academic Press, 1953).

THOMPSON, D. W., *On Growth and Form* (New York, The Macmillan Co., 1942).

WOODBURNE, R. T., *Essentials of Human Anatomy* (New York, Oxford University Press, 1961).

17

Coordination

COORDINATION IS OBVIOUSLY a fundamental necessity for all animals, because even proto-zoa have some method of coordinating their separate parts. *Euplotes* (Fig. 17-1) shows an advanced degree of specializa-tion because it is able to control the move-ment of its cilia from a "nerve" center so that the direction of progression can be changed suddenly. Metazoa such as hydra have a coordinating mechanism in the form of a simple arrangement of nerve cells, the **nerve net.** The first step toward a cen-tralization of nerve cells is seen in planaria, where there is a well-defined anterior brain with two large lateral nerve cords extend-ing posteriorly. Being a larger and more complex animal composed of many cells, a more elaborate coordinating mechanism is essential. Further centralization is con-tinued and elaborated upon through the invertebrate and vertebrate groups as ani-mals become larger and more complicated.

The growth and organization of the in-dividual may be likened to the expansion of a telephone system as a small village grows to a great city. As the latter increases in size, the system becomes more and more intricate until a telephone system like that of New

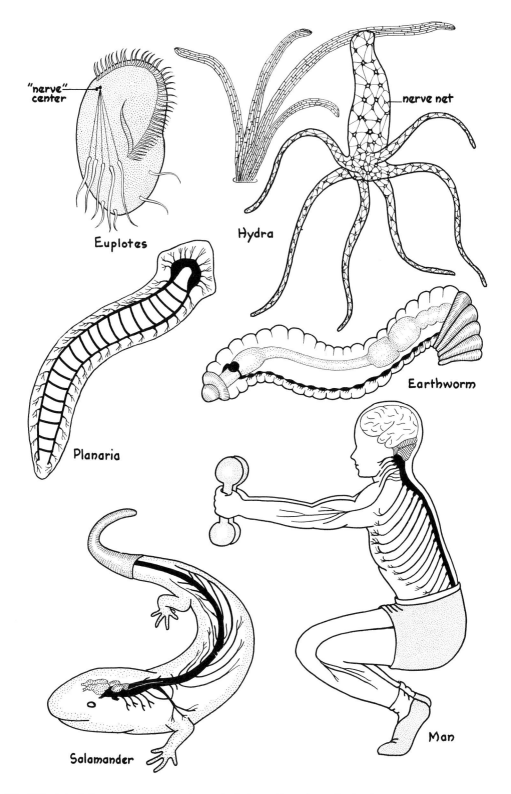

FIG. 17-1. Animals from protozoa to man have solved the problem of coordination in many ways.

York City results which is about as difficult to understand as the nervous system of a grasshopper or a man.

Among higher invertebrates and all vertebrates the network of tiny fibers connecting all parts of the animal has apparently proven inadequate, because a supplementary system has evolved, namely, an **endocrine system.** In this system an entirely different principle is employed; instead of impulses passing over tiny fibers, specific chemicals produced by special glands are released into the blood and circulate to other parts of the body where they produce a specific effect.

In studying coordination we shall begin with a discussion of stimuli from the external world and the internal environment as received by the **sense organs** and other **receptors;** then we shall discuss the nervous system which is the intermediary for the transmission and interpretation of the stimuli, the components called the **adjustors,** and then discuss the **effectors**—muscles and glands—which respond to the stimuli. We shall conclude with a discussion of the endocrine system.

RECEPTORS

The receptors consist of specialized end-organs which are highly sensitive to certain kinds of stimuli. Conspicuous sense organs such as the eye and ear are familiar to everyone; others, such as the tiny receptors located in various parts of the internal body, are not so well known but are just as important in the proper coordination of the organism.

Skin Receptors

It might be expected that the outer covering of the body would be highly sensitive to the environment around it, and this is true. A pin prick in the skin almost anywhere over the surface of the body results in a pain sensation; this fact indicates that these nerve endings are very numerous and widespread. The same is true of the nerve endings for touch, pressure, heat, and cold. A thin section of the human skin will reveal tiny, oval-shaped **tactile corpuscles** from which nerves lead inward. Any pressure brought to bear on them causes impulses to be discharged from the specialized cells within the corpuscle which travel along nerve fibers to the central nervous system. Other kinds of sensory end-organs which respond to pressure stimuli over larger areas are located in the deeper skin and in many internal organs. Free nerve endings which register pain terminate in the epithelium within the internal organs as well as in the skin. The endings ramify and come into contact with nearly every cell, which explains why pain sensations are felt even if only a small area is stimulated, such as in pricking with a pin.

By marking off specified areas on the skin and using a stiff bristle as a stimulus the appropriate receptors can be located, and they will be found to be quite unevenly distributed over the body. It is difficult, for example, to distinguish two points one-half inch apart in the middle of the back, whereas on the tip of the finger or tongue a distance of one-sixteenth of an inch is perceptible. Likewise, if metal pointed instruments (styluses) are used, the hot and cold end-organs can be detected. There are more cold spots than hot spots and that is why, for instance, one shivers at first if suddenly exposed to a hot shower. When all of the end-organs are stimulated simultaneously, as would be the case in the above situation, the total response is that of coldness at first because there are more of the cold than hot spots. Later, the proper interpretation of the stimulation is recognized. Pressure end-organs can be found by applying a blunt metal stylus having the same temperature as the skin to various regions. Other sensory nerve endings are located in the tendons and muscles and respond to tension placed on these tendons and muscles. These are important in bal-

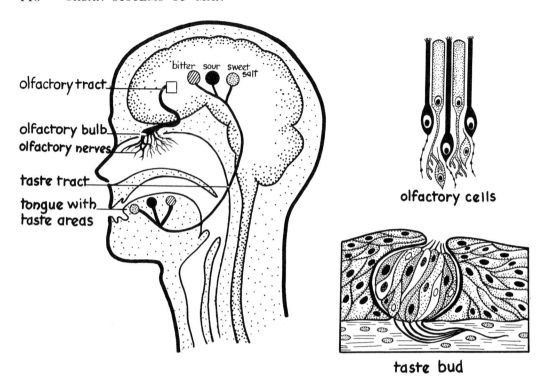

olfactory tract

olfactory bulb
olfactory nerves

taste tract

tongue with
taste areas

bitter sour sweet
salt

olfactory cells

taste bud

FIG. 17-2. The end-organs for chemo-reception are located in the nasal chambers (smell) and on the tongue (taste). They are shown here in detail together with the nerve pathways that conduct the impulses to the brain.

ance and will be discussed under that topic later.

Chemo-Receptors

All of the receptors of the skin have to do with identifying energy changes that occur at or very near the body. In addition, there are chemo-receptors that identify substances dissolved in the saliva of the mouth, giving one the sense of **taste,** and chemicals dissolved in the mucus of the nasal chambers, imparting the sense of **smell.** In the latter case, the organism is made aware of changes in its environment some distance away. The sense of smell is, in this respect, like the senses of hearing and seeing which extend perception to great distances.

Taste. The so-called sense of taste is actually a combination of stimuli coming from the mouth cavity. Stimuli from the end-

organs of taste, touch, heat, and cold located in various parts of the mouth cavity give a composite sensation which is called taste. The difference in the "taste" of hot and cold foods is due to stimuli other than those which are caused by dissolved chemicals. The sense of smell is also important to taste, as anyone with a bad cold is well aware. The end-organs of taste are called **taste buds** and are distributed over the surface of the tongue, laryngeal region, and parts of the roof of the mouth (Fig. 17-2). They are oval-shaped bodies made up of several cells which terminate in a slender sensory process on the end toward the mouth cavity.

There are four kinds of taste sensations and consequently there are four different kinds of taste buds, each with a rather specific distribution on the tongue and other mouth parts (Fig. 17-2). The taste buds registering **bitter** are located at the base of the tongue, **salt** and **sweet** on the tip, and **sour** along the edges. These can all be identified both microscopically and experimentally. No matter how these buds are stimulated the resultant sensation is always sweet, sour, salt, or bitter. Some chemicals stimulate two kinds of taste buds, but in each case the taste bud responds as it should according to its predetermined function. There are some classes of substances which have a consistent taste; for example, acidic substances usually taste sour, basic substances bitter. The threshold (a stimulus that is just sufficiently strong to elicit a response) is very low for the sense of both taste and smell. For example, it is possible to taste quinine in concentrations of one part in two million, and much greater dilutions of odorous substances can be smelled.

The taste of some substances varies widely with different individuals and just what taste registers has a genetic basis. For example, the chemical **phenylthiocarbamide** may taste sour to one person, bitter to another, salty to another, sweet to another, and fail to give a taste response at all to another. Taste is inherited in a definite pattern.

Smell. The olfactory end-organs which are responsible for the sense of smell are located in the nasal membranes, and it is through these organs that gaseous chemical stimuli (odors) are received. While in man the receptive area in the two nasal chambers is only about 10 square centimeters, in most mammals it is much more extensive. It will be recalled that the sense of smell is far more important to ground dwellers than to those that live in trees, where keen vision is of more value. It is not surprising, therefore, that when the primates took to the trees the sense of smell diminished and in the present primate is very poorly developed. The dog, on the other hand, receives a great deal of information about the world through his nose. This sense is so keen that the dog can pick up the odor of an animal

that has passed over a trail some hours before. Most game dogs rely more on their sense of smell than on sight except at close range and, in fact, many bird dogs are very nearsighted.

The olfactory cells give rise to fibers (Fig. 17-2) which coalesce, after passing through the cribriform plate, to form the **olfactory bulb,** which becomes a large nerve leading to the brain. The location of the olfactory end-organs is such as to protect them from the desiccating effects of incoming currents of air during breathing, and the nasal passages are kept continuously moist in order that the incoming odors may dissolve in the fluid bathing them. A dry olfactory end-organ cannot be stimulated any more than can a dry taste bud.

It may be necessary for large quantities of air to pass over the receptors before stimulation is possible. As more air passes over them more of the chemical in gaseous form becomes dissolved in the fluid of the nose, thus increasing the concentration to a point where the threshold is exceeded. This accounts for the constant sniffing of the dog, or man, too, on occasion, to bring more air into contact with the nasal epithelium.

Our knowledge of the sense of smell is very limited, as indicated by the fact that no satisfactory system of classification of odors has yet been set up. Odors are still referred to by the name of the aromatic substance in question, and there are nearly as many names for odors as there are aromatic chemicals. It seems highly improbable that there is an infinite number of kinds of olfactory nerve endings, although when they become fatigued to one odor they seem to respond with normal vigor to another. Different chemicals apparently do not stimulate the same nerve endings. In general, the nerve endings fatigue readily, and it is a familiar experience that an odor which is very strong when one first enters a room soon fades away until it is unnoticed, not because the chemical in the air has

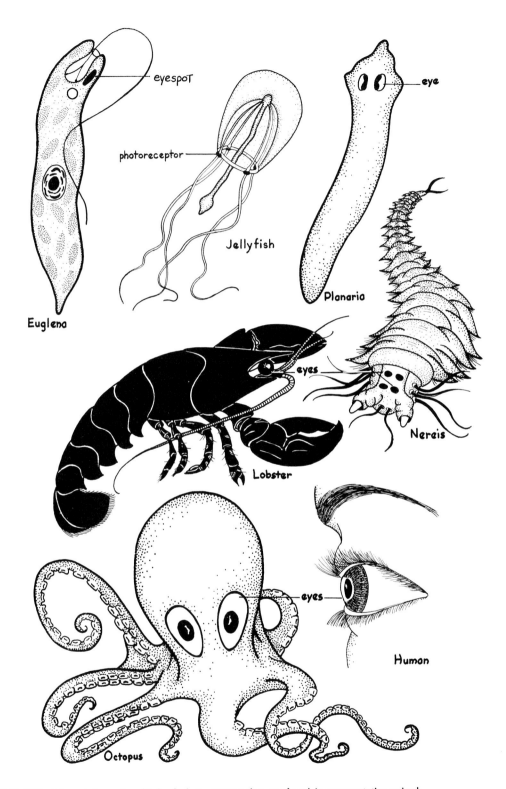

FIG. 17-3. A few of the various kinds of photoreceptors that are found in representative animals.

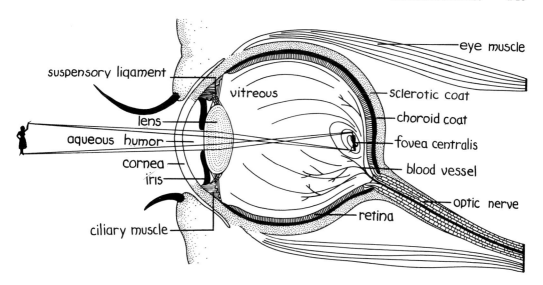

FIG. 17-4. A longitudinal section of the human eye to show its internal structure.

diminished in quantity but because the olfactory end-organs fail to be stimulated beyond a certain brief period. Just why this is so is not clearly understood at present.

Vision

This is the most perfect of the distance receptors. It provides us the means of keeping aware of our environment at small or great distances, whether reading this page or looking at the stars. This sense is the most important not only for man but for all primates, as well, and most of their information concerning their environment comes through this sense.

Nearly all animals from the simplest to the most complex are sensitive to light. Not that they all are sensitive to the same wave lengths that are recorded by the human eye, but nearly all have evolved some sort of receptor which is sensitive to light. It has been proved, for example, that the bee sees shorter light waves than we can see. Dogs, on the other hand, appear to be color blind. It is thus abundantly clear that different animals see, hear, smell, and so forth, quite differently from man. Indeed one must carefully avoid an anthropomorphic attitude with respect to all behavior.

Euglena orients itself with respect to light by means of the stigma (eyespot), and without this photosensitive organelle it would be unable to seek proper illumination necessary for photosynthesis (Fig. 17-3). The delicate jellyfish possesses photoreceptors that help orient it to light in the ocean. Planaria has rudimentary eyes which produce no images but detect direction. Nereis has a set of four eyes which may be superior to those of planaria. The lobster has excellent compound eyes, the details of which were discussed earlier. The octopus, as well as some of its relatives, possesses a remarkably perfect eye. Strangely enough, although it has evolved along an entirely different path, it resembles the vertebrate eye very closely in most respects. This is one of the very interesting cases of **convergent evolution,** where very similar organs have evolved along two entirely different routes (p. 768).

The Human Eye

Although there are some minor differences in the eyes of various vertebrates, the human eye will serve as representative of the group in our discussion (Fig. 17-4).

Whereas insect and bird eyes perform

some tasks better, the human eye in most respects is the most perfect photoreceptor that has evolved. It is extremely sensitive to light and registers color better than eyes of any other animal. It is first necessary to consider briefly the way light behaves before the function of the various parts of the eye, particularly the lens (see also p. 118), can be understood.

Light consists of small particles or corpuscles called photons, each of which has one quantum of energy. Light, therefore, can be measured in quanta. For example, the human eye can detect as little as 6 quanta of light which is equivalent to the light from a candle fourteen miles away. Light travels in straight lines at a speed of 186,000 miles per second in air, but it travels at different rates in other media such as water, glass, and transparent tissues such as the lens. Therefore, when light passes from one medium to another it bends (refracts). It is a familiar fact that when a stick lies at an angle partially in water, it appears bent. Actually, of course, the light is coming to the eye through two different media, water and air, and at different speeds, hence the bending at the juncture of the two media. Light coming through glass is bent in a similar fashion, and when the glass is shaped so that it is uniformly curved on both sides (convex lens) the rays of light are bent toward one another so that they come to a point, or **focus,** as it is called. The amount of bending increases with the increase in angle between the light ray and the surface of the glass. Therefore, a highly curved surface will bring the rays to focus at a very short distance **(focal length),** whereas a more flattened surface will bring them together at a greater distance. Depending on conditions, therefore, a lens is said to have a long or short focal length. Light comes from an infinite number of points on the object and passes through the lens with the result that the image is reversed. With this knowledge of light and convex lenses, let us study the human eye.

The remarkable similarity of a simple camera to the eye will help us to understand how we see (Fig. 17-5). Both have convex

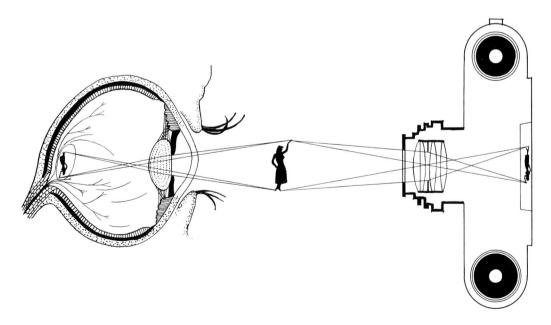

FIG. 17-5. A comparison of the camera and the human eye. Note the likenesses and differences. (For names of parts of the eye see Fig. 17-4.)

lenses which bring the rays of light to focus upon a sensitive plate, the film in the camera and the **retina** in the eye. The amount of light entering the chamber is controlled by the **iris diaphragm** in both cases. The housing is a lightproof case which allows the rays of light to pass through unobstructed; in the camera it is made of an adjustable tube or bellows and in the eye it is composed of a tough outer covering, the **sclera,** and a highly pigmented inner lining, the **choroid coat.** In the eye the space behind the lens is filled with a semiliquid substance, the **vitreous humor,** and the cavity in front of the lens is occupied by the **aqueous** (watery) **humor.** These maintain pressure within the eye and keep it from collapsing.

There are some very important differences between the camera and the eye. First of all, the film and the retina function differently. Once a picture is taken, the film is used up, that is, it must be replaced by another, whereas in the retina continuous series of pictures can be recorded without exhaustion of the sensitive cells. Secondly, the method of bringing objects at different distances into focus on the sensitive plate operates differently, although the end result is the same. In the camera the lens maintains one shape and must be moved forward and backward until the image is in focus on the film. In the eye, however, the lens itself changes its shape, becoming more curved for close objects and less curved for distant objects. This change in shape of the lens is called **accommodation.** Most of the light is brought to focus upon the retina by the **cornea;** only the slight differences that are needed to produce a sharp picture are accomplished by the lens itself. This slight variation, however, makes the difference between clear, sharp vision and poor, fuzzy sight. Accommodation is effected by the action of the **ciliary muscle,** located near the point of attachment of the **suspensory ligament** which supports the lens (Fig. 17-6). When this muscle contracts, pressure changes occur within the eyeball which cause the lens to become more curved, that is, thicker, which brings near objects into focus. When the muscle relaxes, the ligament tightens and the pressures are shifted so that the lens flattens out, causing distant objects to come to focus on the retina. Therefore, the ciliary muscle is active only when one is looking at close objects (under 30 feet), which is the reason why the eyes can be rested by looking out the window at a distant object.

The amount of light entering the eye is controlled by a sheet of circular muscular tissue, the **iris,** which contains the pigment granules responsible for eye color. Both radial and circular muscles are present in the iris and it is the antagonistic action of these muscles that do the job of enlarging or constricting the opening, the **pupil.** They are under the control of the autonomic nervous system and therefore beyond voluntary control. When the eye is exposed to bright light, the circular muscles contract, constricting the pupil, whereas in dim light the radial muscles contract, causing dilation of the pupil. Thus a delicate arrangement is provided to project just the right amount of light on the retina to obtain the best possible picture reception.

Exactly how light rays are transformed into the nerve impulses that pass over the optic nerve to the brain is not understood. The conversion from light energy to nerve energy takes place in the retina, which is composed of numerous cells, some of which are sensitive to light. These are the **rods** (sensitive to white light) and the **cones** (sensitive to colors) (Fig. 17-6). There are about 125,000,000 rods and 4,000,000 cones in the human retina. The cones are crowded around a central region, the **fovea centralis,** where visual acuity is most pronounced. Elsewhere in the retina the cones are mixed with the rods and vision is not so clear.

The retina is so arranged that the light must traverse the layers of neurons (ganglion and bipolar cells) before it reaches

FIG. 17-6. Accommodation is accomplished by changing the thickness and curvature of the lens. The amount of light entering the eye is controlled by the iris diaphragm. The image recording mechanism is the retina.

the sensitive rods and cones. The latter are functionally interconnected by synapses and all finally leave the eye through one place to form the **optic nerve.** At this point of exit the retina is interrupted so that no images can be formed here and is therefore called the **blind spot.** In order to see clearly, it is necessary to look directly at the object so that the image falls on the fovea— all other vision is peripheral and is less clear. The rods are more sensitive to light than the cones, and detection of weak light sources is best made when looking to one side of the source. Fliers search for beams at night with their peripheral rather than foveal vision.

It is well known that when light falls on the rods in the retina chemical change takes place which is the basis for light reception. The rod cells contain a photosensitive purplish-red pigment, **visual purple** (rhodopsin), which, when struck by light, is bleached by a photochemical reaction forming the compound **retinene,** a derivative of Vitamin A and the protein **opsin.** The important outcome of this reaction is that energy is released which stimulates a neuron setting up a nerve impulse to the brain (Fig. 17-7). Visual purple is restored by the recombining of retinene and opsin with the aid of ATP. Vitamin A is readily converted into retinene by reduction (loss

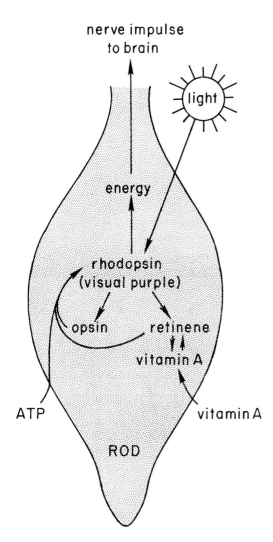

nerve impulse
to brain

light

energy

rhodopsin
(visual purple)

opsin   retinene

vitamin A

ATP   vitamin A

ROD

FIG. 17-7. The reactions that occur in a rod cell of the retina. See text for explanation.

pigment **iodopsin** of cone cells. It is known that cones in some reptiles and birds contain one of four different pigments: red, orange, yellow, and white. The pigment is in the form of a globule resting on the tip of the cone. All light passing through the globule is filtered out except that of the particular globule. The colored cones are distributed over the retina so that color images are possible. Color blindness may be a result of a reduction in certain of the cones. It is interesting to observe that chickens have mostly cones with very few rods in their retinas and therefore see poorly in dim light; this accounts for their habit of going to roost with the setting sun.

Eye Defects. The most common defects of the eye are caused by the inability of the focusing mechanism (cornea and lens) to form clear images on the retina. If the rays come to focus in front of the retina, the person suffers from **myopia,** or **nearsightedness;** if they come to focus behind the retina, the defect is known as **hyperopia** or **farsightedness** (Fig. 17-8). In order to correct these conditions it is only necessary to place in front of the eye a lens ground so that it bends the rays of light just enough to compensate for the defective focusing mechanism. In the case of nearsightedness a biconcave lens is needed, while in farsightedness a biconvex lens will bring about the proper correction. When either the cornea or lens is irregular in its curvature, the defect is called **astigmatism.** This can be corrected by using lenses that are ground in such a manner as to compensate for these variations in curvature.

Sometimes, as a result of disease or for other reasons, either or both the lens and the cornea may become fogged over so that vision is dimmed or completely obliterated. If the lens becomes fogged, it can be removed and a substitute lens placed in front of the eye in the form either of conventional glasses or of contact lenses which fit tightly against the eyeball. If the cornea

of H) of part of the molecule under the influence of an enzyme. Continued exposure to bright light sometimes causes visual purple to be bleached at a more rapid rate than it can be regenerated; if this occurs *snow blindness* results. A deficiency of Vitamin A may result in *night blindness,* that is, difficulty in seeing in dim light.

The exact nature of color vision is not well understood, although it is known that light brings about a chemical change in the clouds over it can be replaced by one from a normal eye, restoring the vision to normal. This is an extremely delicate operation but one that is becoming more and more common. People often "will" their corneas to others at the time of death; this custom is prevalent enough now that cornea "banks" have been established.

Hearing

Hearing is another sense that records stimuli coming from a distance. This is a convenient supplement to vision in that sound travels around corners and in the dark, two very important adjuncts in the problem of orientation. Nearly all groups of animals have some means of receiving water or air vibrations (Fig. 17-9). Underwater forms such as fish receive vibrations in the water and can, therefore, hear, although they possess none of the apparatus found in higher vertebrates that is used to receive and amplify sound. They do possess the inner ear structures that are essential for hearing. Apparently these can receive only vibrations set up in their own bodies. Air breathers, both vertebrate and invertebrate, have not only solved the problem of receiv-

ing air vibrations but also of setting up such vibrations. The katydid, for example, produces its chirp by rubbing its wings together, and the sound waves are received by special "ears" located on the tibias of the front legs. This form of communication serves in bringing the sexes together in mating and may also be important in notifying other members of the species of food sources.

When the vertebrates evolved onto land they, too, started to solve the problem of sound making and sound receiving in air, although fish not only received sounds in water but some even made sounds. The frog has a crude ear and emits a very simple sound. It is interesting to note that in providing for this change old structures, the gill arches, which now serve no special function, were employed in making the new organs. For example, the tips of the jaws and the hyoid arch which evolved earlier from gill arches became the **ear bones,** and some of the remaining gill arches became the **larynx** (voice box) as well as other elements of upper breathing system (Fig. 26-12). Strangely enough, those mammals that returned to the sea, such as the por-

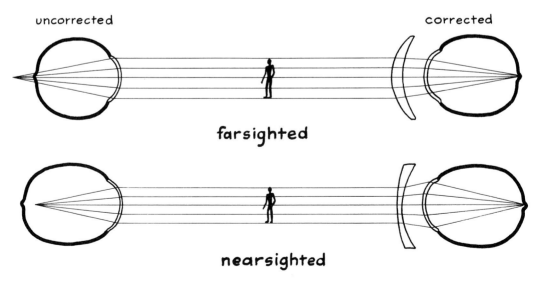

FIG. 17-8. Common human eye defects and how they are corrected with lenses (spectacles).

FIG. 17-9. Some animals and the manner in which they produce and receive vibrations in the air and water.

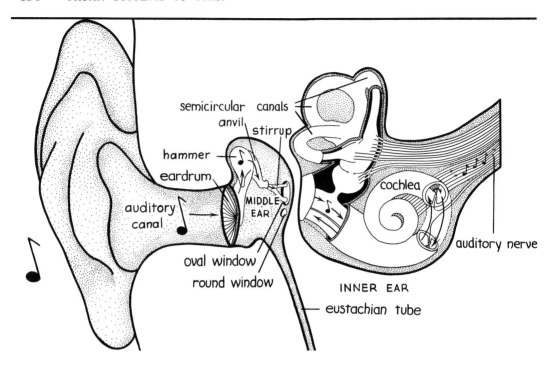

FIG. 17-10. The human ear dissected in order to show the various parts that have to do with receiving sound and the part that is concerned with balance.

poises, have retained excellent underwater hearing. They also produce a variety of sounds which are used to communicate with one another. In man, the production of sound has probably been carried to its greatest perfection, birds excepted, although the sound-receiving apparatus of some other vertebrates, such as the dog, has a greater range than the human ear.

Intimately associated with and usually considered as a part of the ear in the vertebrates is another organ that is physiologically quite separate from the sense of hearing. This is the organ of equilibrium, which is a receptor for changes in conditions of balance and rotation. In the invertebrates these two organs are quite unrelated. Organs of equilibrium are found in many invertebrates, from the jellyfish to the crayfish.

Among the lower vertebrates such as the sharks and skates both the hearing organ and the organ of balance are connected to the brain through the eighth cranial or auditory nerve. It is generally believed that hearing came later in evolution and merely took over a part of the eighth cranial nerve which had initially functioned only in conveying impulses from the organ of equilibrium. A discussion of the organ of equilibrium will be found in a later section (p. 459).

The Human Ear. The human ear is composed of three portions, the **outer,** or **pinna,** the **middle,** which connects with the throat by means of the **eustachian tube,** and the **inner,** where the **cochlea** (sound receptor) and **semicircular canals** are located (Fig. 17-10). The outer ear is merely a skin-covered, cartilaginous projection from the head, designed to catch and concentrate sound waves. It surrounds the opening which leads through the **auditory canal** and terminates at the **tympanum,** or **eardrum.** The walls of the canal are supplied with glands that produce wax which discourages small creatures such as insects from entering.

The middle ear consists of a chamber connected to the pharynx by the eustachian tube. Bridging across this air chamber is a series of three bones (ear ossicles) which conduct vibrations of the tympanum to the cochlea. Although the eustachian tube is advantageous in equalizing the pressure on both sides of the eardrum, it does have a disadvantage in that microorganisms in the mouth can make their way through this tube and infect the middle ear region. Such infections can be dangerous, sometimes leading to deafness. The tiny bones are named the hammer, anvil, and stirrup (malleus, incus, and stapes, respectively) because of their shapes. Together they produce a lever arm which diminishes the amplitude of the tympanic vibrations but at the same time intensifies them. The hammer is attached to the eardrum and the anvil, while the stirrup, attached to the anvil at its opposite end, fits into the oval window of the cochlea. Vibrations conducted through the chain of bones are conveyed to the liquid-filled cochlea. Another membrane-covered opening, the round window, allows the fluid to vibrate freely without being lost from the closed chambers. Since liquids do not compress, the vibrations retain all of their vigor until they are delivered to the sensory cells which generate impulses that are transmitted to the brain over the auditory nerve.

The highly complex cochlea can best be studied by uncoiling and cutting across it in order to examine its internal structures (Fig. 17-11). It is a long tapering tube which is divided into three chambers, all filled with fluid. The middle chamber contains the organ of Corti (named after its discoverer), which consists of a basilar membrane composed of tightly stretched connective tissue fibers which are longer at the top of the spiral and shorter at the larger or lower end. Above this membrane are the so-called hair cells which send out nerve fibers that make up a part of the auditory nerve. Overlying the hair cells is the tectorial membrane, a thin sheet of tissue, which lies very close to the tiny hairs projecting from the hair cells. There are other structures, too, which need not be considered in this discussion.

Sound is perceived when the fluid in the canals of the cochlea is set into vibration by the stirrup entering the oval window. It seems probable, although no one has seen it, that these vibrations set the basilar membrane into sympathetic undulations which cause the hair cells to touch the tectorial membrane, and that such touch stimuli set up impulses in the nerve fibers of the hair cells. The short fibers of the basilar membrane that lie at the large end of the cochlea respond to higher notes, whereas those at the top of the spiral are stimulated by the low notes. This can be borne out by experimentation. If an experimental animal is exposed to sound of high pitch and considerable amplitude (loudness) for a long period of time, the hair cells in the lower end of the cochlea are destroyed and the animal is deaf over this range. The same phenomenon has been observed in people suffering from the so-called boiler makers' disease where the constant din of a trip hammer over many years finally destroys that portion of the organ which records the same pitch as that of the hammer. It seems, then, that vibrations coming in stimulate various parts of the organ of Corti according to the frequency of the vibration (pitch). When vibrations of various pitches come in simultaneously the corresponding segments must be stimulated. This is quite remarkable when it is recalled how many different tones can be distinguished when listening to a symphony, for example.

Hearing Defects. The human ear can detect low and high tones ranging from about 20 to 16,000 vibrations per second. A young

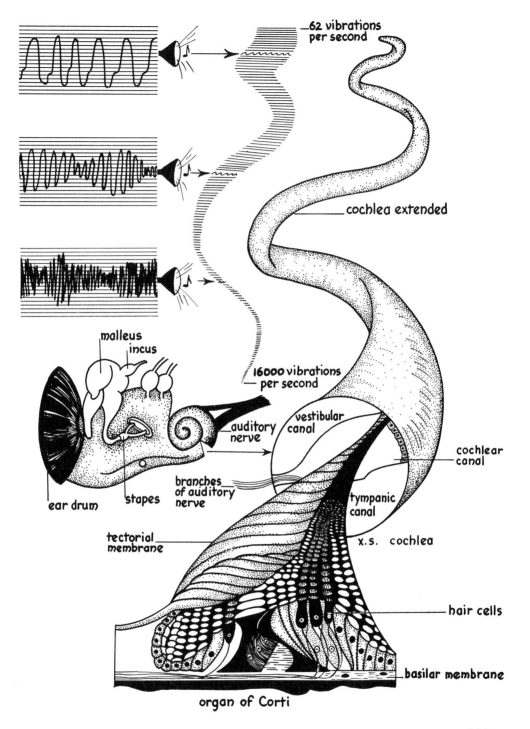

62 vibrations per second

cochlea extended

malleus
incus

16000 vibrations per second

vestibular canal

auditory nerve

cochlear canal

branches of auditory nerve

tympanic canal

ear drum

stapes

x.s. cochlea

tectorial membrane

hair cells

basilar membrane

organ of Corti

FIG. 17-11. The cochlea uncoiled and cut in cross-section to show the organ of Corti in detail. The parallel lines to the left indicate the wave lengths of the various notes and the approximate position in the cochlea where the organ of Corti picks them up.

child can hear even greater ranges, and some animals such as the dog and bat can hear vibrations considerably beyond those detected by the human ear. In man, the range diminishes in the upper limits with advancing years.

Deafness is usually caused either by faulty transmission of sound through the middle ear or by some difficulty in the cochlea, rarely by any deficiency in the central nervous system. One of the common causes of deafness is middle ear infections. Infectious bacteria can make their way up the eustachian tube to the middle ear where they can cause damage to the ear bones or drum. With the refinement of electronic equipment, hearing aids have gradually been perfected to a point where they are very useful to those who have imperfections in the transmitting portion of their ears. Obviously defects in the cochlea cannot be compensated for by hearing aids. These instruments merely amplify the tones so that sluggish or imperfect ear bones will, by sheer force of the vibrations, pick up and transmit them to the inner ear. Some very remarkable surgery of the ear bones, replacing one or more, in recent years has restored the hearing to many people.

Sense of Balance

There are three different organs which have to do with the sense of balance and movement. The eyes, when functioning, operate continually in this capacity. A second very important organ of equilibrium is a portion of the inner ear, the **nonacoustic labyrinth,** while the third organ is the system of **proprioceptors,** which are tiny sensory endings located in the muscles and tendons.

The nonacoustic labyrinth is composed of three **semicircular canals** and two small chambers, the **utriculus** and the **sacculus** (Fig. 17-12). In all vertebrates the inner ear includes the organ of equilibrium. The parts of the nonacoustic labyrinth operate differently. The semicircular canals function when change in rate or direction of movement of the head occurs, and the utriculus and sacculus have to do with the position of the head.

The three canals are semicircular tubes arranged at right angles to one another so that no matter how the head is moved, two of the canals (one in each ear) function. They are fluid-filled and each has a small swelling called the **ampulla** which houses a tuft of hair cells that are sensitive to the movement of the fluid. Any acceleration or deceleration of head movement causes the fluid to flow in definite directions in the canals, thus stimulating the hair cells to send impulses to the brain which results in the sensation of movement. When this occurs in a horizontal plane—the one people are accustomed to—no particularly unpleasant sensation results. However, if the head is moved in a vertical plane, such as in the abnormal movements of flying or riding in an elevator, some very unpleasant sensations are experienced; in fact, they may become so distasteful that nausea occurs, as in seasickness. Just why such movements should affect the stomach and bring about disagreeable feelings is not very clear. Fortunately, one can usually become accustomed to such movements so that eventually there is no more response to them than to horizontal movement.

Head position, that is, static position, is determined by the utriculus and sacculus. These two chambers are also filled with a fluid and, in addition, each contains a tiny lime pebble (the **otolith**) attached to the sensory hair cells. Since the otolith is free to move in the chamber, when the head changes its position the pull of gravity shifts the tiny weight so that the hairs are bent in synchrony with its movement (Fig. 17-12). This is very similar to the operation of the statocyst in the crayfish (p. 305). It is the perception of this movement that makes a person conscious of the position of the body with respect to gravity.

Not only is it important to register the

FIG. 17-12. The non-acoustic labyrinth with the sacculus and one of the semicircular canals cut in cross-section to show their internal structures. The lower figures indicate schematically how the otoliths aid in setting up stimuli coordinated with head movements.

position and movement of the body as a whole but, if coordination of all the complex movements is to be had, there must be some way of bringing about this interrelationship. This is done by the hundreds of **proprioceptors,** tiny sensory endings located in each muscle and tendon. These are sensitive to changes in tension. As the various muscles contract, proprioceptors send out impulses which eventually bring about an interplay of muscles and tendons to perform a coordinated act. This goes on without conscious knowledge and functions without vision, since, for example, a person is able to play a piano in the dark. It is necessary not only to know that a muscle is contracting but also to know where the appendage is at all times. In a way, the muscles can be considered sense organs because sensory impulses are coming from them almost as rapidly as motor impulses are going to them, though the cells involved in the two cases are different. The tendons are also abundantly supplied with proprioceptor end-organs but they receive no motor nerves and cannot contract.

It is because of the proprioceptors that one can judge weight. If a 24-pound weight is compared with a 25-pound weight, it is difficult to distinguish between them. There is no difficulty, however, in deciding that a 5-pound object weighs more than a 4-pound weight. In other words, one can determine the **relative differences** in weight; and the heavier the objects the greater must be the difference to be discernible. For example, in the illustration above, there is a one-pound difference between the two lighter objects which is a 20 per cent difference; in the heavier weights, although there is also a difference of one pound, the relative difference is 4 per cent. People show considerable variation in their ability to detect this difference, and this skill probably plays an important rôle in manual dexterity. Some people have great difficulty in using their hands effectively whereas others are very proficient in this regard. In select-

ing a life work such ability should be taken into consideration, and certain kinds of vocational aptitude tests are designed to determine this ability.

We must consider next the portion of the coordinating mechanism that adjusts incoming impulses. This is the central nervous system.

ADJUSTORS

The Nervous System

The brain together with its many ramifying nerves is most conspicuous even to the beginning student. Early anatomists, however, thought the brain was inert and could assign no function to it. Today the anatomy of the nervous system is well known, although how it functions is not completely understood.

In its evolution it might be expected that the nervous system originated from the external part of the body, because it is this part of the organism that contacts the outside world directly. Embryology and the history of the animal groups both bear this out. As animals became more complex, certain cells in the outside layer became specialized to receive and transmit stimuli. These cells became adapted to receiving stimuli and thus developed into the receptors or sense organs such as the eye and the ear. Transmission of the impulses was left to other cells which combined to form the **sensory nerves.** These, in turn, carried the impulses to a central station, the brain and spinal cord, where adjustment and interpretation took place. Another set, the **motor nerves,** carried the adjusted impulse to the glands and muscles where the final response was executed. With such a system it was possible for an animal to reach great size and complexity and still be intricately coordinated. The analogy of the centralized telephone system may be recalled to good advantage at this point.

It may seem surprising to learn that

this very complex system is composed of only one general kind of cell, the **neuron.** Here the telephone analogy breaks down, because, while the organization may be similar, the nature of the wire itself is vastly different from the neurons which go to make up the entire nervous system.

The Neuron. Although all cells may conduct an impulse within themselves, the neuron has developed this characteristic to an advanced stage. Anatomically the neuron is divided into three parts: the **cell body,** containing the nucleus, the **dendrites,** which consist of numerous protoplasmic outgrowths from the cell body, and the **axon,** a single, much longer extension terminating in a brush-like filament (Fig. 17-

13). The cell body resembles many other cells in appearance and the dendrites merely extend its surface of contact. The axons are usually covered with a fat-containing **myelin sheath** which is enveloped by a single layer of fat cells, called the **Schwann sheath.** Together they function like an electrical insulator. Only the Schwann sheath is found in nerve fibers of the autonomic nervous system. It has been postulated that the myelin sheath promotes conduction of the nerve impulse owing to its insulating properties. It has been shown that the nerve impulse travels about four times faster in myelinated nerves than in those without the myelin sheath.

Recent studies with the electron microscope indicate that the Schwann cell gives

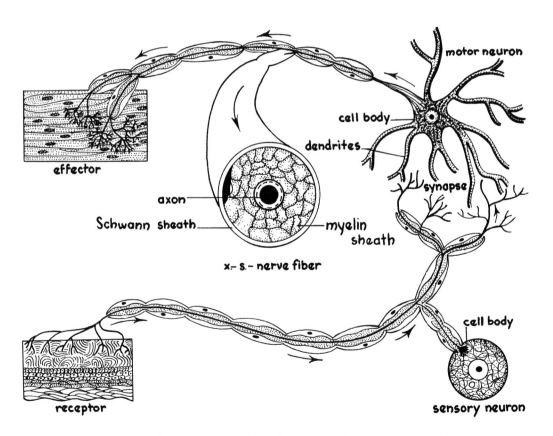

FIG. 17-13. Neurons, motor and sensory, with a myelinated nerve fiber shown in cross-section. The two neurons constitute a reflex arc.

rise to the myelin sheath by the elaboration of its outer membrane as indicated in Figure 17-14. It forms a tightly packed spiral around the axon. Unmyelinated axons, while embedded in Schwann cells, do not possess the elongated spiraled membranes.

The Schwann sheath functions in nourishing the nerve fiber and brings about its regeneration in case of injury. If the axon is severed the distal part from the cell body degenerates. If, however, the Schwann sheath remains intact and heals, a new axon will replace the degenerated one. If the laceration is so severe as to make the healing of the Schwann sheath impossible subsequent regeneration will be disoriented and the sheath will probably never innervate the cells as it originally did. Occasionally this can be corrected by rerouting the Schwann sheaths by surgery.

The axons are usually long. An extreme example is illustrated by the giraffe, in which the axons extend from the tip of the toe to the back, a distance of 6 feet or more. Many axons are bound together to form the nerve trunk, spoken of as the "nerve" by anatomists, which is covered by a tough sheet of tissue. This is remarkably similar to a telephone cable where each wire is insulated from all the others.

There are several major kinds of neurons located in specific parts of the nervous system. In the brain and cord they are highly specialized and occur only in certain locations. These neurons are called **association neurons,** and they function in connecting various parts of the brain and cord. Those that conduct impulses from the distal parts of the body **to** the brain or cord are called **sensory** or **afferent** neurons and those that conduct the impulses **away** from the brain and cord are called **motor** or **efferent** neurons. Some nerve trunks are composed entirely of one or the other, in which case they are called **sensory** or **motor nerves.** Most, however, carry both kinds of fibers and are called **mixed nerves.** In the

vertebrates the cytons for the sensory neurons lie on each spinal nerve in a swelling, the **dorsal root ganglion,** just outside the cord, whereas those for the motor neurons lie within the cord itself in a region that is grayish in color (Fig. 17-18).

In order for a nerve impulse to complete its circuit, it must pass over more than one neuron; in fact, a great many are probably involved even in the most simple action. Neurons are not directly connected with each other but come in close association only. The region or area where the dendrite of one neuron is in close proximity

FIG. 17-14. Schematic representation of the nerve fiber as seen through the electron microscope. See text for explanation.

with the axon of another is known as the **synapse** (Fig. 17-13). This is a very important part of the nervous system because it is here that a selection is made as to whether or not an impulse is permitted to pass on to the next neuron. The impulse can travel both ways within a neuron but where the neurons are in a series, as they always are, the impulse travels **toward** the cell body on the dendrites and **away** from it on the axon. The synapse, therefore, acts like a traffic signal on a one-way street.

Electron micrographs of the synapse show numerous vesicles and mitochondria in the axon where it comes in close proximity (200 Å) with the dendrite which has

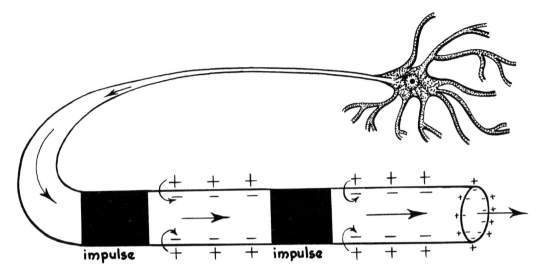

FIG. 17-15. The nerve is normally polarized, being positively charged on the outside and negatively charged on the inside. This polarity is lost coincident with the nerve impulse (indicated in black).

very few of these particles. The current view regarding these vesicles is that they contain a transmitter substance (p. 480) which may pass from axon to dendrite facilitating the one-way transmission of the nerve impulse.

Nature of the Nerve Impulse. Up to the present time, attempts to solve the nature of the nerve impulse have been made only with peripheral nerves, that is, those outside the cord and brain. Very little progress has been made toward an understanding of how they work within the brain itself, though there is no reason to doubt that in a general way the functioning is similar.

Once an impulse passes over a nerve fiber there is a short period when the nerve is incapable of transmitting a second impulse, that is, it refuses to accept any further stimulus. This is known as the **refractory period** and is very short in most nerve fibers, lasting 0.001 to 0.005 second. It means that some reorganization is essential before the nerve fiber can once again be stimulated. This, in turn, is due to the physical make-up of the nerve fiber itself. The outside membrane of the nerve fiber

is positively charged while the inside is negatively charged (Fig. 17-15), and is therefore said to be **polarized.** This condition is maintained until an impulse passes along which brings about a chemical change; this results in the mixing of the charged ions through the outer permeable membrane, and in the membrane becoming **depolarized** or neutral in the region of the impulse. It is known that the change is chemical as well as electrical because the nerve fiber consumes oxygen and gives off carbon dioxide, respiring just as all cells do. The depolarized condition is coincident with the refractory period and therefore lasts a very short time. Impulses pass along a nerve in rapid succession and it is highly unlikely that a single impulse brings about a specific action. Impulses come in "bursts" like bullets from a machine gun.

The fact that the nervous impulse continues throughout its course with equal vigor indicates that something is added to it as it travels. It might be compared to a path of inflammable material where each portion ignites the succeeding part so that the entire trail burns with equal intensity. A minimum amount of heat must be supplied for ignition, but once ignited the flame burns with equal vigor from the point of ignition forward. Furthermore, any excess heat beyond the minimum necessary to ignite the material will not change the situation. It is likewise with a neuron; once stimulated, the impulse travels with equal intensity throughout the course of the cell. The neuron, like the muscle cell, obeys the "all or none" principle. In other words, if a given stimulus elicits an impulse, the impulse starts and continues throughout its course with full vigor. No matter how the minimum stimulus is altered, the impulse travels with its full force or it does not travel at all.

The simplest way to study the nerve impulse is to observe the action of a muscle to which it is attached. The classic setup for such study is the sciatic nerve of the frog attached to the large gastrocnemius (calf) muscle and a mechanical device for recording the contraction of the muscle (Fig. 16-12). Various stimuli can be used to stimulate the nerve, but an electrical one is the best and most convenient. Whenever the nerve is stimulated the muscle twitches, indicating that some change set up in the nerve has traveled along the nerve to the muscle, causing it to contract. This change is called the **nerve impulse.**

If a special instrument designed to detect minute electrical currents is placed on a nerve over which an impulse passes, there will be a definite response, indicating that the impulse has an electrical aspect (Fig. 17-16). If it were electricity, it would travel with the speed of electricity, namely, 186,-000 miles per second. An early experiment, however, demonstrated that the impulse travels at a much slower speed, 30 meters, or about 100 feet, per second in the frog and only four times that rate in man. The nature of stimulation bears no relation to the speed of transmission and whether the nerve is stimulated with heat, pressure, or electricity the impulse travels at exactly the same speed. Furthermore, once the im-

FIG. 17-16. Electrical changes occur in a nerve when an impulse passes over it (A to E) as indicated by the deflection of the galvanometer needle. Similar changes occur in a contracting muscle.

pulse is started it continues with equal vigor throughout its course, unlike electricity which as it travels along a wire gradually diminishes in intensity the farther it goes.

So far, consideration has been given only to the transmission of the impulses within the neuron itself. How does the impulse travel between nerve cells and from nerve cells to muscle cells? It has already been suggested that the gap is traversed by chemical means. This will be discussed under the autonomic system.

Divisions of the Nervous System. In an attempt to understand some of the more simple reactions effected through the nervous system, it is useful to divide it into parts, all of which, however, are very interdependent. The **central nervous system** is composed of the brain and cord while the **peripheral** system is made up of the nerves which connect the brain and cord to all parts of the body. Impulses enter the central nervous system through the afferent fibers of the peripheral nerves. Interpreting the incoming messages and subsequently dispatching them is the function of the brain, the cord acting primarily as a relay. The impulses leave the brain and cord for the muscles and glands on the efferent fibers. The simplest type of this action involving the peripheral and central nervous system is called a **reflex.**

The Cord and Reflex Action. Every person has experienced the operation of a simple reflex in his own body, as, for example, the quick withdrawal of his bare foot when it encounters a sharp object. It is difficult to determine whether the foot was removed after or just prior to the sensation of pain. A simple experiment with a frog can show that the reaction could have taken place without the sensation of pain. If the brain is removed and the skin irritated with acetic acid, the frog will withdraw its foot by appropriate leg movements (Fig. 17-17). The stimulus can be repeated again and again

but the response will always be the same. Remember, there is no brain to interpret the message, yet the response is just as effective as if the brain had been intact. Similarly, people with certain regions of their cord injured feel no pain though they respond to the stimulus. It is apparent in these cases that the impulse from the stimulus must have traveled only to the cord, returning from it to the appropriate muscles for bringing about that response. Various portions of a frog's cord can be destroyed, but the reflex will persist as long as the region where the sensory and motor nerves join the cord is intact. The complete action, then, must take place in a very localized region.

In order to understand how a reflex can take place, a little information about the anatomy of the cord is in order. A spinal nerve bifurcates as it approaches the cord to enter on the dorsal side as the **dorsal root** (sensory) and on the ventral side as the **ventral root** (motor) (Fig. 17-18). The dorsal root bears the **dorsal root ganglion,** in which the cell bodies of the sensory neurons are located. The cell bodies of the motor nerves are located in the ventral gray matter of the cord (called the **ventral horn**). The function of these roots can be definitely identified by cutting them and artificially stimulating the stumps. When the ventral root is cut, no impulses reach the muscle from the cord, but when the cut end on the muscle side is stimulated a response will be evoked. Likewise, by severing the dorsal root no impulses will reach the cord, but when the stump on the cord side is stimulated a response will take place. The dorsal root thus contains only sensory fibers and the ventral root only motor fibers. The spinal nerve, which is a union of the two, contains both, of course.

A simple reflex begins with an impulse coming from a sense organ and traveling over an afferent nerve fiber to the cord via the dorsal root (Fig. 17-18). Here it comes in close contact (synapse) with one

FIG. 17-17. The frog has had the cerebrum removed by a cut just back of the eyes. The cord is intact. Acetic acid has just been brushed on the thigh of the right leg (left). The right leg flexes and the toes scratch the region which is irritated by the acid (right).

or more association neurons. The impulse is then dispatched to the proper muscle or gland over an efferent nerve fiber via the ventral root. With few exceptions reflexes involve more than the three neurons just described. The incoming sensory neuron usually connects with more than one motor neuron through association neurons in the cord. Thus the impulse may not only elicit the simple response but may also pass along the cord to stimulate other efferent neurons and in turn cause a large group of muscles to contract. Indeed, this is the manner in which it usually happens. When applied to man, the simple reflex accounts for many of our daily movements. These actions do

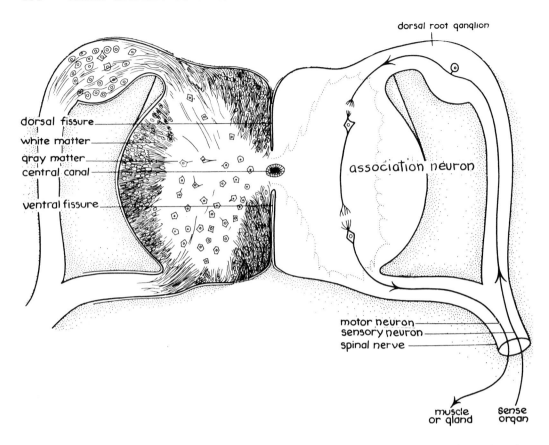

FIG. 17-18. A schematic view of the spinal cord in cross-section. The arrangement of the nerve cells is indicated on the left and the simple reflex pathway on the right.

not have to be learned, they are innate—one is born with them.

Not only are different levels of the cord involved but also neurons on the opposite side of the cord. There is a crossing over of the association neurons so that an impulse may travel to both sides of the body (Fig. 17-19). If, for example, acetic acid is applied to one side of the ventral surface of a frog whose brain is destroyed, the leg on that particular side will attempt to remove the irritating acid while the leg on the opposite side will extend (Fig. 17-17). Presently, the impulse will spread to the front legs so that eventually all of the legs are moving in such a manner as to rid the animal of the offending substance, and the body also begins to make mass movements

as it would in attempting to crawl away from the irritation. To be sure, the first pathway is simple, but as the stimulus spreads many other pathways are involved until the whole animal is thrown into movement. Under these conditions the higher centers also are involved (Fig. 17-19).

In man, when the various parts of the brain are included, the impulse becomes a part of consciousness and one is aware of the reflex. When one steps on something sharp, for example, his foot may be withdrawn through simple reflex, but very shortly certain parts of the brain are involved, even to the cortex where reasoning and memory are possible. He may even consider the advisability of wearing shoes, or the injury may be sufficiently severe that

FIG. 17-19. A series of sketches showing the nerve pathways in the cord and brain. The lower and middle figures show those where only the cord is involved while the upper figure indicates the pathways to and from the brain.

he will remember the event for a long time.

It seems that the impulses usually travel over certain paths but these can be altered on a moment's notice and new paths are then followed. In other words, many conditions can determine the pathway over which an impulse may travel. There are many choices; which it chooses depends on a large variety of circumstances.

An illustration of how the reflex may be interrupted may be seen in the sneeze reflex. Sneezing is caused by a stimulus originating in the nasal chambers; its ultimate fruition is an explosive expulsion of air through these chambers to dislodge the irritation. If, when the sneeze sensation begins, a second stimulation is set up by producing pressure on the upper lip, the first pathway will be blocked. In other words, a new set of conditions blocked the original reflex pathway. Neurologists believed at one time that certain pathways were set up not only in the cord but in the brain as well, and that each pathway was traversed by the impulse in exactly the same manner, thus making it "deeper" until it was well established. There seems to be no evidence for this idea, and it is now well known that the impulse may travel over different pathways and may never take the same course twice. Furthermore, pathways may be employed by different reflexes at different times. Which specific pathways are followed, and why, is one of the most important problems in neurology today.

Brain. This part of the nervous system is the most complex and, of course, the most difficult to understand. Recalling our present scanty knowledge about how the brain functions, one is inclined to doubt the probability of ever understanding it, but to accept such an attitude would be highly unscientific. A great German scientist once said that the speed of the nerve impulse would never be measured, and yet, just six years later, another scientist measured it very accurately; today any beginning student in physiology can duplicate the experiment with good precision. Such statements of finality are dangerous, especially for a scientist.

Nerve impulses come to the brain from all over the body on **afferent** nerve fibers like messages coming to the admiral of a fleet. Just as the admiral must make decisions that will be sent by messages to various parts of the fleet in order to accomplish a certain goal, likewise decisions are made in the brain and impulses are sent out over **efferent** nerve fibers to various parts of the body in order to execute certain actions. Decisions are made for the most part in a routine manner, based on inherited principles or on experience gained through having made similar decisions before. Most of the decisions are made by the brain without breaking through to consciousness, so that one is not aware of most of its activity. This great center is indispensable to the harmonious working of the entire body. Aberrations in the brain, so slight that they cannot be detected by any physical change, produce such stark changes in personality and emotional stability that our society is forced to build special institutions such as prisons and asylums to house people so afflicted.

For a better understanding of the human brain it is best to start with a lower vertebrate type brain, which is relatively simple in structure, and follow through to higher forms. In the discussion of invertebrates it was shown that the obvious location for the brain is in the animal's anterior end, which is the part that arrives in any new environment first. Among vertebrates the brain likewise has its beginnings and its subsequent development in the anterior end of the organism, and as we progress from fishes to mammals (Fig. 17-21) it becomes increasingly prominent.

The three major regions of the brain, **forebrain, midbrain,** and **hindbrain,** are clearly marked off very early in the embryonic development of every vertebrate (Fig.

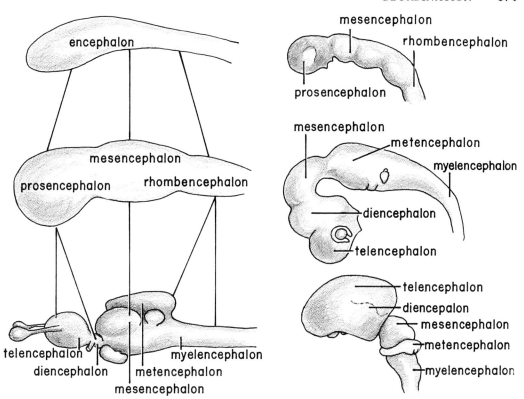

FIG. 17-20. The vertebrate brain begins as a hollow sac which subsequently divides first into three distinct regions and later into the many parts shown (left). The embryology of the human brain parallels that of other vertebrates as shown by the series of figures to the right.

17-20). These three regions soon subdivide into five regions. The forebrain becomes the **telencephalon** and **diencephalon,** the midbrain remains undivided and is known as the **mesencephalon,** and the hindbrain divides to form the **metencephalon** and **myelencephalon.** Each of these becomes modified and develops other parts as the brain becomes more complex in higher animals. In the human brain the **cerebrum** comes from the telencephalon, the posterior lobe of the **pituitary** (an endocrine gland) and the **optic chiasma** from the diencephalon, the **corpora quadrigemina** from the mesencephalon, the **cerebellum** and **pons** from the metencephalon, and the **medulla oblongata** from the myelencephalon. There is a clear relationship between the size of a particular part of the brain of an animal

and its importance in the life of the animal. Detecting odors is one of the most important abilities possessed by fish and frogs, who also have proportionately large olfactory lobes; whereas in birds, where the sense of smell is poorly developed, this part of the brain is proportionately small (Fig. 17-21). In the lowest vertebrates the cerebrum is nonexistent, or almost so, whereas in the birds it begins to dominate the anterior end of the brain and in mammals it overgrows all other parts to become the most prominent part. In man, this trend is carried to the most extreme point of development.

Elaboration of various parts of the brain seems to be associated with the kind of life its owner leads. The part of the brain that controls muscular coordination is the

FIG. 17-21. The relative sizes of the various parts of the brains of different vertebrates vary according to activity. Animals that fly or swim have better muscular coordination than do those on land, hence their cerebellums (solid black) are proportionately large. Likewise a well-developed cerebrum (stippled) is essential to mammals, hence this part of their brain is best developed.

FIG. 17-22. The anterior portion of the head, which includes the cerebrum, has been cut away in this frog. When placed in water it swims in a normal fashion, indicating that this portion of the brain has little, if any, function in performing this act.

cerebellum, which is large in animals that move in three dimensions, such as birds and fish (Fig. 17-21). Amphibians, reptiles, and land dwelling mammals (mouse and man), on the other hand, confine their movements for the most part to two dimensions and by comparison their cerebellums are proportionately smaller than those of animals moving in three dimensions.

The cord takes care of the simplest activities in the organism, and that part of the brain which lies at its anterior end, the **medulla oblongata,** is the center for the activity of such vital organs as those of breathing and transportation. Even in man, both the cord and medulla function in much the same manner as they do in lower vertebrates. The cerebellum functions in muscular coordination, particularly during highly complex movements, and the cortex of the cerebrum, which evolved last, is the center of such highly complex activities as thought and reasoning.

As the vertebrate brain evolved, there was a gradual shift of function from the lower part, the brain stem, to the higher part, the cortex. This shift can be demonstrated experimentally. When the cerebrum of a frog is removed, its normal activities are influenced only slightly. It jumps normally when stimulated and it can swim in a perfectly normal fashion (Fig. 17-22). Even a "decerebrated" reptile shows very little concern about its loss. Such an operation on a bird or mammal, however, brings about striking changes. The ability to locomote is destroyed and all actions which require considerable muscular coordination are lost. This simply means that the higher vertebrates have shifted their nerve centers from the lower brain stem to the cerebral cortex.

This shift has given these higher forms much greater plasticity in the control of their muscle coordination. For example, when certain muscles in man have lost their nervous connection with the brain in the disease known as facial paralysis, functional cranial nerves passing to relatively weak and less useful muscles can be transplanted to the larger more important muscles and eventually become functional through long retraining. In other words, impulses can be sent to a muscle via a wholly new nerve with the result that the muscle can eventually respond in its usual manner. In man, the cortex so completely dominates the body that it is physiologically possible by intense effort to learn to move muscles in almost any manner. This is well illustrated by the many human feats performed, activities that could never be executed by other animals because their nervous systems are constructed in such a way as to make it impossible. This shift of control to the cortex accounts for man's great versatility and is one of the major reasons for his success. It has also made possible the development of our type of society.

As the cerebrum increased in size in reptiles, birds, and mammals, it became necessary to increase the surface area while retaining a reasonable volume. This has been done by the formation of wrinkles or **convolutions.** Starting in the lower mammals with only very few convolutions, the number and extent of these increase as the brain increases in size, reaching a maximum in man. Naturally, as the cortex has increased in size, the entire brain has increased with respect to the cord. The relative weights of these two structures for several common animals are shown in the following figures:

	Ratio of Weight of Cord	Weight of Brain
Frog	1.0	1.0
Cat	1.0	4.0
Monkey	1.0	15.0
Man	1.0	55.0

In general, the size of the brain is an indication of intelligence, although there are some notable exceptions; for instance, the brain of both the whale and elephant weighs more than that of man. Dogs, gorillas, and men of approximately the same body weights have brain weights of about 140, 450, and 1,350 grams, respectively. Within limits of normal variation in a single species, brain size does not indicate intelligence. For example, woman generally possesses a brain which averages about 100 grams less than man, but what man would be so brave as to imply that she is less intelligent! Likewise, there is a wide variation in the size of brains of different individuals of the same sex, just as there is in stature and body weights. Famous brains have been preserved and weighed, out of morbid curiosity or for scientific purposes, and it has been shown that a variation of 800 grams exists between brains of apparent equal intelligence. So, within limits, brain size alone is not a criterion of intelligence. Intelligence is probably due to such things as the number of cell bodies or the number of association neurons in the cortex of the cerebrum which, in turn, is an indication of the number of pathways over which impulses may travel.

The two cerebral hemispheres are each divided into five lobes, and the nerve cells associated with various functions are localized in these lobes (Fig. 17-23). The center for sight is located in the **occipital** or posterior lobe. Areas for smell, hearing, and taste are located in the lateral or **temporal** lobe, while centers for muscle movements are centered in the anterior or **frontal** lobe. Skin sensations lie in the **parietal** lobe. The fifth lobe (**insula**) lies beneath the frontal and parietal lobes and cannot be seen from the surface view. Large areas of the cortex are spoken of as "silent areas" because it appears that injuries to these regions result in no particular loss of sensory or motor function. These are the great unknown areas of the brain which have stimulated so much research in recent years.

The complex life human beings live in modern society has produced intricate mental "patterns" in man's cerebral cortex, and in a so-called normal person these pat-

FIG. 17-23. Localized brain areas are concerned with special functions.

terns are satisfactory for the solution of day-to-day problems. There are no physical patterns that can be detected by examining the brain, merely repeatable cortical activity. In certain instances various aberrations in behavior indicate severe mental disturbance. It has been found that by subjecting certain people in specific instances to severe shock by means of insulin, electricity, and other agents, these abnormal responses can sometimes be corrected. More recently certain drugs, such as reserpine and its derivatives, have been useful in the treatment of certain types of mental diseases.

The medical profession is learning that more and more of the common ailments of mankind are due to an overactive cerebral cortex rather than actual organic disease; that is, people imagine they are sick, and this can be carried so far that actual symptoms from heart disease to stomach ulcers occur. This has resulted in a new field of medical research known as **psychosomatic**

medicine. With proper treatment, certain neurotic tendencies can be overcome and the person miraculously "cured." This type of medical research is commanding increasing attention and holds hope for a different approach to the study of certain diseases.

The Autonomic Nervous System

A great many activities of the body such as peristaltic movement in the intestines, breathing, and heart action go on unnoticed and without voluntary control. These are all under the influence of the so-called **autonomic nervous system.** The name implies that the system is a completely automatic one, which is not the case, but it has become fixed by usage.

Anatomically, part of the autonomic nervous system can be seen as two rows of ganglia (lateral sympathetic ganglia) lying on each side of the spinal column in the thoracic and abdominal cavities (Fig. 17-24). The ganglia are secured to the spinal

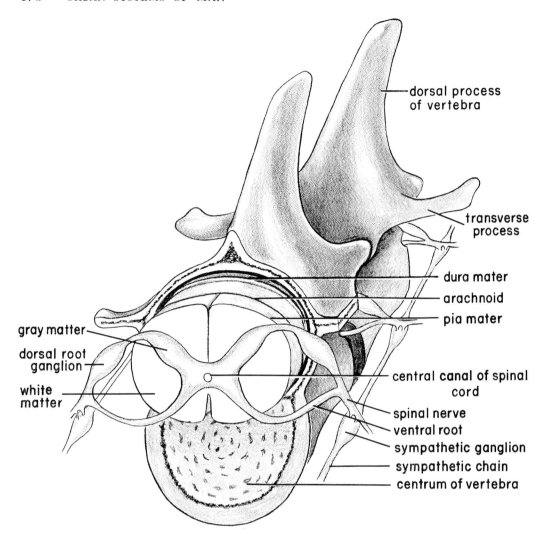

dorsal process
of vertebra

transverse
process

dura mater

arachnoid

pia mater

gray matter

dorsal root
ganglion

white
matter

central canal of spinal
cord

spinal nerve

ventral root

sympathetic ganglion

sympathetic chain

centrum of vertebra

FIG. 17-24. The spinal column with nerve cord and associated nerves. Note how well these delicate structures are protected from possible injury.

nerves by means of two short connectives, a **white** and a **gray ramus** (Fig. 17-25). Distally they extend as small nerve fibers to the various organs of the chest and abdominal regions. The incoming (afferent) fibers pass through the dorsal root just the same as the voluntary nerve fibers, and the cell bodies are located in the dorsal root ganglion. The notable difference between the two systems is that the efferent fibers of the autonomic system have a chain of at least **two neurons** between the central nervous system and the organ innervated, whereas in the voluntary system there is but one. The latter also has a myelin sheath, whereas the former has only the Schwann sheath (p. 463).

The first autonomic cell bodies of the efferent neurons lie in the lateral portion of the gray matter of the cord, while the second neuron cell bodies lie outside of the cord in the ganglia already mentioned; sometimes the second ganglia lie directly on the organ itself some distance from the sympathetic chain. The second neuron may return to the ventral root and pass along with the spinal nerve fibers to such parts of the body as the blood vessels of the skin and sweat glands which are under the control of the autonomic nervous system. Others may pass through to a large ganglion (**collateral sympathetic ganglion**) outside the sympathetic chain where synapsis occurs with the second neuron. Fibers leading from the central nervous system to the ganglia outside the cord are called **preganglionic fibers,** those leaving the ganglion, the **postganglionic fibers.** Such a system of fibers makes it possible for stimuli to come from the internal organs and to effect a response elsewhere in the body. For example, an impulse can come from the stomach (Fig. 17-25), causing some action to occur

in the duodenum, initiating a peristaltic wave, perhaps. Moreover, pain impulses might come from the stomach which, by the intermingling of the two systems (central and autonomic), project through to the cerebral cortex where they are registered as an uncomfortable feeling about which something might be done. Likewise, impulses might arise in the temperature end-organs of a too warm skin and pass through the circuits (Fig. 17-25) giving rise to efferent impulses that cause the sweat glands to pour their secretion over the skin, and thus cool the body. Thousands of these pathways are continually carrying messages to and from parts of the body, most of them unknown to the owner.

The autonomic nervous system is divided into two rather distinct parts: the

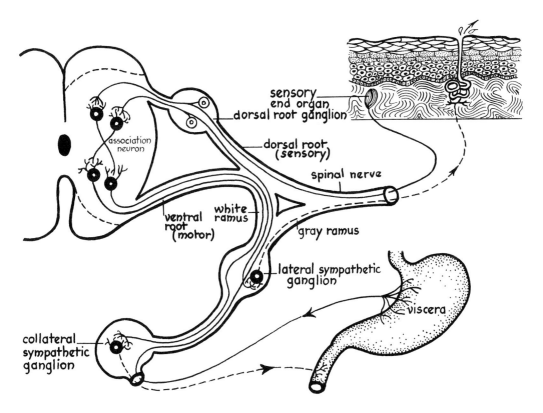

FIG. 17-25. A schematic drawing of the nerve pathways involving both the autonomic and the central nervous systems. Impulses arising from a temperature sense organ in the skin can stimulate sweating. Also impulses arising from the stomach can cause some action in other parts of the viscera. Dashed lines indicate the postganglionic fibers.

FIG. 17-26. A schematic drawing of the sympathetic and parasympathetic nervous systems, separated for clarity, to show how they function. Note that each organ is supplied with nerves that cause it to be activated or inhibited.

thoracolumbar (sympathetic) which is composed of the double chain of ganglia already noted; and the craniosacral (parasympathetic) which originates in the posterior portion of the brain (midbrain and medulla) and the sacral region (Fig. 17-26). The thoracolumbar system has short preganglionic fibers and generally long postganglionic ones. The opposite is true of the craniosacral system, and in fact, the ganglia lie in some cases, such as the heart, embedded within the organ itself. These two systems send nerve fibers to all of the organs operating involuntarily so that each has a double innervation. However, the two systems produce opposite effects. For example, if the nerve from the thoracolumbar system to the heart is stimulated, the beat is accelerated; but if the nerve from the craniosacral system is stimulated, the beat is slowed down. Stimulation of one nerve may cause excitation in one organ and inhibition in another, thus stimulation of the vagus (craniosacral) inhibits the heart but excites the stomach. The value of such a mechanism is obvious. It is the interaction of these two systems that regulates the flow of blood to various parts of the body, differing with each condition in which the animal finds itself. It also causes the pupil of the eye to dilate or constrict, depending on the amount of light that is needed for vision. These and hundreds of other routine jobs the body does quietly and efficiently and entirely without the knowledge of the owner. This system has certainly taken the drudgery out of operating the body, and has left for the higher centers the job of getting the whole organism in a position to obtain food or to do the many other things that are essential for life. If the central nervous system were burdened with the job of operating this machinery, little else could be done. It would be like requiring the President of the country to see that the proper amount of water flows through a certain aqueduct in New York City.

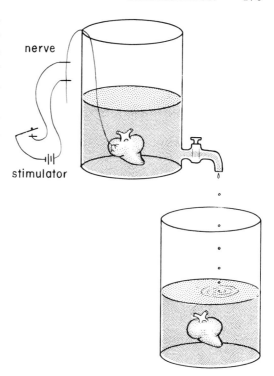

FIG. 17-27. A schematic representation of Loewi's classical experiment in which he demonstrated that when the vagus nerve was stimulated in one frog heart, the other was inhibited even though the only connection between the two was by a saline solution.

The puzzling question of why impulses arriving in an organ via either part of the autonomic system cause acceleration or inhibition even though the nerves appear to be identical, was cleared up by some ingenious experiments performed by Loewi in 1921. He removed the hearts of two frogs, leaving the nerve supply intact on one of them, and then placing them in a salt solution in separate containers (Fig. 17-27). He then stimulated the vagus (parasympathetic fibers) nerve of one and permitted the salt solution to perfuse through the other. The rate of beat slowed down in both hearts. He then stimulated the sympathetic fibers and the rate of both increased. Obviously some substance was being released by nerves of the first heart and was having the same effect on the second heart. Further investigations demonstrated that two substances, called **neurohumors,** were produced. The parasympathetic system secretes **acetylcholine** and the sympathetic system secretes **sympathin.** Thus, in order to complete the mission of delivering a message to a muscle or gland, a physical and a chemical action must take place. It is also believed that acetylcholine plays a role in transmitting the impulse across the synapses in other parts of the nervous system, and perhaps in the transmission of the impulse along the neuron. An enzyme known as **acetylcholinesterase** is always present, which neutralizes acetylcholine thus preventing cumulative effects which would be disastrous. The action of sympathin is much like that of epinephrine, the endocrine secretion from the medullary portion of the adrenal gland. Indeed, these cells are themselves modified postganglionic sympathetic fibers. There seems to be no inhibitor for sympathin and it must be destroyed by oxidation some time after it is formed. Its slow destruction may account for the slow and sustained response of this part of the autonomic system.

The discovery of specific neurohumors in the autonomic nervous system that bridge the gap between nerve endings and muscle has naturally led scientists to postulate that perhaps the same mechanism causes the bridging of the gaps between neurons in the central nervous system. Impulses passing to the synapse differ in both frequency and duration from those leaving the synapse, which would indicate that something happens to them as they pass through the gap. Not only is there a delay in the transmission of the impulse as it passes through the synapse, but something happens in this junction which allows the impulse to cross it in only one direction. These characteristics of the synapse may indicate that the neurohumoral explanation is the correct one, although there is more work to be done on the problem before this can be stated positively.

EFFECTORS—THE ORGANS OF RESPONSE

The principal effector organs of higher animals are the **muscles** and **glands,** although there are other types of effectors in use throughout the living world. For example, there are **chromatophores,** found in a large group of vertebrates and invertebrates, that are responsible for rapid color change in the skin. Some animals possess **luminous organs** which radiate light when stimulated and still a few others possess **electric organs** that generate electrical discharges under suitable conditions. Each of these effectors will be discussed briefly with the exception of the muscles which have been treated rather thoroughly in Chapter 16.

Glands

Skin glands have already been discussed (Chapter 16), but there are other glands in the body which are stimulated directly by the nervous system. Just how a gland cell secretes is not well understood. Its job is to extract the product of secretion from the blood or lymph on one side and discharge it on the other into a lumen or tube that conducts the product to its proper place, either to the outside of the body, in the case of sweat glands, or into the digestive tract, in the case of digestive glands (Fig. 17-28). In such glands as sweat and tear glands no special substances are synthesized; their secretion is merely extracted directly from the blood. However, in the case of many other glands, the digestive and endocrine glands for example, while the raw materials are extracted from the blood stream, the final product is synthesized within the cell itself. Suggestions as to how this is accomplished were discussed earlier (p. 101).

Glands respond to stimuli from the nervous system and most of them secrete only when stimulated. Some endocrine glands, however, apparently secrete con-

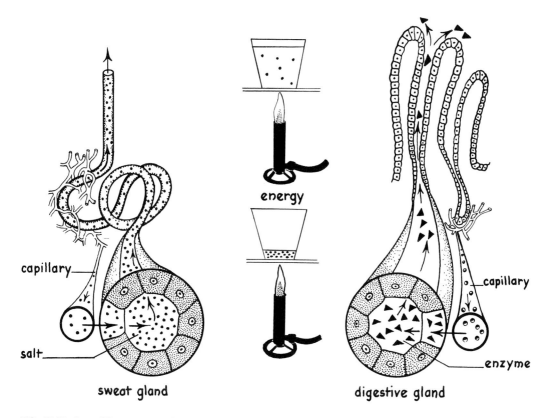

FIG. 17-28. Two different types of glands and how they function. Sweat glands merely extract the substance from the blood, concentrate it, and secrete it. Digestive glands, on the other hand, must manufacture the enzyme from raw materials supplied from the blood, and then secrete the finished product. In both instances energy is required.

tinuously, although the rate may be affected by nervous excitation or by hormones from other endocrine glands. There is considerable energy utilized during glandular activity. Thus the sweat glands produce a fluid with a salt content considerably higher than that of the blood, and energy is required to increase this concentration just as it would be if heat were used to evaporate an equal amount of dilute salt water to a similar concentration (Fig. 17-28). Careful measurements of gland cells demonstrate that some respire at a higher rate than any other cells of the body, even those of the heart.

Chromatophores

Although color change is not found in human beings other than the gradual tan-

ning of the skin as a result of exposure to sunlight, many lower animals are equipped with a very efficient and often spectacular color-changing apparatus. In some animals such as the squid (p. 267) the variety and rapidity of change in color are almost fantastic. It can change from pearly white to intense black almost instantaneously. Others such as fish and reptiles change more slowly, but the final product is equally dramatic. Such fish when moved experimentally from an aquarium with a black bottom, over which they become very dark, to one of white sand will shortly become a very light color. Furthermore, some, like the flounder, will actually produce the mottled effect of colored stones on the ocean floor. Lizards will change from the color of the bark on the tree trunk to the intense ment granules of the cell into compact "pin points." On a dark background the same pigment granules spread out at the surface, darkening the entire area.

Although most of the pigment cells in animals are primarily under the influence of the nervous system, some, such as those of Crustacea (Fig. 17-29) and Amphibia (Fig. 17-30), are controlled by hormones, although the initial stimulus is via the eyes. Pieces of frog skin, for example, can be stimulated to change color simply by dipping them in solutions containing specific hormones. When in contact with the hormone *intermedin* (from the intermediate lobe of the pituitary), the skin darkens, and the opposite reaction can be induced with epinephrine. However, under normal conditions, stimuli from the eyes excite the endocrine glands whose secretion causes the chromatophores to respond. It is a chain reaction.

FIG. 17-29. The shrimp, *Crangon*, is hidden because of its ability to match its background. The chromatophores bring about a mottling effect which resembles the sand particles. In addition, it half buries itself to bring about still further concealment.

Electric Organs

Powerful electric discharges can be produced by a few species of fish. They are "triggered" by stimuli coming from the nervous system. The electric eel and ray possess special "electric organs" that are composed of a great many modified muscle cells so arranged as to accumulate their individual action currents and build up a considerable voltage. In some forms as much as 400 volts have been recorded, which is sufficient to stun or even kill a small fish. When a small light bulb is placed in the circuit, flashes have been recorded. Horses wading through shallow water where the large electric eel resides have been shocked enough to throw their riders.

green of the leaf. The protective value of such a mechanism is obvious.

This color change is accomplished by the movement of pigment either in the effector end-organ in the skin or in parts closely associated with it. In vertebrates, the pigment is confined to single cells which are scattered throughout the skin of the animal. When light falls on the eyes of the fish, stimuli are sent to the chromatophores which adjust the amount of pigment that spreads out on the surface to obtain just the right shade of color to match the background. Blind fish remain one color no matter what the background. On a light background, the normal response of each chromatophore is to concentrate the pig-

Muscles and glands occur in nearly all metazoa. The additional effectors—pigmentary and electric—are much more restricted in their occurrence. They demonstrate how far animals are able to modify certain parts of their bodies to perform very special functions. It is interesting to speculate how, through the millions of years of evolution, these animals have been able to select such aberrant, though practical, modifications.

CHEMICAL COORDINATION— THE ENDOCRINE GLANDS

An important adjunct to the nervous system in bringing about coordination of the vastly complex animal body is the **endocrine system.** This is made up of glands located in various regions of the body which secrete powerful organic compounds, called **hormones,** directly into the blood stream. Their activity is manifest in other parts of the body. While the nervous system is responsible for quick action, the endocrine system functions in bringing about the much slower reactions which may extend over some period of time.

The glands which are known to be endocrine in nature today were described by early anatomists. Thus, Galen, in the second century A.D., described the tiny pituitary gland of mammals, although he could assign no function to it. Indeed, it was not until nearly the end of the last century that actual experimentation began to bring to light the function of these mysterious glands.

The British physiologist E. H. Starling, studying the functions of the pancreas in 1905, named the endocrine secretions, **hormones,** and defined their function. As our knowledge increases of the numerous hormones found in both plants and animals it becomes clear that these are specific chemical compounds which are manufactured by special regions of the organism. They either diffuse or are transported in the blood stream to another region of the organism where, in very low concentration, they regulate and coordinate cellular activity. Chemically they are steroids, amino acids, or proteins and are, therefore, very diverse. This wide variation in chemical composition makes it impossible to define them as belonging to any group of chemical compounds. Normal body function is pos-

FIG. 17-30. The leopard frog changes from a light color where the spots are very prominent to a darker color where the spots are obscured. The activity of the chromatophores which are responsible for these varying colors is shown magnified in the enlargement of the portions of skin shown on the right. This activity is controlled by hormones.

483

sible only when all of the hormones are present in optimal concentrations. They are intricately dependent upon one another as we shall see.

The Endocrine Glands and Their Secretions

The endocrines evolved after the nervous system, so it might be expected that they would be found in the more highly specialized animals where the nervous system could not take care of the multitudinous jobs assigned to it. However, hormone-like substances from plants and protozoa have been described. Among the invertebrates endocrine glands have been found in mollusks, annelids, crustacea and insects where they are important for coordination or other functions. They probably exist in all groups of animals. They are consistently found among the vertebrates, even in such low forms as the cyclostomes. The glands themselves are derived embryologically from various sources and in their evolution have performed different functions. For example, the hormones that control chromatophore activity in the amphibia can exercise no comparable function in birds and mammals because they have no chromatophores. Yet, the hormone is still present, as can readily be demonstrated by the injection into a frog of the proper extract. Undoubtedly, such recently acquired hormones as those that stimulate lactation in mammals are derived from similar hormones present in lower vertebrates where they perform a different function. There has been a long, slow, biochemical evolution of these complex compounds which have an intricate interrelationship in the higher animals today. This very complex relationship has been the subject of a tremendous amount of research during the past 60 years.

From the first, experimental research in **endocrinology,** as this branch of biology is called, has required the use of certain techniques in understanding the function or functions of a suspected gland. The simple removal of the gland and assigning whatever changes that appear in the animal thereafter as a result of the hormone produced by that gland may or may not be correct. It so happens, as we shall soon learn, that the normal functioning of any organ or organ system is due to a number of hormones working together (synergism) or against one another (antagonism); hence symptoms resulting from the removal of a single gland may be caused by more than the mere lack of that hormone. Other hormones, now uninhibited, may be in part responsible for the observed abnormalities. Therefore, the experimental design may involve the removal of a number of glands simultaneously, and the substitution of purified extracts for each one. In this way the function of each may be defined.

A common practice in defining the function of an endocrine gland is to substitute another gland from another animal for the one removed or to feed dried glands, or better yet, to inject purified extracts of the gland. The degree to which recovery is observed will give some evidence of the function of the gland or the extracts. Here again the design of the experiment must be carefully planned if the results are to be meaningful.

A great deal of effort in the past few years has been made to purify hormones so that the chemical formula of each could be written. Since the amount of a hormone in the gland, blood, or urine is extremely small, enormous quantities of these materials are required to find even a trace of the hormone. For example, it requires over two tons of pig ovaries to yield a few milligrams of estradiol. Even so, many hormones are being defined today chemically.

In human beings, the occasional dysfunctioning of endocrine glands because of tumors or other abnormalities has given physicians and biologists abundant material for study and, in some cases, for experimentation.

TABLE 1

Vertebrate Hormones and Their Functions

SOURCE	HORMONE	FUNCTION
Stomach	Gastrin	Gastrin secretion
Duodenum	Secretin	Pancreatic secretion
	Enterogastrone	Inhibits gastric secretion
	Cholecystokinin	Controls gallbladder
Pancreas		
Beta cells	Insulin	Sugar metabolism
Alpha cells	Glucagon	Sugar metabolism
Testes	Testosterone	Development of male characteristics
Ovary		
Follicle	Estradiol	Development of female characteristics
Corpus luteum	Progesterone	Changes associated with pregnancy and child-birth
Placenta	Chorionic Gonadotropin	With other hormones maintains pregnancy
Ovary and placenta	Relaxin	Relaxes pelvic ligaments
Thyroid	Thyroxin	Increases basal metabolism
Parathyroids	Parathormone	Calcium and phosphorus metabolism
Adrenal medulla	Epinephrine	Supplements action of sympathetic nerve action
	Norepinephrine	Increases blood pressure
Adrenal cortex	Hydrocortisone	Aids in the conversion of proteins to carbohydrates
	Aldosterone	Metabolism of sodium and potassium
	Adrenosterone	Stimulates male characteristics
Anterior lobe of pituitary	Somatotropin	Controls growth
	Thyrotropin	Stimulates thyroid function
	Adrenocorticotropin (ACTH)	Stimulates adrenal cortex
	Follicle-stimulating hormone (FSH)	Affects growth of parts of ovary and testes
	Luteinizing hormone (LH)	Affects production and release of gonadal hormones
	Prolactin	Affects mammary glands
Intermediate lobe of pituitary	Intermedin	Controls pigment in chromatophores
Posterior lobe of pituitary	Oxytocin	Controls contraction of uterus
	Vasopressin	Controls contraction of smooth muscle; antidiuretic action

Results of experiments on lower animals have also revealed a great deal of information that has been applied directly to the alleviation of many endocrine aberrations in man.

The ultimate goal in experimentation with endocrines is to find the exact chemicals that are involved and to be able to prepare them in the laboratory. Once the chemical structure of these substances is

FIG. 17-31. The location of some of the endocrine glands and some of the results of their normal activity and malfunctioning.

known, they can be synthesized and used in animals with deficiencies to restore normal conditions. This has been accomplished for some hormones, but there is still much to be learned.

The vertebrates have seven clearly recognized endocrine glands: the gonads, pancreas, duodenum, thyroid, parathyroids, adrenals, and pituitary. Although they are referred to as ductless glands, the first two do have ducts—the endocrine secretion does not leave the gland through the ducts but instead enters the blood stream directly. These two, together with the duodenum, have two separate glandular functions. The gonads function in the production of eggs and sperm in addition to their endocrine function of producing hormones that are responsible for the secondary sexual characteristics. The pancreas produces digestive enzymes in addition to insulin, and the duodenum has several functions besides producing secretin. Moreover, a single gland such as the pituitary produces several hormones, each with a strikingly different function. Other endocrine glands may be found, although this appears much less likely than the possibility of discovering new functions for the glands already known.

We shall briefly survey these seven glands that are fairly well known. Their location is indicated in Figure 17-31 and their functions in Table 1.

The Duodenum

Two British physiologists, Bayliss and Starling, found that the highly acidic food passing from the stomach into the duodenum stimulated the walls of the latter organ to produce a substance which circulated in the blood stream to the pancreas, causing it to secrete its products into the digestive tract. This substance they called **secretin.** We shall learn more about secretin in the chapter on digestion. With their pioneer work, the field of endocrinology was initiated.

Other hormones produced by the intestinal wall are **enterogastrone** and **cholecystokinin.**

Pancreas

This compound gland has ducts and its most obvious function is producing digestive enzymes which are drained off to the duodenum through the pancreatic duct. The digestive function of the pancreas will be discussed later; here we are concerned only with those portions of the pancreas which produce hormones.

Lying scattered among the pancreatic juice-secreting cells are clusters of cells called **islets of Langerhans** which function in secreting hormones. There are two kinds of these cells; the alpha cells which produce **glucagon** and the beta cells that secrete **insulin.** Both of these hormones function in controlling sugar metabolism. Before discussing them let us take a look at the historical background that leads up to the discovery of insulin.

The story of the discovery of insulin is one of the more fascinating sagas in the annals of biological science. As far back as 1890 it was known that if the pancreas were removed from a dog, death followed in a few weeks. The salient point that came out in the early experiments was the appearance of large quantities of sugar (glucose) in the urine of such dogs. The two German workers who first performed these operations noticed that ants were attracted to the cages of these dogs and found that it was the sugar in the urine which was attracting them. This reminded them of human diabetes, a disease that had been known for centuries. A long series of experiments followed by workers all over the world, and it was soon proven conclusively that the islets of Langerhans produced a hormone called insulin that was responsible for retaining and storing sugar in the body. If these islets were destroyed, as in the case of human diabetes, sugar no longer was retained in the liver and other tissues, but poured out through the kidneys into the urine and was lost from the body. This was a great discovery, but what could be done about it now that the cause of this dread disease was known?

The first step was to try to find a substitute for the nonfunctioning islets. Feeding the whole pancreas to depancreatized dogs failed to produce the slightest effect. The hormone was digested in the alimentary tract; consequently, it never got into the blood stream where it could be carried to the liver and tissues in which it would work. The next step was to inject an extract into the body, but because of the difficulty encountered in getting a pure product, no satisfactory results were obtained for 20 years. During this long period experimenters were attempting to obtain a pure hormone from the whole glands of various animals, mostly domestic animals such as cattle, sheep, and hogs.

It occurred to a young Canadian physician, Dr. Frederick Banting, that perhaps the digestive enzymes produced by the pancreas destroyed the insulin before it could be extracted. This was later shown to be true. Banting reasoned that since the embryonic pancreas was known to produce the islet tissue before the enzymes appeared in the pancreas, if such glands were used, perhaps the hormone could be isolated in an active state. In 1922, he and three other men—Best, McLoed, and Collip—working together, set out to isolate the hormone. After a great deal of labor, they eventually prepared a product which caused no ill effects on the dogs when injected under their skin and which alleviated their diabetes. It was a short step to the treatment of humans, where success was immediate. Thousands of diabetics then had, for the first time, some means of staving off an early death from a disease that had always been fatal.

With the ensuing years insulin was produced in more concentrated and purified form, and today its chemical structure is known. Through the brilliant work of the English biochemist, Sanger, insulin is known to be a protein (molecular weight—12,000) consisting of two peptide chains, one containing 21 amino acids, and the other 30. It was discovered that most commercial insulin preparations contain another hormone, called glucagon, which has the opposite effect of insulin; namely, it increases blood sugar levels instead of reducing them as insulin does. Glucagon has been found to be a protein also and is secreted by the alpha cells as already mentioned.

Both glucagon and insulin function primarily in the control of carbohydrate metabolism, although hormones from both the pituitary and adrenal glands also play a part. Insulin has several effects all of which are related. It brings about the conversion of glucose in the blood to glucose phosphate within the cells which is reflected in a decreased blood glucose level. It also promotes the storage of glycogen in the liver and muscles, and increases the burning of glucose to carbon dioxide and water. If insulin is produced in insufficient quantities sugar utilization is correspondingly decreased and with this faulty carbohydrate metabolism the metabolism of fats and proteins is seriously interfered with. Glucagon increases blood sugar by its action on the enzyme **phosphorylase** which controls the conversion of liver glycogen to glucose.

Insulin is responsible for the near-normal lives of hundreds of thousands of men, women, and children. The hormone is either taken by mouth or injected under the skin at rather frequent intervals, depending on the severity of the disease.

The Nature of Diabetes. Without treatment a diabetic suffers from insatiable thirst, excessive urination, a gradual loss in weight, general body weakness, and finally a coma which terminates in death. During this course the sugar in the blood and urine is found, by measurement, to be abnormally high (as much as 8 per cent in the urine), the liver loses its glycogen and finally, in the coma state, acetone and partially degraded fats also appear in the blood and urine. Before death the acetone may reach such concentrations that it can be detected on the breath. All of these symptoms are immediately relieved with the administration of insulin.

The first, most obvious function of insulin is to maintain normal carbohydrate metabolism in the body. For some reason, in the absence of insulin the liver fails to store glycogen, and glucose is oxidized very poorly. Strangely enough, the abstinence from carbohydrates in the diet does very little good in preventing any of the symptoms. In fact, it seems that without insulin the body mobilizes all of the sugar at its disposal and discharges it from the body via the urine. Even the amino acids are deaminized at an abnormally high rate, so that the sugar residue is added to the already heavily sugar-laden urine. Furthermore, the fats are withdrawn from storage and only partially oxidized, leaving the unoxidized fractions in the blood and urine. It seems that all the forces of the body are put forth to produce sugar which is then wastefully thrown away. Death is the inevitable answer to such a course, unless insulin from an external source can intervene.

In some diseases of the pancreas the islets are stimulated to produce more than the normal amount of insulin. The results are the same as when a diabetic gives himself too much insulin. The blood sugar is dropped to such a low level that the brain becomes irritable and finally the person goes into the severe condition called **insulin shock**. Most diabetics are familiar with the possibility of this condition and accordingly carry sugar or some other sugar-containing substance that can be taken quickly to overcome the lowered blood sugar level. Because of his liability to insulin shock or coma, either of which may render him unconscious, it is advisable that the diabetic carry among his possessions a card or tag identifying his disease, so that in event of collapse his condition will not be mistaken for some other malady or even drunkenness.

The Gonads

The testes and ovaries are also compound glands whose primary function is the production of sperm and eggs; in addition, they have very important endocrine functions which have developed in the evolution of the vertebrates. They are concerned with those organs which function in the caring of both the gonadal products (eggs and sperm) and the early embryo. The complete process of reproduction becomes highly complex in mammals where the young are few in number and are cared for both within the body of the mother long before birth and for some time after they have made their appearance in the outside world.

The gonad's primary function of producing eggs and sperm will be discussed later in Chapter 21 and only such anatomy as is necessary for an understanding of their endocrine function will be given at this time.

The Testes. Located among the sperm-producing tubules of the testes is a special type of tissue (interstitial) which produces several hormones, the most active being **testosterone,** a steroid, which is secreted directly into the blood stream. It affects the general metabolism which results in protein synthesis and subsequently body growth. It also stimulates the production of the **secondary sexual characteristics** in all male vertebrates, characteristics which are associated with maleness. They are the very obvious traits which separate the male from the female both morphologically and physiologically. The comb and brilliant plumage of the cock, the antlers and massive body of the bull moose (Fig. 17-32), and the beard of man are all secondary sexual characteristics. The absolute proof that these characteristics are associated with the testes can be demonstrated by **castration,** or removal of these glands, an ancient custom practiced by man not only on his domestic animals but in some cases also on his fellow man. The castrated cock shows none of the comb and wattles of the normal male; the steer is quite different in both its anatomy and behavior from the bull; the gelding has none of the fire nor cantankerousness of the stallion. In ancient times it was customary to castrate slaves, produc-

is associated with puberty when pubic hair, change of voice, and increased size of the genitalia occur.

If testosterone is injected into a castrated animal or a testis is transplanted into some part of the body where it can grow and secrete testosterone into the blood stream, the male secondary sexual characters will be restored. Such injections given to a castrated female will cause her to develop masculine characteristics. A perfectly normal egg-laying hen can be induced to become a functional father rooster with comb, wattles, and crow and all by castration followed by a series of injections of testosterone. By removing the single ovary from

FIG. 17-32. Sexual dimorphism in birds and mammals.

ing **eunuchs** who would then be docile, subservient beasts of burden and trusted keepers of the harem. When it was desired to retain the soprano voice of a particularly talented youth, castration did the trick, and thus choirs could be produced with remarkable musical qualities. Occasionally, the loss of the testes in a young boy has resulted in an adult with a high-pitched voice, without a beard, obese and with little of the usual emotional characteristics associated with the male. Castration after maturity, however, seems to initiate few, if any, of these changes.

The onset of interstitial tissue activity

a seven-week-old chick a normal "rooster" will result (Fig. 17-33). This can be accomplished in female birds because they possess a residual testis and no external genitalia. Sex reversal in mammals is limited to the secondary characteristics only.

Occasionally the testes in mammals fail to descend normally into the scrotal sac as they should do during the last few weeks of gestation. This condition is known as **cryptorchidism** and males in which it occurs are invariably sterile. If, however, the testes are brought down into the scrotum by surgery, they very soon become functional and produce viable sperm. A cryptorchid is perfectly virile in every way although he is infertile; that is, he possesses all of the normal characteristics of the male including sex drive. This is because his interstitial tissue is unimpaired, so that testosterone is produced in proper amounts to allow for normal development of his masculine characteristics. Upon microscopic examination, these testes will show perfectly normal interstitial tissue but degenerate sperm-producing tubules. Experiments show that if the normal testes of mammals are placed back into the body cavity or heated to the internal temperature of the animal the sperm tubules degenerate. Therefore, sterility of the cryptorchid is due to the higher temperature existing in the body as compared to the scrotal sac. This is difficult to correlate with the fact that the internal testes of birds are fertile and the temperature is even higher than that of mammals. In the long evolution of mammals one fails to note the advantage of placing these organs, upon which the race depends for its perpetuation, in such a hazardous position when they would be much safer housed within the body cavity as are their counterparts, the ovaries.

Radiations of various kinds, such as X-rays, if given in large doses have a lethal effect upon the sperm-producing portion of the testis. In smaller doses the effect may simply alter the genes which ultimately might produce far greater casualties in the human race than mere sterility in a few individuals. At any rate, people who work around X-ray machines must guard themselves carefully or they will become sterile, although none of their secondary characteristics will be affected.

Chemically, testosterone is well known and is found to be similar to one of the female hormones, both being steroids. Other related testicular hormones are collectively called **androgenic compounds** and seem to be generally distributed throughout the body. They are probably substances which are utilized in the production of testosterone or they are products of its breakdown, because they are found in the urine. Strangely enough males produce female sex hormones (estrogens) and females produce male hormones (androgens). It is the relative amounts of each that determine the development of the secondary sexual characteristics.

The pituitary is intimately associated with gonadal hormones. If the pituitary is removed all cells of the testes regress resulting in the loss of androgen secretion and the secondary sex characters. Apparently, normal gonadal development requires pituitary hormones (LH, FSH) as well as testosterone.

After the testes had been associated with male vigor, the intriguing idea of transplanting them or injecting their extracts into the body of a senile male caught the imagination of early biologists. Long ago, Brown-Sequard, a famous physiologist, injected himself with testicular extracts which he professed renewed his vigor. This

FIG. 17-33. The removal of the single ovary in birds results in the subsequent development of a testis and male characteristics. In these photos the chickens on the extreme ends are female and male respectively. The animal in the middle had its ovary removed at seven weeks of age and shows a well-developed male comb.

FIG. 17-34. A Graafian follicle from a rat, sectioned to show the egg.

initiated a long series of experiments both on animals and on man himself. The results have all been disappointing, and today it is believed there are no beneficial effects from either the administration of testosterone or the grafting of testes. It can be concluded that testosterone does initiate and maintain the secondary sexual characteristics and probably contributes to sexual behavior and urge. In man, however, the latter function is so complexly interwoven with psychological reactions that it is difficult to determine just how much effect the hormone really has.

The Ovary. A far more complex battery of hormones is produced by the mammalian female generative apparatus than by the male. This is due to the recently acquired though intricate mechanism of caring for the developing embryo, both before birth and immediately after. These hormones are produced in the ovary, although others occur in various parts of the genital tract.

At birth and throughout the early life of a female, the potential eggs lie dormant in the outer region of the ovary. From puberty on they begin to grow. As an egg grows, there develops about it a fluid-filled space called the **Graafian follicle** (Fig. 17-34). These follicles produce a hormone, **estradiol** (estrogen), which is the counterpart of testosterone in the male. The influence of estradiol in the blood stimulates the onset of changes both in body contours and in the female organs; these changes result in the mature human female. A similar process occurs in all mammals. Before the completion of maturity, another hormone, **progesterone,** is produced by a special part of the ovary called the **corpus luteum.** After the rupture of the Graafian follicle and the liberation of an egg which moves down the oviduct toward the uterus, the cavity left fills with the corpus luteum which, in turn, produces progesterone. This hormone prepares the uterus to receive the egg. If no fertilized egg reaches the uterus the menstrual cycle is initiated.

The **menstrual cycle** in humans and other primates has its counterpart in the **estrous** or "heat" **cycle** in other mammals. It involves a distinct rhythmic cycle of sexual activity during some part of which the female is receptive to the male. Such a cycle is completed every 14 days in guinea pigs, twice a year in dogs, and once every 5 days in rats. In humans and anthropoid apes the menstrual cycle is complex, involving a periodic sloughing off of the highly vascular lining of the uterus every 28 days by menstruation. In other mammals the uterine lining returns to the resting state with no sloughing off or bleeding. The word *menstruation* comes from the Latin *mensis,* which means month. The menstrual flow consists mostly of the epithelial lining of the uterus together with the incorporated gorged blood vessels. The course of events that precede this are rather well known, but just *why* it must occur, since it is not found in lower mammals, lacks an immediate explanation.

Since we are dealing with a cycle, description can start at any point in it (Fig. 17-35). The beginning of the menstrual flow may arbitrarily be taken as the starting point for this discussion. About 4 days later a Graafian follicle begins to grow in the ovary and as it increases in size it produces more and more estradiol. Maturity is reached in about 12 to 18 days at which time a rupture occurs in its wall and the egg is released. This marks the end of estradiol production from this structure but not of the hormone itself. The empty follicle is quickly converted into the corpus luteum, which continues to produce in increasing amounts the closely related hormone, progesterone, from the 15th to the 26th day. These hormones, in addition to bringing on the changes, already referred to, at puberty, are also responsible for the

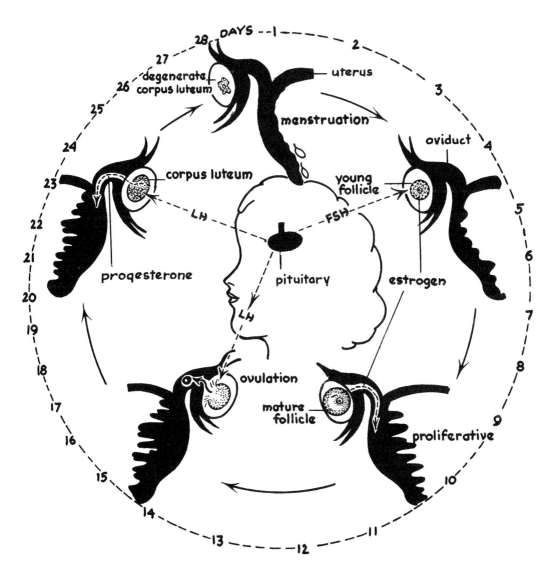

FIG. 17-35. Graphical outline of the events that occur during the menstrual cycle in man.

rhythmic menstrual cycle. The production of both estradiol and progesterone has a stimulating effect on the walls of the uterus, causing it to proliferate and to become highly vascular in preparation for the fertilized egg, if and when it makes its way into the uterine cavity. What happens from this point forward depends on whether or not the egg is fertilized.

If the egg is **not fertilized** the corpus luteum suddenly retrogresses and progesterone is reduced to zero during the 25th to 27th days of the cycle. This results in the sloughing off of the uterine wall known as the menstrual flow, which continues over a period of 4–5 days. Another Graafian follicle then begins to grow and the cycle is started over again. The pituitary hormones, which will be discussed a little later, play an important part in this process. It might seem that a rather elaborate preparation is made each month for the event of pregnancy and that an unnecessary waste results when fertilization fails to occur. One speculates whether a little less preparation might be satisfactory until it is certain that fertilization has taken place.

If the egg **is fertilized** as it passes down the oviduct, the corpus luteum is retained and goes right on producing progesterone until just a few days before the end of gestation. The zygote is implanted in the uterine wall wherever it happens to touch. In fact, the highly vascular wall is so receptive to tiny particles that almost any small object is readily picked up by it at this time. The walls also produce mucus rich in glycogen, which probably acts as a source of energy for the early stages of the embryo until it gains a secure foothold and can withdraw nourishment through its placenta. With the developing stages of pregnancy, progesterone continues to cause further accommodations of the uterine wall for the enlarging embryo. It also causes the mammary glands to increase in size, prevents any further Graafian follicles from forming, and inhibits uterine contractions.

The placenta (p. 391) which develops from the uterus wall and embryonic membranes supports the embryo but also has endocrine functions which are involved with pregnancy. It secretes **chorionic gonadotropin,** a protein hormone which functions in stimulating the corpus luteum to remain active. Chorionic gonadotropin appears early in pregnancy (about 2 to 3 weeks) and can be detected by injecting urine into a frog, which will promptly shed sperm, a positive test for pregnancy. The placenta also secretes estrogens and progesterone which supplement that produced by the ovaries. The ovary as well as the placenta produce the protein hormone **relaxin** which relaxes the pelvic ligaments to permit the passage of the fetus through the birth canal.

As the end of pregnancy approaches, the corpus luteum ceases to produce progesterone and the uterine wall, which has during this time become an accessory in producing the hormone, reduces its output. This precipitates changes which are similar to the beginning of menstruation, that is, in the absence of progesterone the uterine wall begins to degenerate, therefore becoming incapable of nourishing the fetus any longer. Furthermore, without the inhibiting effect of progesterone, the muscles of the uterine wall begin powerful contractions which eventually result in the expulsion of the fetus. The production of milk by the mammary glands occurs after birth due to another hormone, **lactogen,** which is produced by the pituitary gland and will also be discussed later.

It takes some time after the birth of the offspring for the hormones to readjust themselves and the menstrual cycle once again to reestablish itself. This usually does not occur until the amount of lactogen from the pituitary subsides, which means, of course, that the offspring has ceased to rely on the mammary secretion as its principal source of food.

The Thyroid

The thyroid, together with the remaining glands, is purely endocrine in function. The thyroid has various shapes in different vertebrates but in man is bilobed and lies on either side and under the larynx (Fig. 17-31). The two lobes are connected by a narrow strip of tissue, called the **isthmus,** passing across the trachea. The presence of the gland can be determined by merely feeling it with the fingers.

This gland was seen by early anatomists, and its importance suspected because they noted that in certain individuals it became enlarged, seeming even to cause their death. At the beginning of the Christian Era the Greek physicians prescribed the drinking of sea water as a cure for **goiter** (the term used for the swollen gland). Later, others gave their patients products of the sea, such as dried seaweed leaves, which undoubtedly gave some relief because all sea products are rich in iodine, the important ingredient in the production of the thyroid hormone, **thyroxin.** The exact function of the thyroid was not known until replacement experiments in 1885 demonstrated that the gland did produce a hormone. This was isolated in pure form in 1916 and synthesized in 1927 by Harrington and Barger, two English investigators. When this substance is administered to an animal deprived of its thyroid, the animal remains perfectly normal in every respect. If it is denied such treatment, stark metabolic changes occur which, if prolonged, may terminate the life of the animal. What is the specific function of this gland?

It is generally agreed that the thyroid gland secretes thyroxin, which controls the level of basal metabolism. The secretion of thyroxin is controlled by the pituitary hormone, **thyrotropin,** and vice versa. That is, if thyroxin drops in the blood the pituitary sends out more thyrotropin which stimulates the thyroid to produce more thyroxin,

a nicely tuned "feedback" system (Fig. 17-36).

Special cells (follicle cells) in the thyroid accumulate iodide from the blood and incorporate it into the protein **thyroglobulin,** which is subsequently hydrolized by enzymes to thyroxin, a derivative of the amino acid, tyrosine. Thyroxin then diffuses into the blood stream and thence to

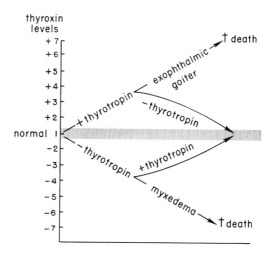

FIG. 17-36. Under normal conditions thyroxin levels in the blood remain relatively constant owing to a carefully controlled feedback mechanism. As a result of thyrotropin stimulation the thyroxin output is increased. If this continues, exophthalmic goiter results, and ultimately death. When the flow of thyrotropin is cut back, less thyroxin is produced and the normal level is maintained. Likewise when too little thryotropin is produced by the pituitary, the thryoxin level drops eventually, resulting in myxedema and death. This is normally prevented by an increased output of thyrotropin which causes the level of thyroxin to return to normal.

the tissues where it does its work. It functions in stimulating the oxidative processes in all body tissues.

Thyroxin must be produced at a uniform rate in order that these important processes proceed at what is spoken of as a normal level. If more or less is produced, these processes accordingly increase or decrease in speed with accompanying symptoms that are very definite and easily recognized. A diseased thyroid merely produces too little or too much of its secretion. If continued in either direction too long, death inevitably results.

Underactivity. When the gland fails to produce the proper amount of thyroxin, the effects are somewhat more pronounced in a young animal than in an adult. For example, if the thyroids are removed from tadpoles or pups the animals will not mature properly. The tadpoles will not metamorphose into frogs, and the pup will not mature into an adult dog. Likewise in human beings, if a child has a deficient thyroid he becomes a **cretin.** Such a child is small and badly formed, with pudgy, puffy skin and swollen tongue, and his mental development is at a rather complete standstill. If given thyroxin in the early stages of the disease, the child responds remarkably well and can grow into a normal adult. Obviously, if a human cretin is allowed to live for twenty years without treatment, thyroxin will do him little good because his body tissues will have completed their development and can be changed but little.

If the thyroid becomes atrophied for some reason and fails to produce an adequate supply of thyroxin in the adult, a familiar disease known as **myxedema** results. The obvious symptoms of the disease are general loss in vigor, reduction in mental activity, increase in weight, and a thickening of the skin to give it a puffy appearance. Less obvious symptoms are a drop in basal metabolism, the improper burning of food, sometimes as much as 40 per cent below normal, a slowing of the heart rate, and a lessening in the sex drive. It seems that the entire machinery of the body slows down. The administration of proper amounts of thyroxin or thyroid extracts restores the rate of metabolism to its normal level, and subsequently all symptoms of the disease disappear. Sometimes in surgery too much of an overactive gland is removed and the patient may then find that he is suffering from myxedema and must take thyroxin all the rest of his life. Fortunately, the digestive enzymes have no effect on thyroid extract, thyroxin, or even the dried gland in contrast to insulin, a fact which permits administration by mouth, an important detail in the treatment of any disease.

Fifty years ago the presence of an unsightly enlarged thyroid was very commonplace in certain parts of the world. Surprisingly, these regions were rather well defined and in them even the domestic animals had goiters. An examination of the soil and water showed that there was a marked deficiency of iodine. Along with this discovery, the thyroid secretion was found to be remarkably rich in iodine; it was not difficult to fit the two together and conclude that goiter appeared in regions where there was very little iodine available in the food products and water. These areas were spotted over the world. In the United States they are concentrated along the St. Lawrence River and Great Lakes regions. For example, in 1924, 36 per cent of the schoolchildren in Detroit showed incipient endemic goiter, but within seven years after the addition of potassium iodide to table salt the incidence had dropped to 3 per cent. In view of this experience, it has been proposed that the word *salt* be legally recognized in Michigan as iodized salt and that the sale of any other salt in food stores be prohibited.

The presence of a goiter does not necessarily mean that the gland is under- or overactive. It does mean, however, that there is some sort of disturbance in the thyroid output. It may be compensating for the lack of iodine and does this by producing more thyroid tissue in an effort to supply sufficient thyroxin to keep the body at a normal basal metabolic level. Such compensating action is not uncommon in other parts of the body, for example, an enlarged heart muscle. If the thyroid cannot maintain a normal level of thyroxin, myxedematous symptoms may be evident. If it can supply the proper amount there are no symptoms of the disease, although the individual harbors the greatly enlarged gland on the front of his neck which is at least inconvenient, if not embarrassing.

Overactivity. For some unknown reason, the thyroid sometimes begins spontaneously to produce more thyroxin than the body needs, and this may be accompanied by a slight enlargement of the gland. It differs from the simple goiter described above because while it may not be enlarged, or only slightly so, its output is far greater. Obviously, abnormally high amounts of hormone in the blood stream increase the rate of burning foods (30 per cent or more) and speed up all the bodily activities. More food is consumed, yet there is a wasting away of the body. Profuse sweating occurs, the heart is overworked, and external heat cannot be tolerated. All this step-up produces a highly irritable and nervous individual who is continually on the move but accomplishing very little. The action is like running an automobile at top speed with the brakes set. It is clear that such activity will soon result in the destruction of the organism itself.

This condition, which is called **exophthalmic** (from the fact that it sometimes causes the eyes to bulge out of their sockets) or **toxic goiter,** is controlled by destroying a part of the cells that produce the hormone (Fig. 17-37). This is easily accomplished by surgery and such operations are very successful. In this age of the atom a new method has been discovered which is sometimes employed when for some reason or other it is inadvisable to operate. It is the use of radioactive iodine. Iodine, when subjected to atomic radiations, becomes radioactive itself. Such a form is called an **isotope.** Since the thyroid picks up about 80 per cent of all the iodine taken into the body, the exact amount that will be de-

FIG. 17-37. A case of hyperthyroidism.

livered to the gland shortly after swallowing isotopic iodine can be determined beforehand. Furthermore, radiations are known to destroy thyroid tissue; therefore, by feeding radioactive iodine "cocktails" to the patient, a certain amount of success in destroying a part of the gland has been achieved. Its more satisfactory use, however, is in the treatment of cancer of the thyroid.

The Parathyroids

In the early studies of the thyroid much confusion resulted because in removing the gland the four tiny parathyroids embedded in the thyroid were inadvertently removed also (Fig. 17-31). The symptoms that followed this were the result not only of thyroid deficiency but also of parathyroid de-

497

ficiency. The small parathyroid glands were discovered in 1891 and many years later their true function was determined.

If the parathyroids are removed from an animal, injections of the hormone **parathormone,** produced by the glands, will keep that animal in good health. If no hormones are given, the animal suffers from severe muscular tremors, cramps and finally convulsions. The composite symptoms are called **tetany,** and without treatment the animal passes into a coma and death soon follows. It is now known that the parathyroids actually produce two hormones, both of which seem to have the same function, maintaining proper levels of calcium and phosphorus in the blood, but through different pathways. One leads to increased phosphorus excretion through the kidneys and the other functions in controlling the amount of phosphorus and calcium that is deposited in the bones. When the glands are removed the blood calcium level falls rapidly, which correlates with the symptoms of the disease. Administration of calcium will prevent symptoms of parathyroid deficiency. If the glands produce an overabundance of the hormone, the calcium level in the blood then rises too high and even the calcium of the bones is sacrificed, so that a weak, twisted skeleton is the result, rendering the unfortunate individual a cripple.

The Adrenals

The adrenals are located on the upper inner edge of each kidney, as one might guess from their name (Fig. 17-31). Their combined weight is no more than an ounce, and each is composed of two parts, an outer covering called the **cortex** and an inner dark-colored mass called the **medulla.** The gland is therefore a composite one and each part has a separate origin, the cortex coming from the mesodermal lining of the coelum whereas the medulla is derived from a part of the neural tube. One might expect structures of such different origins to have different functions and they do.

The Medulla. The medullary portion of the adrenal produces two closely related hormones, **epinephrine** (sometimes called **adrenin** or **adrenaline**) and **norepinephrine.** Chemically they are amino acids derived from tyrosine and their functions are similar. They have also been synthesized from sources other than adrenal glands. Related synthetic compounds such as **ephedrine** produce similar effects when administered to animals.

If the medullary portion of the adrenals is removed from an animal, death does not follow nor is the animal markedly affected by its loss. If injections of medullary extract are given to such an animal or one with intact adrenals, characteristic changes occur rather rapidly. The heart action becomes stronger and the blood vessels to the skin and viscera constrict, sending most of the blood to the muscles, brain, and lungs. The hair "stands on end," the pupils dilate (wide-eyed), and the skin blanches. The spleen constricts, forcing its reserve of blood out into the general circulation, and simultaneously the blood's ability to clot is stepped up. More glycogen in the liver is converted to glucose, so that the total amount in the blood is definitely increased. This chain of events prepares the body for undue stress such as occurs in a fight or a sudden retreat. The body is made ready to function to the maximum of its ability in case a sudden burst of energy is needed. Provision against possible injury is afforded by the increased speed of blood coagulation. This whole series of effects is similar to excitation of the sympathetic nervous system. Thus, both the nervous system and the adrenal medulla play an important rôle in fear and anger. Knowledge of this fact has led to the so-called emergency theory of adrenal function.

Epinephrine has clinical use in cases of asthma where it dilates the breathing passages. It is also useful in starting a heart that has suddenly stopped beating.

The Cortex. The **cortex** of the adrenal is essential for life, although when even such a small portion as one-fifth of the total gland tissue is present, life is undisturbed. Its products are numerous; in fact, over 30 compounds have been isolated in recent years. The first crude extract, isolated in 1930, was called **cortin** and was effective in treatment of people suffering from Addison's disease, which is the name identified with a deficiency of this portion of the adrenals. Since that time many compounds have been extracted, the best known and most effective being **hydrocortisone** and **cortisone** which function in the conversion of proteins to carbohydrates. Another is **aldosterone** which controls sodium and potassium metabolism. A third, **adrenosterone,** is an androgen which influences the development of male characteristics. The function of the other hormones is not clear. All, however, are steroids and are synthesized from cholesterol; they are closely related to testosterone and progesterone.

If the cortex fails to function, marked changes occur which are fatal if uninterrupted by treatment. Addison's disease develops and as a result the carbohydrate metabolism is greatly affected, as indicated by a drastic drop in blood sugar, because of the inability of the enzymes to convert the proper amounts of proteins to carbohydrates and then to convert the latter to sugar in the liver. Salt (NaCl) is lost from the blood and tissues at a rapid rate which reduces the entire blood volume and with it the blood pressure. As Addison's disease progresses, the skin bronzes owing to the deposition of melanin and the sexual functions fail due to an actual atrophy of the Graafian follicles and the seminiferous tubules.

If, on the other hand, the gland becomes overactive as a result of irritation caused by a tumor, changes of a different kind occur. Carbohydrate, salt, and water metabolism is disturbed and the person becomes weak and tends to waste away. In males, the maleness is greatly enhanced, accompanied by excessive hair growth. If it happens to a very young male child, the sex organs may become fully mature (except the testis) within the first or second year of life, and the hair, musculature, and voice resemble those of an adult man. These are very rare cases, fortunately. In females, the situation is even worse. If the overactivity occurs in an adult woman, the changes are all toward maleness; the beard grows (the bearded lady in the circus), the body becomes more muscular, and the voice deepens. Even the female sex organs begin to atrophy and become nonfunctional.

These hormones, particularly hydrocortisone (cortisone), are used clinically for suppressing allergies, tissue inflammation, and tissue proliferation in the joints which causes rheumatoid arthritis.

The Pituitary

The last and perhaps the most complex of all the endocrine glands is the **pituitary,** or **hypophysis.** Located approximately in the middle of the head, it lies in a bony capsule and is attached to the base of the brain by a slender stalk, the **infundibulum** (Fig. 17-31). Like the adrenals, the hypophysis is a compound gland, composed of three lobes: the **anterior** and the **intermediate** lobes arise embryologically from an outpocketing of the roof of the pharynx; and the **posterior** lobe originates as a solid outgrowth from the floor of the brain (hypothalamus). The point of contact with the brain through the infundibulum is retained while all connections with the pharynx are lost very early in embryological development. The anterior lobe is the larger of the three and has no nerves but is amply supplied with blood vessels. This abundant vascularization provides means for receiving hormones that stimulate it to produce its own secretions and a means for their escape. The posterior lobe is composed of

FIG. 17-38. Case of giantism. The men on either side are of normal height.

From these observations it is clear that the pituitary certainly gives rise to more than one hormone and that its influence is far-reaching in the animal body.

The Anterior Lobe. Five well-known hormones are produced by this lobe, and there may be others. The five are named according to the part of the body that they affect, with the addition of the suffix *tropic:* **somatotropic** (growth), **thyrotropic** (thyroid), **adrenocorticotropic hormone** (adrenal cortex), **gonadotropic** (gonads) and **mammotropic** (mammary). The hormone is sometimes named by adding the suffix *in,* that is, thyrotropic hormone may be called thyrotropin. Each of these will be considered briefly in this order.

Somatotropic effects. The function of the pituitary was brought to the attention of early anatomists by the fact that an enlarged gland was always associated with giantism. These huge men (Goliath, whom David slew, was undoubtedly one) reach a height of nearly 9 feet and are rather well proportioned, with the exception of the extremities which are longer than normal. (Fig. 17-38). An examination of the anterior lobe of the pituitary always reveals a greatly enlarged organ, sometimes reaching the size of a hen's egg. On the other hand, when the gland fails to produce the proper amount of hormone a midget results. It is to be noted that giants or midgets are produced only when the gland either overfunctions or underfunctions in the young child.

Both dwarfism and giantism can be produced in animals simply by removing the pituitary in the first case and supplementing with grafted pituitaries or extracts (somatotropin) in the second. Dogs can be forced into giants by placing glandular material under the skin or injecting purified extracts of the anterior lobe of the pituitary. If the gland is removed in a pup, growth takes place very slowly, if at all, and the dog becomes a midget. In human beings

nonmyelinated nerve fibers coming to it from the hypothalamus. It is also supplied with blood vessels but they are distinct from those going to the anterior lobe.

Although it is very difficult to operate on the pituitary in man, experimental animals such as the frog and rat lend themselves to such surgery. By perforating the roof of the mouth the pituitary can be neatly removed and subsequent effects observed. When this operation is performed on a young mammal, growth is inhibited at once, sexual maturity never occurs, and both the thyroid and the adrenal cortex atrophy. With the injection of pituitary extracts, the animal develops normally and the associated symptoms never appear.

FIG. 17-39. A case of acromegaly. Note particularly the protruding lower jaw, massive brows, and the enlarged hands.

with overactive anterior lobes, removal is the only remedy known so far. In pituitary midgets, injections of refined extracts are sometimes beneficial.

If increased activity occurs after maturity has been reached, as it occasionally does when a tumor forms on the pituitary, the person does not then become a giant, although deep-seated changes do occur. Since the body has already ceased growing, the effort to produce a giant by further increase in size is restricted to the regions of the joints and the face. Consequently, a person so afflicted becomes barrel-chested, beetle-browed, and long-jawed, while the

feet and hands grow very large (Fig. 17-39). Such a condition is spoken of as **acromegaly.**

Thyrotropic effects. Very little is known about the relationship between the pituitary and the thyroid except that thyroxin will not supplant hormones from the pituitary in correcting pituitary deficiency. A hormone from the pituitary, **thyrotropin,** initiates or stimulates the thyroid to produce varying amounts of thyroxin.

Corticotropic effects. The adrenal cortex and its production of hormones are directly under the control of a specific hormone from the pituitary called **adrenocorticotropic hormone** (ACTH). This substance has been isolated and its chemical composition determined. It is a peptide containing 39 amino acids. Its action parallels cortisone in every respect, which proves that its action is through the adrenal cortical hormone. Therefore ACTH must control the cortisone output. By increasing ACTH, cortisone is also increased.

An interesting sidelight on the discovery of ACTH came from a common observation, namely, that during pregnancy arthritic women recover from their rheumatism. Shortly after the child is delivered the disease returns. Both cortisone and ACTH have the same remitting effect as pregnancy. Apparently, the added burden of childbearing stimulates a greater output of ACTH which, in turn, stimulates a greater production of cortisone, the combined action of which improves the arthritis. Just what the specific action is on the disease itself is not known.

Both of these hormones have proven beneficial in cases of extensive body injury such as that caused by severe lacerations or burns. They serve to muster all the body's potentials toward regenerating new tissue as well as preventing shock and the other symptoms associated with severe trauma.

Gonadotropic effects. A young hypophysectomized animal never becomes sexually mature, and if the operation occurs after maturity there is prompt atrophy of the sex organs. There is thus a close and important relationship between the pituitary and the sex glands. There are at least two gonad-stimulating hormones produced by the anterior lobe of the pituitary gland: one is called FSH (follicle-stimulating hormone) and the other LH (luteinizing hormone). Both are complex proteins and have only recently been isolated in pure form. If no FSH is produced, Graafian follicles fail to form in the female and seminiferous tubules cease to function in the male. Without LH none of the Graafian follicles will release their eggs, nor will the interstitial tissue of the testis produce testosterone. Restoration

of these two hormones to a hypophysectomized animal allows normal development of the sexual organs and in the female insures normal functioning all the way to pregnancy and full term development of the fetus. The development and subsequent function of the testis is under the influence of FSH and LH. Both are essential for normal spermatogenesis. LH also influences the interstitial cells of the testis to produce testosterone.

Mammotropic effects. As was pointed out in an earlier section on the gonadal hormones, the mammary glands develop under the impetus given them by estradiol, progesterone, and possibly another hormone. Even after they are fully formed, lactation (secretion of milk) will not occur unless still another hormone, *prolactin,* or lactogenic hormone, is produced by the pituitary. This is sometimes referred to as the "maternal instinct" hormone, because it will produce certain mothering behavior in animals which normally do not possess such instincts, an old male dog, for example. If such an animal is given this hormone in sufficient quantities over a period of time, it not only will mother pups but will also produce milk to feed them.

The Posterior Lobe. The posterior lobe of the pituitary is no longer considered an endocrine gland in spite of the fact that hormones are released from it. The hormones are actually manufactured by neurosecretory cells deep in the brain and pass to the hypothalamus from which they are released via the posterior lobe. If this structure is removed or damaged the body water balance is greatly disturbed. Water is not reabsorbed by the kidney tubules, which results in great urine flow (from 3 to 10 gallons a day). This disease is known as **diabetes insipidus** and, without treatment, is fatal.

The hormone **oxytocin** has been isolated from the posterior lobe and has recently been synthesized. It is a peptide consisting of nine amino acids. It has a pronounced effect on uterine muscles, causing them to contract with increased vigor; hence this compound is often used following childbirth to contract the uterus. Another interesting function of oxytocin is that in cows it functions in milk let-down. If there is little or no hormone present in the blood of the animal, milk will be produced in a normal fashion but cannot be released. **Vasopressin,** another posterior lobe hormone, is chemically very much like oxytocin; it varies only in two different amino acids, yet its action is vastly different. It brings about the constriction of small arteries of the body causing a marked elevation in the blood pressure. It also functions in regulating water balance and when given regularly to a person suffering from diabetes insipidus normal water balance can be maintained indefinitely. For this reason it is called **antidiuretic hormone** (ADH).

Because of the many hormones produced by the pituitary, it was once thought of as the "master gland." It is now becoming clear that all of the glands affect one another, so that their integrated action brings about coordinated body activities.

The hypothalamus exercises considerable control over the pituitary. Neurosecretions from the hypothalamus are carried in the blood to the anterior lobe where they stimulate the release of ACTH. Perhaps the other pituitary hormones are released by a similar mechanism.

The control of the pituitary output of hormones is very complex. It is now believed that the release of each anterior lobe hormone is under the control of the quantity of the specific hormone in the blood. Hydrocortisone inhibits the release of ACTH, thyroxin suppresses thyrotropin, and estradiol and progesterone inhibit the secretion of FSH and LH. Thus we see a "feedback" mechanism always in operation so that the pituitary hormones and their "target" organs are in equilibrium to

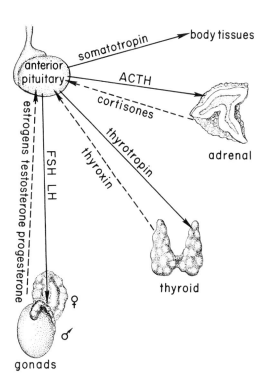

FIG. 17-40. The feedback mechanism operates between the pituitary and the glands it controls. The hormones produced by the anterior pituitary are indicated by the solid line, those produced by the other glands by dashed lines. If there is a feedback hormone from the body tissues, it has not been identified.

maintain the so-called normal conditions in the body (Fig. 17-40).

Other glands in the body, such as the **thymus** in the neck region and the **pineal** in the brain, have been suspected of having endocrine functions. There is some recent evidence that the thymus is involved in the production of antibodies. Also a hormone called the **melanocyte-stimulating hormone** (MSH) has been isolated from beef pineal glands which darkens the skin of frogs and man. It is responsible for the increased pigmentation noticed in pregnancy. This hormone is closely associated with hydrocortisone and ACTH.

Stress and Hormones

Considerable attention in recent years has been given to the role played by hormones during environmental stress. Han Selye and his collaborators at the University of Montreal have been particularly interested in this problem. During the life of an animal environmental hazards such as cold, starvation, hemorrhage, burns, and lacerations occur more or less frequently and it is under these conditions that certain endocrine glands are stimulated to increase their output compensating for any damage that might accrue from these stresses. For example, following trauma, particularly with severe bleeding, the adrenal medulla increases its output of epinephrine. The increased epinephrine triggers the release of increased ACTH from the anterior pituitary which in turn releases increased amounts of adrenal cortical hormones and these bring about changes in the carbohydrate and mineral metabolism. These changes are such as to counteract the effects of the injury and permit the tissues to repair rapidly. If the stress is of long duration, such as severe cold or starvation, the tissues become adapted to the stress as a result of hormonal action. However, there is a limit beyond which the body cannot tolerate further strain; if this limit is taxed, the body goes into shock from which it is not likely to recover.

In this chapter we have seen how the many parts of a complex animal are coordinated into an integrated whole. We shall examine in the next few chapters the organ systems responsible for the energy that keeps the machine going.

SUGGESTED SUPPLEMENTARY READINGS

BEACH, F., *Hormones and Behavior* (New York, Paul B. Hoeber, 1947).

BEKESY, G. Von, "The Ear," *Scientific American,* 197(2) (August, 1957), 66.

BRAZIER, M. A. B., "The Analysis of Brain Waves," *Scientific American,* 206(6) (June, 1962), 142.

COBB, S., *Foundations of Neuropsychiatry* (Baltimore, Williams and Wilkins Co., 1952).

GRAY, G. W., "The Great Ravelled Knot," *Scientific American,* 179(4) (October, 1948), 28.

GRAY, G. W., "Cortisone and ACTH," *Scientific American,* 182(3) (March, 1950), 30.

KATZ, B., "The Nerve Impulse," *Scientific American,* 187(5) (November, 1952), 55.

LOWENSTEIN, W. R., "Biological Transducers," *(Scientific American,* 203(2) (August, 1960), 98.

MILLER, W. H., RATLIFF, F., and HARTLINE, H. K., "How Cells Receive Stimuli," *Scientific American,* 205(3) (September, 1961), 222.

PAVLOV, I. P., *Conditioned Reflexes* (New York, International Publishers, 1941).

PROSSER, C. L. and BROWN, F. A., *Comparative Animal Physiology* (Philadelphia, W. B. Saunders Co., 1961).

RANSON, S. W. and CLARK, S. H., *The Anatomy of the Nervous System* (Philadelphia, W. B. Saunders Co., 1959).

SELYE, H. *Textbook of Endocrinology* (Montreal, University of Montreal Press, 1949).

THOMPSON, E. O. P., "The Insulin Molecule," *Scientific American*, 192(5) (May, 1955), 36.

TURNER, G. D., *General Endocrinology* (Philadelphia, W. B. Saunders Co., 1961).

WALD, G., "Eye and Camera," *Scientific American,* 183(2) (August, 1950), 32.

WIENER, N., *Cybernetics* (New York, John Wiley and Sons, Inc., 1948).

WOODBURNE, R. T., *Essentials of Human Anatomy* (New York, Oxford University Press, 1961).

YOUNG, W. C., ed., *Sex and Internal Secretions* (Baltimore, Williams and Wilkins Co., 1961).

18
The Digestive System

PROCURING FOOD and extracting the energy from it is one of the most important activities confronting animals. This is true because all animal activities require energy which can be obtained only by releasing it from food. All animals, from amoeba to man, have special means for bringing about this conversion. The first steps in this complex energy-releasing mechanism are ingestion and digestion of food.

Animals procure and digest food in many ways. The amoeba engulfs its food to form tiny vacuoles in which the food is finally digested and absorbed into the surrounding cell protoplasm (Fig. 18-1). In ascending the animal scale—to hydra with its spacious gastrovascular cavity, to planaria with its sacculated blind gut, to the earthworm with its "one way" tube, to the vertebrate with a more elaborate tube—we see the evolution of a complex digestive apparatus. Whereas the digestive enzymes in the earthworm are secreted solely from the walls of the tube, in the vertebrate there are, in addition, special glands some distance away from the gut, and their secretions are carried to the gut through ducts. It must be remembered that while the di-

FIG. 18-1. Some of the ways in which animals handle the problem of digestion.

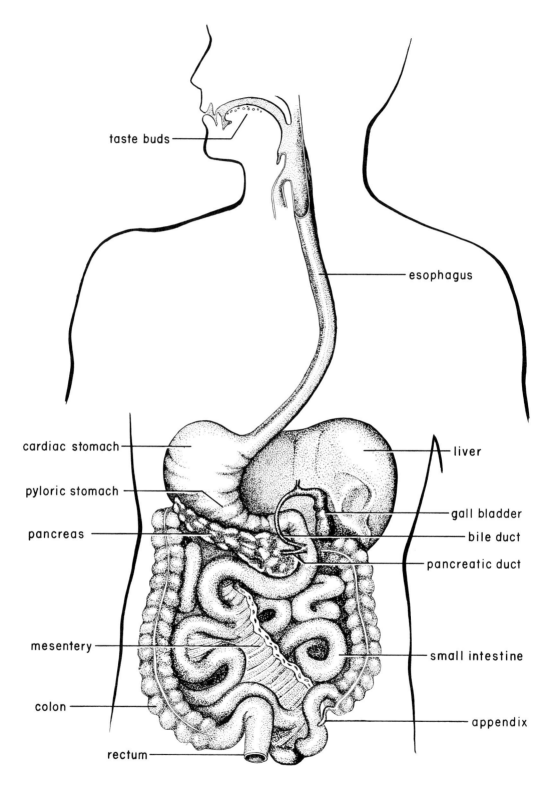

taste buds

esophagus

cardiac stomach

liver

pyloric stomach

gall bladder

pancreas

bile duct

pancreatic duct

mesentery

small intestine

colon

appendix

rectum

FIG. 18-2A. The human digestive tract. A dorsal view has been drawn in order to show some parts more clearly.

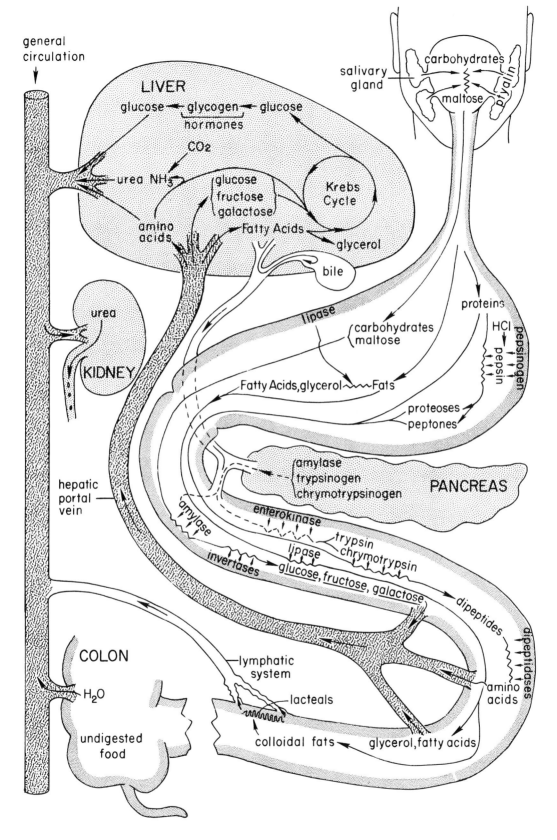

FIG. 18-2B. A partial history of food as it passes through the body.

gestive apparatus itself has become more complex with the increasing bulk of the animal housing it, the fundamental principle of digestion remains unchanged from amoeba to man. The sole purpose of digestion is to break down the large insoluble food molecules to absorbable small molecules which can then be transported to distant parts of the animal body for energy and for building protoplasm.

Let us take a "tour" through the digestive tract and examine what happens on the way. In order to elucidate the story of digestion Figures 18-2A and 18-2B have been provided. The former shows the morphology of the human digestive tract and the latter indicates the principle chemical reactions of digestion as well as absorption and where both occur. It will be helpful to refer constantly to these two figures during the following discussion.

THE MOUTH

Food is taken into the **oral cavity** through the mouth, where it is crushed into smaller

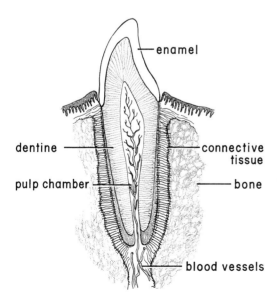

FIG. 18-3. A mammalian tooth in sectional view to show its internal structure. A part of the jaw is also shown to indicate how the tooth is fastened to the bone.

particles by the teeth. During this procedure it is thoroughly mixed with **saliva,** a secretion from the three pairs of **salivary glands** (submaxillary, sublingual, and parotid) (Fig. 18-4). The tongue arises from the floor of the oral cavity where its functions as a handy organ in moving the food about and pushing it to the back of the mouth when it is to be swallowed. The tongue is not only highly sensitive to chemicals, as has already been pointed out, but also to touch. A small baby always wants to put things in its mouth, the apparent purpose being to satisfy its acute sense of touch. The use of the tongue in forming words needs no further comment. The oral cavity is lined with mucosa which secretes mucus, thus keeping the lining moist at all times; this, together with saliva, aids in lubricating the food so that it can slide down the esophagus with little friction. The teeth are such important structures from both the utilitarian and esthetic points of view that further consideration should be given them.

The Teeth

It should be recalled that some parts of the teeth arise from the ectoderm and that they are modified scales similar to those found in the shark (Fig. 16-4). The tooth consists of the **crown** which protrudes into the oral cavity, the **neck,** a narrow region where the gum comes into contact with it, and the **root** which is firmly cemented in a socket in the jaw bone (Fig. 18-3). The crown is covered with hard **enamel** which affords a good grinding surface. Under this is the **dentine,** which is softer, and lying at the center is the **pulp** chamber which contains the nerves and blood vessels. The living tooth is porous and is nourished by the blood stream.

Man has two sets of teeth during his lifetime. The first set, the **milk** teeth, begin to appear in the first year of life and are fully formed by the eighth year. Before they are all well established, however, the front ones start falling out because of the pressure of the second set coming from underneath. During the first twelve to sixteen years of life the individual is experiencing a continual loss and replacement of his teeth. The second set, when fully formed, is composed of 32 teeth, eight on each side of both the upper and lower jaws. There are two front cutting **incisors,** one **canine** next (proceeding posteriorly), then two **premolars,** used in grinding food, and finally three **molars** which are the heavy grinders. The last molars, the **wisdom** teeth, may appear late in life or not at all.

Teeth that are so perfectly formed in lower vertebrates and primitive man seem to have difficulty withstanding the inroads of civilization. It has long been known that the civilized man has notoriously bad teeth while his primitive brother may have perfect teeth throughout his lifetime. In recent years much research has been done to solve this preplexing and distressing problem. A high carbohydrate diet has been thought to be responsible for tooth decay, but natives of many of the South Sea Islands live almost exclusively on a starchy diet and yet their teeth are unusually well preserved. However, when sugar (sucrose) replaces starch in the diet, dental caries (decay) appears. Along with this change to sugar there is a marked increase in the numbers of an acid-forming bacterium (*Lactobacillus casei*) in the mouth. If sugar is withheld from the diet for some time the bacteria disappear and there is no further decay of the teeth. It is rather well confirmed today that it is the sugar in the diet that causes dental caries, and since sugar occurs only in small quantities in nature, it can be considered an unnatural food for all animals including man. Teeth cannot withstand the action of acids produced by the bacteria, hence decay is prevalent among sugar-eating people, which includes much of the civilized world. Fluorine in the water is known to be of value in preserving teeth, probably owing to the fact that in addition to the hardness of the enamel it produces, it retards the growth of bacteria in the mouth.

Digestion in the Mouth

The only part of the saliva that has to do with food breakdown is the enzyme **amylase** which converts starches to **maltose,** a disaccharide. Salivary amylase is a very active enzyme, for if only a few drops of saliva are added to a suspension of starch kept at body temperature, the starch will be converted to maltose in about 20 minutes. This demonstrates one of the properties of an enzyme, for to accomplish the same conversion in the laboratory would require drastic treatment with powerful acids for many hours at high temperatures. Salivary amylase has the power to break the large starch molecules into the much smaller maltose molecules, leaving only one more step to the glucose stage when, as a simple sugar, it can be taken into the cells and metabolized. The way most people eat, amylase has only a momentary chance to function before the food departs for the stomach, although its action does continue

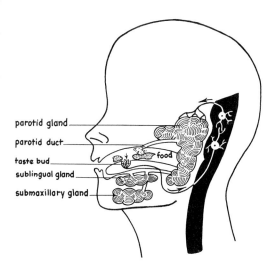

FIG. 18-4. The salivary glands secrete saliva when end-organs in the tongue and mouth cavity are stimulated. The nerve pathway is shown here.

during the swallowing and for a short time in the stomach.

The flow of saliva into the mouth is controlled by nerves which respond to stimuli coming not only from the taste buds on the tongue but also from end-organs in the walls of the oral cavity that are sensitive to the presence of food itself and to the mechanics of chewing. Impulses travel from these end-organs to the brain stem to be routed back along the efferent nerves to the salivary glands (Fig. 18-4) which are stimulated to pour saliva into the mouth through ducts. This is not the only way salivation (secreting saliva) can be induced, as any hungry person knows who smells, sees, or even thinks about food. Such responses are called **conditioned reflexes** and are acquired by learning (p. 516). From past experience one knows the appearance, odor, and taste of food and so one responds reflexly by increasing the salivary output when any or all of these sense organs are stimulated. Salivation is an important response because it prepares the mouth cavity for food before it is introduced.

Swallowing

The problem of getting food from the mouth cavity to the stomach in vertebrates has an interesting evolutionary history. The difficulty arose when animals migrated onto land and the breathing and food paths were forced to coincide. Water, the oxygen-containing medium, passes into the mouth and out the gill clefts in fish, while the food enters the mouth also and merely continues straight back into the esophagus (Fig. 18-5). No difficulty was experienced with such a mechanism. However, when vertebrates moved out on the land the oxygen-containing medium, air, took a new pathway because the lungs evolved from the floor of the mouth cavity. This meant that both food and air had to pass through the pharynx and this could only be accomplished by providing some way of closing

one when the other was functioning. The apparatus developed for this purpose is very simple among amphibians but becomes more complex in the higher forms, particularly in mammals. Here elaborate nerves and muscles have evolved to provide a smooth crossing of food and air. The inadequacies of this system are familiar to anyone who has experienced the difficulties resulting when particles of food accidentally enter his air passages.

Let us see how the process of swallowing takes place in man. When the food reaches a pasty consistency in the mouth, it is forced into the back of the oral cavity (pharynx) and rapidly propelled to the stomach through the small esophagus. When food or fluids reach the pharynx, a chain of impulses is initiated which brings about the pulling forward of the larynx and a tipping of the epiglottis to prevent food from passing into the trachea, together with a simultaneous opening of the upper end of the esophagus (Fig. 18-5). Once all this is started, the food is beyond recall. When it enters the esophagus a peristaltic wave carries it quickly to the stomach. Peristalsis is accomplished by the thick muscles which make up the wall of the esophagus. The presence of food in this collapsed tube causes the longitudinal muscles to relax just in front of the bolus (ball) and at the same time causes the circular muscles to constrict just behind it with the result that the food is pushed along the tube (Fig. 18-9). This is a rapid action, requiring only 5 to 6 seconds for food and less for fluids. Furthermore, it has nothing to do with gravity because a horse can swallow uphill, as indeed it must almost always do, and even a human can drink in an inverted position if he desires. Swallowing is initiated only by the presence of food or fluids in the pharynx; thus it is impossible to swallow twice in rapid succession when no foods or fluids are taken into the mouth. Yet when one drinks fluids one can swallow continu-

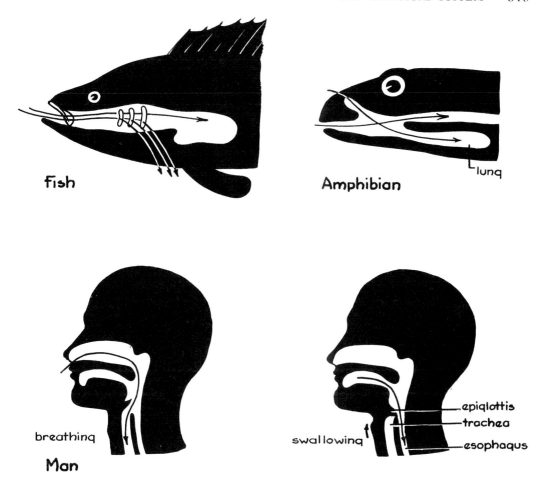

FIG. 18-5. In fish the food and water portal of entry is the mouth. In land-dwellers the air and food passageways cross, as shown here in the amphibian and man. The left lower figure shows the position of the larynx during breathing and the lower right figure shows it during the act of swallowing food.

ously. This means that swallowing can only occur when food or fluids are in the pharynx.

THE STOMACH

After passing through the esophagus, the food drops into the stomach, which is a sac-like expansion of the digestive tube designed not only to store a considerable amount of food (about two and one-half quarts) but to start the digestion of proteins. It is a thick-walled muscular sac lined with **gastric glands.** These are minute, slender pockets in the soft mucosa with tiny openings through which the gastric juice flows into the cavity of the stomach. In addition to the circular and longitudinal muscle layers of the esophagus, the stomach possesses an oblique layer. With this elaborate system the stomach becomes an efficient mixing or churning organ.

The stomach is usually divided into two general regions: the **cardiac region** which immediately follows the esophagus, and the **pyloric region** which is followed by the small intestine. The anatomy and activity of the two portions vary somewhat. The portals of entry and exit to the stomach are guarded by valves consisting of thickened circular muscles which, when strongly contracted, completely close both of these openings. Such valves in a tube are called **sphincters.** Besides these two in the stomach, the **cardiac** at the entrance and the **pyloric** at the exit, there are two others along the digestive tube: one where the small intestine joins the large intestine (**ileocaecal**) and the other at the end, the **anal** sphincter. These valves are important in retaining the food in its proper place until digestion is complete.

As food is swallowed, the stomach gradually expands until full; the reverse process takes place as digestion is completed and the food is moved along to the small intestine. Fluids such as water pass through the stomach in a few minutes, whereas more solid foods remain from 3 to 5 hours, depending on their nature. Some foods digest more slowly than others, for example, those rich in fats. The food is retained in the stomach and churned until it resembles a thick soup, which is called the **chyme.** Peristaltic waves begin in the cardiac region and move toward the pyloric end, so that the food is constantly being forced into that end. So long as the pyloric valve remains closed, the food cannot pass into the intestine, but must continue to be mixed back and forth until the proper consistency is reached. The pyloric valve then opens intermittently, allowing small amounts of the chyme to pass in spurts into the upper end of the small intestine.

These movements are under the influence of the autonomic nervous system. Parasympathetic fibers reach the stomach through the vagus nerves and their action increases the intensity of the peristaltic waves and augments the flow of gastric juice. The opposite action is brought about by impulses coming through fibers from the sympathetic system. Undue emotional strain during a meal excites the sympathetic fibers excessively, thereby slowing up stomach activity and prolonging digestion unduly. For this reason, meal time is no time to discuss weighty or controversial problems.

Most animals have a mechanism for removing anything taken into the stomach that does not "set well." This is particularly true in carnivores, who are apt to eat slightly decayed food that might be toxic. **Regurgitation,** as this chain of events is called, is just the reverse of swallowing, culminating in a complete evacuation of the stomach. Just prior to the event a deep breath is taken in order to hold the diaphragm down; a convulsive contraction of the abdominal muscles then follows which presses the stomach up against the rigid diaphragm. The sphincter leading into the esophagus relaxes and the stomach contents are expelled almost explosively. The action also resembles swallowing in that once it starts it continues until the job is done, regardless of the will of the owner. This safety mechanism is a feature of importance in the survival of a species.

Digestion in the Stomach

The millions of tiny glands in the walls of the stomach secrete **gastric juice,** a highly acidic, watery fluid that contains the enzyme **pepsin** (gastric proteinase). Between 400 and 800 cc. of gastric juice are produced during the digestion of an average meal. The flow of gastric juice, like the flow of saliva, is under the influence of the nervous system, at least in part. Everyone has experienced "mouth watering" when hungry and within sight or smell of good food; the stomach "waters" the same way and probably at the same time. Just how this functions was an attractive subject for investigation even for early biologists, and now the entire mechanism is rather well understood. Let us follow briefly the history behind these discoveries.

At the time of the signing of the Declaration of Independence in this country, a clergyman in Italy attempted some experiments on the activities of his own stomach. This amazing Spallanzani swallowed small metal cages containing bits of meat and after these were left in his stomach for varying lengths of time they were retrieved by means of an attached string. He noticed that the tiny bits of meat had disappeared and concluded that they must have gone into solution and therefore were digested. Another notable series of experiments, begun about 40 years later and continued for many years, was performed by an American army surgeon, Dr. William Beaumont, who had the good fortune of treating a man (Alexis St. Martin) with an unusual bit of accidental stomach surgery. This Indian had been shot through the stomach with a shotgun, and the remarkable thing about the accident was that the load had not only torn away the abdominal wall over the stomach but had also taken a part of the stomach as well. Beaumont plugged the

wound with a wad of cotton and waited for his patient to die. To his surprise the patient not only recovered but the stomach wall healed to the abdominal wall in such a way as to leave a permanent opening, or **fistula,** as such openings are now called. This gave Beaumont an unusual experimental subject for the study of the functions of the stomach. For years afterwards he kept St. Martin close at hand so that he could observe how digestion progressed under all sorts of conditions.

Since that time there have been many cases where the esophagus had been closed because of the accidental swallowing of some strong chemical, making it necessary to provide the person with a fistula in order that he might receive nourishment. Many of Beaumont's observations have been confirmed and a great deal more has been learned. The famous Russian physiologist, Pavlov, produced artificial fistulas in dogs and then studied the rate of flow of the gastric juice under various psychical condi-

FIG. 18-6. Artificial openings into the digestive tracts of two dogs to illustrate how Pavlov performed his basic experiments. The left dog is eating a "sham meal," while the right one is secreting gastric juice from a "Pavlov pouch" into a container.

tions (Fig. 18-6). In such fistulas a small compartment of the stomach is separated off from the remaining portion, but the circulation and nerves remain intact so that the fistula will respond normally. With such an experimental animal Pavlov was able to show conclusively what factors influenced gastric secretion. Another operation which supplemented the findings with artificial fistulas involved the severing of the esophagus and the bringing of the cut ends to the surface of the neck (Fig. 18-6). His discoveries from this experiment were of great importance. For instance, he showed that if a dog were fed a meal which never reached the stomach, since the cut esophagus led to the outside of the neck, about one-fourth of the normal flow of gastric juice took place. He showed further that this was due to reflexes, because the flow ceased when all of the nerves to the stomach were severed. However, if he placed food directly into the stomach without the dog seeing or smelling it, about one-half of the normal flow of gastric juice took place. While the flow in this case was somewhat reduced by cutting the nerves to the stomach, a considerable secretory activity continued. This could mean only that there must be a hormone produced by the lining of the stomach which circulates in the blood and stimulates the gastric glands, at least in part, to secrete. This hormone, **gastrin,** has since been identified. With this type of experiment Pavlov established the principle of **"conditioned reflex"** which is the basis for much of modern psychology.

In order that gastric secretion may be turned off as the stomach empties there must be some other hormone to bring this about. It is **enterogastrone,** secreted by the duodenal mucosa. As foods enter the duodenum this hormone is secreted into the blood stream and passes to the stomach where it inhibits gastric secretions. It also reduces the churning action of the stomach.

The contents of the stomach are very acidic, having a pH of approximately 2.0,

owing to the high concentration of hydrochloric acid. The ions exist as H^+ and Cl^- in the gastric juice. The acid nature of the stomach contents is quite obvious to anyone who has eaten too heartily and sometime later complains of a "sour" stomach. It is even more obvious if he is forced to regurgitate. The acid functions in several ways. It aids in dissolving away the limy material between cells (particularly plant cells), thus making them more readily available for enzyme action. It provides a favorable medium in which the enzymes can do their best work and it has some bactericidal effect on detrimental bacteria which may be taken in with the food.

In addition to HCl, gastric juice contains mucous proteins, water, and the enzymes, **pepsin, rennin,** and **lipase.** Pepsin is manufactured by special gland cells in the stomach lining. It exists in the inactive state when formed in the cells and is called **pepsinogen.** When this substance comes in contact with the acid medium of the stomach, it is transformed into pepsin, the active enzyme. Pepsin, once formed, can itself convert pepsinogen to pepsin. The advantage of producing an inactive enzyme is to spare the lining cells from the powerful proteolytic action of pepsin. Pepsin breaks protein molecules down into **proteoses, peptones,** and **polypeptides,** all of which are soluble in water. The reaction may be expressed thus:

$$\text{Protein} + \text{water} \xrightarrow{\text{pepsin}} \text{proteoses, peptones, and polypeptides}$$

Like all digestive enzymes, pepsin is an hydrolytic enzyme which functions by adding water (hydrolysis); in this case it splits the large protein molecules into smaller molecules. This is the initial stage in protein digestion. Owing to the short time food is in the stomach, not all of the protein molecules are attacked by pepsin; some pass on into the intestine where enzyme action finishes the job.

The enzyme **rennin** is found in the

stomachs of young mammals, and it acts on **caseinogen,** the protein of milk. It is secreted in the inactive state as **prorennin** and, when in contact with HCl, becomes rennin which attacks caseinogen splitting it into **casein** and **whey.** The casein then coagulates in the presence of calcium ions forming **curdles** which are then accessible to pepsin for digestion. The young mammal depends on milk as its sole source of food during the early part of its postnatal existence and the efficient digestion of milk protein is advantageous. The formation of curds permits the protein to remain in the stomach long enough for peptic digestion to occur. Without rennin the soluble caseinogen would pass far into the intestine, just as any other fluid does, before protein digestion could start.

The remaining enzyme in gastric juice is **lipase** which converts fats to fatty acids and glycerol. Most tissue fats are not attacked by gastric lipase, only those in colloidal form such as that found in milk. Moreover, efficient fat digestion requires an alkaline environment and bile salts, a condition found only in the small intestine. Therefore, fat digestion in the stomach is inconsequential.

Like other parts of the body, the stomach is subject to many ills but it seems to suffer especially from emotional strain. In some people happiness seems to center around the contentment of their stomachs. Everyone is familiar with the difficulty experienced in eating immediately following the reception of good or bad news. This is owing to stimulation coming through the autonomic nervous system. Continued emotional strife can even produce organic damage, such as erosion of small areas of the stomach lining (gastric ulcers). Frequently this malady clears up "miraculously" when the emotional strain is removed. In stubborn cases of ulcers or cancer, parts, or even the entire stomach in extreme cases, may be successfully removed. This type of surgery has progressed remarkably in the last

two decades but, needless to say, not to the stage where a goat's stomach can replace that of man—contrary to an idea staunchly held by many people.

Hunger

It might be appropriate to discuss hunger at this point because it was long believed that the stomach controlled this sensation. Hunger pangs were thought to come from the empty stomach and these would disappear only when this organ was filled. It is now known that the sensations of hunger are primarily under nervous control. As a result of a great deal of excellent research on mammals, it has been shown that there are two centers in the **hypothalamus** (p. 475) which have to do with eating. One, the **hunger center,** when stimulated sends out messages to different parts of the body causing the animal to eat. The other, the **satiety center,** has the opposite effect when stimulated. Very clever surgery on rats revealed this information. Small electrodes were inserted into the two centers, which then could be stimulated at will. By continuous stimulation of the hunger center the animals would eat more or less continuously and become overweight, whereas if the satiety center was stimulated they would starve in the presence of abundant food. Therefore, the food intake of mammals, and perhaps other animals including man, is controlled by nerve impulses coming from these two centers. Whether one or the other is stimulated depends on the glucose level in the blood. Fasting causes a very slight drop in blood glucose and this difference stimulates the hunger center; the opposite results following a meal. Here again we see the "feedback" mechanism in operation. Unfortunately, in man at least, it is not quite so simple. Deep-seated psychological factors can influence man's behavior in many ways, and one of these is in his eating habits. A perfectly operating control mechanism may function erratically as a result of outside influences, a fact we all are aware of.

THE SMALL INTESTINE

The small intestine is a narrow tube with a length of over 23 feet which extends from the stomach to the large intestine. Although it is possible to get along without a part or all of the stomach, it is absolutely necessary that the small intestine remain essentially intact, because it is here that almost all digestion is completed and **absorp-** substances. The small intestine is thus adapted to retain food for a considerable period of time in order that digestion may be completed and absorption take place. In this respect, it should be recalled that carnivores possess shorter intestines than herbivores because meat is more readily digested (Fig. 18-7).

The entire gut is supported by a dorsal **mesentery** which holds such parts as the stomach and duodenum in place but at the same time allows the rest of the small intestine considerable freedom of movement. In

FIG. 18-7. The length of the digestive tracts of animals varies with the diet, as shown in these figures. The carnivore (dog) has the shortest tract (with respect to trunk length), the herbivore (rabbit) has the longest, while the omnivore (man) has a gut of intermediate length.

tion of the end products of digestion takes place. The small intestine is divided into three parts that differ slightly from one another in their anatomy. The first 10 inches is the **duodenum,** into which the ducts from the **liver** and **pancreas** empty. This is followed by about 10 feet of a region known as the **jejunum,** which is particularly rich in intestinal glands. The remaining portion is the **ileum,** and is characterized by the vast number of tiny finger-like projections of its lining, the **villi** (Fig. 18-10). These structures increase the surface area of the intestine tremendously, thereby making possible the adequate absorption of digested food lower vertebrates there is evidence that a ventral mesentery was once present which held the entire digestive tract in a line from mouth to anus. As the gut increased in length this ventral support was lost. Actually, it no longer performed any particular function, since the animal lived in a horizontal position where its gut hung like clothes from a line. However, when man decided to walk on his hind legs, the dorsal mesentery could not continue to support the gut as well as previously, and so the gut had a tendency to slide posteriorly into the pelvis. In youth, the abdominal muscles are adequate to compensate for this deficiency but as age advances the gut tends to sag more and more, resulting in the potbelliedness of advancing years. It requires a great amount of physical effort to keep it in place, a price that a tired body and a genial philosophy will not condone.

Specialized gland cells in the duodenum secrete **intestinal juice,** which contains the following enzymes: **enterokinase, dipeptidase, amino-peptidase, invertases, amylase,** and **lipase.** The function of each will be discussed later.

The Liver

This, the largest gland in the body, is located on the right side just under the diaphragm (Fig. 18-2A). It is tunneled with spaces and with vessels which are filled with large quantities of blood, and because of its construction will not tolerate injury. Fatal internal injuries suffered in car accidents frequently involve the liver. Unfortunately, the steering wheel of the automobile is located over this area of the body, and since any sudden stopping of the car throws the driver against the wheel, the liver, being the most vulnerable organ in that area, is most apt to be damaged.

Bile, which is drained from all parts of the liver by tiny tubules, accumulates in one large duct, the **bile duct,** which eventually joins the pancreatic duct just before the two empty into the duodenum. However, there is a storehouse for the continuously secreted bile, the **gallbladder,** which is located in a hollow on the underside of the liver. It is a thin-walled sac connected to the bile duct by a small duct of its own. Between meals the bile accumulates in this sac and when bile is needed the walls contract, forcing the stored bile into the duodenum in large quantities.

In so far as digestion is concerned, the only function of the liver is the production of bile. In a sense, bile is an excretory as well as a secretory product because the residue from broken-down red blood cells accumulates in it and is thus eliminated

from the body, at least in part. Bile also contains considerable quantities of sodium bicarbonate, which functions in greatly reducing the acidity of the chyme in the duodenum. The organic constituents of bile are **bile pigments, bile salts,** and **cholesterol,** each of which has specific functions.

The bile pigments, **bilirubin** (red) and **biliverdin** (green), are responsible for the color of bile. While in man bile is strawcolored, in other vertebrates it ranges from green to red with all intermediate shades. When mixed with the chyme in the gut, the bile pigments undergo further chemical change, turning to dark brown or black, thus contributing the brown color of **stools.** The first sign of faulty bile elimination is the gradual loss of this color, and when the bile fails altogether the stools are gray in color.

Of the numerous constituents making up bile, only the **bile salts** function in digestion. They are responsible for emulsifying the fats in the food so that the fat-splitting enzyme from the pancreas can work more effectively. They also seem to **activate** this enzyme, because without them the fats are poorly digested and appear in large quantities in the stools. They are conserved by reabsorption in the lower end of the small intestine and circulate in the blood back to the liver to be used over again.

The organic compound **cholesterol** is important in the bile because of the trouble it sometimes causes. It does not accumulate if the concentration of bile salts is sufficiently high to keep it in solution. However, if the bile salt level drops, cholesterol will sometimes precipitate out in the gallbladder, forming **gallstones.** These are harmless in themselves but if one is forced into the tiny bile duct as the gallbladder contracts in emptying, it may occlude the tube and produce trouble. Peristaltic waves in the tube wall attempt to pass the stone along and this causes extreme pain. If the contractions are successful, the stone eventually passes into the intestine where it will do no more harm. If, on the other hand, it remains lodged in the duct, bile fails to reach the intestine and all the symptoms resulting from an absence of bile in the gut ensue. The stools lose their color, fats fail to digest, and the bile pigments, since they are excretory wastes, accumulate in the blood and eventually in the skin, causing it to yellow, or **jaundice**. Removal of the stones is a simple surgical operation, and when accomplished the person is usually restored to health very quickly.

The Pancreas

This long, flat, light-colored organ lies between the stomach and duodenum, and by means of its **pancreatic duct** connects with the bile duct. The gland has two functions: endocrine, which has already been discussed, and digestive. It produces several digestive enzymes, all of which are essential to complete the digestion started in the mouth and stomach. In addition, the **pancreatic juice,** like bile, contains large quantities of sodium bicarbonate, which functions in neutralizing the acid chyme from the stomach. Even with this large amount of sodium bicarbonate the chyme remains slightly acid during its trip through the small intestine, a fact contrary to earlier beliefs.

The pancreatic juice also contains a starch-splitting enzyme **amylase** (amylopsin), the protein-splitting enzymes **trypsin, chymotrypsin** (secreted as trypsinogen and chymotrypsinogen) and **carboxy-peptidase;** and the fat-splitting enzyme **lipase** (steapsin). It should be noted that pancreatic and intestinal lipase has almost the entire job of digesting fats because gastric lipase is ineffective in this operation. The other enzymes are approximately duplicated in the mouth and stomach.

Control of Pancreatic Juice and Bile Flow

The pyloric sphincter relaxes when the content of the stomach reaches a certain consistency, though precisely how this is controlled is not well understood. Once the chyme reaches the duodenum, however, the control of the bile and pancreatic juice flow is rather well known. The wall of the duodenum contains a substance called **prosecretin** which, when brought into contact with hydrochloric acid, is converted to a hormone called **secretin**. Some of this gets into the blood stream where it circulates to the pancreas, causing it to deliver pancreatic juice (Fig. 18-8). The proof of the action of secretin can be had by simply injecting an extract from the wall of the duodenum that has come in contact with hydrochloric acid into an animal which has had all of the nerves to the stomach and pancreas cut in order to rule out nervous control. The result is copious secretion of pancreatic juice.

The flow of bile from the gallbladder is caused by a somewhat similar mechanism. The presence of fats and acid in the duodenum causes the formation of a hormone named **cholecystokinin,** which circulates in the blood and causes the gallbladder to contract and deliver its contents.

Digestion in the Small Intestine

As the chyme spurts through the pyloric sphincter into the duodenum, it is eventually mixed with bile and pancreatic juice, together with the intestinal juice from the duodenal wall. Together these function in the final stages of digestion. The chyme is rendered less acid by the highly alkaline nature of both bile and pancreatic juice. Inactive trypsinogen and chymotrypsinogen coming from the pancreas are converted to active trypsin and chymotrypsin by the enzyme **enterokinase,** a constituent of intestinal juice. Actually enterokinase activates the conversion of trypsinogen to trypsin and this enzyme then influences the conversion of chymotrypsinogen to chymotrypsin. Trypsin and chymotrypsin attack whole protein molecules that have survived the effects of pepsin in the stomach, break-

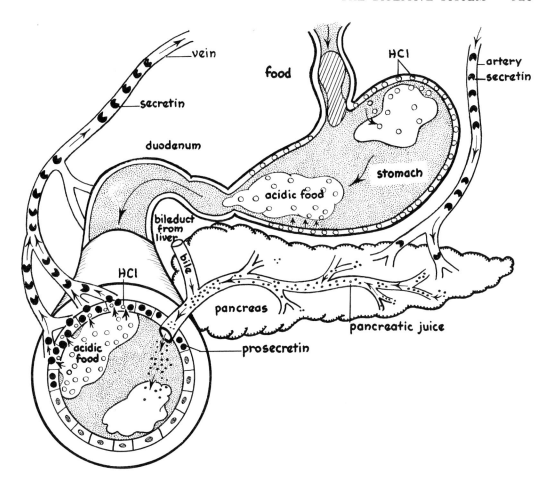

FIG. 18-8. The hormonal control of the secretion of pancreatic juice. The acidic food causes prosecretin (black spheres) in the duodenal lining to be converted to secretin (black spheres with a notch) which circulates in the blood, eventually reaching the pancreas where it stimulates the flow of pancreatic juice.

ing them down to proteoses, peptones, and polypeptides. Further action is necessary before protein digestion is complete.

Further splitting of the proteoses, peptones, and polypeptides is accomplished by amino-peptidase from the intestinal juice and carboxy-peptidase from the pancreas. These two enzymes attack different bonds in these complex molecules, the end result being relatively simple two-amino acid compounds, the **dipeptides.** The last step in degradation of the protein molecule is brought about by the enzyme **dipeptidase** (intestinal juice) which reduces the dipep-

tides to amino acids which are then absorbed into the blood stream.

Intestinal carbohydrate digestion follows a similar path. Pancreatic and intestinal amylase take up where salivary amylase left off since nothing happened to these food molecules in the stomach. Salivary amylase, as was pointed out earlier, does not have a full opportunity to do its work so that considerable amounts of polysaccharides reach the small intestine. These amylases, then, break the remaining polysaccharides to the double sugars, disaccharides, which are then reduced to monosaccharides by the **invertases** in the intestinal juice. There are several of these which are specific for particular sugars; for example, sucrase splits sucrose to glucose and fructose, maltase converts maltose to two glucose molecules, and lactase attacks lactose and converts it to glucose and galactose. These are the end products of carbohydrate digestion and the molecules then are absorbed into the blood stream.

Fat digestion is continued and com-

thus transported to all parts of the body where they are utilized for energy, growth, and repair. With the exception of alcohol, which is absorbed in the stomach, nearly all organic and inorganic compounds are absorbed in the small intestine. Complex modifications of the digestive tract facilitate the process of absorption. In the first place, the small intestine is 23 feet long and, secondly, the *villi*, previously referred to, multiply the surface area with which

TABLE 1

Enzymes of Digestion

SUBSTRATE	ENZYME	SOURCE	END PRODUCT
Polysaccharides	Amylase	Salivary glands	Polysaccharides, disaccharide
	Amylase	Pancreas	Disaccharides
	Amylase	Intestinal glands	Disaccharides
Maltose	Maltase	Intestinal glands	Glucose
Sucrose	Sucrase	Intestinal glands	Glucose and fructose
Lactose	Lactase	Intestinal glands	Glucose and galactose
Proteins	Pepsin	Gastric glands	Proteoses, peptones, polypeptides
Casein	Rennin	Gastric glands	Coagulates casein
Proteins, proteoses Peptones, polypeptides	Trypsin Chymotrypsin	Pancreas	Peptides
Peptides	Peptidases	Pancreas & Intestinal glands	Amino acids
Fats	Lipase	Gastric glands	Fatty acids and glycerol
Emulsified fats	Lipase Lipase	Pancreas Intestinal juice	
Colloidal fats			Colloidal fats

pleted also in the small intestine. Not all fat is reduced to fatty acids and glycerol; some remains as finely divided fat particles which are absorbed as such. That which is digested is split by intestinal and pancreatic lipase into the end products, fatty acids and glycerol, which are then absorbed. This complete story is portrayed in Table 1.

ABSORPTION

The end products of food digestion are absorbed into the circulatory system and are

the chyme comes in close contact, giving every absorbable particle an opportunity to find its way into the blood stream.

The important anatomical unit that facilitates absorption is the villus (Fig. 18-10). It is a thin-walled projection lined with capillaries and with a central space, the lymph vessel or **lacteal.** As the watery chyme bathes the villi, an osmotic equilibrium is constantly strived for between the blood and the intestinal contents, but since the blood is moving rapidly through the capillaries, the flow of absorbable materials is toward the circulating blood. In addition to this passive absorption, work is required to move some molecules across the mucosal membranes. The fact that such molecules as fructose, glucose, and galactose, all of the same size and chemical composition, are absorbed at different rates indicates that some **selection** is made. The "active" transporting mechanism involves temporary phosphorylation of the sugars, which "pulls" them into the cell on one side and "releases" them, unchanged on the other (p. 65). Other molecules pass through by simple diffusion, as mentioned above.

The end products of protein, carbohydrate, and fat digestion, together with inorganic salts, vitamins, and water, are absorbed into the capillaries of the villi and are transported via the **hepatic portal system** directly to the liver. The colloidal fat droplets, however, enter the lacteals and are carried by the lymphatic system into the general circulation, by-passing the liver (p. 509). Excess water as well as other molecules that do not enter the capillaries may also find its way into the lymph. The end result is that all food products eventually reach the blood stream, where they are distributed to all parts of the body.

Small Intestine Movements

While the chyme is in the small intestine (5–10 hours), it is in constant motion. The purpose of this movement is to mix it thoroughly and thus insure proper digestion and absorption. One of the most important sources of our knowledge about these and other movements of the alimentary tract has come through X-ray pictures taken during various stages in digestion. If a person consumes a meal heavily laden with barium (or bismuth), it can be readily followed through the digestive tract because barium is opaque to X-rays. When observed with a fluoroscope, such a mass appears as black shadows on the screen; and if pictures are taken, the contours of the alimentary

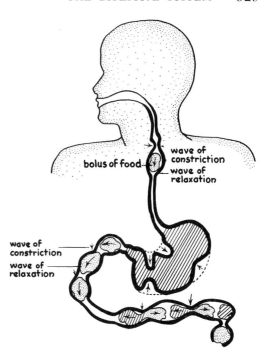

FIG. 18-9. Food moves along the digestive tract by peristalsis. The motion is rapid in the esophagus, where its purpose is to get the food to the stomach as soon as possible. In the stomach and remainder of the gut there are two kinds of movements: one that moves the food along, as shown in the duodenum above; and the other which brings about a mixing of the food (segmental and pendular) as shown in the stomach and lower intestine.

canal can be made out very easily. This is common practice in determining abnormalities or diseases of the digestive system.

There are two types of mixing movements in the small intestine: **segmental** and **pendular**. Both are confined to the limits of a single loop of the gut. The segmental movements start by constricting at regular intervals throughout the loop (Fig. 18-9). Relaxation appears in 10 minutes or so and another series of constrictions occurs which are between the first series. This results in the breaking up and mixing of the masses of chyme. It is supplemented by the pendular movements, which consist of mild peristaltic waves that move the chyme back and forth within the intestinal loop but do not go beyond it. The chyme is moved pro-

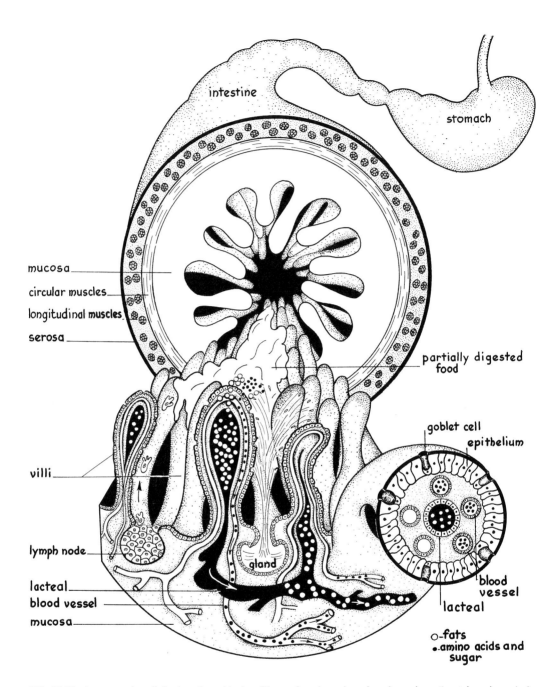

FIG. 18-10. A cross-section of the intestine with the villi greatly enlarged to show how absorption takes place. Amino acids, sugars, and fatty acids and glycerol (not shown) enter the capillaries of the villi. Colloidal fats are taken into the lacteals of the villus. One villus is shown contracted while the other is gorged with fat. This "pumping" action aids in moving the lymph.

gressively along the gut by means of peristaltic waves that occur both gently and in sudden rushes. The action is a slow progressive movement with a sudden rush, at times, of the entire contents from stomach to colon. The combined movements result in a continuous progression of the chyme through the small intestine until it reaches the large intestine.

THE LARGE INTESTINE

The small intestine joins the large intestine (colon) in the lower right region of the abdominal cavity (Fig. 18-2A). The opening is guarded by the **ileocaecal sphincter.** Chyme that passes into the large intestine is still in a very fluid state, but as it passes through this region of the digestive tract much of the water is reabsorbed. The reabsorption of water is a conservation measure, for if it were retained in the gut the intake of water by mouth would necessarily be much greater. Such demands would impose insurmountable problems for an animal that needed to go any distance for its source of water. Since the chyme moves very slowly through the large intestine (12–14 hours), there is ample time for the water to be reabsorbed. During this time bacteria grow so abundantly that they constitute about half of the weight of feces. Bacteria cause no harm and are responsible for the production of vitamin K in man. In some herbivorous vertebrates, however, bacteria are thought to be beneficial, aiding the digestion of cellulose.

The sac-like **caecum** at the beginning of the colon terminates in a finger-like evagination called the **vermiform appendix** because it is worm-like in appearance. This is a remnant of a once functional portion of the caecum. Herbivorous animals possess a very large caecum in which a certain amount of bacterial digestion takes place. The appendix in man sometimes becomes infected, and since it does not drain well, the infection may reach such proportions as to burst the intestinal wall, liberating the contents of the appendix into the coelomic cavity. This is serious because the bacteria then attack the extensive covering of the visceral organs, resulting in a general infection that can be fatal. However, with the use of antibiotics and a surgeon's skill there is usually little danger today of such an infection proving fatal.

From the caecum, the colon extends anteriorly along the right side as the **ascending colon,** crosses to the left side as the **transverse colon,** passes down the left side as the **descending colon,** then bends in an S-shape (**sigmoid flexure**) to become the **rectum.** The digestive tract terminates in the **anus** which is closed by two powerful muscles, the **anal sphincters.**

Colon Movements

The chyme, which is now referred to as **feces,** is gradually moved through the colon by mild peristaltic waves as well as periodic, over-all massive contractions. When feces reach the rectum, which is normally empty, a desire to defecate becomes very pronounced. During defecation a large peristaltic wave moves over the entire colon, aided by voluntary contractions of the abdominal muscles.

Failure of regular bowel movements, commonly referred to as constipation, is the subject of much discussion and more misinformation. If feces are not regularly eliminated from the lower bowel, they tend to accumulate and the mere pressure caused by their presence may produce headaches and the usual symptoms associated with constipation. Similar symptoms can be elicited by simply packing inert material, such as cotton, in the lower bowel. Therefore, no toxins are produced during constipation, although this is usually thought to be the case. The various cathartics that are so well advertised to relieve this condition act in various ways. Some, such as cascara, stimulate the reflex centers in the brain which, in turn, initiate peristaltic contractions;

others such as epsom salts (magnesium sulfate) are not readily absorbable, and since they are taken in high concentrations they produce a tendency for water to remain in the digestive tract. Castor oil as well as magnesium sulfate strongly irritate the nerve endings in the lining of the gut which bring about violent peristaltic activity reflexively. Usually, a controlled diet will relieve constipation, eliminating the necessity of resorting to these artificial means. Much of the catharsis to which people subject themselves is not only unnecessary but harmful.

FOOD

Food must provide the body with the proper amounts and kinds of substances from which it can synthesize its own parts. Just as the carpenter or mason must have lumber, bricks, cement, and other materials, so must the body have its building materials. The digestive process breaks down the large, complex molecules to small or simpler ones that can be rebuilt into the specific molecules needed for human protoplasm. The process of reconstruction will be taken up later. What concerns us now is the kinds of food which, when reduced to the simple state, will provide all of the essential materials in sufficient quantities to build and maintain the body. Returning to the house analogy, if the carpenter

does not have enough lumber and nails, or the mason enough bricks and cement, they will be forced to cut corners and produce a house that will not function as it should. Similarly, food must contain all of the essential substances if the body is to be properly constructed. The types and kinds of food have a profound effect on growth (Fig. 18-11). Food must also supply a source of energy to maintain the body at a constant temperature and to permit movement. Let us consider the kinds of food that contain these two types of materials.

Foods for Building

The simplest of these are the inorganic salts. The analysis of any animal will reveal a considerable amount of iron, calcium, phosphorus, and other minerals. Moreover, the animal body excretes minerals every day, in man about 30 grams. This means that the animal must get these from the food supply.

The minerals that are most apt to be deficient in human diets are calcium, iron, and iodine. Calcium is essential for building bone and should be maintained at a high concentration in the diets of children and pregnant women. The old adage that a woman loses a tooth with each child may have some truth in it, because the demands of the fetus for calcium are great and calcium can come only from the mother's blood. If her diet is deficient in calcium, her teeth may be sacrificed. Although calcium is present in small amounts in vegetables and cereals, it is particularly rich in milk—hence, the constant urge for an adequate supply of this food for children. Iron is necessary for the formation of hemoglobin, the chief constituent of the red corpuscles, and a low iron diet will result in anemia. Meats and eggs are rich in iron, as well as many kinds of fruits and vegetables, and ordinarily, under normal circumstances, it is not necessary to supplement the diet for this mineral. Iodine is required for the proper functioning of the

FIG. 18-11. The value of a complete diet is spectacularly demonstrated by these three litter mates, which were fed on rations that were popular in the years indicated. The diets improved over these 43 years chiefly because of intensive research on vitamins and antibiotics.

thyroid gland, as was pointed out earlier. Near and at the seashore, and in regions covered by the sea in past geological time, this element is in adequate supply in the water and food grown in the region. Sea food in particular is always rich in it. In other areas, however, particularly those remote from the sea, the iodine is not sufficient for an adequate diet and must therefore be supplemented.

While sodium chloride (table salt—NaCl) is probably adequately supplied in most meats, it is less abundant in plant products; for that reason, food is usually salted during cooking and the salt shaker forever adorns the table, just in case. Salt is essential for normal body maintenance. Hydrochloric acid, for example, is produced in the cells of the stomach, using the Cl from the NaCl. With severe sweating there is a gradual loss of salts; if prolonged it will result in "miner's cramps," where large muscles go into painful spasms. The victim suffers from extreme thirst, but the more water that is taken the more severe the spasms, because the salt loss is proportional to the water loss.

Since the body is primarily water and since approximately 2,000 cc. are normally lost each day, it follows that this important substance must also be replaced continuously. One can survive many weeks without food but only a few days without water.

In addition to minerals and water, the protoplasm-building proteins must be present in the diet in considerable quantities. Larger amounts of protein are essential for the growing body than the 50 grams per day required by the adult. This amount must include all of the amino acids (about 10) that the human body cannot synthesize from simpler compounds. These are the so-called essential amino acids. There are many others that can be manufactured by the intracellular enzymes, providing the raw materials are available. Some proteins, such as those derived from milk, meat, eggs, and wheat, contain all of the essential amino acids, whereas others, such as those from gelatin and corn, lack one or more. A diet including only one of these two proteins would be inadequate. It is therefore best to eat a variety of proteins in order that all of the amino acids be supplied in sufficient quantity for proper growth and repair.

Foods for Energy

All of the energy utilized by the body must come from the food brought to it. No energy is derived from breaking the large molecules of protein, carbohydrate, and fat down to absorbable size during digestion. The energy comes from further breakdown by glycolysis and oxidative metabolism referred to earlier (p.   ). When carbohydrates, fats, and proteins are metabolized to the same end products, either in the body or artificially outside the body, they deliver the following numbers of calories per gram: proteins and carbohydrates—about 4 calories; fats—about 9 calories. As far as energy requirements are concerned, one food is as good as another. Carbohydrates, of course, oxidize readily to supply energy. One can also derive all required energy from protein alone by conversion of the amino acids (about 40 per cent), following deamination, to pyruvic acid and the subsequent oxidation via the Krebs citric acid cycle. With fats the situation is different. For some reason, when over 50 per cent of the caloric intake is fat, oxidation is impaired, and fats burn best when there is an adequate amount of carbohydrate present in the tissues.

Accessory Foods—the Vitamins

The discovery of vitamins has a long and fascinating history. When man first began to isolate himself from natural fresh foods and to live on stored or dried foods, the "deficiency diseases" made their appearance. Among the many diseases that appeared, **scurvy** was the best known, and the first for which a remedy was discovered.

That was some 350 years ago, long before anybody knew anything about vitamins, or much else concerning nutrition. The British navy Captain Cook discovered that when his men were down with scurvy after many months at sea, their fresh foods exhausted, they recovered almost miraculously if the ship docked where fresh fruits were available. He, therefore, took fruit, particularly citrus fruit, aboard and discovered that small daily rations kept his men from getting the dreaded scurvy. It has been said by some that the use of this knowledge was responsible in part for the success of the British navy. Within the present century a great deal has been learned about this vitamin, as well as many others that have since been discovered.

Vitamins are effective in extremely small quantities, so small that they cannot be considered energy-producing in the sense that proteins, carbohydrates, and fats are. They are specific, relatively simple organic compounds which must be included in the diet for normal health. Most organisms produce some vitamins. Plants manufacture all they need but animals require those in their diet that they cannot synthesize. If vitamins are absent over a period of time, definite symptoms appear which grow progressively worse, terminating in death. Animals vary in their vitamin needs. Rats, for example, can synthesize vitamin C and man can exist without thiamine. In the latter case, however, this vitamin is manufactured by bacteria living in his digestive tract. By trial and error experiments the vitamin requirements have been determined for most laboratory animals, such as the rat, mouse, guinea pig, and rabbit, so that they can be employed in vitamin research. However, in recent years it has been found that microorganisms, such as certain species of bacteria and protozoa, also require vitamins, and their needs are so precise that these tiny organisms have become very important in determining not only the presence of particular vitamins in foods but also the

amount present. This method, called **microbiological assay,** is becoming more important as further studies are made on nutrition.

The role of vitamins is becoming clear as research on the subject continues. Since they are needed in such small quantities in the diet and yet are essential for life of the organism, it was early suspected that they might play some part in metabolism. This has proven true as we shall see.

Since not all of the needed vitamins are synthesized by the animal, those which it cannot produce must be included in the diet; therefore, animals are dependent ultimately upon plants for the vitamins which they do not make themselves. It is interesting to speculate about how this situation arose. Probably the distant ancestors of animals could manufacture all of their own vitamins, or vitamin-like substances, but in the subsequent millions of years they lost this ability. Losing the capacity to synthesize a vitamin would not be too serious if the vitamin could be readily obtained in the available food, so animals survived more or less unhampered. This continued until as many as 8 vitamins were required. Moreover, animals lost the capacity to synthesize about 10 amino acids, all of which must be present in their diets.

Vitamins are usually grouped according to their solubility: those soluble in fats and oils (A,D,E,K) and those soluble in water (B-complex and C). The use of letters to identify the vitamins is disappearing as their molecular structures become known and they are given specific names. There are more than 30 vitamins described. Some of the better known ones are listed in Table 2 together with their sources and the diseases caused by their absence from the diet of man.

Fat-Soluble Vitamins

Vitamin A. This vitamin is derived from the orange-colored pigment of plants called **carotene.** The vitamin exists in two chem-

TABLE 2

Important Vitamins

NAME	SOURCE	FUNCTION	EFFECTS OF MARKED DEFICIENCY
Fat-Soluble			
Vitamin A	Yellow and green vegetables, oils, butter	Chemistry of vision; health of epithelial cells	Night blindness, xerophthalmia, infections
Vitamin D	Liver oils, milk, eggs	Ca and P metabolism	Rickets
Vitamin E	Most foods	Gamete formation	Sterility in some vertebrates
Vitamin K	Most foods	Prothrombin formation	Blood clotting time increased
Water-Soluble			
B complex:			
Thiamine (B_1)		Carbohydrate metabolism	Beriberi
Riboflavin (B_2)		Oxidative metabolism	Skin defects
Niacin (B_5)	Whole grains, yeasts, meats, eggs, milk, green vegetables	Oxidative metabolism	Pellagra
Pantothenic Acid		Coenzyme A precursor	Uncertain in man
Folic Acid Cobalamin (B_{12})		Nucleic acid metabolism	Anemia
Biotin		CO_2 metabolism	Uncertain in man
Pyridoxine (B_6)		Amino acid metabolism	Uncertain in man
Vitamin C	Citrus fruits, fresh vegetables	Amino acid oxidation, maintainance of capillary walls	Scurvy

ical forms. Carotene is present in all green plants and it is most abundant in those that are yellow or red. Carrots, for example, are rich in vitamin A. Some animals have a tendency to store it in great quantities in their livers. This is particularly true of such fish as the shark, cod, and halibut, hence the well-known names—shark-liver oil, cod-liver oil, halibut-liver oil. Note that it is found in the oil of these livers. Its fat or oil solubility is one of its characteristics.

For some unknown reason, the vitamin A concentration in the liver of newborn infants is low. Apparently it is not transmitted through the placenta and therefore must be acquired during the first few weeks of life. Human milk is rich in vitamin A, particularly the **colostrum** which is the milk secreted by the breast immediately following birth. Cow's milk fed to babies should contain high amounts of vitamin A, especially during the first few weeks of life.

In severe cases of vitamin A deficiency,

rarely observed in this country, the eyes become infected and the cornea becomes very dry and ulcerated (**xerophthalmia**). Another symptom is the inability to see at night, which is called **night blindness.** The retina of the eye cannot synthesize **visual purple** in the absence of this vitamin and consequently does not respond to dim light (see p. 452). It is true of vitamin A, as it is with most of the others, that severe symptoms resulting from a marked deficiency rarely show up among Americans, because of our diversified diet. Mild cases, on the other hand, are relatively common but can be corrected simply by supplementing the diet with vitamin A.

Vitamin D. Whereas only a single vitamin is mentioned here, there are about ten related compounds included in the group of D vitamins. Chemically they are all derivatives of **sterols.** The most important is D_2, or **calciferol,** which is formed by the action of ultraviolet irradiation on **ergosterol,** another sterol. It aids in calcium absorption from the digestive tract and, together with parathormone, controls calcium mobilization in bone formation.

Vitamin D is found naturally in fish liver oils along with Vitamin A. Irradiated fats contain D vitamins in abundance. Often milk is advertised as being irradiated which means that some of the ergosterol has been changed to vitamin D. Exposing fats to sunshine will do the same thing; even exposing one's own body to the sun produces this vitamin, hence the name, "sunshine vitamin." When vitamin D is deficient in the diet of children there is failure of proper deposition of phosphorus and calcium in the developing bones, causing the disease known as **rickets.** A rachitic child has a malformed skeleton. Fortunately, very few rachitic children have been seen in recent years, compared to two decades ago. In climates where there is a great deal of sunshine the vitamin deficiency is rarely seen. However, in northern climates during the winter months children are very apt to deplete their stores of vitamin D. For that reason, it is important that children's diets be supplemented with this vitamin during winter.

Vitamin E. This vitamin is called **tocopherol** and it has three different molecular configurations. It apparently functions in hydrogen transfer during aerobic respiration which is reflected, when deficient, in the degeneration of the germinal epithelium, the production of inactive sperm, and resorption of mammalian embryos. In chickens the liver becomes necrotic, hemorrhages occur, and the testes degenerate when this vitamin is lacking in the diet. Nothing is known about its effect in man, owing primarily to the fact that deficiency is very unlikely because it occurs so abundantly in plant and animal foods.

Vitamin K. This vitamin occurs in two forms, both of which are known chemically. It plays a role in photosynthesis, hence is widely distributed in plants. It is produced by bacterial action in the digestive tract and a sufficient amount of the vitamin is absorbed to prevent symptoms under normal conditions. Newborn infants may sometimes show a deficiency. In mammals it functions in the synthesis of prothrombin (p. 569), an essential factor in blood coagulation. When bile fails to reach the digestive tract, as in gallstone occlusions, the bacteria do not produce vitamin K in sufficient quantities to allow normal clotting of blood, thus making surgery hazardous. Today the surgeon does not worry, because the administration of vitamin K in several treatments restores the clotting time and bleeding is no problem. It is also given before childbirth in order to prevent unusual hemorrhaging.

Water-Soluble Vitamins

B Vitamins. This is a group of water-soluble vitamins that occur abundantly in high-protein foods such as meat, liver, nuts, whole grains, and particularly yeast. In the early days of vitamin research, a single B vitamin was described; now a large number, about 12, are known to belong to this group which is sometimes referred to as the **B-complex.**

Thiamine (B₁). This vitamin functions in intermediate metabolism. When it is deficient in the diet, the conversion of pyruvic acid to acetic acid is impaired, and respiration is faulty. Thiamine produces dramatic results when administered to a laboratory animal, like a pigeon, with marked symptoms of **avitaminosis, polyneuritis.** Within 30 minutes the completely helpless animal regains its posture and appears normal in every respect. Thiamine forms the active part of enzymes involved in the metabolism of carbohydrates. Severe thiamine deficiency in man produces **beriberi,** a disease that was common among the rice-eating peoples of the world when modern methods of removing the hulls were introduced. The thiamine was in the hulls, and hence was lost in the processing of the rice. The processing of wheat today is just as impractical from a nutritional standpoint. Nearly all of the vitamins are removed from the wheat grain when it is processed into the white flour that is demanded by the American housewife. Present-day methods of milling have become a little more scientific, however, for an effort is now made to put the vitamins back in again. It seems rather ridiculous to engage in the labor and expense of removing many nutritious parts of the rich wheat kernel, and then be obliged to restore them, for the sole purpose of keeping the flour white. About all that is accomplished is the production of a white but nutritionally inferior flour at a higher price.

Riboflavin (B₂). This vitamin is necessary for hydrogen transport in respiration. It is converted into a **flavoprotein** which is one of the hydrogen acceptors in the conver-

sion of ADP to ATP (p. 85). When deficient, skin disorders result in man as well as in laboratory animals. Small amounts taken daily will often restore the skin to normal appearance.

Niacin (B₅). This vitamin also plays an active part in respiration. It functions as a precursor to the synthesis of diphosphopyridinenucleotide (DPN) and triphosphonucleotide (TPN), both hydrogen acceptors. When it is lacking in the diet, the disease **pellagra** results. This is a disease in which the skin and digestive tract are affected; it is fatal in severe cases. It is found in certain regions of the South where the diet consists almost exclusively of molasses, meat, and corn. Small amounts of yeast, which contains niacin as well as other members of the B-complex, will cure the disease very quickly. This is probably the only severe vitamin deficiency disease that exists in this country today.

Pantothenic Acid. This vitamin functions as one of the precursors in the synthesis of coenzyme A, which is used in the transfer of acetyl from pyruvic acid to the Krebs citric acid cycle (p.   ). The vitamin is synthesized by bacteria in the colon of man. It is not known what the human requirement is. Its deficiency in rats causes hemorrhages and destruction of the adrenal cortex.

A recently discovered vitamin, **thioctic acid,** also is associated with coenzyme A formation. It, together with thiamine, pantothenic acid, and niacin, is essential in this phase of cellular metabolism.

Folic Acid. This vitamin is required for purine and pyrimidine synthesis. Probably all animals require it in small amounts. In man it is synthesized by intestinal bacteria although a folic acid deficient diet leads to anemia.

Cobalamin (B₁₂). This is a cobalt containing vitamin which occurs in natural waters.

It functions in protein synthesis and is required by many organisms. A diet deficient in this vitamin causes anemia in mammals because of its importance for the maturation of red blood cells. Man requires about 1 mg. per day to prevent anemia.

Biotin. The function of this vitamin involves the metabolism of carbon dioxide, probably through oxaloacetate synthesis. Interestingly egg yolk contains it while egg white is rich in an antibiotin factor which nullifies its action. It is synthesized by intestinal symbiotic bacteria in many animals. If the bacteria are destroyed mammals require biotin in the diet. The requirement for man is very small, less than 10 micrograms per day.

Pyridoxine (B_6). This vitamin is associated with the metabolism of amino acids. It has been known for a long time that it is required for normal growth of rats and there is some evidence now that it may be essential for health in humans. Rats fed a diet deficient in pyridoxine stop growing and show marked lowering of resistance to disease because of a resulting loss of both white and red cells in the blood. Its rôle in the human is still not ascertained.

Vitamin C (ascorbic acid). The function of this vitamin is poorly understood. It seems to be involved with oxidation of some amino acids. The fact that it occurs in the mitochondria would indicate that it is probably involved in respiratory metabolism.

Vitamin C is found abundantly in citrus fruits and fresh vegetables. Cooking destroys it rapidly and stored foods soon lose their vitamin C content. The chief symptoms of scurvy are due to the weakening of the walls of the capillaries and small arteries, causing the characteristic bleeding at the joints, gums, and under the skin. There is some evidence that it influences the formation of substances that bind cells together. In scurvy it probably is the failure of this function of vitamin C that brings on the symptoms of the disease. Dental caries is supposed to be due, in part, to a low vitamin C intake.

In a nation where most people are not confronted with the problem of how to get enough food but what kind of food to select, good advice is to eat a highly varied diet. Such a diet should be particularly rich in fresh vegetables and fruits, with an ample supply of meat and lesser amounts of the foods high in carbohydrates, such as potatoes, bread, and so forth, which add weight but have few vitamins. Eat sufficient, but not too much, food. A slightly underfed rat is the healthiest, and there is reason to believe that the same holds true for man.

SUGGESTED SUPPLEMENTARY READINGS

BEAUMONT, W., *Experiments and Observations on the Gastric Juice and the Physiology of Digestion* (New York, Dover Publications, 1959—original published in 1833).

CARLSON, A. J., and JOHNSON, V., *The Machinery of the Body* (Chicago, University of Chicago Press, 1962).

FULTON, J., *Selected Readings in the History of Physiology* (Springfield, Ill., Charles C Thomas, 1930).

MAYER, J., "Appetite and Obesity," *Atlantic Monthly* (September, 1955), 58.

ROMER, A. S., *The Vertebrate Body* (Philadelphia, W. B. Saunders Co., 1962).

WOODBURNE, R. T., *Essentials of Human Anatomy* (New York, Oxford University Press, 1961).

WOODWARD, J. P., "Biotin," *Scientific American,* 204(6) (June, 1961), 139.

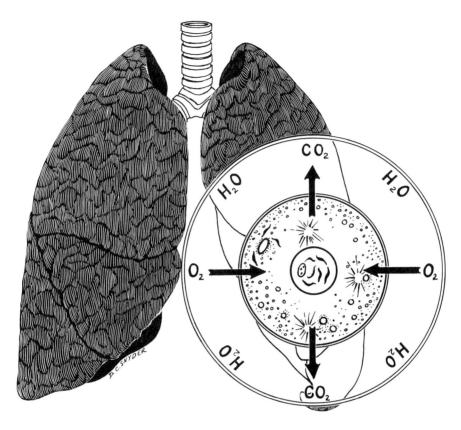

19

The Breathing System and Gas Exchange

IN THE PREVIOUS CHAPTER we saw how energy-rich food is broken down and absorbed into the blood stream, ready for distribution to all of the cells of the body where it is used for growth, repair, and energy. In order that the energy in food molecules may be released, *oxygen* must be present, because most energy obtained by a living organism is through oxidation. Each cell, then, must not only have a supply of fuel and building materials but also have oxygen to burn the fuel. The function of the breathing system in animals is to provide a means of getting oxygen out of the air or water

and into the vicinity of the cell so that it can be utilized. Another function is the elimination of CO_2. In animals with considerable bulk, where the cells are a great distance from the surface, the circulatory system performs the job of distributing the oxygen, thus working hand in hand with the breathing system to solve this complex problem of oxygen supply.

The definition of respiration is not breathing but the actual oxidation of the food in the cells, releasing energy and the waste product, carbon dioxide. Breathing, on the other hand, is merely part of the mechanism by which cells obtain oxygen. Lungs, gills, and other structures remove oxygen from the air or water and pass it on to some sort of transportation system by which it can reach every cell. It is important that the distinction between breathing and respiration be kept in mind. We shall deal with the former in the following discussion leaving the latter for another chapter.

The methods employed by different animals to bring oxygen to their cells are highly varied and become extremely complex in large animals. Such a system may be compared to the ventilating system of a large building. The larger and more complex the building, the more intricate the system becomes, and each new expansion of the edifice means the addition of more powerful blowers and an ever increasing number of ducts. A point might even be reached when it would be impossible, or at least impractical, to attempt to provide ventilation for all parts of the building. In animals, likewise, the problems become more complex with increasing size, which has doubtless been one of the factors in limiting the size of animals.

Single-celled animals such as amoeba have no special parts for breathing. Oxygen diffuses through the cell membrane and carbon dioxide leaves the cell the same way. A similar situation exists in hydra. In planaria, however, the more complex body requires that diffusion be retarded, hence the animal is limited in size. Modifications had to evolve before any increase in bulk could occur. In the earthworm this was accomplished by the introduction of a circulatory system which carries oxygen from the skin to all cells of the body (p. 281). Bulkier animals required special breathing organs which appeared in the form of gills in aquatic animals and lungs among the land forms. Let us compare the breathing systems of animals living in water and air.

Breathing organs of both have one feature in common. They are arranged so that the oxygen in water or air comes very close to the cells requiring it, or to the circulating blood which transports the oxygen to the body cells. Among the air breathers this is accomplished in two ways. The most common method is by means of thin-walled sacs which are surrounded by capillaries, thus as the blood flows through, the oxygen in the sac diffuses readily across the cell membranes and into the blood (Fig. 19-1). The composite structures of huge numbers of these sacs are the **lungs.** Insects and spiders have a method of breathing that is unique in the animal kingdom. They possess a system of tubules (tracheae) which carry oxygen directly to each cell (p. 313). Owing to the friction caused by moving air through such a system, size limitations are probably imposed on these creatures.

The larger aquatic animals possess **gills** which are again complex thin-walled structures in which the blood in the capillaries comes close to the surface being only two cell layers removed from the external water environment. Diffusion of both oxygen and carbon dioxide is readily accomplished. In some smaller forms such as marine worms, the capillaries merely approach the outer layers of the animal where diffusion can occur. This is true of some small air-breathers also, as has already been referred to in the case of the earthworm. Let us examine more carefully the complex breathing mechanism of man.

HUMAN LUNGS

The lungs of man, like those of all vertebrates, arise in the embryo from an outpocketing of the floor of the pharynx. When fully formed, they almost fill the entire **thoracic cavity.** The complete breathing system consists of the **nasal chambers, larynx, trachea, bronchi, bronchioles,** and **alveoli** (Fig. 19-2). The nostrils are the normal portals of entry for air, and they open

FIG. 19-1. Gaseous exchange in aquatic and air environments requires thin membranes of no more than two cells in thickness. This is accomplished in air-breathers by tracheae in insects and lungs in vertebrates. Water-breathing vertebrates possess gills. Some invertebrates also have gills; in others, the capillaries lie close to certain areas of the skin which is extremely thin. Sketches on the right show diagrammatically how these breathing organs are constructed at the microscopic level.

into the spacious nasal chambers which are especially adapted for warming the incoming air. The surface area is greatly increased by sheets of bony tissue, the **turbinates,** that hang down into the nasal passages. These are covered with a layer of mucous epithelium that is kept constantly wet by the mucus-secreting glands located in this layer of tissue. It is also highly vascularized, giving warmth to the entire nasal chamber. The result is that as air passes through these passages it is not only warmed to approximately body temperatures but is also humidified to some extent.

Another important feature is the provision made to filter particulate matter out

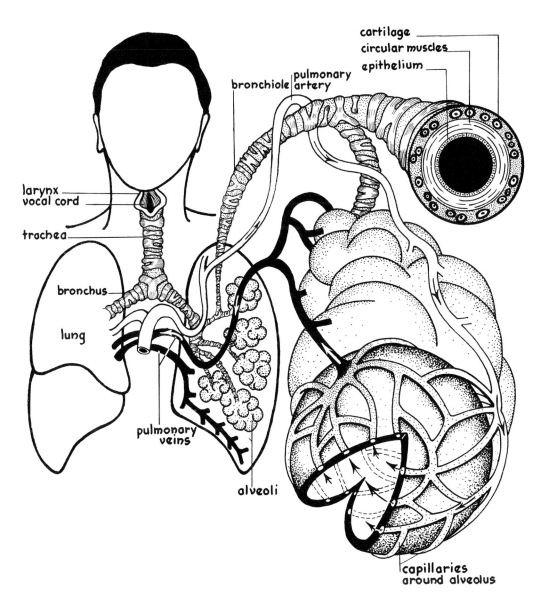

FIG. 19-2. A schematic view of the breathing system of man with one alveolus and associated parts greatly enlarged.

of the incoming air. The nose is lined with hair which strains out the larger particles, and smaller bits which pass the hair are caught in the mucous secretion and eventually discharged with it. The breathing passages are lined with ciliated epithelium which functions in moving mucus toward the nasal chambers. Proof of the efficiency of this mechanism is noted by observing the color of the nasal secretions after working in dust-laden air. The mucous secretion also has some hygienic value, because bacteria are caught by this mechanism as well, thus preventing them from reaching the lungs where they might cause disease. However, some bacteria and viruses may establish themselves in the nasal areas, as in the case of head colds. Later they may make their way into the deeper portions of the breathing tract where characteristic symptoms appear. The nasal secretions have some bacteria-destroying action, and in head colds the cells of these areas are stimulated to produce large amounts of mucus to prevent the organisms from getting a foothold. This reaction accounts for the "running nose" at the beginning of a cold. Unfortunately, this is frequently carried to such extremes that swelling of the walls closes the air passages, forcing the victim to breathe through his mouth. This makes him liable to infection from the same or other organisms, since the air has not been filtered in the nasal passages as it normally would be.

Once past the nasal passages, the air is carried down into the **pharynx** and into the **larynx** on its way to the lungs. The larynx, or **voice box,** is a cartilaginous structure at the upper end of the **trachea.** It offers a rigid support for the **vocal cords,** which are stretched bands of tough tissue that vibrate to produce a sound when they are tightened and air is forced over them. While the initial sound comes from the vocal cords, the ultimate sound produced is highly modified by the nasal chambers and mouth cavity. These resonating chambers, together with their movable parts (soft palate, tongue, and cheeks), are responsible for the **quality** of the voice, either speaking or singing. Any interference with these passages has a marked effect on the quality of the voice, a familiar phenomenon in anyone suffering from a cold.

Immediately beyond the larynx is the **trachea,** a single tube whose walls are prevented from collapsing by means of cartilaginous rings. The "windpipe," as it is sometimes called, lies at the front of the throat where the rings can be felt through the skin. The trachea passes into the chest cavity where it divides into two **bronchi,** one going to each lung. These subdivide into **bronchioles** which after many divisions terminate in tiny blind sacs, the **alveoli.**

In the alveoli the actual exchange of gases takes place. All of the mechanism up to this point functions in getting the air to and from these alveoli. The combined surface of all the alveoli of the human lungs is over 1,000 square feet, and all of this is in intimate contact with capillaries. The lungs are covered by a thin layer of epithelium called the **pleura** and the spaces between the alveoli and bronchioles are filled with elastic connective tissue. The lungs remain partially inflated at all times. When removed from the thoracic cavity they collapse to only a fraction of their inflated size, because of the constant tension on the walls of the bronchioles. But, even in this contracted condition they resemble a sponge in consistency and will readily float in water.

THE BREATHING MECHANISM

The lungs almost completely fill the thoracic cavity, which is lined with pleura identical with that covering the lungs. These two layers normally lie close together with no actual space between them, but when the lungs are deflated, the space that results is known as the **pleural space.** The two surfaces are held together because there is no

FIG. 19-3. In breathing the thoracic cavity increases and decreases in size by alternate raising and lowering of the ribs, together with a corresponding elevation and depression of the diaphragm. This can be shown experimentally by placing the lungs and trachea of a dog in a bell jar and covering the open end with a rubber membrane. By pushing up and down on the membrane, simulating the movements of the diaphragm, air passes in and out of the lungs.

FIG. 19-4. Lungs can be deflated by simply forcing air into the pleural space as shown here.

air in the pleural space. In other words, there is a partial vacuum in which the pressure is below that of the outside atmosphere. Therefore, if the walls of this closed cavity move out so as to enlarge the cavity, the walls of the lungs must follow. This creates a decreased pressure in the lungs themselves which, in turn, causes air to rush into the low pressure region deep in the alveoli. The opposite effect results when the cavity is reduced in size. The cavity can be increased and decreased in size by simply raising the ribs (Fig. 19-3) and then allowing them to return. Simultaneous with the raising of the ribs, the dome-shaped **diaphragm** is pulled downward and flattened. The ribs are raised by the contraction of the muscles lying between them (intercostal muscles) and when these muscles are relaxed the ribs fall back into position. At the same time, the diaphragm is returned to its dome-shape by a ligament that keeps it in this position. Therefore, **inspiration** is brought about by the contraction of muscles, **expiration** by relaxation. As a result of these two actions the air in the alveoli is changed.

Under extreme exertion the abdominal muscles also are involved in the breathing movements. On inspiration they relax in order to allow the diaphragm to descend farther, thereby compressing the abdominal organs. In forced expiration the abdominal muscles contract in order to help push the diaphragm upward. These muscles also play an important part in coughing and sneezing. Preceding these actions, the air passages are voluntarily closed and the muscles contract to build up a pressure within the lungs. This is followed by a sudden opening of the passages, resulting in an explosive discharge of air which is designed to dislodge any foreign matter that may have gotten into the air passages.

Accidental puncturing of the thoracic cavity brings about the collapse of the lung because when air within the pleural cavity reaches the same pressure as the outside air, the lung contracts, as pointed out above. Such a lung is nonfunctional and if both lungs collapse at the same time, suffocation follows. Fortunately, there is a partition between the lungs so that one can be deflated while the other functions normally. It even becomes necessary sometimes to col-

FIG. 19-5. In such diseases as poliomyelitis, the motor nerves to the breathing mechanism fail. The iron lung is a device that substitutes for the action of the breathing muscles. A partial vacuum is produced in a rhythmic manner over the entire body, but its specific effect is on increasing and decreasing the thoracic cavity, simulating normal breathing.

lapse one or the other lung artificially in such diseases as tuberculosis. This is easily accomplished by simply forcing a hollow needle between the ribs into the pleural space and allowing sterile air to enter (Fig. 19-4). When the needle is withdrawn the lung will gradually fill the space again after about two years, as the air is slowly absorbed into the tissues and eventually carried away in the blood.

In some diseases, particularly poliomyelitis, the motor nerves to the breathing mechanism fail to function, resulting in death from suffocation if some artificial breathing mechanism is not brought into immediate action. The apparatus used in such cases, commonly called an "iron lung," is merely a device that creates a partial vacuum over the chest region, thus replacing the nonfunctioning muscles (Fig. 19-5). Its use must be continued as long as the muscles remain inactive. Frequently the nerves regenerate, in part at least, so that gradually they are able to carry impulses to the breathing muscles and normal breathing is restored.

LUNG CAPACITY

It is a familiar fact that breathing is slow and shallow when one is at rest, either sitting or lying down, but rapidly becomes faster and deeper with exertion such as running. It is also well known that when resting one can take in a great deal more air at the end of a quiet inspiration and can force out a great deal more air at the end of a quiet expiration. These facts indicate that the lungs have a great deal more capacity than is used in nonstrenuous work. This constitutes a reserve that is always available when needed.

In quiet breathing, about 500 cc. of air is breathed in and out. This is known as **tidal air,** reminiscent of the tides (Fig. 19-6). Upon forced inspiration, 1,500 cc. more can be taken into the lungs. This is known as **complemental air.** Forced expira-

tion can deliver about 1,500 cc. of air, known as **supplemental air.** Therefore, complemental air together with tidal and supplemental air amounts to about 3,500 cc., the total capacity that can be taken in and forced out under conditions of heavy exertion. This amount is called **vital capacity.** There is some variation in this quantity, depending on the size, age, sex, and training of the individual. Athletes usually have slightly more vital capacity than do nonathletes, women slightly less than men.

Some air, about 1,000 cc., is always left in the lungs even after forced expiration. This **residual air** is present to some extent in lungs that have been removed from the body. If the lungs of an unborn child are placed in water they do not float, whereas those of the newborn who has taken a breath do. This test sometimes has legal significance in suspected cases of infanticide.

CONTROL OF BREATHING

Because the demands for oxygen vary with activity, the rate and depth of breathing vary to meet these demands. It is possible to change the rate of breathing voluntarily, although one does not need to think in order to breathe. One can hold his breath for some time, with considerable distress, but eventually he will be forced to breathe again in a normal fashion. The rate of breathing is altered by a number of conditions arising from within as well as from without the organism. Such conditions include emotional as well as physical strain (Fig. 19-6).

Breathing is a result of the coordinated action of a great many muscles which require a rather precise controlling mechanism called the **breathing center.** This consists of a group of specialized cells located in the **medulla** (Fig. 19-7). Bursts of nervous impulses leave this center over the **phrenic** nerves to the diaphragm and over the **cervical sympathetics** to the rib muscles,

FIG. 19-6. Breathing movements can be recorded by such a device as shown here. The movements alter the air pressure in the rubber hose which is transmitted via the rubber tube to the rubber membrane which in turn influences the movement of the lever, the tip of which inscribes the magnified movements on the smoked drum. With this instrument the tracings shown in A and B were made. See the text for an explanation of A. The tracings in B are a result of mental work. A student was given a problem in mathematics to solve which required one minute. How his breathing was influenced during this mental work is shown in the tracing.

causing both to contract, resulting in inspiration. The rate at which these contractions occur depends on several factors influencing the breathing center. If the carbon dioxide content of the blood rises, as it does in exercise or emotional stress, the impulses are quickened. If, on the other hand, the carbon dioxide is diminished, the impulses will be farther apart. If the phrenic nerve is severed or destroyed through disease such as poliomyelitis, the impulses fail to reach the diaphragm and this muscle ceases its contractions. The same is true of the other motor nerves going to the rib muscles. It is possible by taking a series of deep inhalations and exhalations to reduce the carbon dioxide content of the blood to a point where breathing can be held in abeyance until the gas again reaches a sufficient concentration to stimulate the breathing center. A newborn child, as well, will take its first breath only after the carbon dioxide has reached a certain level. When its placental circulation is cut off the gas begins to build up in the blood. Occasionally, even then breathing will not start. This can be remedied oftentimes by forcing air containing 10 per cent carbon dioxide into the lungs.

One of the problems of breathing that was not understood for a long time was how the breathing center could send out these bursts of impulses in a rhythmic fashion. It has been discovered by clever surgery that if all of the sensory nerves leading to the breathing center are severed, inspiration will occur but not expiration. In other words, the muscles of the diaphragm and of the ribs will contract but will not relax, because a steady stream of impulses continues to come to them. This means that the breathing center must be inhibited periodically so that the bursts of impulses coming to the breathing muscles are interrupted. This is accomplished by sensory endings in the walls of the alveoli and other

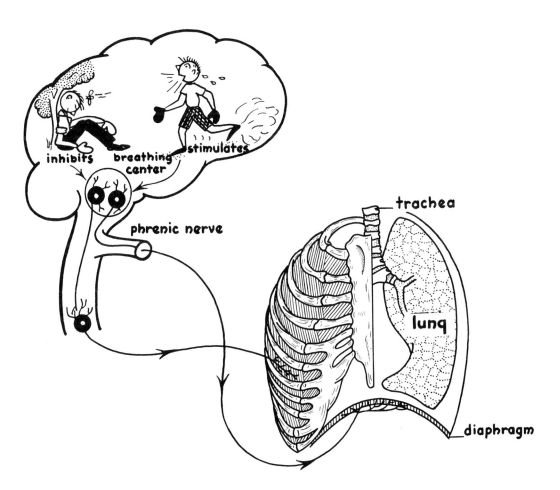

FIG. 19-7. The rate of breathing is controlled by the breathing center which is sensitive to carbon dioxide in the blood. During activity the increased carbon dioxide content of the blood stimulates the breathing center to bring about increased rate of breathing. The opposite effect prevails when at rest.

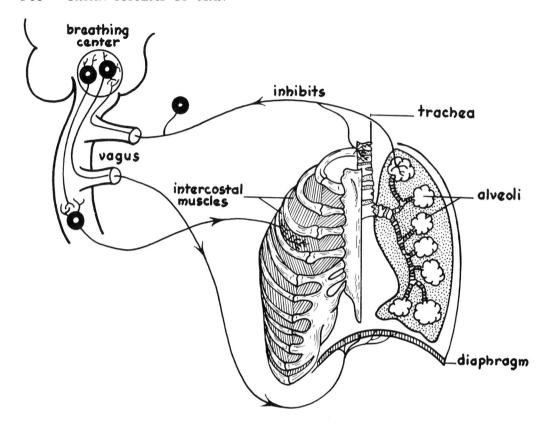

FIG. 19-8. The rhythmic movements in breathing are controlled by the breathing center also. Sensory nerve endings lying in the alveoli send impulses to the center which inhibit its action when the alveoli are stretched on inspiration. During the period of inhibition, no motor impulses come from the center to the muscles, hence they relax, resulting in expiration.

parts of the lungs (Fig. 19-8). When air is drawn into the lungs, the stretching of the walls presses on the nerve endings, causing impulses which inhibit the breathing center. Such is the device by which the lungs are alternately filled and emptied.

The breathing center is also inhibited by impulses coming to it from many other parts of the body. Receptors lie in the walls of the larynx and pharynx which are sensitive to foreign bodies or harmful gases. For example, when a particle of food gets into the larynx, breathing ceases at once thus preventing the passage of the particle farther into the delicate breathing tract. This is followed by a closing of the epiglottis until considerable pressure is built up in the chest cavity. It then lets go explosively in the form of a cough as already described. Likewise, if irritating gases such as chlorine are drawn into the pharynx, breathing ceases instantly with the closing of the air passage by the epiglottis. Here is another safeguard to prevent injury to the extremely sensitive and delicate lining of the breathing tract. Severe pain and sudden chilling will also inhibit the breathing center. One also "catches his breath" because of the action of these nerves on the breathing center. Thus we see how carefully this mechanism is tuned to the job of protecting the important breathing organ so that its function may go on uninterrupted throughout life.

GASEOUS EXCHANGE

By measuring the amount of oxygen and carbon dioxide in expired air as compared to that of the atmosphere, it is easy to demonstrate that some exchange has taken place, as shown in the following figures:

	Inspired Air	Alveolar Air	Difference
Oxygen	20.0%	14.5%	5.5%
Carbon dioxide	0.04%	5.5%	5.1%
Nitrogen	79.0%	80.0%	1.0%

Water and other gases have not been taken into account in the above approximate figures. It is noted that atmospheric air has lost approximately 27 per cent of its oxygen (difference ÷ total inspired air) and has picked up approximately 5 per cent carbon dioxide in passing through the alveoli of the lungs. Blood passing near the alveoli

has lost most, but not all, of its carbon dioxide and has taken on a load of oxygen. Just how is this done?

The oxygen molecules in the air dissolve in the watery mucus covering the lining of the alveoli and pass directly through by diffusion to the blood which is flowing very close to the walls of the alveoli, in fact, only two cells away (one cell layer in the capillary wall plus one cell layer in the alveolar wall) (Fig. 19-9). Oxygen passes from the alveolar air to the blood by simple diffusion, since the concentration of the oxygen molecules is much greater in the alveoli than in the blood. Although oxygen molecules are moving freely across the membranes in both directions, there are more going into the blood than are going into the alveoli, hence the net movement is toward the blood stream. Conversely, the carbon dioxide moves in the opposite direction for exactly the same reason. The inert nitrogen gas remains approximately the same

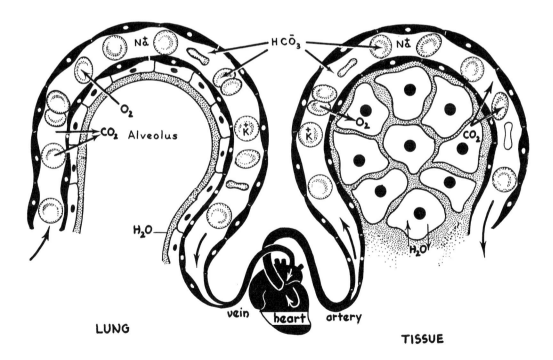

FIG. 19-9. This is a schematic representation of how gaseous exchange occurs in the alveoli and in the tissues. An explanation is found in the text.

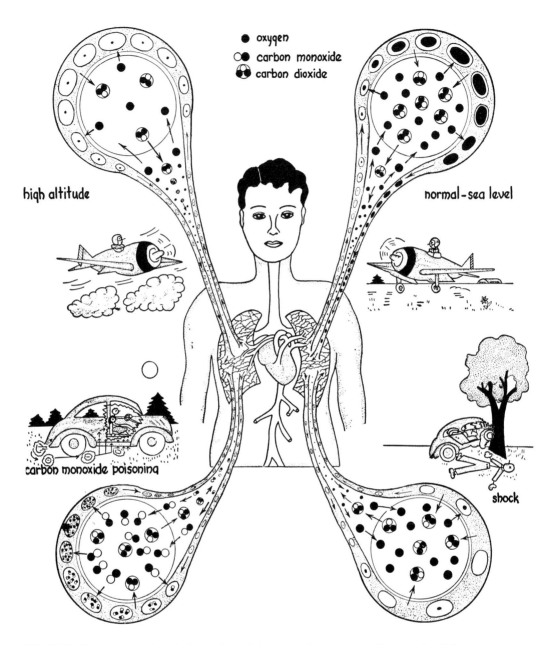

FIG. 19-10. There are several physical and chemical factors in the external environment that influence gaseous exchange. Under normal atmospheric pressures (sea level) the gaseous exchange in the alveoli is adequate. At high altitudes (beyond 14,000 feet) the air pressure is so reduced that an insufficient amount of oxygen passes into the blood to maintain consciousness. In shock (a physiological response often caused by serious lacerations or other trauma) the blood pressure drops so low in the alveoli that circulation is inadequate to pick up enough oxygen to maintain normal body activities. In the presence of carbon monoxide (CO) a stable compound (methemoglobin) is formed in the blood, thus rendering hemoglobin incapable of carrying oxygen. If prolonged, breathing of CO can be fatal.

during breathing. The over-all result, then, is that the blood leaving the lungs is rich in oxygen and low in carbon dioxide, whereas expired air is rich in carbon dioxide and low in oxygen. With the continued breathing movements there is a continual exchange of these gases, and interruptions cannot be tolerated, at least for any prolonged periods of time.

The amount of oxygen in the alveoli depends on the amount in the air, which changes with atmospheric pressure. At sea level it is 760 mm. of mercury, of which about 150 mm. represents the **partial pressure** of oxygen. There is a gradual drop in pressure as one rises above the earth's surface and with this comes a drop in the pressure of oxygen in the alveoli, even though the breathing rate and depth are increased. At about 14,000 feet, no matter how fast or deep the breathing, symptoms called **mountain sickness** appear. These are due directly to a shortage of oxygen in the tissues, resulting from too little oxygen in the alveoli and hence too little in the blood (Fig. 19-10). Airplanes at or above 14,000 feet must, therefore, supplement the oxygen supply. This is done in passenger liners by pressurizing the entire cabin to that of about 4,000 feet, no matter how high the plane goes. People who live at high altitudes (10,000 feet) soon become acclimatized to the rarefied air by producing more red corpuscles, thus increasing the oxygen-carrying capacity of the blood.

In the tissues exactly the opposite condition prevails with respect to the movement of the two gases (Fig. 19-9). The oxygen diffuses from the blood into the tissue cells because the amount of oxygen is higher in the blood than in the tissues, and the carbon dioxide diffuses out of the tissues into the blood for a similar reason. Not all of the oxygen leaves the blood at the tissues, however. Only about 7 cc. out of a possible 19 cc. (per 100 cc. of blood) actually diffuses into the tissue cells.

TRANSPORT OF GASES

The value of the blood as a transporting agent for oxygen and carbon dioxide can be determined easily by measuring the amount of these gases that will be dissolved in equal quantities of blood and water. It will be found that for both O_2 and CO_2 many times more will be picked up by blood than by water. This is primarily because of that amazingly complex organic compound called **hemoglobin** (p. 570). Plasma is little better than water in its capacity to carry these two gases. For example, only 0.2 cc. of oxygen and 0.3 cc. of carbon dioxide will dissolve in 100 cc. of plasma, whereas the same amount of whole blood will absorb 20 cc. of oxygen and 50 cc. or more of carbon dioxide. If it were not for hemoglobin, the blood would need to circulate 35 times faster than it does to accomplish the same job.

About 98 per cent of the oxygen is carried in combination with hemoglobin and the rest is dissolved in the plasma. The molecules unite in a one-to-one ratio, that is:

$$\underset{\substack{\text{Hemoglobin}\\\text{(dull red)}}}{Hb} + O_2 \underset{\text{(tissues)}}{\overset{\text{(lungs)}}{\rightleftarrows}} \underset{\substack{\text{Oxyhemoglobin}\\\text{(scarlet)}}}{HbO_2}$$

Obviously the reaction must be a reversible one, because the oxygen must be as readily released to the tissue cells as it is taken up in the alveoli in the lungs. Hence blood leaving the tissues contains largely hemoglobin, whereas that leaving the alveoli contains primarily oxyhemoglobin. The color difference in these two explains why systemic veins are dull red in color while arteries are scarlet.

Hemoglobin is no less remarkable in its capacity to make it possible for the blood to carry large quantities of carbon dioxide. When this gas leaves the tissues and enters the blood (Fig. 19-9) it immediately enters the red blood cells where, under the influence of the enzyme **carbonic anhydrase,** it reacts with water to form carbonic acid (H_2CO_3), the bubbly ingredient in soda water. Carbonic acid dissociates to form hydrogen (H^+) and bicarbonate ions (HCO_3^-), and since sodium ions (Na^+) are plentiful in the plasma and potassium ions (K^+) in the red cells, the CO_2 is transported to the lungs as sodium and potassium bicarbonates. Almost one-third of the CO_2 is carried in the cells and two-thirds in the plasma. If carbonic acid were not immediately transformed to a harmless bicarbonate, it would render the blood very acid because of the release of free hydrogen ions. This we know does not happen, for the blood has a relatively constant number of hydrogen and hydroxyl ions (pH 7.45) at all times. The numerous buffers (inorganic ions, amino acids, and proteins) make this possible. If, however, the alveoli become unable to eliminate CO_2 as in disease (pneumonia), the carbonic acid will build up in the blood which will then become more acid than usual (it is still alkaline), resulting in a condition called **acidosis.** Tissues cannot tolerate this acid condition and will soon die.

In the lungs, the entire series of events is reversed and CO_2 is released to the alveolar air. The rate at which CO_2 is released from carbonic acid is greatly facilitated by carbonic anhydrase. As the carbonic acid is transformed into CO_2 and H_2O, it is immediately replaced by more from the bicarbonates with which it is in equilibrium. The process is simplified in the scheme below.

exchange in each site. The passage of O_2 into the tissues enhances the release of CO_2 into the blood; likewise, the diffusion of CO_2 into the alveolar air in the lungs fosters the uptake of O_2. Very slight changes in the concentration of the gases in both the alveoli and the tissues have pronounced effects on the chemical equilibria which hold or release O_2 and CO_2 at these sites.

For all chemical purposes, nitrogen plays no part in respiratory exchange in man. However, it does produce some effects which become important only under unusual conditions. In probing into the various corners of his environment man has gotten into trouble with this abundant and omnipresent gas. Trouble starts when he leaves the earth's surface very far, either up into rarefied air or down into the depths of the sea with its tremendous water pressures. Gases under pressure remain in solution as long as the pressure is maintained, but the moment the pressure is decreased they will come out of solution in the form of bubbles. This familiar fact is observed when the cap is removed from a bottle of "coke"—bubbles of carbon dioxide rise rapidly from within the fluid because of the release of pressure.

At sea level there is an atmospheric pressure of 760 mm. of mercury exerted on all parts of the body, inside and outside. Minor differences in pressure, such as those due to altitude changes encountered in driving across the country, have little or no effect, because the change is gradual and the gases in the blood and tissues have a chance to adjust themselves in an undisturbing

$$H_2O + CO_2 \rightleftarrows H_2CO_3 \rightleftarrows H^+ + HCO_3^- + \left\{ \begin{matrix} K^+ \\ Na^+ \end{matrix} \right\} \rightleftarrows \left\{ \begin{matrix} K\ HCO_3 \\ NaHCO_3 \end{matrix} \right\} \text{ BLOOD}$$

(above arrow: TISSUES; below arrow: ALVEOLI)

The loading and unloading of the blood with CO_2 is coupled with the oxygenation of the hemoglobin. The chemical equilibria established in the tissues and the lungs are such as to foster the rapid gaseous

manner. However, if the change is sudden, that is, if one suddenly ascends to 20,000 feet in a minute or two, these dissolved gases begin to form bubbles in the blood which float about and become lodged in the blood vessels, plugging them and thus cutting off the circulation in parts of the body. This results in violent pain which sometimes causes the person to bend over, hence the name "bends." This discomfort is also experienced by deep sea divers when they begin to surface after being submerged to a considerable depth in the sea. Divers must surface slowly to avoid the "bends," although there are considerable differences in individuals, some suffering more acutely than others. With the advent of high speed rocket planes in recent years the necessity for preventing "decompression sickness," as it is referred to now, has become more important than ever. Research has revealed that **helium,** another inert gas, leaves the tissues much faster than nitrogen and for that reason has been employed to prevent the sickness. Aviators breathe the gas a few minutes before taking off, thus replacing the nitrogen in their tissues with helium, and when they reach high altitudes they do not suffer from decompression sickness as they otherwise would.

The matter of ventilation in living quarters has gone through various stages in the past 100 years. It was once thought that night air was bad and that all windows must be battened down tight at night or one would certainly "shiver with the ague." It has since been learned that the "badness" in the night air was mosquitoes and the ague was due to the malarial parasites residing in the body of the mosquito that were transmitted by its bite to people. Then someone mistakenly correlated tuberculosis with a lack of ventilation, so people went into a period of living out in the open. Windows were flung open at night and it was considered in the interests of good health to be covered with snow the following morning while still lying in bed. Today a more sane approach to the problem of ventilation has come about, based on scientific facts.

It is true that oxygen is withdrawn from the inspired air and that in an airtight room after a considerable period of time all of the oxygen would be used up. But who lives in an air-tight room? Most houses are so porous that the exchange through windows, doors, and even walls and roof is adequate to take care of all of the oxygen needs of the people residing within. This air turnover likewise rids the room of the accumulated carbon dioxide. However, everyone is familiar with the "stuffiness" common in crowded theaters and other gatherings. This feeling probably arises from the increased humidity and temperature that comes from rebreathed air, mingled with the usual variety of body odors. Circulating and drying the air restores it to outside freshness. To insure comfort it is necessary only to see that the air in the house is circulated, and this is the principle of air-conditioning which has become popular in recent years.

SUGGESTED SUPPLEMENTARY READINGS

CARLSON, A. J., and JOHNSON, V., *The Machinery of the Body* (Chicago, University of Chicago Press, 1962).

FULTON, J. F., *Selected Readings in the History of Physiology* (Springfield, Ill., Charles C Thomas, 1930).

GABRIEL, M. L., and FOGEL, S., *Great Experiments in Biology* (Englewood Cliffs, N.J., Prentice-Hall, Inc., 1955).

GIESE, A. C., *Cell Physiology* (Philadelphia, W. B. Saunders Co., 1962).

GREEN, D. E., "The Synthesis of Fat." *Scientific American,* 202(2) (February, 1960), 46.

ROMER, A. S., *The Vertebrate Body* (Philadelphia, W. B. Saunders Co., 1962).

WEAVER, W., "People, Energy, and Food," *Science Monthly,* 78 (1954).

WOODBURNE, R. T., *Essentials of Human Anatomy* (New York, Oxford University Press, 1961).

20

The Transportation System

In the previous two chapters we have seen that as animals grow larger, some sort of transportation system becomes imperative to insure that food and oxygen reach the cells. Above the simple metazoa, such a system has evolved in the form of a circulating fluid in which the food and oxygen are transported.

Amoeba and hydra have no need for such transportation because all of the cells are in direct contact with the external environment (Fig. 20-1). To some extent this is also true of planaria. However, its deeply-lying cells, such as those in the mesoderm, may receive their oxygen and food from a fluid, **hemolymph,** that bathes all of these internal cells. There is no means of circulating the fluid except by the body movements. Because this is so slow, the animal itself responds feebly to its environment; hence these are all slow-moving creatures.

Although a rudimentary circulatory system is found for the first time among the nemertines (p. 242), it was not until the annelids appeared that a well-differentiated system of closed tubes was established as an essential organ system. The circulatory system of the earthworm, for example, is a

FIG. 20-1. The problem of food and oxygen distribution and waste removal has been solved in different ways in representative animals. The problem is simple in amoeba and hydra but becomes more complex in the higher forms.

well-defined, efficient system. Like all transport systems, it is composed of a circulating fluid, **blood,** confined to closed vessels which at some point break up into very tiny tubules. These tubules have walls only one cell layer thick and they are in close association with all of the cells of the body. A pump is provided to keep the fluid flowing continuously. Once such a system was established, the bulk of the animal could increase very greatly with safety and this is exactly what happened, as demonstrated by the great dinosaurs of the past and the huge whales of today.

Evolution in the vertebrate circulatory system is one of the many interesting changes that accompanied the transition from aquatic to terrestrial existence as described in an earlier chapter. This can be briefly summed up with the aid of a sketch (Fig. 20-2). In fish, the circulatory flow of blood was between the breathing organs (gills) and the body tissues. The simple fish heart (one auricle and one ventricle) forced the blood through arteries into the gill capillaries where respiratory gaseous exchange occurred. These capillaries coalesced to form arteries which carried blood to tissue capillaries in all parts of the body. The capillaries then united to form veins which conveyed the blood back to the heart—a very simple system.

When vertebrates made the transition to land life, a circuit to care for the newly acquired lungs was established. This meant the construction of a new heart superimposed on the old one. The beginning of this development is seen in amphibians where a second auricle, together with a pulmonary circulation, appeared. This was only a partial solution, for the oxygenated and reduced blood became mixed. In a further step forward, a complete pulmonary heart appeared in the higher reptiles. This proved so satisfactory that it was retained in both mammals and birds. Once the two hearts were formed, the vertebrates were fully equipped for land life and evolution was

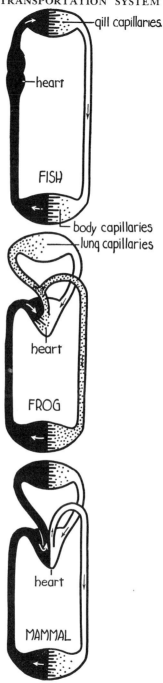

FIG. 20-2. A schematic portrayal of the evolution of the vertebrate circulatory system. While the simple heart was satisfactory for an aquatic form, it could not handle the problem of transporting oxygen in sufficient quantities for the active air-breathing land dwellers. The second heart (pulmonary heart) had its beginnings in the amphibians and reached its full-fledged condition in the higher reptiles, birds, and mammals.

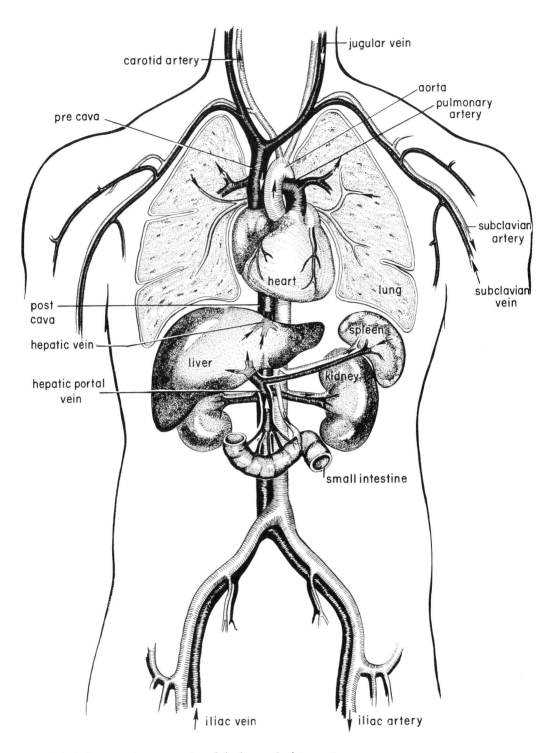

carotid artery

jugular vein

aorta

pulmonary artery

pre cava

subclavian artery

subclavian vein

heart

lung

post cava

hepatic vein

spleen

liver

kidney

hepatic portal vein

small intestine

iliac vein

iliac artery

FIG. 20-3. A diagrammatic representation of the human circulatory system.

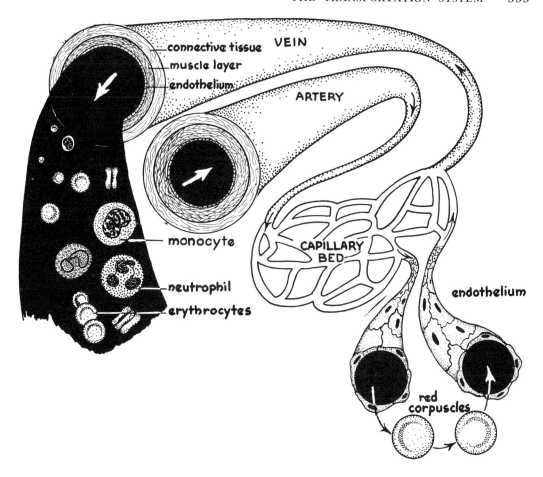

FIG. 20-4. Arteries and veins differ only in thickness of their walls, whereas capillaries are composed only of the layer of cells that lines the larger vessels. In this figure the arrows indicate the path of the blood. Some of the various cellular components of the blood are also shown.

extremely rapid, as evidenced by the tremendous variety of land forms. Let us examine the circulatory system of man as an example of this system in land vertebrates.

HUMAN CIRCULATION

The over-all design of circulation in man (Fig. 20-3) is similar to that of air-breathing vertebrates in general, differing only in such minor details as the number and location of vessels.

The functional part of circulation is the circulating blood. The elaborate mechanism of the heart, arteries, veins, and capil-

laries is merely a mechanical device to circulate the blood so that its contents may reach every cell in the body.

Before studying the blood itself, let us examine the machinery of circulation.

THE VESSELS

These consist of a closed system of tubes, large and small, which convey the blood continuously within a circuit. The large vessels carrying blood **away** from the heart are known as **arteries;** the large vessels bringing blood back **to** the heart are known as **veins;** and the tiny intermediate vessels are **capillaries.** The last are the most important, since it is through their walls that the real work of the circulatory system goes on.

The Capillaries

These tubules, often so small that blood cells pass through single file, have walls composed of a single layer of cells. These same **endothelial** cells continue as the lining of the larger vessels (Fig. 20-4). The capillaries form a network throughout all the tissues of the body, so vast that a pin prick anywhere usually punctures one, causing blood to ooze out. Because of their thin walls, dissolved substances in the blood can readily pass into the tissues and, conversely, waste substances in the tissues can readily diffuse into the blood and be carried away. In an active animal such as man it is essential that this exchange be a rapid one. Even in the relatively sluggish frog, whose capillaries can be easily observed in the web of its foot, blood cells race through the capillaries in a fraction of a second and yet this is sufficient time for the important processes of exchange to occur.

The Arteries and Veins

On either end of the capillaries are larger tubules, **venules** (little veins) at the end toward the heart and **arterioles** (little arteries) at the end coming from the heart. These venules and arterioles become larger and larger as the heart is approached, where they are designated as veins and arteries.

FIG. 20-5. Cross-section of the human umbilical cord to show the construction of an artery and vein. The largest opening is a vein. Note the thin wall as compared to that of the two smaller arteries just above it. Veins and arteries are similar in structure except that the muscle layer in the latter is heavier.

There is no structural difference between the two except that the walls of the arteries are thicker and stronger than those of the veins (Fig. 20-5). Both are composed of three layers of tissue. The inner **endothelium** is the same tissue that makes up the whole of the capillary wall. As a matter of fact, it lines the entire circulatory system. The outside layer of both arteries and veins is made up of a tough **connective tissue** so that it readily stretches to permit an increase in diameter, but does not easily rend. Between the two is a **smooth muscle layer** which regulates the diameter of the blood vessel, thereby controlling the amount of blood flowing through it. These muscles (**vasoconstrictors**) are under the influence of the autonomic nervous system and the state of their contraction depends on the need of various tissues of the body for food and oxygen. For instance, following a meal the muscles in the walls of the blood vessels going to and from the viscera relax, allowing more blood to flow to and from these organs. On the other hand, during violent exercise they contract in this region but relax in the muscles and breathing system. By such regulation the various parts of the body are supplied with the proper amount of blood at all times. The veins differ from the arteries in that some have **valves** which prevent the blood from flowing backwards in them. High blood pressure in the arteries makes such valves unnecessary.

The walls of the arteries need to be stronger than those of the veins because the blood is under considerable pressure when it leaves the heart and this pressure alternately rises and falls with each contraction of the ventricles. Since the capillaries need a continuous flow, there must be some means of absorbing these high and low pressure levels, and this is taken care of by the elastic arterial walls. When the pressure rises suddenly, as it normally does, the walls stretch, absorbing the pressure. Between beats, then, the resilience of the walls forces the blood through the capillaries at an even flow. If this were not true the blood would gush through at high pressure and stop altogether between beats when the heart is at rest. Indeed, something approximating this happens in advancing years when the walls of the vessels grow hard due partly to deposition of salts. When this occurs, the pressure of the blood rises so high that the brittle vessels are apt to burst and cause damage by cutting off the blood source to vital organs.

THE HEART

The pumping mechanism of animals has had a long history of evolution from the simple pulsating tubes of the annelid to the highly efficient organ of the vertebrate. Much of this history has been portrayed in earlier chapters, and with respect to vertebrates can be summed up briefly by comparing the hearts of several adult forms (Fig. 20-6). The history is correlated with the transition from aquatic to land life. The primitive heart of the shark, as well as the more elaborate one of the salmon, is a two-chambered pump that functions satisfactorily where gills are the breathing organs. With the advent of lungs, a second heart was formed over millions of years of evolution. Today we see how this probably happened in the adult forms of the frog, lizard, and crocodile. The story is also recapitulated in the developing mammalian embryo (Fig. 20-6).

The adult human heart is a muscular organ composed of four principal chambers, two **auricles** and two **ventricles,** and a system of valves to keep the blood moving in one direction (Fig. 20-7). The auricles are thin-walled, sac-like chambers whose principal function is to collect sufficient blood from the great veins to fill the ventricles quickly the moment they are empty. The ventricles, on the other hand, are thick-walled chambers whose sole function is to keep the blood forever on the move

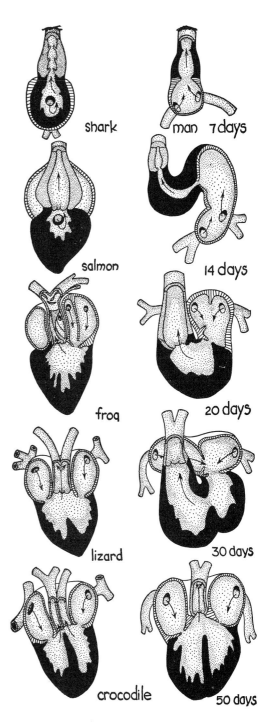

FIG. 20-6. The phylogenetic development of the vertebrate heart from the shark through the reptile is shown on the left, as compared with the embryology of the human heart shown on the right.

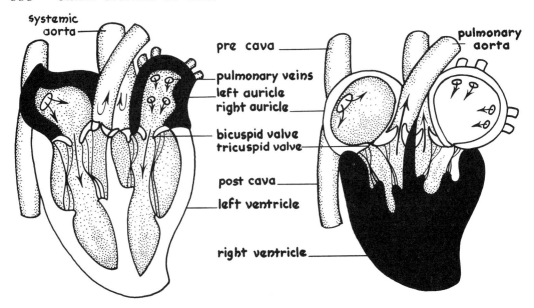

FIG. 20-7. The human heart is shown here cut so that the chambers and valves can be seen. The contracting portions are indicated in solid black, whereas the parts that are relaxed are left white. The two figures demonstrate the way the parts operate during the cardiac cycle.

throughout the vast network of vessels. Because the left ventricle is thicker and larger than the right, it performs the greater task of forcing the blood throughout the body, whereas the right heart merely keeps the blood moving through the lungs. The two hearts, however, are intimately associated and beat simultaneously even though their circuits are distinct and separate. The left auricle and ventricle are separated by a pair of flaps, called the **bicuspid** (mitral) **valve;** similarly, the right auricle and ventricle are separated by three flaps, the **tricuspid valve.** These flaps of tough tissue are held rigidly in place when under pressure by tiny cords that extend to the inner muscular walls of the ventricles.

The ventricles open into large arteries, the left into the **systemic aorta** and the right into the **pulmonary artery.** Very near the openings are half-moon-shaped valves, the **semilunar valves,** which prevent the blood from returning to the ventricles once it is forced out. Each valve is composed of three thin-walled cups that fit very tightly together when under pressure. These, as well as the other valves, are arranged so that the blood can pass only in one direction. This, then, is the pump that keeps the blood circulating continuously throughout life.

The Blood Path Through the Heart

Blood passes from the pre- and post-cavas into the right auricle, the walls of which then contract (**systole**), forcing the blood through the tricuspid valve into the right ventricle (Fig. 20-7). Actually, when the ventricle empties and begins to relax (**diastole**), the blood requires very little force to flow into the ventricle; hence the muscular walls of the auricles are thin. The ventricle fills completely, then suddenly contracts with sufficient force to exceed the pressure in the pulmonary artery, thus opening the semilunar valve which allows the blood to pass to the lung capillaries. The sequence of events during one complete systole and diastole is known as the cardiac cycle. The blood then returns to the left auricle by way of the four pulmonary veins. The path taken by blood passing through the left heart is similar to that of the right, although the force with which it leaves is greater because the blood must go throughout the body as a result of the impetus received from the muscle of the left ventricle. It passes over the semilunar valve of the dorsal aorta and out to the capillaries of the body, eventually returning to the right auricle again through the vena cavas.

How the Heart is Nourished

It is obvious that such an active muscle as the heart must require an enormous supply of oxygen and food continuously. Even though tons of blood flow through the heart chambers, none of it reaches the heart muscle because there are no direct connections to the muscle from the chambers. The heart has a system of blood vessels of its own, however, called the **coronary circulation.** This rather strange name was given to it because the vessels reminded early anatomists of a crown, since they encircle the top part of the ventricles. The two **coronary arteries** leave the systemic aorta just above the semilunar valves (Fig. 20-8) and pass throughout the heart muscle, ultimately becoming capillaries. Blood returns through a system of veins (**coronary veins**) which coalesce and eventually empty into the right auricle via the **coronary sinus.** Approximately one-fourth of the total blood pumped out by the left ventricle passes through the coronary circulation. This is an extremely important system because the slightest impairment, such as a tiny clot of blood lodging in it, profoundly affects heart action. This is one form of heart attack. Sudden death results when the stoppage of blood is sufficient to hinder seriously the contraction of the muscle.

Listening to the heart during health and illness led more alert physicians many centuries ago to recognize that certain sounds could be associated with heart malfunctioning. The characteristic "lub-dub," as heard with the stethoscope, is caused by the closing of the various heart valves to prevent the blood from rushing back into the auricles from the ventricles and back into the ventricles from the great arteries. The low "lub" sound is due to the closing of the mitral and tricuspid valves during the initial stages of ventricular systole, whereas the sharp "dub" which follows the first sound very closely is caused by the sudden closing of the semilunar valves in the arteries. There is a brief pause during which time the heart rests and the auricles fill. Any abnormalities in the closing of these valves can be detected by various "murmuring" sounds that are easily recognized by the trained ear of the physician. During some kinds of infectious diseases, and perhaps allergies, the edges of the valves become inflamed and injured; upon healing they frequently do not fit as well as they once did, resulting in the so-called heart murmur. Such an injured heart can, however, increase its size and output so that even with faulty valves it may still be adequate. Such a heart is often spoken of as a "compensated heart" and within limits may function normally for many years.

The work of the heart is almost unbelievable when it is compared to that accomplished by other muscles of the body. Starting long before birth, indeed, when the embryo is no more than 25 days old, it continues its ceaseless contractions until old age; during all this time it does not falter, and its only rest comes between systoles. Beating at 70 times per minute, over 100,-000 per day, and nearly 40,000,000 per year, the heart does enough work in one year's time to lift its owner nearly 100 miles above the surface of the earth. It is truly a remarkable organ.

Control of the Heart

The heart muscle will function in an apparently normal fashion when removed

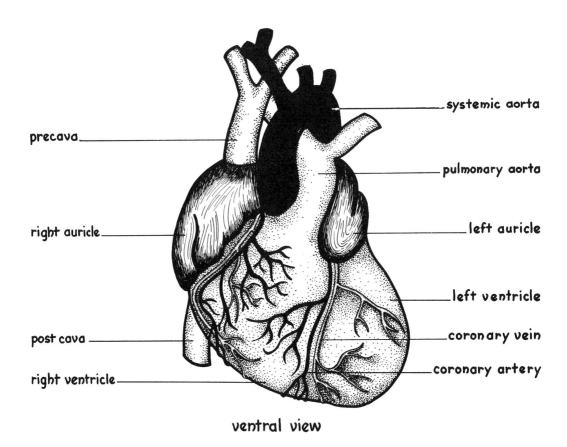

precava

right auricle

post cava

right ventricle

systemic aorta

pulmonary aorta

left auricle

left ventricle

coronary vein

coronary artery

ventral view

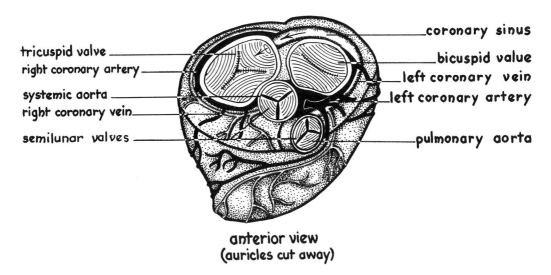

tricuspid valve
right coronary artery

systemic aorta
right coronary vein

semilunar valves

coronary sinus
bicuspid value
left coronary vein
left coronary artery

pulmonary aorta

anterior view
(auricles cut away)

FIG. 20-8. The heart is here shown in ventral and anterior view with the auricles cut away in order to illustrate the nature of the coronary circulation.

from the body that houses it. Histologically, cardiac muscle is unlike either smooth or striated muscle (p. 105). The nuclei lie deeply embedded in the muscle fiber as in smooth muscle, but cross-striations are present, much as in voluntary muscle. Most important, however, all of the fibers are directly connected to other fibers so that the entire mass of muscle fibers is continuous, forming a syncytium.

Skeletal and smooth muscles contract only when they are stimulated by nervous impulses or by hormones. The vertebrate heart, on the other hand, may be removed from the body and if placed in the proper nutrient fluid at the proper temperature will continue beating for hours. Moreover, the rate of pulsation may be quite normal even though it is isolated from any nervous or hormonal control. This might seem to indicate that the heart is not influenced by either of these types of control, but a check of one's own pulse under varying conditions of excitation or physical exertion quickly shows that such is not the case. This means only that the **intrinsic** nature of the

heart muscle is to contract in a rhythmic manner. The rate of this beat, however, may be influenced by outside factors. This can be demonstrated in an excised heart. When placed in a cold fluid it slows down, whereas in a warmer one it speeds up. Therefore, temperature affects its rate. Certain drugs do the same.

The manner in which the heart beats has been determined rather precisely in studies of the excised heart. It has been shown, for example, that if the heart is subjected to reduced temperatures in various parts, its rate of beat is changed only when a specific region is cooled. This region lies near the base of the great veins where they enter the right auricle (Fig. 20-9). There is a discrete bundle of specialized tissue lying here called the **sinus node** or "pacemaker" which is responsible. This is clearly shown by the following experiment. If an excised heart is clamped in the region between the auricles and the ventricles, the former continue their rhythmic beating whereas the latter remain quiet. This demonstrates that impulses pass from the pacemaker through the auricles to the ventricles. We have learned further that in passing from auricles to ventricles the impulses travel over a bridge called the **auricular-ventricular node** (Fig. 20-9). In the contraction of the heart as a whole, the auricles beat first, the ventricles second. Nerve pathways in the heart have been traced from the auricular-ventricular node down through the septum between the ventricles and anteriorly through the muscle, and each beat is synchronized with an impulse that follows this pathway.

Even though the heart will beat autonomously in the intact animal, its beat is carefully regulated by two sets of motor nerves which carry impulses directly to the sinus node (Fig. 20-10). Branches from the **vagus** (cranial-sacral) may inhibit the beat, whereas many branches from the thoracolumbar autonomic system in the cervical region may accelerate it. These are influ-

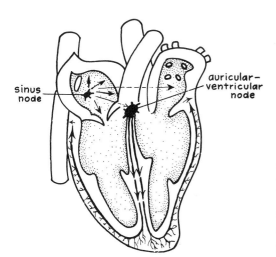

FIG. 20-9. The sequence of the contraction of the various chambers of the heart is under the influence of the sinus node and the auricular-ventricular node. The beat is initiated in the sinus node, from which it travels over the heart as indicated by the arrows.

enced by emotions, a fact familiar to all.

Additional sources of regulation come from three groups of sensory endings close to or in the heart itself. One group originates in the aortic arch and terminates in the **cardiac center** (depressor center) in the **medulla**, and these nerves are called **depressors** because they slow down the heart beat by stimulating the vagus when the pressure is unnecessarily high in the aorta. Another set of nerves comes from the carotid arteries which also record elevated pressures in these vessels. Such action occurs following exercise when the muscles no longer need a large volume of blood. A third group arises in the right auricle and terminates in the **cardiac center** (accelerator center). When the large skeletal muscles are in vigorous action, blood flows into the right auricle in greater amounts than normally. As a result the walls are stretched, stimulating the accelerator nerves to make the heart beat faster with the result that the muscles receive the additional blood they need. Thus, by the combined action of these sets of governors, the heart is able to maintain a rate that supplies all parts of the body with an adequate amount of blood under variable circumstances.

Other Controls of Heart Rate. Many factors other than nerve impulses affect the heart rate. These usually stimulate the heart directly. We have already mentioned that heart rate is influenced by temperature change. The rate is increased with increasing acidity and decreased with increased alkalinity. Carbon dioxide increases the heart rate as well as the rate of breathing, noted earlier. Hormones, such as epinephrine, have a pronounced effect on heart rate. Actually there is almost no change in the body that does not affect the heart in one way or another. This must be so if it is to do its job properly.

It was brought out in an earlier chap-

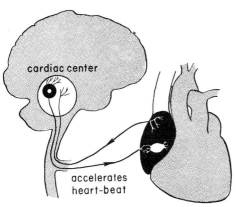

FIG. 20-10. The rate of heart-beat is under the control of the cardiac center in the medulla. The upper figure demonstrates how emotions control the beat. The middle and lower figures show how the rate is regulated according to physical needs.

ter that when a muscle contracts, a minute electrical impulse is set up which can be detected with delicate instruments. This fact has been employed in diagnosing heart difficulties. The instrument employed is the **electrocardiograph.** It records slight electrical changes that occur when the various parts of the heart muscle contract. A normal heart produces a characteristic series of peaks and valleys. Any deviation in this pattern indicates abnormality, the exact nature of which can be discerned rather accurately.

BLOOD PRESSURE

If a vein is severed the blood oozes out in a gentle flow, whereas if an artery is cut it shoots out in spurts which are synchronized with ventricular systoles. It is obvious that the blood is being forced along under pressure, and that the arterial pressure is much higher than the venous pressure. The highest pressure is maintained in the aorta. As the blood passes through the thousands of miles of capillaries, the pres-

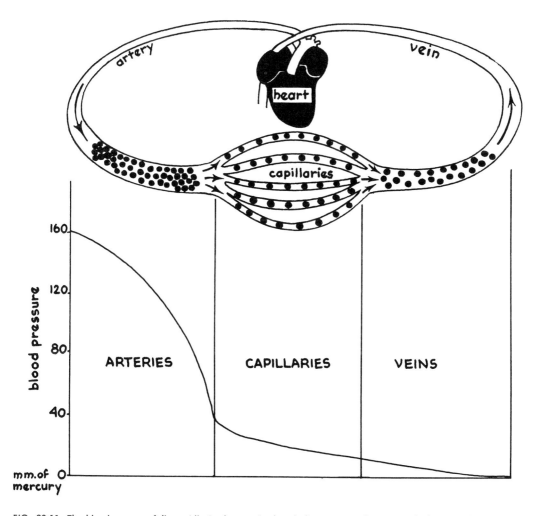

FIG. 20-11. The blood pressure falls rapidly in the arteries but declines at a much more gradual rate in the capillaries and veins. It is highest when leaving the heart and lowest in the large veins that empty into the heart, as indicated by this sketch.

FIG. 20-12. Blood pressure readings can be obtained in this manner. With such a device much information can be gained about the circulatory system.

sure gradually falls, owing primarily to the friction of the walls of these tiny tubes (Fig. 20-11). By the time it reaches the veins, much of the pressure has been spent and, in fact, when it reaches the large veins entering the right auricle it has a slight negative pressure. In other words, the blood is "sucked" into the heart.

The pressure in the arteries rises and falls with each heart beat. This can be observed by "taking the pulse," which can be felt over the wrist artery or any other artery that is near the surface. The artery swells and collapses in a rhythmic manner. This interested an eighteenth-century English clergyman, Stephen Hales, to the point of experimentation. He placed a crude can-

nula (a small brass tube), connected to a long glass tube, into the carotid artery of a horse and noted that the blood rose to a distance of over 9 feet. He also observed that the blood rose and fell gently in the tube with each heart beat. He therefore concluded that the pressure in the artery was sufficient to maintain a column of blood 9 feet high, and that the variation in height was due to the contracting ventricle.

Blood pressure is measured even today in a similar manner, although with more refined instruments. For experimental purposes, where blood pressure recordings are desired over some period of time, the blood from an artery is allowed to flow into a tube fitted to a recording device (Fig. 20-12).

Continuous recordings can be made in this manner. This would be a rather formidable way to observe the blood pressure of a patient in the physician's office and there would be few who would submit to such treatment. The years following Hales' discovery led to much experimentation, and before the turn of the nineteenth century, other methods had been devised to obtain blood pressure without entering an artery.

The most successful method is universally employed today. It consists simply of placing a rubber bag that can be inflated around the upper arm where it will squeeze the arm artery until no more blood can be forced through it. The bag is attached to a mercury or air **manometer,** an instrument that records the pressure in millimeters of mercury. Mercury is used because it is a heavy fluid and changes in pressure can be recorded with a small instrument. Water could be used, but the instrument would be very inconvenient because the tube would have to be several feet long. Once the blood is prevented from going through the arm artery, the pressure in the cuff is slowly released, barely allowing blood to pass through at the highest pressure, called **systolic pressure** because it is the point of greatest force due to ventricular systole. This can be heard through a stethoscope placed over the artery at the elbow. As the pressure is released still further, more and more blood flows through the artery and the sound becomes louder and louder, suddenly falling off sharply. The pressure reading just before this point is reached is referred to as the **diastolic pressure,** because the blood is moving during the entire cardiac cycle and it therefore records the pressure which is maintained in the arteries when the semilunar valves are closed. In other words, it is the lowest pressure in the arteries or when the heart is at rest. A great deal of important information can be obtained by the physician about the condition of the arteries and heart by taking blood pressure readings, and they have be-

come a routine part of medical examinations.

Blood Pressure Control. Blood pressure depends on three major factors in the circulatory system: the blood volume, size of the blood vessels, and the force of the heart beat. Blood volume is controlled by the intake and loss of fluids and plays little or no part in rapid changes in blood pressure. It is effective over long periods of time; for example, a gradual loss of blood would decrease blood volume and lower the blood pressure. The remaining two factors are important in rapid blood pressure change, a phenomenon which may be very important to the animal, and which may even save its life.

Blood vessel space is controlled by the changing size of the vascular system. This is accomplished by the contraction and relaxation of the smooth muscles in the walls of the arteries and veins. There are none in the capillaries. The diameters of the vessels are reduced when the muscles contract (called **vasoconstriction**), and increased when the muscles relax (called **vasodilation**). The blood pressure rises with vasoconstriction and drops with vasodilation. The muscles are under the control of nerves which terminate in the **vasomotor center** located in the brain very near the breathing and cardiac centers. Nervous and chemical stimuli influence the vasomotor center, much the same as they affect the cardiac and breathing centers. Under normal conditions there is a "built-in" safety mechanism to prevent the blood pressure from rising too high or dropping too low. The same stretch reflexes operate here also; nerve branches from the aorta and carotid arteries lead to the vasomotor center and when the pressure is high it dictates general vasodilation which causes the blood pressure to drop over the entire body. Vasoconstriction is brought about by dropping the blood pressure in the aorta and carotid arteries.

Blood pressure levels are dependent also on the force of the beat which controls the amount of blood that flows through the heart. As the flow of blood to the heart increases the heart muscle becomes stretched which brings about a reflex action causing the muscle to contract with more vigor. Any muscle works more forcefully when under tension. An upper limit is soon reached, however, when the carotid and aorta are sufficiently stretched to send impulses to the vasomotor and cardiac centers which slow the heart rate and dilate the blood vessels thus maintaining or lowering the blood pressure. When a feeble flow of blood enters the heart, the heart beat is weak and the blood pressure is low. The rate of the heart beat is not necessarily correlated with the flow of blood; a rapid weak beat may not force out as much blood as a slow forceful one. On the other hand, the beat can be fast and forceful, or slow and weak; in other words heart rate is not an index of the efficiency of the heart. Low blood pressure will immediately rise when, through exercise, the venous return increases thus stretching the vena cava and right auricle which then sends impulses to the cardiac and vasomotor centers. These in turn bring about increased heart rate (and force) and general constriction of the blood vessels, both of which cause an immediate rise in blood pressure. We see here then that vasodilation, vasoconstriction, and force of the heart beat are all carefully coordinated to bring about the proper blood flow to supply the demands of the tissues of the body.

Chemicals also have profound effects on blood pressure; indeed this is the basis for the treatment of patients with unusually high or low blood pressure. Normally, carbon dioxide in the blood influences the vasomotor center just as it does the breathing and cardiac centers. As it increases the vasomotor center sends out signals which cause constriction of all the blood vessels, thus raising the blood pressure. The re-verse happens when the carbon dioxide content of the blood is low. It is interesting to observe what profound effects can be produced by carbon dioxide. This is reasonable since this gas is a good indicator of the metabolic state of individual cells.

Endocrine secretions also influence blood pressure. Epinephrine, for example, causes vasoconstriction in all of the body vessels except those in the skeletal muscles which dilate. This is understandable when we recall the function of this hormone. During an emergency when maximal strength is needed, the skeletal muscles receive the greatest supply of blood. Many drugs influence the blood pressure through different pathways; some affect the vasomotor center, some the cardiac center, and some the blood vessels directly. Recently great progress has been made in controlling high blood pressure (hypertension) through drug therapy.

Distribution of Blood. It has already been indicated that blood distribution is not uniform; that is, localized areas may receive more or less blood under varying conditions. For example, following a meal the blood vessels to the viscera dilate, permitting more blood than usual to go to this region of the body. This is advantageous in facilitating digestion and subsequent distribution of food molecules. During this period skeletal muscles receive less blood owing to the constriction of their vessels. This accounts for the lethargy following meals. The opposite action takes place when the digestive tract has completed its job and body action is called for.

When one suddenly moves from a horizontal position to standing, there is an instant shift in the tension on the blood vessels to compensate for the difference in hydrostatic pressure between the two positions. The same is true when one moves against gravity such as in rising in an elevator or airplane. Temperature also induces changes in the size of the blood vessels, as is familiar to everyone. Cold brings about constriction of the surface blood vessels whereas heat causes them to dilate, both accounting for the change in skin color under these conditions.

We see here, as we have seen in other systems of the body, "feedback" systems geared to the needs of the body tissues. Wherever blood is needed to permit the organism to function at its best advantage, the interlocking regulatory systems (heart, breathing mechanism, and vasomotor system) come into play to bring about the desired results.

THE BLOOD

It is interesting to recall that not too long ago it was considered sound medical practice to withdraw blood (blood-letting) from the veins during disease, while today such a procedure would be considered "fatal," if not for the patient, certainly for the doctor who attended him! Medical practitioners today conserve the patient's blood, or even add to it by transfusion in certain types of illness and in cases of serious injury. Many thousands of lives have been saved because stored blood is now available for immediate use.

In spite of earlier blood-letting customs, blood has been held in high regard from ancient times, and today still plays a part in rituals of many primitive tribes. Such terms as "blood lines" in breeds of domestic animals or "good or bad blood" or "blue blood" denote the hereditary importance that has been attached to blood. Despite such common beliefs, it is now known definitely that there is no difference of this sort between either the bloods of individuals or various races of man alive today. Any efforts to perpetuate this fallacy are based on emotion rather than fact.

The more we learn about blood, the greater its importance becomes. Let us review its function in nutrition and metabolism by following it on a routine trip through the body (Fig. 20-13). Blood leaving the left ventricle goes to the liver, digestive tract, kidney, and body tissues. The blood coming from the liver contains more urea, that from the kidney less urea, that from the intestines more amino acids and glucose, and that from the general body tissues less food and more waste products. Moreover, all of the blood leaving these organs is low in O_2, which must be replenished in the lungs at the same time that CO_2 is lost. The urea which is formed in the liver must make a complete circuit through the lungs before it reaches the kidneys, where it is extracted from the blood. Fats are absorbed into the lymphatic system which eventually joins the blood system, making possible the distribution of this food. As the blood passes through the endocrine glands, food products are absorbed and converted into hormones which are then secreted into the blood. The performance of all of these functions and many more makes blood truly a most remarkable fluid.

Closer examination shows that blood is a tissue like muscle, nerve, or bone, even though it exists in a fluid state. The fluid portion of the blood is called the **plasma.** Suspended in the plasma are certain **formed elements, erythrocytes** (red blood cells), **leucocytes** (white blood cells), and **platelets.** In addition, the plasma carries many substances, some of which still are not well understood. Like all tissues, blood is mostly water, about 80 per cent in weight; the 20 per cent of solids consists of approximately 18 per cent protein and 2 per cent other chemical substances. When the formed elements are separated from the plasma, they are found to make up nearly one-half of the volume (45 per cent). The total amount of blood in a normal person is 5–6 liters, or approximately 8–10 per cent of his body weight. One can lose somewhat less than half of this amount and survive. However, a special mechanism for **coagulation** or **clotting** is present to prevent such blood loss.

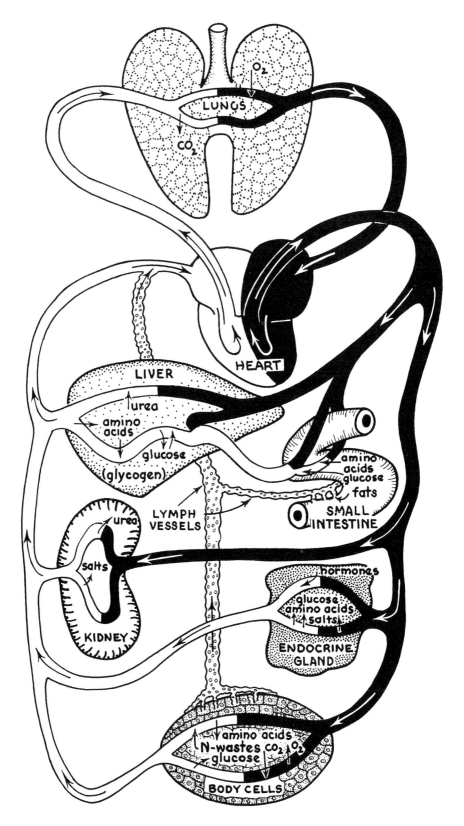

FIG. 20-13. The blood performs many functions as it flows through the body, some of which are portrayed in this sketch. Note what happens to the blood as it enters and leaves each organ.

Blood Clotting

The survival value of any mechanism that prevents the loss of blood is obvious. Blood coagulates even more rapidly in the earthworm, for example, than in man. The blob of jelly-like substance on the windshield of a speeding car demonstrates the rapidity with which the insect's blood coagulates. Animals have very short clotting times when compared to the three minutes required for man's blood to clot, for the speed with which the clot forms often spells the difference between life and death.

The exact series of chemical reactions that takes place in forming a blood clot is not completely understood. The clot is made up of a mass of threads of a protein called **fibrin,** which enmeshes red blood cells so that a semisolid plug is formed. It starts as a small clot but grows rapidly until it is of sufficient size to fill the opening in the vessel. If the vessel is too large or the pressure too great from behind, as in the large arteries, the clot fails to stop the blood flow and death of the animal results. Ragged injuries produce better and faster-forming clots than do clean cuts, the explanation of which will follow shortly.

There are several observations on blood that need to be known before the clotting mechanism can be understood. If blood is collected in a vessel containing sodium citrate or oxalate, it fails to clot; and if it is allowed to flow into a paraffin-lined vessel, it clots only very slowly. In the first instance, the chemicals must have blocked the clotting action of the blood, and in the second, the nature of the paraffin surface must have been involved. It is now known that the sodium citrate or oxalate combines with the calcium in the blood, removing it from solution. Therefore, calcium must be essential for clotting. The smooth paraffin is similar to the lining of the blood vessels; therefore, rough surfaces such as often form in ragged injuries must aid in the formation of clots.

If freshly drawn blood is stirred vigorously with stiff bristles, fibrin shortly begins to collect on the bristles, and if the stirring continues all of the fibrin can thus be removed, leaving what appears to be perfectly normal blood except for its failure to clot. This is called **defibrinated** blood. There must have been a precursor protein, much like fibrin, that was in solution in the blood but which became insoluble with the stirring. This is known as **fibrinogen.** The problem is: Why did fibrinogen become fibrin? What initiated the chain reaction?

Something must happen when the blood is taken out of the vessels, because clots do not normally form within the circulatory system itself. Careful chemical analysis has revealed another substance, **thrombin,** in the plasma which is responsible for the conversion of fibrinogen to fibrin. Obviously, thrombin cannot occur freely in the blood stream, or clots would form within the vessels. This happens only rarely and even then only under pathological conditions. Again experimentation has revealed a precursor, **prothrombin,** that is normally present in the blood. The next problem is: What starts prothrombin to form thrombin?

Another careful search has demonstrated that the platelets and probably other tissues of the body contain an enzymatically active substance called **thromboplastin** (or thrombokinase) which is essential in starting this long chain of reactions. It was stated earlier that calcium was also essential. Just what the relationship is between these substances is not clear at present. Probably when a hemorrhage occurs, the broken cells in the vicinity of the injury, together with the disintegrated platelets, release thromboplastin. Thromboplastin, reacting with calcium and prothrombin in the blood in some unknown manner, produces thrombin and this, in turn, changes fibrinogen to fibrin. Summarized:

Hemorrhage → thromboplastin
thromboplastin + calcium + prothrombin
→ thrombin
thrombin + fibrinogen →fibrin
fibrin + red blood cells → clot

Plasma clots the same as whole blood which means that the cells play no part in the clotting mechanism. After the clot is formed, it shrinks and squeezes out a straw-colored fluid, called **serum,** which does not clot owing to the fact that it has no fibrinogen. In other respects it is similar to plasma.

Earlier in the chapter on nutrition there was mention made that vitamin K had something to do with blood clotting. If too little is formed in the digestive tract, the clotting time increases dangerously, so much so that surgery is inadvisable until large quantities of this vitamin are given to restore the normal clotting time. It is now thought that vitamin K is associated with prothrombin formation, and hence its effect on clotting time.

Clotting can be prevented by precipitating out the calcium, as has already been referred to, and by a number of anticoagulants called **hirudin,** secreted by blood-sucking invertebrates such as leeches, bedbugs, and mosquitoes. You will recall that hirudin permits the blood sucker to obtain a meal without being interrupted by a clot.

A sex-linked blood-clotting defect that has been known for a long time and has been a particular concern of certain royal families because of their close interbreeding is **hemophilia.** The slightest wound can be fatal to hemophiliacs because their blood clots very slowly. Analysis of their blood indicates that it is normal in all respects except that the platelets do not disintegrate as readily as they do in normal blood. Just why they do not and what can be done about it still remains an unsolved mystery.

Red Blood Corpuscles

Red blood corpuscles are the most numerous and most conspicuous of the formed elements of the blood (Fig. 20-4). A blood smear will reveal them as tiny, circular, biconcave disks without nuclei. All vertebrates except mammals possess nucleated erythrocytes; just why nuclei are absent in the latter group is difficult to understand. However, it must be admitted that since the red blood cell lives only about 120 days and never reproduces, it would seem to be a waste of effort to utilize the space in the cell for a nucleus when it could be occupied more profitably by **hemoglobin,** the oxygen-carrying pigment. The erythrocytes possess nuclei when they first form in the **red marrow** of the bones, but lose them just before entering the blood stream. The cells are a light yellow in color under the microscope, although in combined numbers they render the blood a typically red color. Normally there are from 4,500,000 (women) to 5,000,000 (male) cells per cubic millimeter of blood. This number varies with disease and nutritional deficiencies. A drop either in the number of red cells or their hemoglobin content results in **anemia,** which can be serious if prolonged because the blood is unable to supply the cells with the proper amount of oxygen.

During embryonic life of the mammal, red cells are formed in the kidney, spleen, and liver; but as the animal matures the red marrow of the bones takes over this task. Red cell production is regulated by the amount of oxygen that the blood carries. If the level drops, red cells are produced more rapidly; and conversely, if the level rises red cell production is inhibited. Simultaneously, the sites of red cell destruction (spleen and liver) are correspondingly stimulated or inhibited. The red cells are formed and destroyed at a tremendous rate, over 10 million per second. Since one of the chief elements of hemoglobin is iron, there must be a continual supply in the diet. The amount is small (0.01 gm. per day) and most diets contain an ample amount. However, it is now known that copper is also essential for proper hemoglobin formation. The need for copper

FIG. 20-14. With a break in the skin, the leucocytes (certain kinds) move out of the blood vessels into the injured area where they engulf and destroy any invading bacteria. Bacteria that are not eliminated by the leucocytes may find their way to the lymph nodes where they are usually destroyed. If, however, they get past these barriers, they are free to invade the circulatory system and the entire organism.

lies in the production of an enzyme necessary for hemoglobin formation. Some serious deficiencies in the bone marrow cause a drop in hemoglobin production, resulting in fatal anemias. Recently these have been arrested by administering very small doses of two of the B-vitamins, folic acid and vitamin B_{12} (p. 529). These vitamins are extracted from liver, which was a logical place to find them, since large doses of liver extract were used for years to lessen the symptoms of this particular disease.

The oxygen and carbon dioxide carrying capacity of erythrocytes has been discussed earlier (p. 547).

White Blood Cells

White blood cells are called **leucocytes** because they are colorless. They are not so numerous as the red corpuscles, and there are several different kinds, all with nuclei (Fig. 20-4). They can be distinguished by the way they take certain stains, and when counted they serve as an excellent criterion for determining certain kinds of diseases. They usually increase rapidly in number (normal count is about 7,000–9,000 per cubic millimeter) during an infection, because some of them (neutrophils and monocytes) act as scavengers and attack the bacteria by engulfing and digesting them (Fig, 20-14). Such a process is termed **phagocytosis.**

White blood cells have the ability to move like an amoeba, and in a localized infection they migrate between the cells of the capillary walls out into the infected region where they do their work. Pus is primarily leucocytes. They probably also aid in healing by transforming into other types of cells in order to repair damaged tissue. Other functions have been assigned to them, but considerable information is still needed to understand their complete rôle in the body.

The Plasma

The **plasma** is the fluid portion of the blood and it is chemically very complex. Its composition remains essentially the same although it is constantly receiving and discharging substances. It is composed of about 90 per cent water, 7–8 per cent soluble proteins, 1 per cent inorganic salts, and approximately 2 per cent simple organic molecules such as glucose, amino acids, fatty acids, glycerol, urea, and hormones. The principle proteins are **fibrinogen, albumins,** and **globulins,** all of which play important roles in maintaining a stable internal environment. In general the proteins, water, inorganic ions, and glucose maintain rather constant levels in the plasma whereas carbon dioxide, oxygen, hormones, food molecules, and other substances vary from time to time. In addition to its function of delivering food molecules and oxygen to cells and relieving them of their waste products, the plasma also acts as a communicating mechanism between all cells by means of its neurohumors, referred to earlier.

We have already seen the part fibrinogen plays in clotting. The enzymatically active prothrombin also is involved in this process but there are other plasma enzymes whose function is obscure. Albumin functions in maintaining blood viscosity and osmotic pressure, whereas the globulins cause **blood type** differences and are the molecules responsible for **antibodies** which resist infections. The plasma proteins, together with hemoglobin, also function as **buffers** which maintain a constant hydrogen ion concentration.

Antibody formation is an important mechanism in most, if not all, organisms. This fact was first discovered many years ago by Pasteur. Whereas the exact nature of antibodies is still unknown, their importance and mechanism of action is gradually yielding to intensive research. It is best to describe an actual experiment in order to understand the production of antibodies and what they do.

Antibody Production

It was learned in the chapter on digestion that proteins must be degraded to amino acids before they can be absorbed into the blood stream. Any more complex compound of this sort initiates deleterious reactions. For example, if rattlesnake venom is injected into the blood, serious complications follow, hence the value of venom as a defensive and offensive mechanism. If, on the other hand, a very tiny amount of the venom is injected into a large animal, such as a horse, the reaction is not severe, and if the injections are gradually increased at short intervals the horse will eventually tolerate a tremendous dose; enough that, had it been injected in one initial dose, it would easily have killed the animal. Just what has taken place to protect the animal from this poison?

The snake venom is a **foreign protein** and, like any foreign protein, initiates a reaction in the body of the horse. The reaction produces a substance that can combine with the snake venom and neutralize its effect. This substance is called an **antibody** and the snake venom is the **antigen.** Any foreign protein can act as an antigen. In fact, this is a convenient method for separating and classifying specific proteins. The test is more delicate than most chemical tests. There are millions of proteins and each animal possesses its own specific proteins for which there is no chemical means of separation. Using an animal for a test tube, it is possible to determine by experimentation the many different kinds in a very precise manner, even to the point of determining from what animal a bit of blood or tissue originated. This is done by withdrawing the blood from an animal that has previously been injected with a foreign protein, for example, egg albumin, and then separating out the cells by whirling the blood in a centrifuge (an instrument for increasing gravity). If some of the original albumin is then added to this clear serum, a white precipitate will form. This reaction will occur for only one protein and no others; it is, therefore, highly specific. This has many practical applications, such as identifying whether or not a specimen of blood is from man or a lower animal.

One interesting use of this reaction was employed by Nuthall of England years ago in the classification of animals. He built up antibodies in experimental animals against the blood of other animals.

For example, he might inject the blood of the ape into a rabbit and after a time draw off a sample of the blood from the experimental animal, centrifuge out the cells, and to the clear serum add some of the serum (antigen) of a closely related animal, say a gibbon. He discovered that the closer the animals were related, according to the usual system of classification, the heavier was the precipitate that formed. In this case, the serum of the gibbon would give a rather heavy precipitate, whereas the serum from a pig would give much less, and that from a snake none at all. Interestingly enough, he was able to confirm the classification based on morphological structures.

The graded precipitate of the **precipitin reaction,** as this is called, is a distinct value not only in the relationships pointed out in the preceding paragraph but in determining the closeness of the chemical relationship of different proteins.

Undoubtedly antibodies are formed in tissues other than the blood, but just where is not known although the lymph nodes and liver are likely sites. They do appear,

FIG. 20-15. A schematic representation of the antigen-antibody reaction. When a harmless antigen is inoculated into the blood, an antibody forms on its surface and is then released into the plasma. If, at some later time, a harmful antigen of similar configuration enters the blood, it is inactivated by combining with the antibody, thus protecting the tissues of the body.

however, in the plasma, and since this is a readily available tissue, most of our knowledge of antibody formation has come from studies of the blood. It might be thought that antibody formation could occur in a test tube. What an excellent way to prepare it, if this were true! Unfortunately, it forms only in the living organism. When antibodies are needed in large quantities, they are produced in horses by appropriate injections of antigen and by subsequent withdrawal of blood which contains the antibody in the serum.

Antibodies are globulins and they function in neutralizing or destroying the effects of antigens by combining with them in some such manner as an enzyme combines with its substrate (p. 54). The antibody possesses a molecular configuration which "fits" the antigen, thus destroying whatever deleterious effects it might have on the tissues of the host animal (Fig. 20-15). Just how the antibody is made remains a mystery. It is thought that somehow the globulin molecules accumulate about the antigen thus making a "mold" which is then released in the plasma and functions at some later time in combining with more invading antigens. By artificially introducing a very closely related harmless antigen, antibodies can be produced in large quantities which will react with a harmful antigen that may enter the blood at some later time. This is the basis for **active immunization.** Let us consider how this antigen-antibody reaction is effective in defending the body against invading microorganisms.

Body Defense. In addition to the phagocytic action of the leucocytes already referred to, the blood and tissues of the body employ the antigen-antibody reaction to destroy invading microorganisms that produce disease. Bacteria as well as animal parasites are protein in nature and therefore induce antibodies when they get into the blood stream and other tissues. The para-

site is toxic to the host, so **antitoxins** (antibodies) are produced that will either destroy the parasite or render it helpless so that the leucocytes may engulf and destroy it more easily. Often the parasite gives off a protein product which is also toxic to the host, and again an antitoxin is built up against this product, so that it is neutralized and can no longer harm the body. The end products of this reaction are removed from the body through various channels.

The production of antitoxins is spoken of as **immunization,** a very familiar term. Once the antibodies have been produced, they are active for some time against a second invasion of the parasite. How long they are active seems to be specific for the parasite. For example, immunity against typhoid fever may last a year or two, whereas one may expect never to have a second case of whooping cough, the antibodies for which last throughout the lifetime of the individual. Immunity built up by the actual participation of the parasite in question is called **active immunity.** A similar immunity can be produced artificially by introducing a weakened or even a dead strain of the parasite into the body so that it will bring about antibody formation but will not cause the disease or, if it does, only in a very mild form. In the case of immunization against smallpox, a weakened strain of the virus (developed in cows) is injected which brings about active antibody formation but causes only minor .discomfort itself. This type of active immunization lasts a long time and has been very effective in stamping out certain diseases.

Recently a remarkable human experiment was undertaken in the fight against poliomyelitis. This disease is caused by a virus (actually the several forms of the disease result from infection with different viruses) against which active immunization has been known for several years. Since all people who are exposed to the virus do not get the disease, because of varying amounts of natural or acquired immunity, the effectiveness of using a vaccine (the killed virus) could only be revealed by immunizing human populations on a large scale. The experiment involved the cooperation of many state and national health agencies who helped to get the general public to participate in such an undertaking. This, the largest human experiment ever attempted, was remarkably successful; the final tabulations indicate clearly that the vaccine had been effective in protecting children against poliomyelitis.

This project followed the tenets of a good scientific experiment. The population was divided into two principal portions, each containing representative numbers from all walks of life (habitats). One-half was offered a solution containing the vaccine, the other was offered a *placebo* (the solution with no vaccine present). No one, except those in charge, knew which was which. The effectiveness of the vaccine became evident only when the data were accumulated and arranged in tabular form. Poliomyelitis may ultimately come under control, as smallpox has, as a result of the knowledge acquired through this experiment.

Another method of bestowing active immunization in a person is by employing an altered toxin, such as that used in building up active immunity against diphtheria. The toxin taken from the diphtherial organism is treated so that it has lost none of its antigenic properties but is no longer toxic to tissues in the body. This substance is called **toxoid.** When a small quantity of toxoid is injected, antibodies (antitoxins) are produced, so that if at any subsequent time the diphtherial organism enters the body its effect will be neutralized at once and it will be unable to obtain a foothold. This type of treatment has made cases of diphtheria very rare and they could be nonexistent if everyone were thus protected.

Sometimes, as in the case of advanced tetanus, it is necessary to build up the sup-

ply of antibodies immediately. There is not sufficient time to allow the body to produce them in the usual slow manner. It is possible, then, to add them directly by injections of antitoxin that has been previously produced in a horse. The type of immunity received from this treatment is called **passive immunity,** because the person himself contributes nothing toward the production of the antibody. Passive immunization is short-lived, which is its chief disadvantage, but in certain diseases it can save a life. It is wiser to prevent the appearance of the disease by active immunization rather than attempt to cure the disease once it has struck—hence the popularity of immunization programs in our schools and the absolute enforcement of such programs in the armed forces.

Blood Types

From the foregoing discussion on the relatedness of animals, it might be expected that all animals of the same species have the same specific proteins. In general this is probably true. However, there are minute variations of which we have become aware primarily through our efforts to transfuse blood from one person to another. They have also been called to our attention in plastic surgery, where attempts are made to graft tissues from one person to replace the destroyed tissues of another, as in cases of severe burns, for example. One wonders why the healthy, intact organs of people dying in accidents could not be saved and transplanted in the bodies of those who are dying because the same organs are no longer functioning properly as a result of some organic or infectious disease. So far we have been limited to blood, some bones, and corneas of the eyes in this regard, primarily because of the specificity of proteins of individuals. In other words, the proteins of one person are slightly different from those of another, so that such transplants are incompatible and will not "take."

FIG. 20-16. A schematic representation of how blood types (AB, A, B, O) can be determined. The sera of the four blood groups contained in the pipettes is added to whole blood in test tubes from the same groups. Agglutination occurs when sera containing a specific antibody is mixed with blood containing red cells of a certain type. The antibodies are indicated by specifically shaped particles that fit into spaces cut out of the circular discs which represent the red cells. When they fit agglutination occurs. See the text for further details.

A B O blood types. At the turn of the century, Karl Landsteiner, an American Nobel Prize winner, gave us the first explanation of why people sometimes suffer severely when they are transfused with blood from another person. These occasional catastrophes made the blood transfusion business a rather risky procedure to be used only as a last resort. Landsteiner showed that the red cells of the blood contained two proteins, called **A** and **B,** and that they existed in people singly, in combination, or not at all. Persons could accordingly be classified into groups, depending on the nature of their blood: those with protein A were placed in blood **Group A,** those with B in blood **Group B,** those with both proteins in blood **Group AB,** and those with neither protein in blood **Group O.** The serum of each of these groups contains the antibody for other groups but not for its own, that is, the serum of Group A has anti-B but not anti-A, Group B has anti-A but not anti-B, Group AB has neither antibody, and Group O has both. These antibodies are naturally present in the serum of people, and their kinds must be known in any case before blood can be transfused without possible ill effects.

The groups can readily be determined by mixing sera and whole blood from the various groups in the manner indicated in Figure 20-16, where it immediately becomes apparent that the only safe transfusions are between people of the same blood group. In practice, however, this is not true. Persons with Group O have been called *universal donors* because it is possible to transfuse their blood into people with any of the other blood groups without ill effects. The complete answer for these observed facts is not entirely clear, although two points help in the solution. In the first place, the erythrocytes have no antigenic proteins, so there can be no reaction between them and the antibodies in the recipient's plasma. Secondly, introduced anti-A and anti-B antibodies are diluted so

rapidly by the recipient's plasma that they have little opportunity to cause the red cells to agglutinate. If the blood is added too rapidly or in too large amounts, some agglutination might occur. People possessing blood group AB are spoken of as *universal recipients* because they may receive blood from any of the other groups with no harm done. The explanation for this situation is similar to that for universal donors. It seems that, in general, the presence of antibodies in the donor's plasma is unimportant, whereas the presence of the antigens in the donor's red cells and the presence of antibodies in the recipient's plasma determine the safety of transfusions.

Like other blood groups, described below, these groups are inherited in a definite manner, which will be considered in a later chapter.

The Rhesus Factor

Recently another group of red cell proteins has been discovered, designated as the **Rhesus** or simply the **Rh factor** because it was first discovered in the Rhesus monkey. A survey of various populations showed that it occurs in about 85 per cent of the people. If a person possesses the protein he is said to be **Rh positive,** whereas if his red cells do not contain the factor he is **Rh negative.** Normally there is no anti-Rh in the serum, and of course no difficulty is encountered unless for some reason or other the blood of an Rh positive and an Rh negative are mixed. Under these conditions the protein containing the Rh factor acts like a foreign protein in the Rh negative person, giving rise to the anti-Rh antibody. If, then, at some subsequent period such a person receives another transfusion of Rh positive blood, agglutination of the donor's red cells will occur because the anti-Rh is present in the recipient's serum (Fig. 20-17). Such clumped blood cells will produce serious reactions and even death. For this reason, before blood transfusions are given, the Rh condition of the blood is de-

FIG. 20-17. If Rh positive blood is transfused into an Rh negative person, anti-Rh is built up in the latter's blood. If, at some later time, another transfusion of Rh blood is given, complications may arise because the anti-Rh will bring about the clumping of red cells.

termined and a history of any previous transfusions is important.

The Rh factor also explains the cause of a disease of newly born infants called **erythroblastosis fetalis.** This disease results in the death of a small percentage of babies shortly after birth, and was heretofore a complete mystery. It is now known that the Rh positive factor is inherited as a **dominant,** and the Rh negative factor as a **recessive.** This means that positive factor will appear in either half or all of the offspring of an Rh positive father and an Rh negative mother. When the developing fetus of this combination inherits the Rh positive factor from its father, it is possible that trouble will follow (Fig. 20-18). Normally the blood of the mother does not come into direct contact with the blood of the fetus, but occasionally a very small number of red cells apparently do get into the maternal circulation, perhaps by the accidental breaking of small capillaries in the placenta. Once Rh positive red cells get into the mother's circulation, Rh antibody is produced. Since the antibody is present in the serum, it can easily diffuse through into the fetal circulation, causing damage to the red cells of the developing fetus. Such a child, when born, will be highly deficient in red blood cells, which results in a severe jaundice, and unless immediate treatment is given will die. The child may be saved by numerous blood transfusions during the first few weeks of life.

The situation is not as serious as it might appear, as attested by the small number of babies born with this disease. This is due, perhaps, to the fact that not all cases of pregnancy result in a mixing of the fetal and maternal blood. Furthermore, not enough antibody is generally produced to cause trouble on the first pregnancy so the condition does not usually show up until the second and subsequent pregnancies. Since only 15 per cent of the population is Rh negative, the chance combination of an Rh positive man with an Rh negative woman is not great. Although it is important to know the Rh condition of the mother before and during the pregnancy, it is not sufficiently important to cause alarm on the part of an Rh negative woman who is contemplating marriage to an Rh positive man.

It is important, however, to know the Rh factor condition of a young girl about to receive a transfusion. Suppose an Rh negative girl receives large amounts of Rh positive blood in a transfusion. She may develop such a high concentration of anti-Rh that it might be impossible for her to ever bear an Rh positive child. Furthermore, if at some subsequent time another transfusion were necessary and she were given Rh positive blood again, she would suffer a severe, perhaps even fatal, reaction. Concern for the type of transfusions used is not confined to the female alone. Rh negative males can also suffer severe reactions if transfused intermittently with Rh positive blood. As a result of this information, blood is routinely typed for the Rh factor.

It has been shown recently that there are at least 35 different proteins in human blood which are sufficiently distinguishable to be identified and to have their inheritance followed. This is a very active field of research today, and there is no doubt that much fruitful information will come from it in the years ahead.

Other Functions of the Blood

Among the many functions of the blood must also be included body defense, pH and temperature regulation, and water balance. These will now be briefly considered.

Acid-Base Balance. All of the cells of the body are very sensitive to the amount of acid or base that is present in their environment, and can withstand only very slight changes in the concentration of hydrogen ions. Since the blood controls the internal environment, it follows that it, too, must be very constant. Such is indeed

FIG. 20-18. Complications may arise when an Rh positive man marries an Rh negative woman, as indicated in these figures. The explanation is given in the text.

the case. In whatever part of the body the **hydrogen ion concentration** or **pH** of the blood is measured, it will be found to be remarkably constant, being slightly alkaline (pH 7.45). This may seem difficult to understand in view of the many compounds being "dumped" into and withdrawn from the blood continuously. It is made possible by substances in the blood, appropriately called **buffers,** which maintain a constant pH. They combine with both acids and bases so as to prevent any important change in the relative number of hydrogen and hydroxyl ions. The most important buffers in the plasma are the proteins, amino acids, phosphates, and bicarbonates. Acids that form in the cells as a result of metabolic activity are passed through the cell membrane into the blood where the buffers absorb the extra hydrogen ions, thus preventing an excess and hence an increase in acidity. Carbon dioxide coming into the blood from all the cells would form carbonic acid if it were not for the sodium ions which convert it to bicarbonate, thus maintaining a constant pH. The carbon dioxide is lost in the lungs, an important factor in removing acid conditions from the blood. Likewise, acidic substances are removed from the circulation in the kidneys. All of these factors work together in order that the blood can remain constant as far as the acid-base balance is concerned.

Water Balance. Water is constantly being added to and withdrawn from the blood because it is the only way that this important compound can be delivered to and taken away from the body cells. This is extremely important, since all life processes are maintained in a water medium within the cells. Therefore, they must have the proper amount at all times. Water is taken into the blood from the digestive tract and lost through the skin as sweat or through the kidneys as urine. Excess water is normally lost through the urine, so that a delicate water balance is maintained in every cell of the body at all times.

Temperature Regulation. Because the body is exposed to widely varying external temperatures, several different mechanisms have been provided to regulate the body temperature. The added muscular contraction brought about by shivering in mammals causes a greater burning of the sugar, thus raising the temperature of the entire body. When the body is exposed to low temperatures, the skin becomes pale and cold, due to vasoconstriction, which prevents blood from coming close to the external surface where it would be unduly cooled. The opposite effect, flushed skin, is noted following violent exercise or during particularly hot weather. This is caused by vasodilation in the skin which allows the warmer-than-normal blood to come near the surface where it can lose its excess heat. This control of the size of the small blood vessels in the skin is a very important temperature-regulating mechanism. In addition, the sweat glands pour out water which, by evaporation, provides an important cooling device.

Certain special provisions are present in some animals for increasing surface area to make the cooling process more effective. For example, elephants and rabbits are thought to employ their large ears for this purpose as well as for collecting sound waves. Bats are thought to rely on the circulation in the skin of their wings for heat regulation. Man, of course, covers his body with various fabrics, the color and texture of which are changed depending on the temperature. Hair and feathers are excellent insulators against temperature change. Thus the bodies of the warm-blooded birds and mammals are reasonably well suited to withstand the varying temperatures they encounter in their particular environments.

The Lymphatic System

A swelling following a blow on any portion of the body is gorged with a fluid called **lymph,** which is much like plasma except that it does not contain so much protein material. It does, however, contain some white cells, principally **lymphocytes.** Lymph fills all of the spaces between and around cells and thus bathes every cell of the body. It functions as a medium between the capillary and the cell, a continuum through which food, oxygen, and wastes can enter and leave the cells.

Lymph passes out through the capillary walls around the cells, and from there moves slowly on into a system of vessels which coalesce and eventually reach the circulatory system in the neck region where the large lymph vessels join the large neck veins (Fig. 20-19). This is as intricate as the venous system and resembles the latter in many respects. It merely is an alternate route by which water and wastes from the cells can reach the general circulation. In other words, it resembles a "sludge pump" in its action.

The lymph glands which produce the

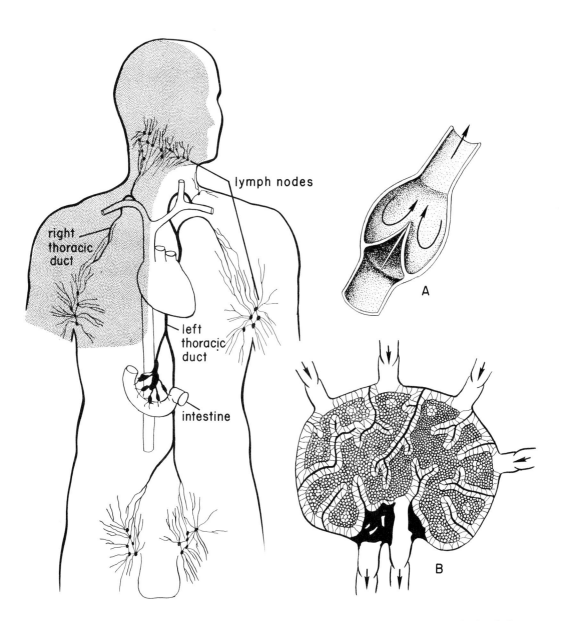

FIG. 20-19. The lymphatic system of man. The vessels are provided with valves (A) which keep the lymph flowing in one direction. A detailed drawing of the lymph node is shown (B).

lymphocytes of the blood lie along the lymph channels, through which they are dumped into the blood. The lymph glands have another function, namely, as filters. Foreign particles such as dust, debris, and bacteria float in the lymph and finally make their way to the lymph glands where considerable phagocytic activity goes on. This can be so active as to produce noticeable swelling of these glands, particularly under the arms if the source of infection is in the hand, or in the groin if the difficulty arises from some portion of the leg or foot. They function in stopping the infection before it gets into the general circulation where it may do a great deal of damage. Carbon particles are inert, so that those entering the body from air laden with coal smoke will lodge in the lymph glands, contributing a dark color to them if the person has lived in cities where smoke is abundant.

There is no pumping station in the lymphatic system of man, although such mechanisms are present in some of the lower animals. The movement of the lymph is due to the continual massaging of the lymph channels by the contracting muscles, both visceral and skeletal. The contraction of the villi in the intestinal walls, as well as the negative pressure created at the point of entry into the large neck veins, aids in bringing about lymph movement. Any stoppage of this movement results in swelling, as in the case of certain roundworms that invade the lymph glands, thereby clogging them so that the lymph cannot pass through. In such cases a leg may weigh as much as 100 pounds (p. 252).

We have seen how the circulatory system provides for the needs of the individual cells in a complex animal. What happens to the food elements that have been carried to the cell? Obviously, they must be utilized in construction, repair, and the releasing of energy through oxidation. These will be considered in the next chapter.

SUGGESTED SUPPLEMENTARY READINGS

BURNET, M., The Mechanism of Immunity, *Scientific American*, 204(1) (January, 1961), 58.

CARLSON, A.J., and JOHNSON, V., *The Machinery of the Body* (Chicago, University of Chicago Press, 1962).

FULTON, J., *Selected Readings in the History of Physiology* (Springfield, Ill., Charles C Thomas, 1930).

HARARY, I., "Heart Cells in Vitro," *Scientific American*, 206(5) (May, 1962), 141.

LAKI, K., "The Clotting of Fibrinogen," *Scientific American*, 206(3) (March, 1962).

ROMER, A. S., *The Vertebrate Body* (Philadelphia, W. B. Saunders Co., 1962).

WOODBURNE, R. T., *Essentials of Human Anatomy* (New York, Oxford University Press, 1961).

ZWEIFACH, B., "The Microcirculation of the Blood," *Scientific American*, 200(1) (January, 1959), 54.

D.C. SNYDER

21

Metabolism and Disposal of Wastes

WE HAVE SEEN in the last several chapters how complex food molecules have been rendered soluble and reduced to the proper chemical configuration to be transported to the individual cells of a complex animal. In addition, we have seen the method by which oxygen has been made available for oxidation of these energy-rich molecules. The next step is to consider the processes by which energy is released and how this energy is utilized by the cells in doing all of the things that living things must do, such as, grow, move, produce heat, and many other things. This most important series of processes is called **metabolism**. Once metabolism is completed certain toxic end products are left over that must be disposed of. In this chapter we shall consider both metabolism and the mechanism the body has for ridding itself of wastes.

METABOLISM

We learned many chapters back (p. 80) that metabolism goes on within the individual cells and we also learned the chemical steps involved. We must now refer once again to this information and, in addition, describe how metabolism takes place in a complex animal.

Metabolism involves two processes: releasing energy and the utilization of this energy. In the former, the food molecules are oxidized, thus providing the energy to propel the machinery of life. These two processes complement one another. The first makes the second possible; protoplasm can do all of the things it does only if energy is available. Conversely, without the fabric of protoplasm there would be no means by which energy could be released. In other words both processes are interdependent and must proceed simultaneously.

We learned earlier that the only source of energy in organisms is through respiration, and this occurs in each individual cell. The raw materials are fats, carbohydrates, and proteins, each of which goes through a complex series of steps in degradation before the energy is finally stored in the form of ATP. The immediate energy is derived when ATP is converted to ADP. If this were completely so then one could compute the amount of energy in any food molecule in terms of ATP molecules, and when an animal consumes these molecules the energy stored as ATP should equal the amount of energy taken in. In this case the efficiency of the organism would be 100 per cent, and we know this is not so. Then how can we determine the energy transformations that go on in an animal; that is, how can we study intake as compared to outgo? Obviously the energy is taken in as potential (stored) energy in the form of food molecules, and it comes out in the form of chemical work, mechanical work, and many other forms of activity. In order to do this we need to convert all of the intake and outgo energy into a single unit. The easiest to measure and one into which all other forms of energy can be converted is heat, expressed in **calories** (Cal.). By definition one calory is the amount of heat required to raise the temperature of one kilogram of water through one degree centigrade. With this unit one has a means of comparing different forms of energy.

It is very simple to measure the number of calories in food molecules. They are merely burned and the heat given off is expressed in calories. For example, 1 gram of glucose or protein equals about 4.0 calories and 1 gram of fat equals 9 calories. This has been done with most foods and lists are available showing the number of calories contained in each kind of food. One can use them in computing the exact number of calories which are consumed in any specified time. This is useful information when it is desired to control weight. Does all of this stored energy become available in the form of useful energy, that is, in the form of ATP? In other words does all of the potential energy in foods show up as ATP as a result of respiration? This can be answered by comparing some experimental data. For example, when 1 gram of glucose is oxidized in cells, the equivalent of 1.7 calories of energy is captured as ATP. When compared with the 3.8 calories a gram of glucose actually contains, we see that respiration has an efficiency of 44 per cent, which is very high when compared to machines built by man. The remaining energy is lost in the form of heat.

In order to determine the amount of energy derived through respiration it is necessary to use some other criterion rather than that of simply measuring the number of calories consumed, owing to the fact that not all of the food is converted to energy. Some may be unused, some used in growth, and some stored. Moreover some organisms are more efficient in food utilization than others. A far more reliable method of determining energy utilization of animals is to measure the **oxygen consumption** because oxygen is used only in respiration. It is a simple matter to measure the amount of oxygen consumed by any organism per unit of time. This is done routinely with man and the results often have medical significance.

Basal Metabolism. Most oxygen consumption data are taken from records on man. The oxygen consumption, and therefore the energy utilization, varies widely among human beings. It depends on age, sex, weight, body configurations, and activity. Therefore, a standard procedure must be followed if any abnormalities are to be detected. The rules are that a person must be completely at rest and must not have eaten for at least twelve hours. The energy utilized then is just sufficient to keep his heart beating, to keep him breathing and to maintain body temperature. The rate at which he consumes oxygen under these conditions measures his **basal metabolic rate** (BMR). For a young mature male this is about 1,600 calories per day; for a young woman about 5 per cent less. By taking thousands of these records standard tables have been established which can be referred to when measuring the BMR of anyone. These are useful in diagnosis of certain diseases which may be reflected in changes in the BMR.

A person pursuing a sedentary occupation requires about 2,500 calories per day. Heavy physical labor boosts this total to as much as 6,000 calories per day. One's weight remains constant providing the intake of calories is equal to those burned. With age the tendency is to continue eating at the same rate as when young, but muscular activity is reduced. This inevitably results in an increased waistline, the bane of middle age.

On the other hand, a caloric intake which does not satisfy the energy requirements forces the body to draw on its reserve food stores. The first reserve foods to be used are the carbohydrates (glycogen) of the muscles and liver. The next to go are the stored fats, which in an average person will supply enough energy for about six weeks. The last to go are the proteins, starting with the least used parts, such as certain muscles. Finally the essential organs such as the heart and brain are reduced to a point of failure, which then terminates the life of the organism. It is interesting to note that one can tolerate starvation for long periods without apparent harm.

Metabolism of Carbohydrates. Starches and sugars are the chief sources of energy for herbivorous and omnivorous (man) animals. Carnivores, however, do not rely on these foods for their primary energy source, but on proteins and fats.

It will be helpful during the following discussion of metabolism to refer to Figure 21-1. Once the complex carbohydrates (polysaccharides) are digested they are absorbed into the hepatic portal system as the three simple sugars (monosaccharides), glucose, fructose, and galactose. When they reach the liver they are converted to **glycogen** which may be stored or immediately reconverted to glucose, depending on the energy requirements of the organism, which change from moment to moment. The glucose level in the blood must be maintained at a relatively constant level because it is the chief source of fuel for respiration in the cells. This level must not drop below about 60 mg. per 100 ml. of blood. If it does, stark changes become immediately evident in the animal, starting with mental confusion, followed by convulsions and coma, and finally ending in death. Similar symptoms occur following an overdose of insulin (p. 488). These dramatic effects are a result of the sensitivity of brain cells to lowered glucose levels. Since they store little or no glucose a minimal level is required at all times to maintain normal functions. They are equally sensitive to the lack of oxygen, and the symptoms are the same.

As was pointed out earlier the liver releases the proper amount of glucose at all times. This is under the influence of hormones, primarily insulin from the pancreas, although those from both the medulla and cortex of the adrenals, as well as somatotropic hormones from the anterior pitui-

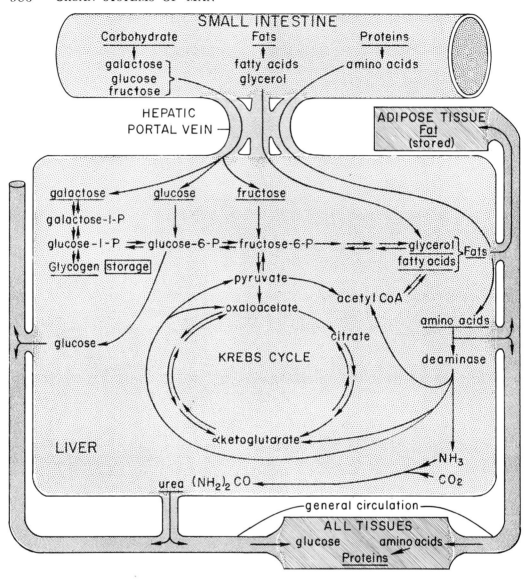

FIG. 21-1. A schematic representation of the metabolism of the end-products of digestion.

tary, are involved. Moreover, the two-way reaction:

$$\text{Glucose} \underset{\text{G-6-phosphatase}}{\overset{\text{hexokinase}}{\rightleftarrows}} \text{glucose-6-PO}_4 \rightleftarrows \text{glycogen}$$

takes place only in the liver because of the enzyme **glucose-6-phosphatase.** Muscle cells can convert glucose to glycogen, just as liver cells do (both have **hexokinase**), but the

reaction will not go the other way due to the lack of the enzyme glucose-6-phosphatase. Muscle glycogen can only supply glucose for the energy needs of muscle cells. In evolution it apparently was of more survival value to have an energy reserve in the muscles than in the brain, although just why this is so is unclear.

Glucose can be stored as fat as well as glycogen. It is common knowledge that an excess of carbohydrates in the diet leads to fat accumulation, in man or beast. The metabolic pathways by which this happens are well known. During glycolysis fructose-1, 6-diphosphate is converted, through several intermediates, to glycerol. The fatty acids are derived from acetyl-CoA. The fatty acids and glycerol are transported by the blood stream to adipose tissue where they are converted to fats and stored. In addition, adipose tissue itself can convert glucose to fats.

Metabolism of Fats. Fats and oils accumulate in both plants and animals and, therefore, appear in the diet of animals. As was pointed out earlier, they are rich in energy, containing over twice as many calories per gram as either carbohydrates or proteins. Their high energy yield is accounted for, in part, by the fact that they contain little water and oxygen. When they oxidize they require an abundance of oxygen. They are excellent materials for the storage of energy, which is one of their chief functions. Fats also have an important function in the construction of membranes within and surrounding cells. They, together with protein, make up the framework of these membranes. Another function of fats, which may be secondary, is to form an insulating layer beneath the skin to prevent heat loss which also serves in cushioning internal organs from shock with body movements. Another incidental function of fats is that they contain the fat-soluble vitamins.

Fats are essential for life but since they are present in most foods, there is little likelihood of one suffering from a fat deficiency. The body is able to synthesize most of the fatty acids, although some are **essential** and must appear in the food. However, the diet would need to be extremely low in fats before a deficiency in the essential fatty acids would be evident.

Fats which are split to fatty acids and glycerol in the digestive tract are absorbed into the hepatic portal system. Colloidal fats by-pass the liver and go, via the lymphatic system, into the general circulation (p. 581). The fatty acids that reach the liver are those present in the original fat that was taken into the digestive tract. That is, they may have come from corn oil, animal fat, or from many other sources. These then are reassembled in the liver to form human fat, which is then absorbed in the blood stream and carried to adipose tissue where it is stored. Or it may be utilized in the manufacture of cell membranes.

It has been known for many years that fats oxidize readily only when in the presence of carbohydrates. The reason for this observation is now known. Oxaloacetic acid, which results from carbohydrate metabolism, is needed to combine with the acetyl coenzyme A which is derived from fatty acids, in order for fat metabolism to proceed. Whenever carbohydrate metabolism is interrupted, fat metabolism is also involved. Diabetes, for example, is a disease in which carbohydrates are not properly metabolized as a result of the loss of the hormone insulin (p. 488). Symptoms of the disease are the accumulation of fat in the liver and the appearance of so-called acetone bodies in the urine. Improper metabolism of fatty acids in the liver cause these abnormalities. Other hormones influence fat metabolism. Those from the adrenals, sex glands, and pituitary are involved but just how is not fully known.

Metabolism of Proteins. Every cell of the body must rebuild or replace itself from time to time. During the growing stage of the whole animal, and in some cases during adulthood, cells also duplicate themselves. This means that protein must be synthesized in each cell more or less continuously, and this is done by the utilization of the amino acids that come to the cell from the blood stream. The amino acids are assembled in the proper sequence to form proteins that are specific for the particular species of animal. This is done under the influence of specific enzymes, and just how this is accomplished in cells will be described later (p. 649). The source of an amino acid, such as glycine, does not matter since it is the same whether it be from a cow, oyster, or plant. As it combines with others, however, the resultant protein is highly specific. This relationship may be compared to bricks in a house. The red bricks are all alike no matter from which brick yard they came, and they only become distinctive when they form a part of a particular house. They are then a constitutent of a pattern which in this case is Smith's house, not Johnson's or Kennedy's. Likewise with the construction of proteins from amino acids, the numerous amino acids (about twenty) are precisely selected by cellular enzymes, and built into the final protein structure.

It, therefore, becomes necessary that all of the amino acids be present in the circulating blood. During the course of evolution animals have lost the capacity to synthesize all of the amino acids that are required for growth and repair. This has come about by the loss of specific enzymes, probably because the amino acids were present in the diet making it unnecessary to manufacture them. The amino acids that the body can manufacture are the **nonessential** amino acids and are not needed in the diet, although they can be utilized if available. The amino acids he is unable to synthesize are the **essential** amino acids and must be included in the diet, referred to earlier. Man requires ten of these and this requirement varies with other animals. For example, if a person ate nothing but gelatin as a source of protein he would starve to death, because it lacks three essential amino acids. Corn lacks two, lysine and tryptophan. Meat, eggs, and milk contain all of them and for that reason are considered complete proteins. Usually one eats a variety of proteins so that amino acids lacking in one are present in another. However, there is always the matter of quan-

tity; monotonous diets consisting of a single protein which may be low in one essential amino acid would require that the individual consume large quantities in order to satisfy his minimal needs. If, on the other hand, the amino acids were perfectly balanced one could take in as little as 25 grams of protein a day to maintain normal health. Actually from 80 to 100 grams are customary in most diets.

One must have a continual supply of proteins because they are not stored in the body, hence during starvation the tissue proteins are sacrificed to replace the other nitrogenous compounds lost from the body. It is possible to measure quantitatively the nitrogen ingested in the form of protein and that excreted as urea and determine whether or not the body is maintaining a protein "balance." This is useful information, particularly during such disturbed conditions as disease or following severe injury. At these times the body often loses more nitrogen than it takes in and is said to be in "negative nitrogen balance." This results in a wasting of the body tissues and, if continued, terminates life.

Just what part hormones play in protein metabolism remains obscure, although there is no doubt that they exert a profound influence. Certainly the growth hormone from the anterior pituitary and the adrenal cortical hormones influence the synthesis of protein. We have already seen that insulin is important in carbohydrate metabolism and probably also influences protein metabolism. Other hormones such as those from the gonads also influence protein metabolism but exactly how is unknown.

Fate of Excess Proteins. Excessive proteins taken into the body are converted to carbohydrate or fat and can then be used for energy or stored. But, as you already know, proteins contain nitrogen which is not true of fats and carbohydrates. This nitrogen must be removed by a process called **deam-**

ination before amino acids can be utilized as fat or carbohydrate. This occurs in the liver and requires energy which is evidenced by an increase of as much as 30 per cent in the BMR shortly following protein intake. This can be proven by a simple experiment. Such a rise does not occur following protein intake in an animal whose liver has been removed.

The amino groups of the amino acids are removed and combined with carbon dioxide to form **urea** which is then removed from the blood in the kidney (p. 595). The process by which this is accomplished involves cyclical chemical reactions (Fig. 21-2). The first step in this cycle is stripping the amino acids of their amino groups ($-NH_2$). This is accomplished by numerous specific enzymes called **deaminases** (transaminases). This results in the formation of **glutamic acid** (from α-ketoglutaric acid, a Kreb's cycle compound). The glutamic acid is then decomposed by the enzyme, **glutamic dehydrogenase,** to form α Ketoglutaric acid and ammonia (NH_3). The latter toxic substance is removed by means of the "ornithine cycle."

Three amino acids, **ornithine, citrulline,** and **arginine,** are involved in the ornithine cycle, and it is the sequential conversion of one to the other that provides a means by which ammonia is continuously eliminated from the body. One molecule of ammonia and carbon dioxide first combines with ornithine producing citrulline. A second molecule of ammonia transferred from the amino acid, aspartic acid, combines with this amino acid to produce arginine which then splits into urea and ornithine under the influence of the enzyme **arginase.** This completes the cycle; ornithine starts the cycle over again and the urea, now quite harmless, finds its way to the kidney where it is excreted. You will

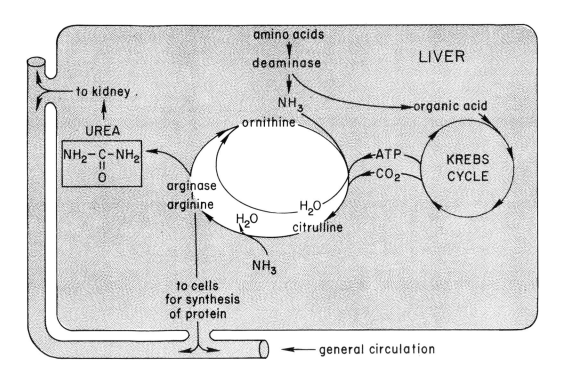

FIG. 21-2. A schematic representation of the ornithine cycle. See text for explanation.

note that the ornithine cycle is dependent on the Krebs Cycle for its operation. Starting from the amino acids the net result is:

$$2\ R - CH\ NH_2COOH + CO_2 + O_2 \rightarrow$$

$$CO(NH_2)_2 + 2\ R - \overset{\overset{O}{\|}}{C} - COOH + H_2O$$
$$\text{urea}$$

Many aquatic animals do not produce urea, but are able to tolerate ammonia in the blood until it is excreted in the urine. Insects, birds, and reptiles excrete their nitrogenous wastes as **uric acid,** which has the advantage of requiring little or no water to flush it out of the body since it is in crystalline form. For this reason these animals can survive better in desert regions. We shall have more to say about this a little later.

Interconversion of Food. From the foregoing discussion it is clear that fats, carbohydrates, and proteins can be used as energy sources, but only protein is essential for building protoplasm. One can survive on protein as the sole source of energy but not on carbohydrates or fats. By consulting Figure 21-1 again you will be able to follow the interconvertibility of the three types of food molecules.

The monosaccharides glucose, fructose, and galactose, which result from polysaccharide breakdown, enter the liver and are converted into glycogen and stored, or they may be transformed into glucose and released into the general circulation, or they may be converted to fructose-6-phosphate and undergo glycolysis, ultimately entering the Krebs cycle where their stored energy is converted to ATP. Some may be converted to glycerol and combine with fatty acids to produce fats, which then enter the general circulation and are stored in adipose tissue. Considerable fat is also synthesized in this tissue. Hence we see how carbohydrates are converted to fats.

Fats are digested to fatty acids and glycerol in the small intestine and pass to the liver where the fatty acids may enter the Krebs cycle and supply energy just as carbohydrates do. They may also recombine in a specific pattern to form fats characteristic of the organism.

The amino acids from protein digestion also reach the liver where they follow several pathways. Some may immediately return to the general circulation and pass to the cells where they are synthesized into proteins under the influence of cellular enzymes. Others may lose their amino groups (deamination), and the remaining organic acids may take part in supplying energy via several pathways. Some fragments enter the Krebs cycle directly whereas others enter via pyruvate. Thus proteins are a source of energy.

This elaborate biochemical mechanism makes possible the most efficient use of all foods, for the maintenance and growth of the body. Whereas plants can manufacture all of their needs from very simple compounds (carbon dioxide, nitrates, salts, and water), animals cannot and therefore have come to depend on plants for many of their food molecules. As was pointed out much earlier, there is a satisfactory balance between the two so that neither overruns the earth.

Molecular Turnover. As one observes a plant or animal over a period of time it seems to remain about the same as far as its general appearance is concerned. It was thought until recently that the molecular composition of the framework of organisms was stable, that is, they remained relatively constant throughout life. It was thought that either food molecules were burned to supply energy or they were utilized in the production of new cells or to replace those that wore out. In other words there was very little turnover of the molecules that composed the organism.

With the advent of tracer techniques with which food molecules could be labelled with radioactive or heavy isotopes and followed during their circuit through the body, a whole new concept emerged. It was shown that labelled amino acids are rapidly incorporated into the proteins of the body even though there is no obvious growth. Likewise, labelled fatty acids become a part of the body fat without increase in the bulk of fat. Even bones become labelled very quickly indicating that these stable structures are changing constantly. Obviously molecules making up the body framework are constantly being replaced by others, the framework being built and destroyed continuously. This is a dynamic equilibrium, in that the body remains essentially the same while this turnover is going on.

The rate of incorporation of labelled atoms into man indicates that one half of his tissues are replaced about every 80 days. Not all tissues are replaced at the same rate; some such as those of the liver turn over much faster than those of the skeletal muscles. Eighty days is an average figure for all tissues of the body. We now know that our bodies change from day to day, as far as their chemistry is concerned. The incorporation of radioactive isotopes into our bodies, as well as into those of all organisms has considerable bearing on the problem of radioactive fallout and should be of great concern to everyone.

DISPOSAL OF WASTES

Once the food molecules are metabolized, the resulting waste products must be removed promptly from the body. Retained, they act as toxic substances, causing death within a short time. In this discussion we are primarily concerned with the removal of the end products of protein metabolism which contain nitrogen, although carbon dioxide is also an excretory product which was discussed earlier. The nitrogenous waste products are urea, uric acid, and ammonia.

At this point we should be certain that there is no confusion about the term, waste products. Undigested food which accumulates in the colon and is periodically removed (defecation) is not metabolic waste. Such materials (feces) have actually never been inside the body, since they follow a one-way passage from mouth to anus without having ever entered the cells where metabolism takes place. Metabolic wastes, on the other hand, result from chemical change that occurs within the cells of the body. Carbon dioxide and nitrogenous end products are such metabolic wastes.

In reviewing the evolution of excretory systems we find that in unicellular organisms, such as amoeba, wastes are removed very simply (Fig. 21-3). Even in multicellular animals such as hydra the process is simple diffusion. Indeed, wherever all or even most of the cells are still in contact with water in the external world, there is no problem, for the CO_2 and nitrogenous wastes diffuse through the cell membranes into the surrounding water. When many of the cells of the animal body lie deeper, the elimination of metabolic wastes requires special organs. This has resulted in the evolution of the excretory systems: gills or lungs for the removal of CO_2, and kidneys for the removal of inorganic and nitrogenous wastes. Sweat glands in some mammals also aid in excretion.

These systems have all been described in preceding chapters, and we shall here confine the discussion to a brief account of the major steps in the evolution of kidneys. We have seen that the first simple kidney consists of a system of tubules ramifying the body tissues, as illustrated in planaria (Fig. 21-3). Each tubule drains the tiny flame cells which selectively pick up the nitrogenous wastes from neighboring cells, and the entire system conveys those products to the outside through many pores.

The next great step is taken by the annelids, where nephridia replace the flame cells. Not only do the cells at the funnel (nephrostome) pick up coelomic fluid which contains many substances besides nitrogenous wastes, but as this fluid passes down

FIG. 21-3. The problem of ridding the body of nitrogenous wastes is handled in various ways by representative animals.

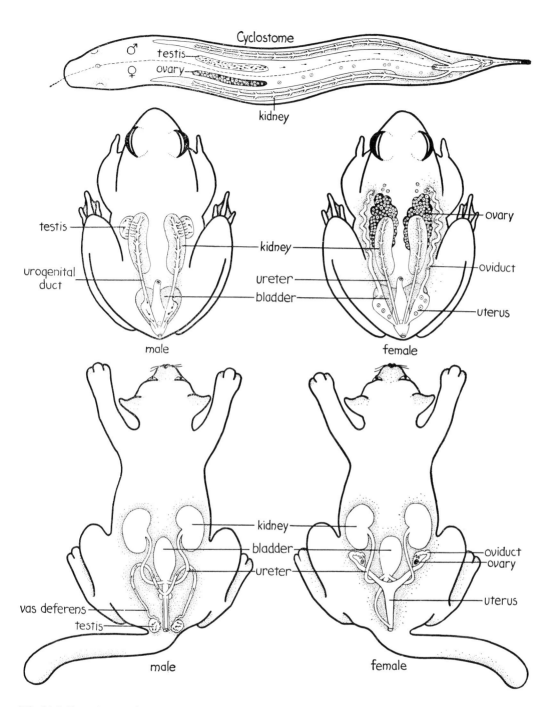

FIG. 21-4. The urinary and reproductive systems were separated in lower vertebrates (cyclostomes) but became intimately associated in higher vertebrates (fishes, amphibia, birds, and mammals). Three forms are shown here to show how this came about. See the text for details.

the tubule selective reabsorption occurs along the way. This principle established in the annelids is retained throughout all higher groups.

In the vertebrates the origin of the excretory system is intimately associated with the reproductive system. Primitive cyclostomes have kidneys that are not greatly different from those found among invertebrates. They are long, thin, paired structures lying in the dorsal wall of the body cavity, one on each side of the vertebral column (Fig. 21-4). Coelomic fluid is drawn into the ciliated nephrostomes which lead into a long tubule much like the earthworm's. The tiny tubules coalesce forming larger tubes, the **urinary ducts,** which terminate in the cloaca. In this animal, the eggs and sperm are shed into the body cavity and find their way out through two openings from the posterior end of this cavity into the cloaca. This is an extremely simple method reminiscent of some of the lower invertebrates. The excretory system and the genital system are thus distinctly separated. Perhaps because this system of getting rid of the germ cells was so fortuitous, it became necessary to provide tubes for this purpose. By chance, or perhaps by proximity, the urinary ducts took over that task, and an intimate relationship became established between the excretory and reproductive systems. This was done very gradually through several groups of animals over a period of many millions of years.

Among the fishes and amphibia, the testes became connected with the upper end of the kidney by means of tiny tubules, the **vasa efferentia.** Sperm cells then made their way out of the body through the same tubes as the urine, namely, the **urogenital ducts** (Fig. 21-4). New ducts, the **oviducts,** were formed for conveying eggs out of the body. The lower ends of these ducts became large and sac-like to form the **uteri** (singular—*uterus*) in order to accommodate the great numbers of eggs that accumulated before deposition. The uteri, too, opened into the cloaca. This seemed to be a very satisfactory arrangement, and not until mammalian evolution was well underway did further radical changes take place.

In a mammal, such as a cat, we find that the kidneys have become "kidneyshaped" and much more compact than the long thin organs of the fishes or even the thicker structures of the amphibians. As in the cyclostomes, the tubes which convey urine away from the kidneys have no affiliation with the genital system. Indeed, these ducts, the **ureters,** are new tubes which formed very late in evolution. They connect with a **bladder** (urinary), thence through a tube, the **urethra,** to the outside. The old urogenital ducts of the frog have lost their urinary function and have been taken over completely by the genital system. Their sole function in the mammal is to carry sperm cells. These tubes, the **vasa deferentia,** connect with the urethra, which is urogenital throughout the rest of its course to the outside of the body. The terminal portion is modified into a copulatory organ, the **penis.**

The path of the eggs in mammals is not greatly modified from that of the frog. They pass into the oviducts from the ovaries and then into the uteri, which may be paired as in the cat or fused as in man. The eggs of mammals are much smaller, of course, but they follow essentially the same path as in the amphibians and fishes. A new structure, the **vagina,** has been added which receives the penis of the male in sperm transfer, an essential for land animals.

The embryological development of the urogenital system of mammals follows basically the same course as its evolution. That is to say, at one time the kidney resembles that of a cyclostome, and a little later, that of a frog. Finally, some time before birth, the true mammalian kidney and associated organs are formed. It must be remembered that, although the excretory and reproductive systems are anatomically intimately related, they bear no relationship to one another functionally. The job of reproduction and excretion are two separate and distinct functions.

The Human Kidney

The two kidneys in man are about 4 inches long and are located near the mid-dorsal line just below the stomach. The ureter and blood vessels emerge from a depression on the medial side. The kidneys lie in a capsule of peritoneum which excludes them from the coelom. If a kidney is sliced lengthwise, it will be seen to consist of an outside layer, the **cortex,** and an inner capsule, the **medulla** (Fig. 21-5), both of which are visible to the naked eye. At the point where the ureter leaves, there is a large cavity, the **pelvis** (not to be confused with the pelvis of the skeleton), which is a depository for the urine as it comes from the millions of tiny tubules of the kidney. The entire internal kidney is tied together

with connective tissue and interlaced with blood vessels, and it is a very complex and extremely delicate organ.

The cortex is made up of **renal corpuscles,** which are the tiny units where the excretory process begins (Fig. 21-5). Each consists of a minute ball of capillaries, the **glomerulus,** surrounded by the double-walled cup-like sac, **Bowman's capsule.** The inner wall of the capsule closely adheres to the glomerulus in order that substances may diffuse readily from the blood stream into the cavity and thence through the long tubule to the pelvis of the kidney. The medullary portion of the kidney consists almost exclusively of these tiny tubules which play an important function in excretion.

Urine Formation. The function of the kidney has long been known but just how urine forms has become clear only in recent

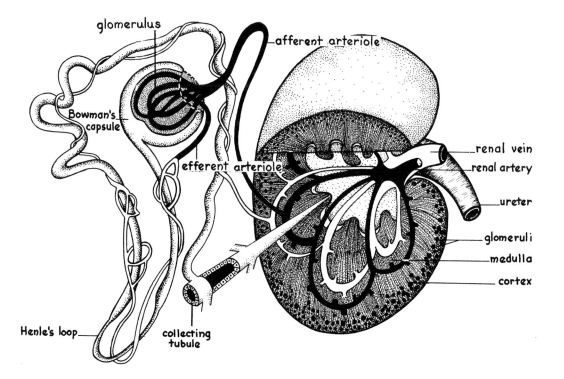

FIG. 21-5. A schematic view of the human kidney cut to show its internal structure and with a single excretory unit (renal corpuscle and tubule) enlarged to show its detailed anatomy.

years. Following through the process as it is now believed to take place, the blood passes into the kidney through the renal artery which immediately breaks up into smaller and smaller vessels until these eventually form the glomeruli of the renal corpuscles. As the blood passes through, most of the substances in the blood except the cells and proteins diffuse through Bowman's capsule by **filtration**. This is purely a physical process which depends entirely on the pressure in the blood vessels, and the amount of fluid passing into Bowman's capsule rises and falls with that pressure. The vessels coming from the glomerulus are slightly smaller than those going to it, so that the pressure remains high in these vessels. About 1 per cent of the blood volume is lost to the **capsular filtrate** as it passes through the kidney.

By some ingenious experiments with tiny micro-needles, Prof. A. N. Richards was able to examine the capsular filtrate and found that it contained urea, sugar, amino acids, salts, and so forth, in about the same concentrations as those in the blood plasma. Obviously, if all of these valuable products remained in the capsular filtrate, the animal would shortly drain its body of the essentials of life. Therefore, these products must be selectively **reabsorbed** into the blood while the fluid passes through the extremely long tubule on its way to the pelvis. This is possible because, when the blood leaves the glomerulus, instead of forming a vein, as is customary in other organs, it becomes another set of capillaries, this time surrounding the tubule that leaves Bowman's capsule (Fig. 21-5). As the capsular filtrate passes down the tubule, the valuable portions, such as the amino acids, sugars, salts, and so forth, are reabsorbed into the blood again. This requires considerable work on the part of the cells lining the walls of the tubules, as indicated by the fact that the kidney requires more oxygen than the heart when calculated on equivalent weights. The secretion is against a diffusion gradient

and therefore is called *active transport* (p. 65). This accounts for the large amount of work that is necessary. If the kidney is denied oxygen, reabsorption stops, although filtration proceeds normally.

With this arrangement it is apparent that the kidney functions as an organ which selects what substances shall remain in the blood and what shall be removed. If there is too much sugar in the blood, for example, the tubules will reabsorb some of it but leave the surplus in the capsular filtrate. Under these conditions the urine will show sugar, which is what happens in diabetics. The same is true of other substances.

The Kidney as a Regulatory Organ. Because of its ability to secrete substances selectively, the kidney is a very important organ in maintaining the proper composition of the blood and other body fluids. As we have seen, the various end products of metabolism are injurious if allowed to accumulate. The kidneys remove just the right amount of each to prevent harmful effects, and yet leave enough to maintain a proper balance of ions and molecules. The kidney figures prominently in the retention or release of hydrogen and hydroxyl ions to maintain their proper balance, and thus hold the pH of the blood constant. If the salt concentration of the blood should rise too high or fall too low, there would be a harmful movement of water which might destroy cells. This too is prevented by the elimination of exactly the right amount of salts through the tubules of the kidneys.

Many substances that are used in medicine are eventually eliminated through the urine. Such compounds as antibiotics, aspirin, and many others are removed from the body via the kidneys. Hence testing the urine is an important criterion of the effectiveness of a drug in treating a specific disease. If the drug appears in the urine shortly after it is given, it can be of little value. Antibiotics, for example, must remain in the body long enough to have an inhibitory effect on pathogenic bacteria. Frequently when searching for a new drug, it is found that the drug does the intended job very well but is lost too rapidly through the urine to be effective.

The kidney is able to return a certain amount of various substances to the blood from the capsular filtrate, but if the amount appearing in the blood is above a certain critical level, which is spoken of as the "threshold" level, the kidney no longer is able to prevent the substance from appearing in the urine. In diabetics (see p. 488), for example, the blood sugar glucose reaches such high levels, owing to the lack of insulin, that a large amount of it appears in the urine. If, in man, the amount of glucose per 100 cc. of blood exceeds 170 mg., glucose will appear in the urine. In other words, that is the threshold for glucose. Other substances have thresholds but they would not necessarily be the same as glucose's.

Blood volume is also regulated by the kidney. Following a severe hemorrhage the blood pressure drops, thus slowing up urine production and conserving body fluids. Similarly, if the blood contains too much water, the blood pressure rises and more fluids are eliminated as a consequence. The amount of urine that is excreted depends not only on the amount of fluids taken into the body but also on the amount of salt that is to be eliminated from the blood. On a salty diet the urine output is greater because more salts must be removed from the blood if a normal balance of these ions is to be maintained. Also it requires more water to pass the high proportion of solids that appears in the urine after a heavy intake of salts. In the case of diabetes there is too much glucose in the capsular filtrate and this produces a high osmotic pressure. For this reason, not much water can be reabsorbed into the blood and so a large urine output results.

Urine volume is also controlled by a hormone (ADH) secreted by the posterior lobe of the pituitary (see p. 502). This hormone controls the rate of water reabsorption in the tubule. If it is insufficient or completely lacking, a disease known as *diabetes insipidus* results. People suffering from this disease may have a urine output of 30–40 liters per day instead of 1.3–1.5 liters, which is average. As might be expected, they also suffer from an insatiable thirst.

A normal kidney restores all of the utilizable substances in the capsular filtrate to the blood except in cases where the retention of such substances might be harmful. However, urea and other substances are highly concentrated as the capsular filtrate flows down the tubule toward the pelvis of the kidney. Once in the bladder it is known as urine. Its concentration will vary, of course, with the amount of water included with it. This can be measured by determining its specific gravity, a routine procedure in diagnosis.

Like most organs of the body, the kidney has a tremendous latitude within which to operate, and can withstand considerable abuse and still do its job satisfactorily. Actually, only one-half of one kidney, or one-fourth of the total kidney tissue, is necessary to handle the normal business of living.

Kidney Function in Adverse Environments

Animals live in a wide diversity of environments, many of which call upon the kidney to assist in keeping the balance of molecules commensurate with that needed for life. Not only the kidney, but often special organs have evolved to keep this balance, particularly among animals that have returned to the sea after having evolved in fresh water or on land.

Most marine invertebrates have little trouble with ion exchange due to the high salt concentration because their body fluids have approximately the same osmotic pressure as sea water, although they may not be in the same proportion. Some, however,

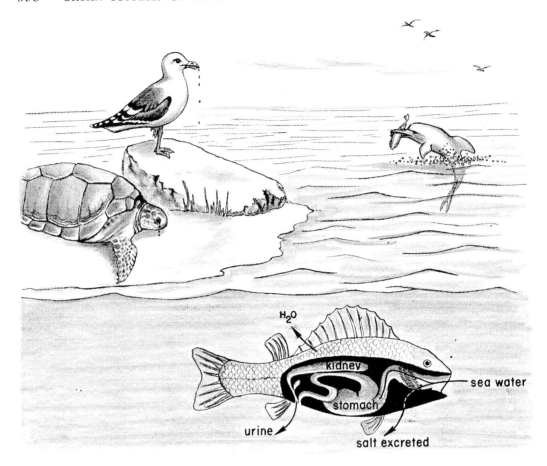

FIG. 21-6. Various methods by which animals maintain water balance when drinking sea water.

such as the shore crab, *Carcinus*, can resist osmotic change as when it moves from the sea into brackish water (mouths of rivers). It is said to have the power of **osmoregulation.** When it moves into dilute sea water its own salt concentration exceeds that of its environment causing an inflow of water which, if continuous, can be fatal. The kidney (green gland), however, excretes water; nevertheless, this alone is not adequate to maintain the high salt concentration of its tissues, hence the gills actually secrete salt into the blood thus keeping it from being diluted. This requires work since the movement of the ions is against a gradient; that is, the salts tend to be lost to the more dilute environment, but by forcing them in via the gills the osmotic pressure of the blood can be maintained. Thus we see again in this marine organism how active transport is required to maintain stability of the ions.

The marine fishes also have osmotic problems because they evolved in fresh water and, therefore, their body fluids have an osmotic concentration of about one-third that of the sea. Since their thin-walled gills are constantly in close proximity with sea water they lose water and must counter dehydration. They drink sea water but cannot eliminate the salt through the kidneys (Fig. 21-6). Instead, the gills concentrate the salt and excrete it back into the sea. Again this requires energy and work on the part of the gill cells (active transport).

The marine mammals, such as whales, porpoises, and seals, also have had to adapt to the high salt concentration of the sea which far exceeds that of their own tissues. Most whales eat fish which have a salt concentration about one-third that of the sea. However, being mammals they excrete nitrogenous wastes as urea, which requires water to flush it out of the body. They also lose some water through breathing, so there is a constant water loss which must be made up. This is accomplished by excreting a highly concentrated urine. The water gained through oxidation of their food replaces that which is lost; consequently they need not drink at all. During certain seasons of the year female marine mammals lose water through another channel, namely, when they are nursing their young. Interestingly, little water is lost this way because their milk is ten times as concentrated (fat) as is cow's milk. This is another remarkable adaptation to prevent water loss.

Marine birds, such as petrels, gulls, penguins, and albatrosses, never drink fresh water, so must also have an osmoregulatory problem. In spite of their ability to excrete uric acid, they still must counteract the high salt concentration of the sea water which they drink. This is accomplished by means of a special gland in the head which excretes salt at a concentration about twice that of sea water. Ducts from the glands lead into the nasal cavity, thus conveying the salt to the tip of the beak. It is a common sight to see gulls at rest dripping salt water from their beaks (Fig. 21-6).

Marine reptiles, such as the giant turtles, solve their salt problem much the same as birds. Their salt glands, however, are located near the eye and the salt is excreted in the form of tears. This becomes obvious when the females come out on land to lay their eggs. They are said to "weep" during this important activity.

Desert animals have a water problem of quite a different sort. In spite of the scarcity of water in these regions of the earth, animals of all kinds abound. Their problem is to get along on little or no water, other than that taken in with their food. They have evolved no new organs to solve their problem but have improved on their kidneys' capacity to concentrate salts and urea in the urine.

The kangaroo rat, a desert rodent, has been studied rather extensively in regard to its capacity to live on dry seeds without drinking at all. When fed on rolled oats in the laboratory it maintains a constant water balance for months without consuming water. It has no sweat glands, being nocturnal, hence loses no water for heat regulation. It conserves on water by producing very dry feces and, most important, by excreting highly concentrated urine, far more than any other mammal. Indeed, its urine is nearly five times as concentrated as man's, and has a salt concentration twice that of sea water.

The camel's reputation for going many days on the desert without water is well known. Just how does it do this when man and most other mammals would perish in a fraction of the time? It has a problem that the kangaroo rat did not have; namely, it works in the heat of the sun and therefore must control its body temperature by heat regulation through water evaporation from the skin. Whereas it has a large compartmentalized stomach, as other ruminants do, it has no extra "water sacks" for a reserve water supply as is sometimes thought. Moreover, the hump contains fat and no water. The camel then seems to have no special devices by which it can store water, and must then conserve what it takes in.

One interesting adaptation is the camel's wide body temperature variation. At night its body cools to about 34°C and during the day it will rise to 41°C before it begins to sweat to prevent a further rise. Man begins to sweat at slightly over 37°C and loses water continuously through this channel. It requires a good many hours in the hot sun before the camel loses water through sweating. Another means of conserving water is the camel's tolerance to dehydration. It can lose as much as 40 per cent of its body water without ill effects whereas other mammals are in serious trouble if they lose 20 per cent. When water is again available the camel can replace this loss in ten minutes. This animal has merely become extremely efficient in water conservation.

SUGGESTED SUPPLEMENTARY READINGS

BALDWIN, E. B., *An Introduction to Comparative Biochemistry* (Cambridge, Cambridge University Press, 1949).

CARLSON, A. J., and JOHNSON, V., *The Machinery of the Body* (Chicago, University of Chicago Press, 1962).

PROSSER, C. L., and BROWN, F. A., *Comparative Animal Physiology* (Philadelphia, W. B. Saunders Co., 1961).

SMITH, H. W., "The Kidney," *Scientific American,* 188(1) (January, 1953), 40.

WOODBURNE, R. T., *Essentials of Human Anatomy* (New York, Oxford University Press, 1961).

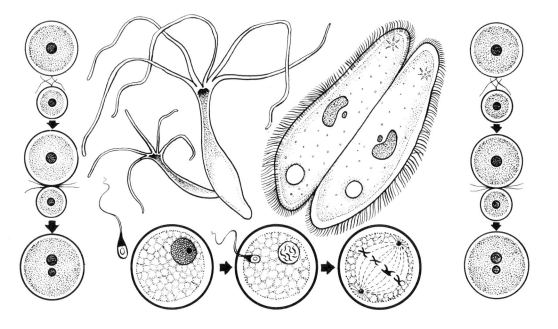

22

Reproduction

In the preceding chapters we have considered in some detail the problems of structure and maintenance in the individual animal body. We shall now turn to the problem of reproduction of the individual. All animals reproduce, from the simplest protozoan to the most complex mammal and, furthermore, elaborate provisions are usually made for this important event. The methods employed by animals today must have had a long and interesting history.

Undoubtedly, the first forms of life duplicated themselves by some sort of fission, perhaps much as many bacteria and protozoa do today. This is one form of **asexual** reproduction, so called because there is no sex involved; the cell simply divides into two parts, usually equal in size (Fig. 22-1). When animals became many-celled, some form of asexual reproduction was still retained by many of the lower forms. Hydra, for example, forms buds (Fig. 22-1) which develop into miniature hydras. Planaria, a more complicated animal, still employs fission. With increasing complexity of body structure in higher forms, this method of reproduction was lost entirely.

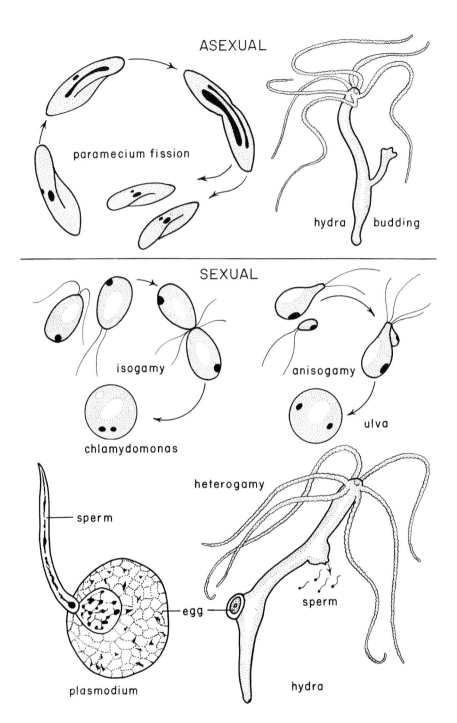

ASEXUAL

paramecium fission

hydra budding

SEXUAL

isogamy

anisogamy

chlamydomonas

ulva

heterogamy

sperm

egg

plasmodium

sperm

hydra

FIG. 22-1. Asexual reproduction occurs among the protozoa and lower invertebrates. Sexual reproduction was initiated among some of the simpler protozoa where it progressed from simple fusion of two similar cells to the union of
highly diverse reproductive cells, the sperm and egg. The steps which brought this about may have been similar to
those outlined here, using animals that are living today.

Sexual reproduction must have been introduced very early in the evolution of living things, because we find it well established even among the single-celled plants and animals. There is a series of single-celled green forms living today that shows a graded sequence from the union of cells that are similar in size and activity to those that are quite unlike in these respects (Fig. 22-1). At certain times, individual cells of *Chlamydomonas* will fuse, forming a **zygote** which will overwinter and continue its asexual method of reproduction the next spring. Since these uniting cells are equal in size, they are called **isogametes** and their union, **isogamy**. A closely related form, *Ulva*, undergoes a similar process, although in this case the cells are unequal in size. The smaller of the two is more active than the larger and in this respect resembles a sperm. Such unlike gametes are called **anisogametes** and their union, **anisogamy**. Among the parasitic protozoa, such as plasmodium (see p. 193), two totally different cells are produced, a large immotile *egg* and a tiny active *sperm cell*. Here there is not only a size difference but also a physiological difference—one moves, the other does not. Once the sex cells reached this relationship in their evolution, they then maintained it throughout all higher forms. The smaller sperm cell is usually motile and is able to maintain sustained movement, while the egg is large and immotile. Such gametes are referred to as **heterogametes** and their fusion, **heterogamy**. After sexual reproduction became established it was retained, and while we see a rather wide range in sizes and shapes of both eggs and sperm, the fundamental plan remains unchanged in all animal groups.

The methods of bringing eggs and sperm together is relatively simple among both the lower invertebrates and the lower vertebrates. The union is purely fortuitous, although some arrangement, such as seasonal aggregation, usually occurs so that the animals are in the immediate vicinity of one another. As long as the animals remain in a fluid environment, all that is necessary is to discharge the sex cells into the water where by sheer chance they are brought in proximity to each other. However, when animals invaded the land the whole process became much more complex. It must have taken a long time to accomplish this transition along with the many others resulting from the pronounced change of habitat. Perhaps the most interesting modifications came about among the vertebrates, some of which we have already discussed.

Care of the Young

Among the vertebrates there are three ways in which young are cared for in their early development (Fig. 22-2). Some are hatched from eggs that are laid, as in the case of most fishes, amphibia, many reptiles (Fig. 22-3), and all birds. These are called **oviparous** forms. Others retain the eggs within the uterus until they hatch, and the resulting young are therefore born in a relatively advanced and active stage of development. These are said to be **ovoviviparous.** Some fish and some reptiles (snakes) are of this type. Still other vertebrates (mammals) produce small eggs without yolk that develop in the uterus, and the young receive most, if not all, of their nourishment from the uterine wall of the mother. These are said to be **viviparous.** Young born thus are, of course, more or less advanced in development.

In general, fishes and amphibians give their young little or no care whatever, and consequently no provisions in the way of accessory structures are found in these animals (Fig. 22-4). However, when the reptiles moved onto land, certain anatomical modifications were essential if the young were to survive in a dry environment. For one thing, the egg became very large, abundantly supplied with reserve food for the developing embryo, thus providing a means for the embryo to reach a rather advanced stage before it had to shift for itself. Be-

FIG. 22-2. Some vertebrates, such as the fish, the frog, and the bird, lay eggs (oviparous) which hatch outside the body. Others, such as the shark, retain the eggs within the uterus (ovoviviparous) where they hatch, and the young are born in an active condition. Still others, such as the mammals, produce young from small eggs (viviparous) and the young receive nutrients from the uterine wall.

sides this food reserve, the egg had to supply a fluid environment in which the embryo could develop. In other words, a tiny bit of its ancestral aquatic world had to be incorporated into the egg. This was supplied by the introduction of the **amnion** (p. 376). Moreover, as the embryo advanced in its development it required more oxygen than could be supplied by diffusion to the embryo directly. The development of the **allantois** (p. 376) met this need (Fig. 22-4).

Large eggs, together with their extraembryonic membranes, served very well for the reptiles and birds. The former reached great heights as dominant world-wide animals during the Mesozoic Era and the latter are a dominant form today.

However, the keen swift-moving mammals that were to follow developed a new approach to this problem. When their embryo began to receive nourishment from the uterine wall via a special organ, the

FIG. 22-3. Hatching pythons (*Python molurus*). Note the wrinkled shell which is soft in reptiles.

Human Graafian Follicle

FIG. 22-4. Special membranes are formed in the eggs of vertebrates that have come out onto land, the reptiles, birds, and mammals. The upper sketch shows the condition found in aquatic forms such as fish and amphibians. The middle figure shows the formation of the amnion and allantois to make embryological development on land possible. In these eggs there is sufficient stored food (yolk) to carry the embryo throughout its early development. In the lower figure is shown the mammalian egg and the condition found in the uterus where, in addition to the membranes seen in the earlier forms, the placenta has evolved, making it possible for the embryo to receive nourishment from the mother.

placenta (p. 391), the large food reserve of the reptilian egg was no longer necessary, although the membranes of the latter were retained. Gradually the yolk disappeared but the yolk sac still remained (Fig. 22-4). Let us examine these extraembryonic membranes a little more carefully.

The **amnion** is an outfolding of the body wall of the embryo and is lined with peritoneum, the lining of the **coelomic cavity.** This membrane continues to grow around the embryo until the latter is completely enveloped and lies in the resulting **amniotic cavity.** The membranes fuse at their point of juncture, so that the cavity is a closed, fluid-filled sac reminiscent of the aquatic environment that was the home of all earlier embryos. Because the amnion is double-walled, an outer layer, called the **chorion,** is formed. In birds and reptiles the chorion comes in contact with the inner layer of the egg shell, whereas in mammals it comes in contact with the uterine wall and ultimately becomes a part of the placenta.

The **allantois** arises as an outpushing from the posterior gut and forces its way into the extraembryonic cavity to become a large sac-like structure, the outer layer of which fuses with the chorion. The resulting intimately fused membrane then lies in close proximity with the inner surface of the shell in birds and reptiles but in mammals eventually becomes a part of the placenta. The allantois functions as a respiratory organ in picking up oxygen and giving off carbon dioxide for the developing embryo; in addition, it absorbs food materials from the large egg (yolk) of birds and reptiles and acts as a repository for nitrogenous wastes.

In higher mammals the allantois, together with the chorion, comes into temporary contact with the uterine wall where the chorion sends out finger-like projections, the **chorionic villi,** deep into the wall's soft tissues. This region of contact is richly supplied with capillaries from the **umbilical artery.** Embryonic blood is sent to this region under the impetus of the fetal heartbeat and returned to the embryo via the **umbilical vein.** Simultaneous with the development of the chorionic villi, the uterine wall in the same region becomes highly vascularized, forming many blood spaces into which the finger-like villi dip. The tissues contributed by both the fetus and the uterine wall constitute the **placenta,** which is shed at birth. It must be remembered that there is no blood connection between the embryo and the mother; each has its own circulation which is kept distinct at all times. The placenta acts like the attachment organ of a fungal parasite—a means of extracting nourishing fluids from the "host." Through this organ oxygen is obtained, carbon dioxide is eliminated, food is absorbed, and nitrogenous wastes (urea) are discharged.

Evolution of External Structures

We usually think of the need for external genitalia to facilitate the union of the sex cells as directly related to the change to life on land. To be sure, such accessory structures were essential for land life, but we must not forget that copulatory organs did evolve among fishes that never left the water. The sharks again are a striking example. The **claspers,** which are modified pelvic fins in the male shark, are utilized as an intromittent organ for carrying the sperm to the cloaca of the female (Fig. 22-2). Many bony fishes also have converted their fins into a copulatory organ. These are unusual cases among the fishes, and most of them have so little external sexual dimorphism that even the best ichthyologists have difficulty in telling male from female.

Among the strict land vertebrates—reptiles, birds, and mammals—a special copulatory organ, the **penis,** has evolved. Among the reptiles it is a pair of elongated masses of erectile tissue with a groove between, the entire structure originating from the floor of the cloaca. In mammals the groove

FIG. 22-5. Among the fishes with cartilaginous skeletons (sharks and skates), two entirely different ways of caring for the young are observed. The top picture is the partly cut away egg case of the barn door skate (*Raja stabuliformis*), showing the embryo skate lying within. These eggs are laid in marine vegetation where the long tendrils on the four corners of the egg case anchor it during the incubation period.

The lower picture is of a small shark (*Mustelus*) embryo removed from the uterus of the mother. The long umbilical cord is attached to the half empty yolk sac which supplies nourishment for the embryo during its early life. In its later embryonic life there is a "placenta" formed in which nutrients and gases pass between the fetal and maternal circulation.

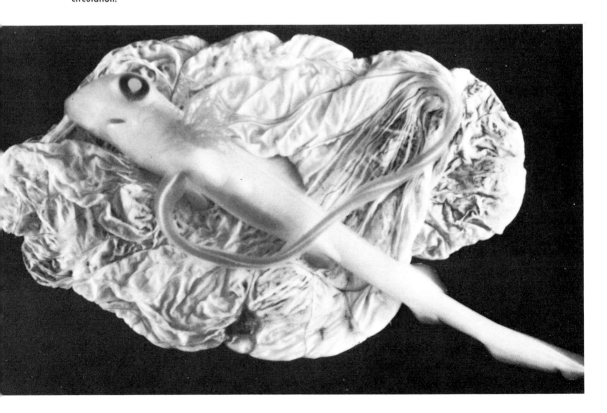

is closed to form a tube which is a direct continuation of the urethra. The terminal portion of the female tract has followed a parallel evolution by becoming transformed into a tube-like receptacle, the **vagina,** for the penis and seminal fluid.

Along with these changes has come the introduction of a large complex of chemical regulators (hormones) and certain nervous modifications which has made copulation not only a necessity for the continuance of the race but a highly gratifying experience. During the breeding period of large mammals such as cattle, both sexes will go to great lengths, even exposure to death itself, in order to tend to the business of bringing about the union of their sex cells. Owners of female dogs are well aware of the semiannual heat cycle of their charges. It is easy to understand how those animals with the greatest sex drive were more apt to become the parents of the next generation, whereas those indifferent in this regard might never have become parents at all, so that the intensity of the sex drive in animals is actually a contributing factor to their survival.

Evolutionary Significance

Viewing the vertebrates in a general way, it is true that giving birth to active young is more advanced than egg laying. There are, however, a number of very interesting primitive vertebrates, the sharks for example, that have progressed a long way toward producing and caring for young in much the same way mammals do. Some sharks inhabit the deep sea and never come into shallow waters to deposit their eggs in safe places. In such species, the eggs are retained in the uteri where they can be better cared for. In one small shark (*Mustelus*) tiny projections, like villi in the intestine, protrude from the yolk sac and penetrate the uterine wall from which the embryo derives nutritious secretions (Fig. 22-5). This condition certainly approaches the placenta of mammals; indeed, these sharks

are called "placental" sharks. Another interesting device for extra-egg nourishment of the developing embryo is found among the rays, close relatives of sharks. In some of these animals, glandular teats grow out from the inner uterine wall and by contractions force their secretion into the mouth or spiracle of the embryo, thus resembling extrauterine feeding of mammals. In spite of these rare cases, it is generally true that evolution of the reproductive system among vertebrates has been from the egg-laying forms to those that retain and nourish their young within the uterus of the mother.

We can make one further generalization, constantly keeping in mind the occa-

FIG. 22-6. A mother flying squirrel (*Glaucomys volans*) carrying her young to a new home. Mammals generally give exceeding good care to their young.

sional exception which prevents one from drawing final sweeping conclusions. Most primitive animals make headway by sheer weight of numbers; millions are produced but only a small fraction of a per cent survive to maturity. As the animals become more complex, fewer and fewer offspring are produced but the early mortality rate drops also. With smaller numbers greater parental care is given, so that the percentage of survival is much greater (Fig. 22-6). The fish deposits its eggs in a scooped-out hollow on the stream bottom and immediately leaves them to the ravages of other fish. A large mammal like a horse bears young only once a year but gives the offspring great care, even to the point of sacrificing her own life (Fig. 22-2). In each case the chance for race survival may be the same. Immediately we can think of exceptions to this generalization. The codfish, for example, lays millions of eggs each season, whereas the shark may have no more than a dozen in an equal period of time, yet the shark is more primitive than the cod. Frogs and toads give their young no care whatever, but the bluegill (fish) will protect its nest of eggs viciously against all intruders. These are good examples to remind us of the caution one must exercise in stating a generalization.

THE HUMAN REPRODUCTIVE SYSTEM

Although there are minor differences in the reproductive apparatus among various mammals, they are all essentially alike, man included. One rather striking variation has undoubtedly had considerable influence on man's habits and indeed his entire social structure. That is the lack of a seasonal or periodic breeding season. The sexes are mutually attractive throughout the year. This fact probably has had some bearing on the establishment of permanent unions that could provide for offspring which required such long periods of time for growth to maturity. This is the basis of the family which, in turn, underlies our whole social order as we know it in civilized nations today. It should not be implied, however, that man is by nature fitted perfectly into the straitjacket of civilization he has fashioned for himself. In fact, he is constantly in trouble with those individuals who tend to break with established convention and to follow basic instinctive urges. This applies to sex urges as well as others. It is important that we recognize these basic urges as normal and regulate our social order accordingly. This attitude has not always been maintained in the past, but as knowledge grows concerning human behavior we shall eventually reach a better understanding of what curbs can be placed on basic instincts that will benefit society and thus make for a more successful civilization.

Male

The sperm-producing glands are the **testes,** which are very similar in their anatomy to the same organ in other mammals. Sperms are produced by rapidly dividing cells located in the walls of the long, tiny, coiled tubules which, taken together, make up most of the gland itself (Fig. 22-7). The paired testes lie in a pendent sac, the **scrotum,** which is located in the pubic region. Sperm cells make their way out of the testes into the **epididymis,** a long convoluted tubule, where they mature and are stored for a time. They then pass into the **vas deferens,** a thickened sperm duct that passes anteriorly through the **inguinal canal,** finally entering the **urethra** and thence through the **penis** to the outside. Near the region where the two vasa deferentia enter the urethra each receives secretions from the glandular **seminal vesicles.** Also at this junction the **prostate gland** surrounds the urethra and pours its secretions into it. Two small glands, **Cowper's glands,** located at the base of the penis, secrete a mucoid fluid which, together with secretions from the prostate and seminal vesicles, constitutes the transport medium for the sperm cells.

The penis is composed of a special tissue with large capillaries called **erectile tissue** which, when gorged with blood, causes the organ to become much enlarged and turgid. In such condition it becomes a satisfactory organ for transferring sperms to the vagina of the female. Erection is accomplished when, under sexual excitement, the small arteries leading to the penis relax, allowing blood to fill the large capillaries; at the same time the veins constrict where they leave the organ, thus trapping blood within it. The organ becomes flaccid by a reversing of the process. The penis ends in a cap-like structure, the **glans,** which is partially covered by loose skin, the **prepuce.**

Because of the anatomical arrangement of the male generative organs, certain difficulties may be experienced, especially by older men. For example, if the prostate becomes enlarged, which it not infrequently does, elimination of urine becomes difficult because the urethra is squeezed shut. Another difficulty arises from the fact that when the testes descend through the inguinal canal into the scrotum some weeks before birth, a weakened area is left at the point where the spermatic cord perforates the abdominal wall. If, at some later time, sufficient pressure is brought to bear on this area, a small segment of the gut may be forced into this canal resulting in an inguinal **hernia.** This sometimes occurs during birth when the child is apt to be squeezed unduly while passing through the small birth canal. If further constriction occurs the circulation to the gut may become so impaired as to kill the region, thus resulting in gangrene which can be very serious.

Female

The egg-producing **ovaries** lie deep in the lower body cavity where they function much as they do in lower vertebrates (Fig. 22-8). Their function is to produce eggs, and since the chances for fertilization in mammals are very good only a comparatively small number are actually generated. The cells destined to become eggs lie in the periphery of the ovary and as they mature migrate into the deeper portions (Fig. 22-9). Several potential egg cells mature in a cluster, only one of which exceeds all others in size and eventually matures into an egg. All, however, produce the hormone **estradiol** (see p. 492). Several layers of cells form around each egg at first; later a liquid-filled cavity appears, in which the egg floats, being attached by a thin stalk to the inner wall. The entire structure is now known as a **Graafian follicle.** When mature it is over 1 centimeter across and is located near the periphery of the ovary once more. The region nearest the outer edge of the ovary thins out and finally splits, allowing the follicular contents to be extruded into the body cavity, a process known as **ovulation.** The tiny egg (about 140 microns across) is carried out with the fluid and is subsequently drawn into the funnel-like terminal end of the oviduct (Fallopian tube), which is lined with beating cilia that create a current directed into the oviduct. Occasionally the egg gets "lost" in the coelom and never reaches the oviduct. If, however, it should be fertilized while outside the confines of the oviduct, which sometimes happens, the embryo may become attached to any convenient organ, including the ovary itself, and develop for some time. It usually is unable to go to full term, however, and aborts, causing severe internal hemorrhages that may be fatal if immediate care is not given.

Fertilization

The union of the egg with a sperm must occur at a rather specific time because neither is long-lived. Fertilization is most apt to occur if sperm are in the vicinity of the egg within a few hours after ovulation, and it usually does not occur if more than three days elapse before the union is pos-

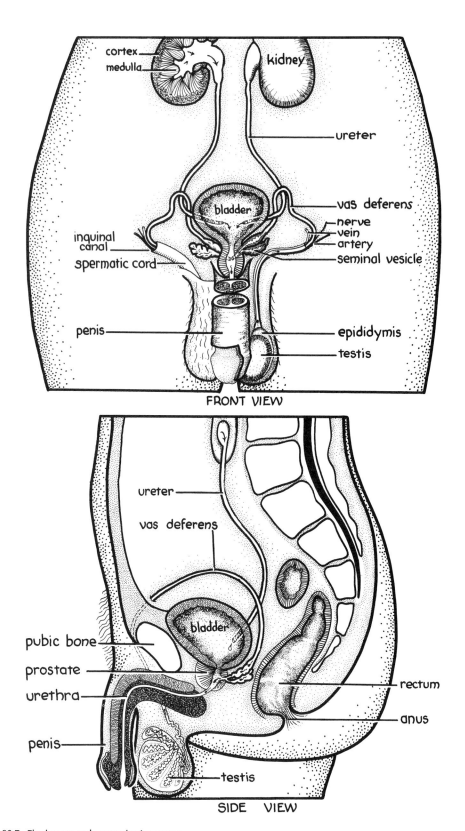

FIG. 22-7. The human male reproductive system.

FRONT VIEW

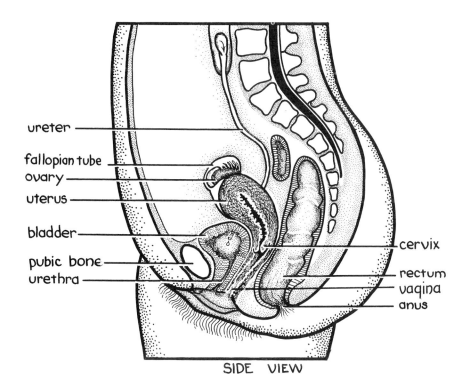

SIDE VIEW

FIG. 22-8. The human female reproductive system.

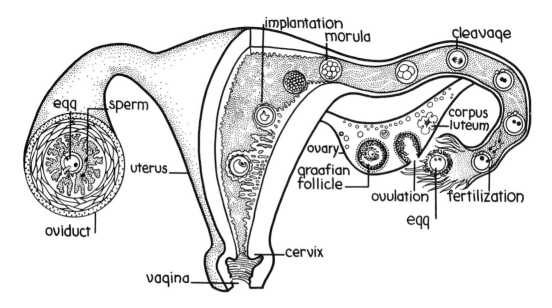

FIG. 22-9. The human ovary and uterus cut in such a way that the pathway of the fertilized egg can be followed. Note that fertilization occurs in the upper end of the oviduct. One of the oviducts is cut in cross-section in order to show the nature of its lining.

sible. Ovulation is definitely timed with respect to the menstrual cycle, usually occurring about the fourteenth day following the onset of menstruation. There may be rather wide variations in unusual cases, but as a rule a day or two before or after the fourteenth day will find the egg in the oviduct where it may be fertilized if sperm are in the vicinity. Sperm deposited in the upper end of the vagina make their way through the **cervix** (Fig. 22-9) and **uterus** into the oviducts in a matter of several hours. It is interesting to note that it seems to be essential that millions of sperm be supplied at once in order that only one reach its destination, even though only one is necessary for fertilization. Apparently the cooperative effort of many is needed to digest their way through the external layers of the egg. The sperm cells move at random in the female genital tract; they are not attracted in any one direction. They reach the egg primarily as a result of the activity of the genital tract itself.

Once the egg is fertilized, it divides several times en route down the oviduct, and by the time it reaches the uterus it is a ball of cells (Fig. 22-9) and is ready for **implantation,** that is, to become attached to the uterine wall. During the time these things have been happening to the egg, the uterine wall has been preparing itself for the reception of the young embryo. When the embryo reaches the uterus, it is actually drawn into the uterine wall because of the receptive nature of the lining itself. Once implanted, the embryo grows rapidly, starting as a tiny reddened spot and finally, after approximately 40 weeks, becoming a full-term **fetus** (Figs. 22-10, 22-11). This entire process is intricately linked with a complex battery of hormones which has been referred to in an earlier section (p. 492).

During intrauterine life the embryo must develop a complete set of organs—lungs, digestive system, excretory system—and all except the circulatory system function only slightly but must be ready to carry on full activity within a matter of minutes after birth. All of its nourishment and oxygen have come to the embryo through the umbilical vein from the placenta, and all of its waste products (carbon dioxide and urea) have been delivered through the same organ. Its lungs have never breathed, its kidneys and digestive tract have functioned but little, yet within a few minutes after it is born all of these organs perform their jobs to full capacity and, almost without exception, they function perfectly from the very start. The most dramatic change occurs in the circulation.

The blood path through the fetus is quite different from that in the adult (Fig. 22-12). Obviously, circulation of blood must start very early in the developing fetus because it is only through the circulation that nourishment and the elimination of wastes can take place. The blood must be pumped to and from the placenta at a rapid rate during **development;** hence the circulatory mechanism is one of the first organs that is well developed in the fetus. The beating fetal heart is easily detected with a stetho-

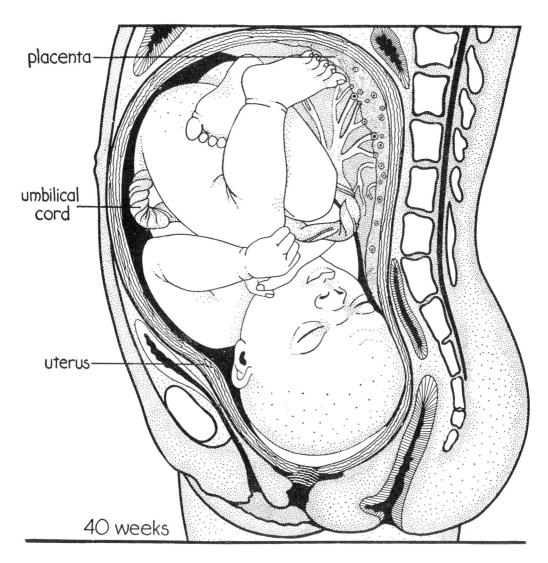

placenta

umbilical cord

uterus

40 weeks

FIG. 22-10. The full-term fetus shown in its normal position just before birth.

FIG. 22-11. A human embryo (about six weeks old) floating in the amnionic cavity. The spherical-shaped body in the lower left is the yolk sac. The feathery nature of the chorion is shown. The part nearest the viewer has been cut away.

scope long before the child is born. Since there is no point in sending blood through the nonfunctional lungs, the heart has modified the main blood flow through itself, and functions essentially as a single organ rather than the double one of the adult. This temporary detour has meant that the fetal heart must be constructed on a slightly different plan than the adult heart. There is an opening between the auricles, the **foramen ovale,** which allows incoming blood from the great veins to fill both auricles simultaneously. When the blood is forced out from the ventricles, that coming from the right ventricle, which in the adult goes to the lungs, is short-circuited through a large, short connection, the **ductus arteriosus,** to the aorta. Very little blood goes to the lungs, so very little comes back to the left auricle. Almost the entire output from both ventricles therefore passes out into the general circulation. This is necessary because the blood must be forced through the paired **umbilical arteries** to the placenta, which is a highly vascular organ requiring large quantities of blood. The blood flows in this path throughout fetal life, while the organ systems are being developed so that at the moment birth occurs they will function properly.

...

blood rich in oxygen
mixed blood
blood low in oxygen

umbilical cord

ductus arteriosus

foramen ovale

umbilical vein
umbilicus

umbilical arteries

placenta

uterus

PRENATAL

POSTNATAL

FIG. 22-12. The blood pathway is quite different during fetal life than it is after birth, as indicated in these sketches.

The basic structure of the human embryo is well delineated by the end of the twelfth week of intrauterine life, although there is a great deal of growth that must take place before the child is ready for the rigorous life that awaits him in the outside world. The uterine wall keeps pace with the growing embryo and the added burden gradually changes the entire body contour of the mother (Fig. 22-13). As the fetus grows it slips posteriorly, with its head low in the pelvis, and by the fortieth week of its life it is ready to be born.

Birth

The process of being born is one of the more remarkable events in the biological world (Fig. 22-14). As the fetus passes

6 weeks

12 weeks

20 weeks

36 weeks

FIG. 22-13. Changes occur in both the uterus and the mother to accommodate the developing fetus.

through the tight-fitting birth canal, the umbilical cord remains attached to the placenta, and until the moment the child takes his first breath, nourishment and oxygen are received from this source. Upon exposure to the external world, stimulation, coming from being chilled and from the high CO_2 in his blood, causes the child to take his first breath. The partial vacuum created in the chest cavity causes the blood to be diverted from the ductus arteriosus into the pulmonary artery and lungs. This is aided by a powerful sphincter muscle surrounding the ductus arteriosus which contracts at this moment and never relaxes. The large volume of blood then makes its way back to the heart through the pulmonary veins, filling the left auricle. Since this chamber is now filled from a new source, it is no longer necessary for an opening to exist between the auricles, hence a flap of tissue closes the foramen ovale. It requires a few minutes for this adjustment to take place, during which time the child is bluish in color, but gradually he becomes pink as the circulation is separated into its pulmonary and systemic parts. It is indeed amazing that with all its complications this process so seldom fails.

However, if the foramen ovale does fail to close or something else goes wrong with the mechanism for separating the blood, the baby remains bluish in color, a condition given the term *blue baby*. He is bluish in color (cyanotic) because the oxygenated and reduced blood are mixed, just as they are during fetal life. Some remarkable heart and vascular surgery has been accomplished in recent years to correct such occasional defects.

We have now completed the story of the *Organ Systems of Man*, starting with the single-celled animals and culminating our discussion with the mammals, man in particular. Now let us discuss the development of an individual from its very beginning and some of the problems involved in this very complex though fascinating story.

FIG. 22-14. A series of models showing the various stages in the delivery of a baby. The placenta remains attached to the uterine wall for some time after the child is born. It is then shed and the uterus returns to its normal size.

SUGGESTED SUPPLEMENTARY READINGS

CARLSON, A. J., and JOHNSON, V., *The Machinery of the Body* (Chicago, Chicago University Press, 1962).

CORNER, G. W., *The Hormones in Human Reproduction* (Princeton, N.J., Princeton University Press, 1942).

TYLER, A., "Fertilization and Antibodies," *Scientific American,* 192(5) (May, 1955), 36.

VILLEE, C. A., ed., *The Control of Ovulation* (London, Pergamon Press, 1961).

WOODBURNE, R. T., *Essentials of Human Anatomy* (New York, Oxford University Press, 1961).

ZAHL, P. A., "The Evolution of Sex," *Scientific American,* 180(4) (April, 1949), 52.

23

Development of the Embryo

WE SHALL now follow the course of events that take place when the sex cells unite to form a zygote which then undergoes millions of mitoses directed specifically toward the formation of a new organism. This subject, **embryology,** is one of the most fascinating, and yet in its fundamental aspects one of the least understood, of any of the fields of biology. To realize the magnitude of the problem, consider how such a tiny object as a fertilized egg can carry within itself the potentialities of producing a living organism as complex as man.

The above question has stimulated speculation among thinking men for many centuries. Aristotle, for example, believed that the male element, or semen, was the seed that gave rise to the new individual. Indeed the word **semen** means seed. The female was thought of as the earth (Mother Earth) in which the seed was nourished so that it might grow. This was a natural deduction, since it was known that castrated animals were sterile; without semen there was no offspring. Furthermore, this was during the time when the male sex was considered all important, the female being

FIG. 23-1. One of the early schools of embryology was that of the spermists, who believed that the child was preformed in the sperm and merely unfolded within the confines of the female uterus. Among followers of this concept was Hartsoeker, who published a drawing in 1678 similar to the one shown here, and advanced the idea of the homunculus. The human sperm as it appears under a modern microscope is shown for comparison.

passive in her social life as well as her biological life. The appearance of characteristics in the offspring was apparently ignored. Moreover, the finding of the placenta attached to the embryo by the umbilical cord furthered the concept that the female functioned only in nourishing the fetus. The idea that both sexes contributed to the offspring came much later.

With the actual discovery of the human sperm by Ludwig Hamm in 1677 the importance of the male retained its place. This was further emphasized by the work of Hartsoeker, who not only claimed to have seen the human sperm first but who also drew a miniature fetus within the head of the spermatozoan and thus advanced the idea of the **homunculus** (Fig. 23-1). This led to the establishment of the **preformation** school which included those who believed that the human embryo was completely formed within the sperm and merely unfolded during its development. Impetus was given to this idea by Malpighi (1672), who concluded that the chick was fully formed, though in miniature, at the time the egg was laid. This was probably due to an error that could easily arise from a study of an egg that had remained several hours (10–15) within the oviduct where development of the chick could proceed, and which might slowly continue development in the warm Italian climate even though unincubated. However, because of the obvious existence of large eggs, such as those of birds and reptiles, there developed another school which believed that the egg was the center of development. This meant there were two schools of thought among preformationists, the **spermists** and the **ovists.**

An interesting aspect of this controversy was the development of the **encasement** theory. One group of followers believed that the child was derived completely from the egg and that the egg contained a minute human being within it. If the egg in question contained a diminutive woman, within the eggs of her ovary were still more minute women and so on, each encased in the preceding. From this point of view the first woman contained all of the future generations wrapped one within the other and the race would come to an end when all of the encased homunculi were exhausted. The absurdity of this theory became apparent with a few mathematical calculations such as Hartsoeker made on the size that an original female must have been to house all future generations. The theory was finally laid to rest with the discovery of the human egg by Von Baer in 1827.

Not all intellectuals of these early times believed in preformation, for some thought that the adult parts were not present at the beginning but developed during embryonic life, that is by **epigenesis.** Actually Aristotle believed this, as did Harvey some two thousand years later. In 1759 the German biologist Wolff published his careful observations on the developing chick, which dealt a severe blow to the theory of preformation. He showed that adult structures do actually make their gradual appearance throughout embryonic life, and his observations have been confirmed many times since; hence epigensis is the view held today by biologists. As we shall see a little later, this does not mean that the egg is completely without organization; but the idea of a fully formed miniature adult is no longer held by anyone.

The various theories of preformation seem strange to us now, but when they were advanced they performed a necessary function in that they stimulated investigators to search more intensively for an explanation of development.

THE PATH OF DEVELOPMENT

Let us examine briefly the stages in the early development of an animal. It might seem more meaningful to select human development for our study, but because of the obvious difficulties in obtaining suitable material we must resort to lower animals. Because the development is relatively simple and yet typical, we shall select the eggs of *Amphioxus,* a primitive chordate, for our study (p. 349). Eggs of starfish and sea urchins also provide excellent material and are frequently used for this study.

Cleavage

In some animals the sperm cell enters the egg before the latter is completely mature, that is, before the formation of the second or even the first polar bodies (Fig. 23-2). This is usually the case in vertebrates and is true of Amphioxus. The first sperm that strikes the membrane surrounding the egg enters head first, dropping its tail the moment it is inside. It enlarges to become the male pronucleus and then lies at rest in the cytoplasm while the egg nucleus completes its last division. When the egg nucleus is mature, the two pronuclei unite and the first division of the zygote follows shortly. In frogs this occurs in about $2\frac{1}{2}$ hours. The split divides the zygote into two equal parts. Cleavage divisions follow in rapid succes-

sion, resulting in a hollow ball of cells, the **blastula** (Figs. 23-2, 23-3), the total being no larger than the original zygote.

Formation of Germ Layers

The ball of cells indents on one side until the two layers of cells almost touch, giving the appearance, somewhat, of a rubber ball which has been pushed in with the finger. This is the **gastrula,** and the single opening formed at one end is the **blastopore.** The newly formed cavity is called the **archenteron,** which will eventually become a part of the digestive tract of the adult animal. The two layers of cells that make up the gastrula are called **germ layers;** the one on the outside is the **ectoderm** and the inner one, the **endoderm.** Presently, tiny pouches push out from the archenteron and pinch off, forming a double layer of cells, the **mesoderm,** with a cavity, the **coelom** (enterocoel, p. 153) between (Fig. 23-2). The coelomic pouches fuse, and the coelom thus formed finally becomes the body cavity in the adult. In higher vertebrates such as mammals the coelom gives rise to the pericardial, pleural, and peritoneal cavities of the adult.

The three germ layers are laid down in somewhat different ways in various animal groups, owing primarily to the presence of yolk in the egg. In the case of Amphioxus, where there is very little yolk, development proceeds in the manner described. However, when the egg contains a great deal of yolk, as in the case of the bird's egg, the formation of the three germ layers is modified, although the end result is essentially the same. In the chick, which is best known and most frequently studied (Fig. 23-4), the embryo forms on top of the yolk mass. The two-layered embryo or gastrula is produced by a splitting of the single-layered embryo, and the mesoderm subsequently appears between the ectoderm and endoderm, spreading laterally from a central axis called the **primitive streak.** The embryo becomes organized anterior to the

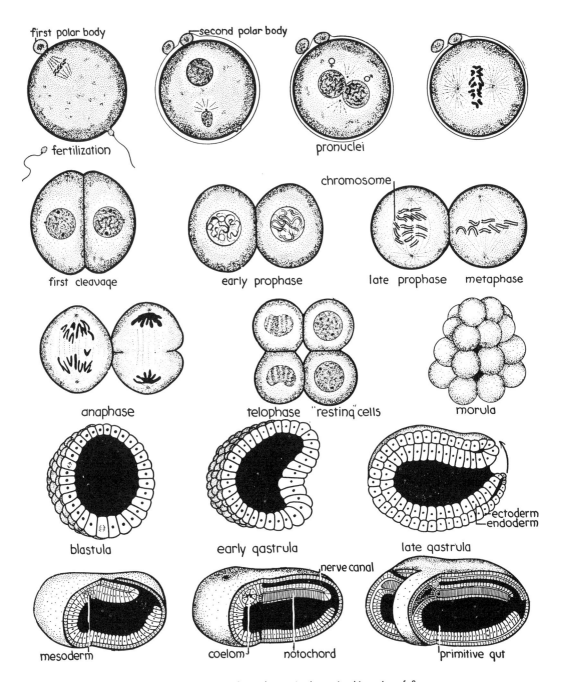

FIG. 23-2. Fertilization and early embryology of *Amphioxus* is shown in this series of figures.

primitive streak. Segmental blocks of mesoderm, the **somites,** appear first in the anterior trunk region of the embryo and continue posteriorly as growth occurs. By the 33rd hour of incubation the notochord and three divisions of the brain can be seen, and the heart is laid down. From these beginnings the embryo body is formed.

With the formation of these three germ layers, a complex metazoan body can be built. The layers grow, fold, and differentiate into the adult structures. In general, the endoderm becomes the epithelial lining of most of the digestive tract and its derivatives. The ectoderm gives rise to the outer layer of the skin, the nervous system,

FIG. 23-3. The early embryology of the starfish. In this photograph the fertilized egg, the two-celled stage, the four-celled stage, a blastula, and the young free-swimming larva are shown.

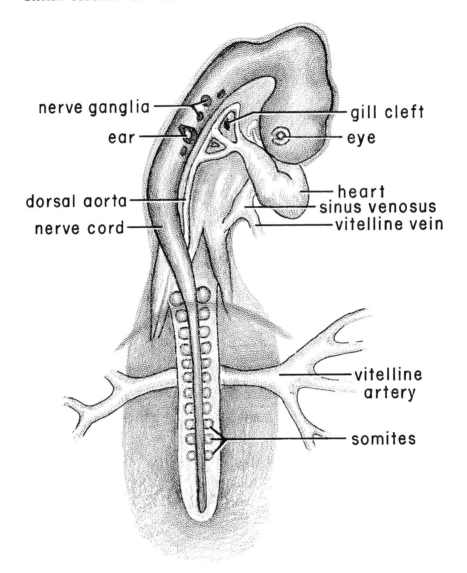

nerve ganglia

ear

dorsal aorta

nerve cord

gill cleft

eye

heart

sinus venosus

vitelline vein

vitelline artery

somites

FIG. 23-4. A chick embryo at 48 hours of incubation. Note the developing eye, ear, heart, and other parts. The large blood vessels carry food-laden blood to and from the yolk for growth and differentiation of the embryo.

and the sensory cells of the adult. The two layers of the mesoderm in the trunk region form different parts: the inner portion becomes associated with the endoderm to form the gut wall, while the outer becomes associated with the ectoderm to give rise to the body wall, thus producing the familiar "tube-within-a-tube" body plan discussed in earlier chapters. Between the two tubes is the cavity of the mesoderm, the

coelom. Derivatives of these layers in man are graphically portrayed in Figure 23-5.

Organ Formation

It is a long, complicated story from the simple germ layers to the full-fledged functional organs which, taken together, constitute the complete animal. The formation of the functional organs is accomplished by several methods. One of the

ectoderm   mesoderm   endoderm

FIG. 23-5. Derivatives of the three germ layers portrayed in a graphic manner.

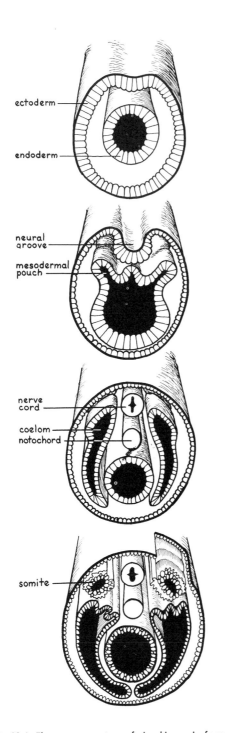

ectoderm

endoderm

neural groove

mesodermal pouch

nerve cord

coelom

notochord

somite

FIG. 23-6. The nervous system of Amphioxus is formed from a groove along the top side of the embryo, as illustrated by these figures from top to bottom. The mesoderm gives rise to the somites and lining of the coelom.

most common is the folding of the layers, which is well illustrated in the formation of the nervous system of Amphioxus and of the chordates in general (Fig. 23-6). It starts by a pushing in of a groove along the dorsal side of the embryo about the time the mesoderm is established. The groove closes over on the dorsal side and sinks below the surface to form a tube which gives rise eventually to the entire nervous system and its associated parts. The retina of the eye forms from an evagination or outpocketing of ectoderm from the brain and the lens from an invagination of the overlying ectoderm of the head. Evaginations from the wall of the digestive tract give rise to the lining of the lungs, most of the liver, and the pancreas, as shown in the human embryo (Fig. 23-7).

Another method of morphogenesis during development is cell migration. Cells once formed do not always remain in their original positions, and during early development individual cells as well as groups of cells migrate a great deal. The mesodermal cells especially, either as single cells or small groups, break loose and wander through the tissues to set up housekeeping in new locations where they differentiate into new structures, such as muscles, blood vessels, and connective or supporting tissue. What forces are operative in directing migrating cells to their proper locations and in causing them to differentiate there into the right kind of cells to do a specific job? For example, how do the tiny processes of nerve cells that migrate out from the primitive nerve tube find their way peripherally to the muscle cells of a developing limb bud? There is a question of time as well as space. If the nerve cells arrived and differentiated before the muscle cells differentiated, would functional neuromotor endings develop? Migration of cells must occur at precisely the right time and to the right location if the final organ is to form and function properly.

Still another essential phase of development must take place after these cells reach their destination. The cells must differentiate into specific kinds of cells in order to produce the definitive organ. In general, such differentiated cells are specialized for particular functions; and it is probable that once they are formed, they do not revert to other cell types. Some cells, however, even in the adult may retain the ability to differentiate into other kinds of cells, for example, the primitive connective tissue cells that fill in the space resulting from a wound.

Final differentiation of cells occurs at the end of a long sequence of changes collectively called the developmental history. Consider, for example, the mesenchymal cells in the interior of the limb buds which eventually form the appendages of vertebrates. These cells all look alike at first but they gradually differentiate into types that are easily distinguished. At an early stage of development, five bumps, the ultimate digits, push out around the distal margin of the limb bud. Soon thereafter cartilage appears in the center of the bud and extends out into each digit. Skeletal muscle, fibrous connective tissue, bone, blood and blood vessels all differentiate from mesenchyme, while nerves grow in from the spinal cord. Growth and development of a typical pattern of arrangement of cell types constitute the later stages of development leading to the form we refer to as the adult.

Differentiation of the germ layers follows a similar pattern in all animals, and the final organs derived from them can be predicted fairly closely from the story of evolution. Layers that first formed ectoderm and endoderm in evolutionary history might be expected to give rise to the covering and the lining of present-day animals. Ectoderm, since it contacts the external world, might also be expected to give rise to the organ system that keeps it in touch with its external environment, namely, the nervous system and its associated organs. Endoderm lined the gut of

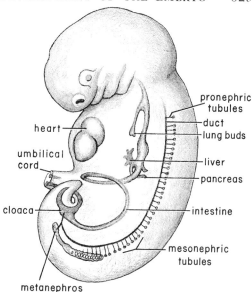

FIG. 23-7. The very young human embryo shows the beginnings of several organ systems. The digestive tract is heavily shaded. Note how the lungs and pancreas are forming as outpocketings from the primitive gut. The nervous system and the kidney are very primitive at this stage of development (under five weeks).

the first metazoa and still performs that same function in the embryos of higher animals, giving rise as well to the epithelial components of the lungs, liver, pancreas, thyroid, thymus and parathyroid glands. The last layer to appear both in evolution and in embryology is the mesoderm, which produces all of the remaining organs such as muscles, blood vessels, skeleton, kidneys, and gonads. Although the three germ layers are destined in normal development to produce specific tissues, deviations can be induced experimentally. Much of the research in the field of **experimental embryology** is concerned with the potentialities of the germ layers under varying environmental conditions.

FACTORS INFLUENCING DEVELOPMENT

Development does not always follow the "normal" pathways, as attested by the oc-

FIG. 23-8.   Parthenogenetic development can be obtained in a rabbit's egg by pricking it with a needle dipped in blood.

casional appearance of malformed (**teratologous**) offspring among all groups of animals. This means that something has gone wrong along the way in the formation of the various systems. At some critical time chemical or physical factors became sufficiently modified to shift the pattern of differentiation into "abnormal" pathways. Since certain kinds of malformations, such as cleft palate or development of extra limbs, can be induced experimentally in certain organisms, the experimental embryologist can frequently make fairly accurate guesses as to the nature of **teratogenic** factors.

Fertilization

The logical place to start in an experimental study of development is fertilization. Is it necessary that a sperm enter the egg? Aside from contributing a complete set of chromosomes, what other functions does the sperm perform?

Even Aristotle knew that the drone bee was a result of an unfertilized egg. Many animals possess **natural parthenogenesis,** which means development without fertilization, during some stage of their life history. It even occurs occasionally among some animals, including mosquitoes and turkeys, whose eggs normally require sperm for development. How does this fact fit into the general assumption that all eggs must be fertilized? The situation in bees as well as other animals led biologists very early to investigate the necessity of the sperm for development. Artificial parthenogenesis can be produced in many animals by simply subjecting the eggs to an appropriate chemical or physical change, such as immersing them in certain chemicals or pricking them with a needle in the presence of blood (Fig. 23-8). This would seem to indicate that the sperm serves two functions: one to contribute a haploid set of chromosomes (p. 659), the other to initiate development of the egg. Apparently the potentialities of development are locked up in the egg, waiting to be released at the right time by the entrance of the sperm. If other suitable physical or chemical factors are applied, they too can perform this second function of the sperm very satisfactorily. The action is probably tied up with enzymes in some sort of trigger mechanism which can be set off by a variety of stimuli.

It is now known that mammalian sperm possess an enzyme, **hyaluronidase,** which is capable of digesting the intercellular cement of the follicle cells surrounding the egg, thus making fertilization possible. Perhaps this is why so many sperm cells are essential to effect fertilization. A few cells would not produce enough enzyme to penetrate the follicle cell of the egg. Eggs of echinoderms give off a protein, called **fertilizin,** which accumulates in the jelly surrounding the egg. Fertilizin causes sperm of the same species to agglutinate. Likewise sperm secrete an antifertilizin which causes eggs to clump. Just how these function in normal fertilization is not known.

Theories of Development

The most important problem in embryology today is: How does one type of cell differentiate into another type? The full impact of this question becomes obvious when we realize that all of the potentialities of the adult animal are locked up in the fertilized egg. All of the different types of cells that compose the adult are derived from this single cell. Obviously from the very beginning of development cells must constantly differentiate from one type to another. Since their genes are probably all the same and since all of the information that is needed to bring about developmental changes came from them, we must look to the subtle environmental changes in the cytoplasm of cells or in the intercellular matrix surrounding them in order to explain development.

Mosaic Development. One of the first attempts to solve the problem of development was made in the latter part of the last century by Wilhelm Roux, who worked with frogs' eggs. He noted that the first cleavage usually coincided with the long axis of the embryo and that the **gray crescent,** a light area near the equator of the egg, appeared shortly before this cleavage. The plane of the first cleavage usually cuts through the middle of the gray crescent, thus dividing the egg into two cells, one becoming the right half and the other the left half of the future animal (Fig. 23-9). About the same time August Weissmann postulated that the zygote nucleus contained **determinants** which were segregated to the daughter cells during the first cleavage. At each subsequent division, according to his hypothesis, determinants were passed to the resulting cells until finally cells contained only those determinants responsible for differentiation of the various types of cells found in the tissues of the adult.

In order to test Weissmann's hypoth-

FIG. 23-9. An idea which convinced some early embryologists of the mosaic theory of development is represented schematically. The egg nucleus (top) was supposed to contain the determinants for the two halves of the embryo. When the egg cleaves (middle), the determinants would segregate to the two cells, each of them giving rise to its corresponding half of the embryo (bottom).

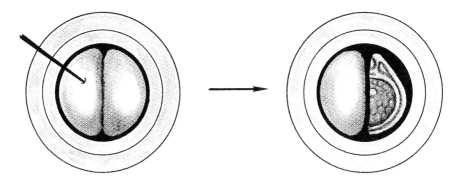

FIG. 23-10. If one cell of a frog's egg is killed when the embryo is in the two-cell stage, only a half embryo develops.

esis Roux killed one of the cells of the two-celled embryo with a hot needle. The uninjured cell cleaved in normal fashion but gave rise to only a half embryo (Fig. 23-10). This experiment seemed to be dramatic proof that the egg is a mosaic of cells, each possessing the capacity to give rise to only a particular portion of the adult animal. This idea was upheld by other investigators experimenting on a variety of embryos, including annelids, mollusks, and tunicates. The experiments were refined to the point where in some annelid embryos

a single cell in the 64-cell stage could be observed to give rise to all of the mesoderm in the adult. The mosaic theory of development seemed to answer all the questions of development. However, when other embryos of other types of animals were studied the theory ran into difficulties.

Regulative Development. Sea urchin embryos provided the first clue that the mosaic theory might not always hold. If the cells of the two-celled embryo were completely separated by shaking, Driesch

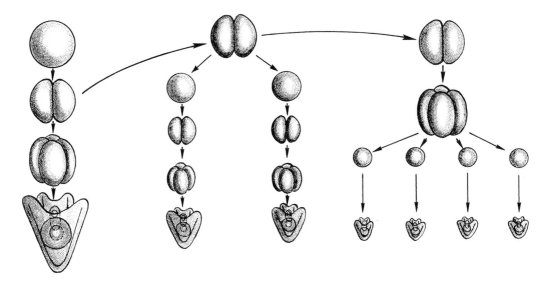

FIG. 23-11. When sea urchin eggs are separated in the two- or four-cell stage, they give rise to fully formed embryos though proportionately smaller.

showed that each gave rise to a perfectly formed embryo though half the size of a normal embryo (Fig. 23-11). This was also true if the cells were separated in the four-celled stage. For this reason the sea urchin embryos were said to be **regulative**. When later investigators finally succeeded in completely separating the first two cells of amphibian embryos, they found that each gave rise to a complete embryo just as in the case of the sea urchin embryo (Fig. 23-12). Separation was effected either by withdrawing one cell with a pipette or by

twins in humans. Spemann, a famous German embryologist working with constricted amphibian embryos, showed that if a loop of hair was sufficiently loose that some part of the first two cells was allowed to remain in contact, a partially double embryo resulted (Fig. 23-12). It seems possible that similar anomalies in fish (Fig. 23-13) or humans may be formed in an analogous fashion. Perhaps cleavage between the two cells starts but is not completed, thus producing embryos attached to a greater or lesser degree. Partially double embryos

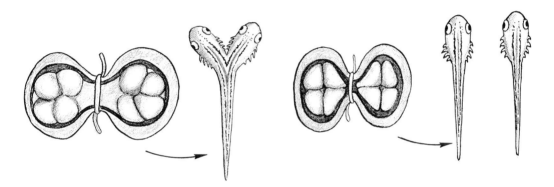

FIG. 23-12. If a hair loop is tied in such a way as to separate the cells partially in a two-cell amphibian embryo, a partially double ("Siamese twins") embryo will result. If the hair loop is pulled tightly enough to separate the two cells completely, two normal, half-size embryos result.

tying a fine thread or hair around the embryo and pulling it tight to separate the two cells. Thus it could be concluded that the presence of the dead cell in Roux's experiment caused the development of a half embryo from the cell left alive. Evidence today seems to indicate that the nuclei of all cells contain a full complement of genes and thus that specific "determinants" are not segregated to determine the many kinds of cells found in the adult. How the nucleus exercises its control of specific cytoplasmic differentiation has become the focus of attention of embryologists today.

A rather interesting outcome of the experiments outlined above was an explanation for the striking anomaly of Siamese

could also result from splitting of the body axis at the gastrula stage. Occasionally in man one embryo grows normally and incorporates the abnormal one inside its body, forming a tumor, known as a **teratoma**. Some teratomas contain skin and hair, indicating that they might have started as partial twins. Teratomas often give trouble in adult life and need to be removed.

The Organizer. Perhaps the most important embryological contribution made in this century was the organizer theory of Hans Spemann. This theory was the outcome of many ingenious experiments on amphibian embryos performed by Spemann and his collaborators. They demonstrated that by transplanting cells from the dorsal lip of the blastopore to an area in a second embryo that would normally form epidermis, a second embryonic axis was established in the new site, even though the host embryo had one of its own (Fig. 23-14). The transplanted cells sank beneath the surface and induced a nerve cord and in some cases almost an entire secondary embryo. From these experiments Spemann came to the realization that the cells of the dorsal lip were the organizing center of the axial structures of the embryo, and hence he referred to the lip cells as the **organizer.** Since

FIG. 23-13. "Siamese twins" in fish. These are probably formed as a result of an incomplete separation of the early embryo, perhaps in the two-cell stage.

the organizer was thought to induce a change in the development of other cells, the action was called **induction.**

Tissue culture experiments with embryonic cells can be explained in the light of the organizer theory. When cells that normally become nerve cord are removed from an early gastrula and grown in a medium away from other cells they form epidermis. However, if the same cells are removed from a late gastrula and grown separately, they differentiate into nervous tissue. Obviously the cells in the early gastrula had not yet been influenced by the organizer, whereas in the later gastrula the organizer had induced the overlying cells to become nervous tissue. The cells of the early gastrula are said to be **undetermined**

as regards their capacity to form a nerve cord. They are said to be **determined** after the organizer has acted upon them. Determination is thus a result of induction. If a piece of embryonic tissue is grown in culture and does not differentiate, it is considered undetermined; if it does differentiate, it is considered to be determined at the time of isolation.

The action of the organizer can be further illustrated in the formation of the vertebrate eye. As the bulb of ectodermal tissue that pushes out from the brain to form the cup comes near the external ectoderm, it induces the latter to form a lens. This will happen even if foreign ectoderm is placed over the eye cup. In this case the eye cup is the organizer. Possibly some chemical compound elaborated by the organizer accounts for formation of the lens in this case and the nerve cord in the previous experiments.

Light was thrown on this possibility when it was discovered that even dead organizer tissue could induce neural structures. Dorsal lip cells could be killed with chemicals or heat yet still would cause undetermined ectoderm to form neural tissue. It should be possible to isolate such a stable chemical compound by proper techniques. From a long series of experiments only confusion resulted, because it was discovered that cells of the gastrula that were noninductive when alive became so when killed. Even adult tissues, such as kidney and liver, and various substances completely foreign to organisms can induce. Efforts to purify the organizer have not been satisfactory. Although there is some recent evidence that the initial organizer is nucleic acid, determination of its exact nature must await further research.

Mosaic and regulative eggs may now be reconsidered. Perhaps the main difference between them lies in the time at which the cells of the embryo are determined, that is, the time when an organizer exerts its influence on specific cells. Mosaic eggs are determined much earlier, evidently when they are formed in the ovary, whereas regulative eggs are determined during embryonic development.

We must now consider the old idea of

in the nucleus of the egg. Once cleavage starts and development proceeds, the genes "give the orders" for each stage of development. They undoubtedly are responsible for the formation of the initial organ-

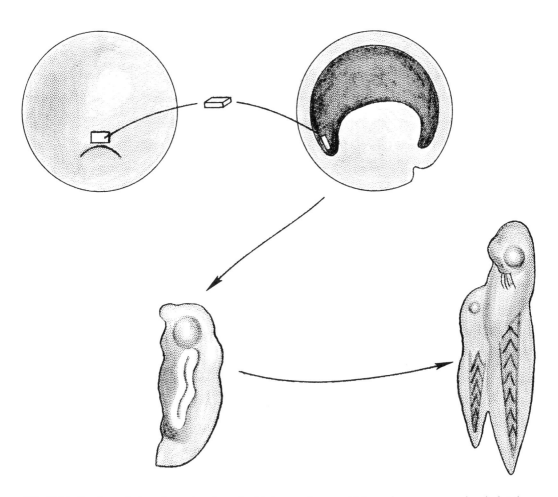

FIG. 23-14. If a few cells from the region above the blastopore of an amphibian embryo are removed and placed on some other region of a second embryo, they will produce a nerve cord just as they would have done had they remained in their original location. The operation is performed in the two top figures and the results are shown on the lower left (early) and lower right (later).

preformation in a new light. Modern genetics has shown that the egg is actually preformed in the sense that the genes have all of the information that is necessary to bring about the development of an adult organism. The genes are derived from the parent during meiosis and are incorporated

izer, and perhaps for all of the subsequent organizers that must form in sequence as each new structure is formed. Organizers are probably produced one after the other as development proceeds. One organ develops as a result of an organizer and this organ, in turn, produces another organizer which induces the development of another organ and so on. To what extent development proceeds by specific induction or alternatively by specific inhibition of differentiating tissues is another of the major questions confronting embryologists.

As was pointed out earlier the question of change in DNA during development does not lend itself well to experimental proof. However, recently some elegant experiments involving transplantation of nuclei in frog eggs suggest that some sort of nuclear change may occur during early embryological development. First the nucleus is removed from the egg and then replaced with one from a cell taken from a blastula or gastrula (Fig. 23-15). The egg, then, contained a nucleus from a cell whose cytoplasm had already undergone differentiation. When such an egg was permitted to develop, some very interesting results were observed.

A normal embryo resulted when the enucleated egg received a nucleus from a blastula cell. However, nuclei from late gastrula cells usually produced grossly abnormal embryos. The type of abnormality proved to be equally interesting. A nucleus from an endoderm cell when transplanted to the enucleated egg gave rise to an embryo with normal endoderm but the ectoderm and other parts were abnormal. Likewise, mesodermal nuclei yielded normal mesoderm but abnormal ectoderm. These experiments tend to support the idea that the loss of differentiative potentialities by the nucleus is somehow related to the part of the embryo from which it originated. This implies, but does not prove, that DNA is altered during differentiation.

Regeneration

In earlier chapters we considered the phenomenon of regeneration among the invertebrates, especially in hydra and planaria where it is particularly striking. Can the observations made on these forms, and others as well, be explained in the light of the information available from experimental embryology?

If the stem of a coelenterate hydroid is cut into two parts, each will give rise to a base and tentacles, retaining the polarity of the parent form (Fig. 23-16). Now if these two parts are placed in a tube and the cut tips exposed to different concentrations of oxygen, the polarity can be reversed. This means that organization of the tissue is labile, that is, it can be changed. In another experiment, one may block circulation in the coelenteron of an isolated hydroid stem by inserting a short length of glass rod into it. In this case, tentacles may form at both ends. This experiment likewise demonstrates that determination of polarity is labile. Perhaps some organizing substance, which is tentacle-forming, is distributed throughout the tissues of the hydroid. Tentacles form where the concentration of this substance is the highest, normally nearest the apical end. How the apical end exerts dominance and represses differentiation of tentacles at the basal end is still unexplained.

Planaria, when cut into several pieces, gives rise to an equal number of whole animals, each with mouth, digestive tract, and nervous system (p. 233). In planaria the situation is much more complicated than in a coelenterate, because of the greater variety of structures, but unequal distribution of head-producing substance along a concentration gradient diminishing toward the posterior end may account for the observed pattern of regeneration in this organism.

Another aspect of regeneration has come to light through metabolic studies of a number of lower animals including planaria. It has been shown that the metabolic rate, as demonstrated by oxygen consumption studies, is greatest at the anterior and least at the posterior end and, indeed, that there is a definite **gradient** running in an anterior-posterior direction. This is con-

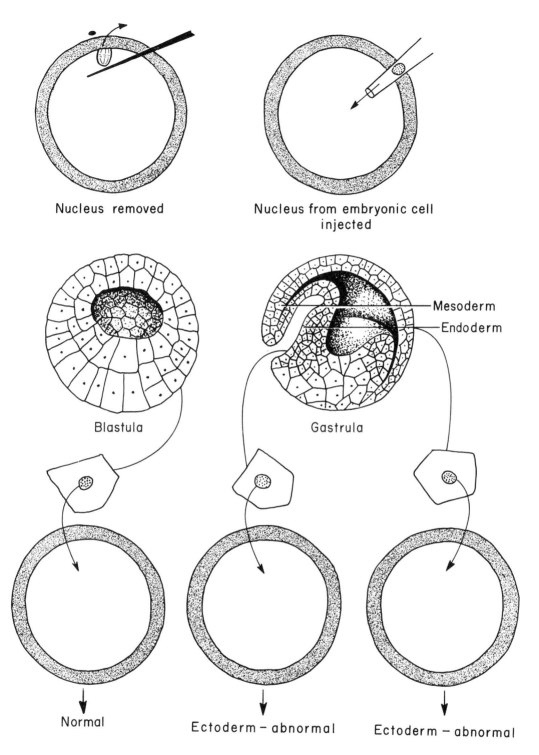

Nucleus removed

Nucleus from embryonic cell injected

Blastula

Gastrula

Mesoderm

Endoderm

Normal

Ectoderm – abnormal

Ectoderm – abnormal

FIG. 23-15. These sketches show the process of removing the nucleus from the frog egg and the results obtained when older nuclei are introduced into them. See text for further explanation.

firmed by applying poisons of various sorts to the animals, in which case the anterior end is always injured first, the effect gradually diminishing in a posterior direction. This same gradient is observed in cut pieces of planaria, for the anterior part of each piece has a higher metabolic rate than the posterior part. The head always develops at the more active end and the tail at the other. This principle has been stated by Child in his **axial gradient theory,**

which has been utilized to explain the origin of some abnormalities appearing in various kinds of embryos, including man. Suppose two centers of high metabolic activity somehow became established along the anterior-posterior axis of a developing embryo. The embryo might subsequently develop with some sort of twinning, partial or complete. Separation of high metabolic centers would have the same effect as the mechanical separation performed in

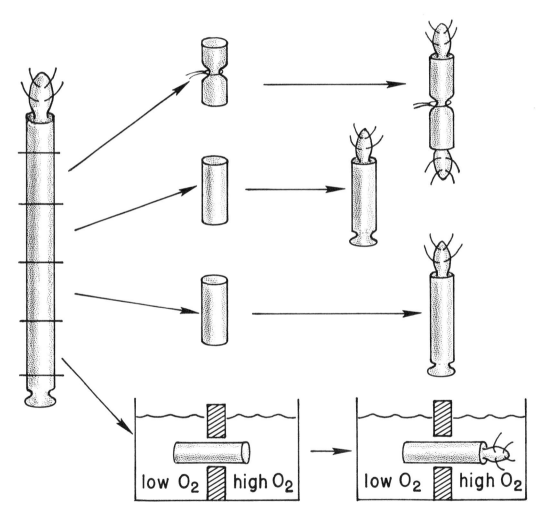

FIG. 23-16. The first character that appears in embryonic development is polarity. This can be demonstrated by performing some experiments on hydroids: Segments cut out of the stem will regenerate tentacles and bases oriented in the same manner as in the parent hydroid. If a constriction is made in the middle of a segment, tentacles form on both ends. If one end is placed in a region of high oxygen level, tentacles will form on that end regardless of its position in the parent hydroid.

Spemann's hair loop experiment, and the end result would be the same.

Study of the regeneration of parts in adult animals is a natural outgrowth of work on embryos. Many interesting questions raise themselves in the field of regeneration. For instance, why do limbs of adult salamanders regenerate completely whereas those of the closely related frogs do not? Further, why have the limbs of higher animals lost most of the power of regeneration? Some interesting experiments have thrown light on these problems.

When a limb of a larval salamander is amputated, the epidermis quickly grows over the cut surface while a concomitant

vents the normal closure over of the wound by the dermis (connective tissue) of the skin and brings about the formation of a blastema. Once the blastema is formed, regeneration proceeds just as it does in salamanders. It appears that normally in the frog the entire skin including the dermis grows over the wound and blocks the formation of the blastema which would bring about regeneration. On the other hand, in the salamander the wound is closed simply by the epidermis; a blastema is formed and regeneration can proceed. It seems, therefore, that in the frog, the ability to regenerate appendages is not lost but merely blocked. The possibility of regener-

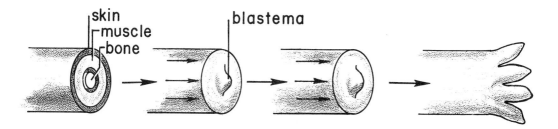

FIG. 23-17. An amputated limb of a larval salamander will regenerate completely as shown here. Why does a mammalian appendage fail to regenerate?

series of changes goes on underneath, resulting eventually in a new limb (Fig. 23-17). The cells of the cut muscle, connective tissue, and bone change in appearance. They appear to **dedifferentiate,** that is, lose most of their specialization, and eventually form a small region of special cells called a **blastema.** Once the blastema is formed, further dedifferentiation ceases. The cell mass then begins to **redifferentiate** into the various tissues of the limb and eventually normal form is restored. Why do these events fail to materialize in frogs and higher vertebrates? A simple experiment performed by Rose gives us a partial answer.

If the cut limb of a frog is placed in saline (salt solution) it actually will partially regenerate. Apparently the saline pre-

ation of appendages or other parts in reptiles, birds and mammals is still under active investigation.

So far we have discussed some of the basic problems involved in development. Since we observe that the embryo grows continually while it is differentiating, let us consider next the problem of growth.

GROWTH

By the end of the eighth week of human life, the embryo has increased to 2 million times its original mass and during the next eight lunar months it will increase another 4,000 times (Fig. 23-18). This tremendous accumulation of protoplasm we call **growth.** In an earlier chapter (p. 129) we

FIG. 23-18. A human fetus undergoes considerable change in body proportions during gestation. These five are compared as to relative size and body shape. Their approximate ages are 8 weeks, 12 weeks, 16 weeks, 6 months, and full term.

studied growth of protozoa in a culture medium and discovered the nature of the **growth curve.** By removing a small bit of embryonic chick heart, for example, and placing it in a flask containing adequate nutrients, growth of the cells will occur according to the same curve as that demonstrated for the protozoa. At first the cells divide very slowly, then increase to a uniform rate, and finally fall off until no more divisions occur. If a small bit of tissue is transferred to fresh medium, the cycle will be repeated; and this can be continued indefinitely. If cells of isolated tissues grow according to the same pattern as do protozoan cells, how do cells grow when they are a part of the intact embryo?

Just as we note limiting factors (nutrients and accumulation of wastes) in the growth of protozoa, we also note limiting factors in the growth of the whole embryo. We know that animals grow to a certain size and stop; they do not grow forever. Something about the community of cells limits the number of divisions that occur. The individual organs also fail to grow after a certain number of cell divisions or after a certain time has elapsed. For example, if bits of tissue are removed from embryos at various ages it will be found that those from older embryos will not grow as well as tissues from younger ones; in fact, some, like nerve tissue, will grow little, if at all, when removed from adult animals. Others like epithelium retain the capacity for growth throughout the life of the organism. Still others, like cancer tissue, grow readily no matter what their source or age. From these experiments we can conclude that cells, when confined to an organism, are subject to factors that limit growth. These factors may be the same as the ones that limit growth in a culture medium. What all of these limiting factors are is a fertile field for research.

In the growth of an embryo, the sizes of the various organs increase at varying rates. The human heart, for example, approximates the growth of the body as a whole, whereas the brain grows tremendously during the first five years of life and thereafter grows very little. Because all of the organs grow at different rates, the general over-all proportions of the human body gradually change. The change is radical during the gestation period (Fig. 23-18), but after that it progresses slowly throughout life (Fig. 23-19).

We have considered in this chapter the development of the individual, where it would appear that most of the problems are yet to be solved. Now let us consider several other problems in biology: namely, how do genes replicate themselves, how do cells divide, and finally what are the mechanisms that make it possible for a race to continue apparently unchanged through generation after generation? In the next part, *Continuity of Life,* we shall examine some of these problems and a few of the answers as we know them today.

prenatal   birth ————————————————————→ adult

FIG. 23-19. Various parts of the body grow at different rates during the life of an animal. Here in the human being many changes occur from prenatal life at the left to the adult at the right. Note particularly the proportionate difference in the head and body size.

SUGGESTED SUPPLEMENTARY READINGS

CORNER, G. W., *Ourselves Unborn* (New Haven, Conn., Yale University Press, 1944).

EBERT, J., "The First Heartbeats," *Scientific American,* 200(3) (March, 1959), 87.

EDD, M. V., Jr., "Animal Morphogenesis," in W. H. Johnson, and W. C. Steere, eds., *In This Life* (New York, Holt, Rinehart and Winston, Inc., 1962).

GROBSTEIN, C., "Differentiation of Vertebrate Cells," in J. Brachet, and A. E. Mirsky, eds., *The Cell,* Vol. I (New York, Academic Press, 1961).

MOSCONA, A. A., "Tissues from Dissociated Cells," *Scientific American,* 200(5) (May, 1959), 132.

PATTEN, B. M., *Human Embryology* (New York, The Blakiston Co., 1953).

RUGH, R., *Experimental Embryology* (Minneapolis, Burgess Pub. Co., 1962).

WADDINGTON, C. H., "How Do Cells Differentiate?," *Scientific American,* 189(3) (September, 1953), 108.

PART VII

Continuity of Life

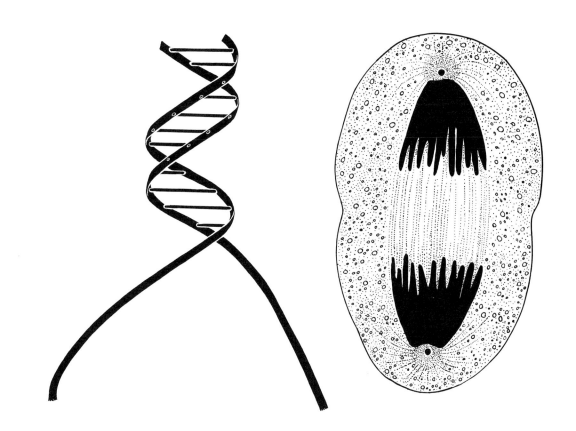

24
Continuity of Cells

ONE OF THE MOST obvious facts in biology is that living things grow by increasing their number of cells. The process of growth can be studied under the light microscope, the details of which were worked out many years ago. We must, however, investigate a lower level of organization, far beyond the resolution of the most powerful microscopes, if we are to learn the initial stages in this duplicating mechanism. We learned in Chapter 2 something about the gene and hinted at its significance in the duplication of cells. We must now return to the gene and try to understand its part in cell division, after which we shall examine that part of the process which can be seen through the microscope.

COMPOSITION OF GENES

The first approach to a study of the composition of genes is to analyze the chromosomes chemically, because once we can describe a substance in chemical terms we have taken the first step toward understanding how it functions. This monumental task has been accomplished to the extent that we know the chromosome is composed of four major kinds of molecules: two proteins, one called **histone** with low molecular weight (about 2,000) and another which is more complex with a much higher molecular weight; and two nucleic acids, one **deoxyribose nucleic acid** (DNA) which has less oxygen than the other, **ribose nucleic acid** (RNA). These latter two compounds were described earlier (p. 78). The four kinds of molecules are combined in some fashion not clearly understood to form chromatin, the stainable material of which chromosomes are composed. Of these, DNA carries the genetic information and it is about this molecule that we know the most, probably because it has been the most exciting to study.

Workers in both Europe and America learned in the 1940's that the nuclei of germ and somatic cells of any one species contained the same amount of DNA for each set of chromosomes. This evidence pointed to the fact that DNA was the essential molecule in genes. This idea was confirmed sometime later when it was discovered that it was possible to change one type of *Pneumococcus,* the causative organism of pneumonia, to another (there are many types) by exposing one to DNA extracted from the other. Such transformations have been accomplished with other microorganisms which definitely establishes DNA as the molecule which carries genetic information. It is interesting to note that whereas we have only very recently understood what DNA does in the cell, it was first isolated by Miescher in 1868, long before the existence of genes was even suspected!

It has been shown that DNA is a long unbranched molecule (sometimes called a "macromolecule" because of its large size) of variable molecular weight. Most DNA molecules are composed of four repeating nucleotides. The deoxyribose and phosphoric acid are the same in all DNA molecules; they differ only in the arrangement of their bases (purines and pyrimidines). The purine nucleotides are **deoxyadenylic**

and **deoxyguanylic** acids; the pyrimidines are **deoxythymidylic** and **deoxycytidylic** acids. The chemical structures of the bases are given in Figure 24-1. The configuration of the DNA molecule was discovered as a result of the following observation. When DNA was extracted from different cells and the relative proportions of the various nucleotides measured, it was discovered that the amount of purine always equalled the amount of pyrimidines in any given cell type. Even more astonishing was the fact that the number of deoxyguanylic acid molecules equalled the number of deoxycytidylic acid molecules; likewise, the number of molecules of deoxyadenylic and deoxythymidylic acids were equal. This specific 1:1 relationship formed the basis for an understanding of the architecture of the molecule itself.

James Watson and Francis Crick of England, using this as well as other information, were able to construct a model of the DNA molecule. They suggested that it is composed of two strands that spiral about one another, sometimes called a double helix (Fig. 24-1). The "backbone" of each strand is made up of deoxyribose and phosphate with the bases (adenine, guanine, thymine, cytosine) pointing toward the middle of the spiral and being held together by hydrogen bonds. The sequence of the base-pairing is such that adenine in one strand always pairs with thymine in the other strand and guanine with cytosine. The salient features of the model are its double strands and their complementary nature. This makes it possible, as suggested by Crick and Watson, to understand how information can be stored in the DNA molecule. The sequence of the base pairs can occur in any number of combinations which means that an infinite number of DNA molecules are possible. The molecule may be compared to a tape upon which an alphabet of four letters could be encoded. By employing each letter as often as desired it would be pos-

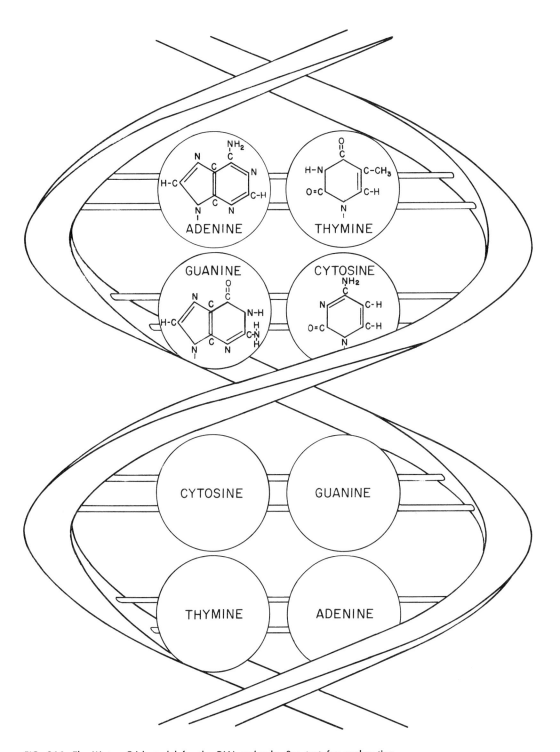

FIG. 24-1. The Watson-Crick model for the DNA molecule. See text for explanation.

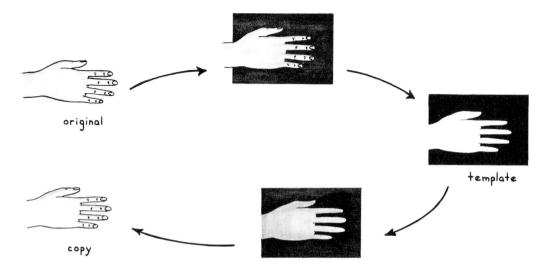

FIG. 24-2. The template principle gives us a possible explanation of how a structure with complex surfaces may be accurately copied. It has been given as a possible explanation for DNA duplication.

sible to make an almost infinite number of tapes with no two being identical. With the Watson-Crick model from which to start, it has been possible to formulate theories on the replication of DNA as well as to speculate on the way in which the coded information stored in the DNA molecule is transferred to RNA and subsequently to the synthesis of specific proteins.

Replication of DNA

The complex DNA molecule with its double spiral configuration appears to be most difficult to duplicate, which of course it is. It seems that it somehow unwinds and then forms a second strand in the immediate vicinity of each of the parent strands. But the surface of such strands would be extremely complicated and how could replicas be made of them? Methods used in industry can help out in a solution to this problem. Very irregular and complex surfaces of objects have been faithfully copied for a long time by craftsmen by employing the **template** principle. A template is made from the original which is then used as a mold to produce the copy (Fig. 24-2). It is possible that the surface of the DNA

molecule is replicated in the same manner. Indeed, as we shall soon see this same principle may well explain RNA and protein synthesis.

Evidence for the correctness of this hypothesis, as well as for the nature of the DNA model, comes from several sources. One is the actual synthesis of DNA in a test tube without the presence of cells. A. A. Kornberg placed the four nucleotides and an enzyme **polymerase** in a test tube and to this mixture added a small amount of DNA called "primer" DNA. The result was that long chains of DNA were formed and more importantly, the synthesized DNA had the same physiochemical structure as the primer. The structural identity held when DNA from different sources (virus, bacterial and animal) was used. Obviously, according to the Watson-Crick model, the double helix must unwind or uncoil and a new complementary chain form along each chain. The above reaction progresses more rapidly if the DNA is heated with formaldehyde which has the effect of uncoiling the helices, thus making single chains. Let us consider how DNA is replicated in the cell naturally.

We may indicate the DNA molecule in simplified form, emphasizing only the relationships of the bases, which requires that we flatten out the helices, as shown in Figure 24-3. Adenine is bonded to thymine, and guanine to cytosine. The first step in replication requires that the hydrogen bonds break and the helices uncoil and separate. The separated strands can do one of two things; they can form a complementary strand of DNA or they can form a strand of RNA. Let us consider the replication of DNA first.

We must assume that nucleotides are present in the nucleoplasm and are readily available for DNA synthesis. The complementary base pairs are attracted to each other so that a new strand of DNA is formed, thus restoring the DNA molecule to its original double-stranded condition. The important point to note is that the new strand is an exact replica of the original strand. Replication of the DNA molecule can thus go on endlessly and always retain its specificity, an absolute necessity if genetic continuity is to persist as we know it does.

Origin of RNA

We have already learned that RNA is responsible for protein synthesis and we know that it originates in the nucleus from DNA (p. 78). We must assume also that it somehow receives information from the DNA so that specific proteins can be made. Just how is this information passed from DNA to RNA? This problem is beginning to be solved.

When the DNA strands separate, they may replicate another strand of DNA as we have already pointed out or they may produce a strand of RNA (Fig. 24-3). Again we must assume that nucleotides for RNA synthesis are available in the nucleoplasm. The RNA nucleotides are similar to the DNA nucleotides with minor exceptions. First of all the sugar is **ribose** instead of deoxyribose which simply means that it contains more oxygen, and secondly, deoxythymidylic acid is replaced by **uridylic acid.** The assembling of the RNA strand is identical with that for DNA synthesis, that is, by base-pairing. Such a strand possesses the same information as the DNA strand. It then separates from the DNA strand and is free in the nucleoplasm, ready to carry on the business of protein synthesis, which we shall consider presently.

This story is based on certain crucial experiments, most of them done with microorganisms, but the evidence is sufficiently abundant even now to convince scientists that genetic information is coded on a double-stranded structure which has the capacity to replicate precisely without losing its integrity during the process. Furthermore, the coded information on these strands can be faithfully passed on to other strands that are instrumental in building the proteins of the cell. Many of these proteins are enzymes which are essential in the construction of the DNA molecule in the first place. We see, then, that each step in this complicated cycle depends on a preceding step and that the entire process runs full cycle.

RNA and Protein Synthesis

Enzymes and perhaps all proteins are under gene control, and since the business part of the gene is DNA, it follows that DNA controls the arrangement of amino acids in proteins. Proteins contain some 20 amino acids arranged in a multitude of combinations, hence the difference between them. Then the question arises, how can DNA with only four bases—a four-letter alphabet—be so coded that it can spell out the sequence of the 20 amino acids in a protein? It would seem that a 20-letter alphabet would be required. Just how this can be done requires considerable speculation but sufficient evidence is available to make it worthwhile.

It is possible to arrange groups of several nucleotides with different sequences in

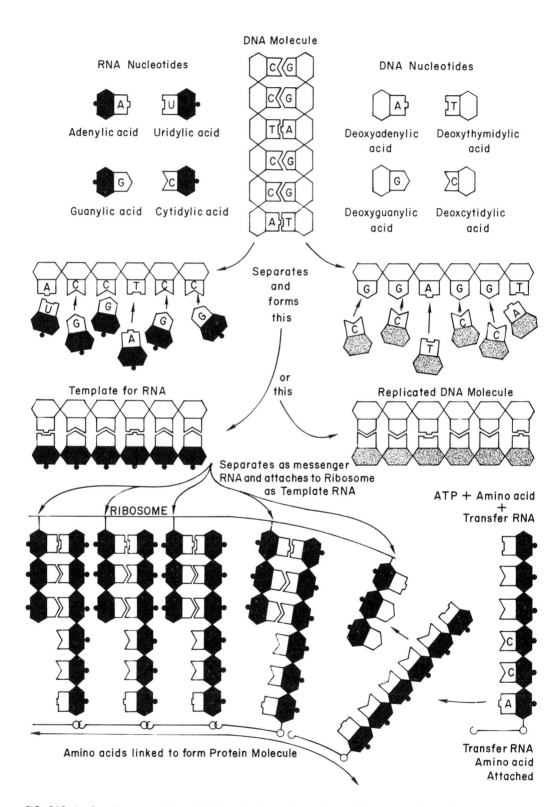

FIG. 24-3. A schematic representation of DNA replication and protein synthesis. See text for explanation.

which each group corresponds to an amino acid. Thus the DNA alphabet with only four letters can be made to spell out the structure of a protein molecule composed of an alphabet of 20 letters (Fig. 24-3). With such a model it is possible for the DNA molecule to bring about the synthesis of protein by passing on its coded information to RNA. Does it do this directly within the nucleus or in the cytoplasm? Evidence for the site of RNA formation comes from experiments with many organisms, from bacteria to cockroaches. For example, by exposing cells with large chromosomes to labelled uracil (RNA pyrimidine base) it is possible to actually see the sites of RNA formation when such chromosomes are placed on a photographic plate. The RNA forms along the chromosomes and in the nucleolus. These are large RNA molecules, sometimes called **messenger** RNA, which then find their way into the cytoplasm; possibly through the pores in the nuclear membrane.

Evidence for the movement of RNA from the nucleus out into the cytoplasm comes from several sources. In some cells it may move out in massive quantities, for example in the ciliate *Tetrahymena pyriformis* it is possible to actually observe this process with the electron microscope. By treating mass cultures of cells with heat-shocks (about 40°C.) at 30-minute intervals five or six times, the cells become synchonized so that they will all divide simultaneously. This makes it possible to study the steps in division in a large number of cells. At a specific period in the division cycle (just before division) the nucleoli in the macronucleus aggregate at the nuclear membrane and push out into the cytoplasm in the form of blebs. These apparently pinch off, thus transferring large amounts of RNA to the cytoplasm.

Once in the cytoplasm where does the messenger RNA go? Experimental evidence points to the ribosomes (p. 77) as being the sites of most of protein synthesis (90%);

hence messenger RNA apparently becomes attached to these particles, where it is known as **template RNA**. RNA in the ribosomes is, therefore, responsible for arranging the amino acids in the proper sequence to produce a particular protein. Template RNA is of high molecular weight (several million) as one would expect since it must contain sufficient information to assemble hundreds and even thousands of amino acids in the job of making the complex protein molecule.

Considerable evidence has accumulated to demonstrate that protein synthesis occurs in the presence of template RNA. When cells are broken up and fractions prepared by centrifugation, those containing RNA (ribosomes) incorporate labelled amino acids into proteins in proportion to the amount of RNA present in the fraction. Likewise, in whole cells, protein synthesis occurs most rapidly in cells with high RNA content when compared with those with low RNA content.

Apparently another type of RNA is formed in the nucleus which also makes its way into the cytoplasm. It has been shown that this type of RNA is soluble in the nucleoplasm and is of low molecular weight (10,000–15,000). Moreover, there is experimental evidence to show that this type of RNA functions in transferring the amino acids to the template RNA, hence it is referred to as "transfer" RNA. It is now assumed that there are at least 20 different transfer RNA's, each specific for one of the 20 amino acids. It is further assumed that each transfer RNA has the capacity to recognize specific sites on the RNA templates in the ribosomes. Before the transfer RNA molecule can carry out its function the amino acid must become "activated," which is accomplished by ATP and an enzyme. The activated amino acid is then linked to its corresponding transfer RNA by a high energy bond derived from the ATP molecule. The transfer RNA then transports the amino acid to the template

RNA in the ribosome where it finds its proper place by means of the sequence of its nucleotides. Likewise, other amino acids are carried to appropriate sites on the template, thus aligning themselves in a specific sequence. The amino acids are then locked together to form the polypeptide chain or protein. This is done by means of the so-called peptide linkage in which water is dropped from the COOH and NH_2 groups which always lie in proximity to one another (p. 53). The amino acids fall into place, starting at one end and continuing until the entire polypeptide molecule is completed, which has been shown to occur in less than two minutes even for a large protein molecule such as fibrinogen (molecular weight over 1 million). The newly formed protein molecule then separates from the ribosome and performs its predestined function.

This remarkable story explains how replication occurs at the molecular level and how the most complex of all molecules are formed. The proteins, thus produced, not only make up the architecture of the cell itself but are also the enzymes which are instrumental in the synthesis of many other molecules, such as carbohydrates, fats, sterols, purines, pyrimidines, amino acids, hormones, pigments, and many others. As has already been pointed out, much of this synthesis goes on in the nucleus; therefore, enzymes formed in the cytoplasm must make their way back into the nucleus to supervise the building of other compounds. Here again we see a feedback system in operation, in other words a very carefully tuned cycling of events which constitutes life itself.

CELL DIVISION

The first visible evidence that DNA, which makes up the genes, and its associate proteins, have doubled, occurs in the cell nucleus and ultimately in the entire cell, which cleaves into two identical daughter cells. Nuclear division was first seen by Flemming in 1882 and was named **mitosis** by him. In most cells, nuclear division is immediately followed by a division of the cytoplasm (cytokinesis). In a few tissues, such as skeletal muscles (p. 105), nuclear division is not followed by division of the cytoplasm; such tissues are said to be **syncytial.**

The most significant aspect of cell division is the remarkably equal distribution of the chromosomes to the daughter cells. This is essential because the genes control the future metabolism and ultimate success or failure of the cell. The importance of the nuclear material is illustrated by removing small portions of the cytoplasm of an egg and following the nucleated part in subsequent development. Such an egg will produce a normal embryo. If, however, a chromosome is removed from the nucleus of an egg, it usually fails to develop normally. Even though it should develop to some extent, the resulting embryo would be quite abnormal. Chromosomes are irreplaceable, because the genes of which they are composed are vital to the life of the entire cell.

You are familiar with the morphology of the chromosomes from an earlier study of the cell (p. 78). We are interested now in how the chromosomes, as well as other cell parts, behave during mitosis.

Mitosis

The process of cell division is no less precise than replication of DNA or protein synthesis. It is equally complex and many aspects are not as well understood. The central theme revolves about the "splitting" of the chromosomes and their subsequent segregation into the daughter cells. It is now known that chromosomes do not split; rather, a second chromosome which is an exact replica becomes synthesized in the immediate vicinity of the parent chromosome. We also know that the DNA doubles in amount which can be determined

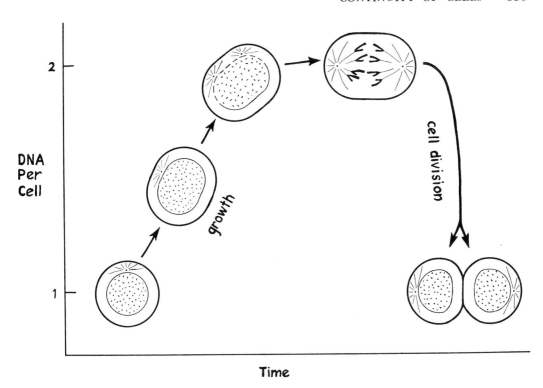

FIG. 24-4. DNA is synthesized during growth and is doubled just before division, at which time it is reduced to one half.

by taking measurements during the various stages of division (Fig. 24-4). The two chromosomes lie so close together that they appear as one. They can be distinguished as two only long after the actual duplication has taken place.

The process of cell division can best be seen in large cells that have been cut into thin slices and stained with different dyes that will differentiate the chromosomes from other regions of the cell. Excellent preparations have been made of a large variety of dividing cells. Among them the early whitefish embryo affords some of the best material (Fig. 24-5). The various stages in cell division of whitefish material are shown in Figure 24-6 but in order to understand the details of cell division, it is best to follow the steps in a generalized cell as portrayed in Figure 24-7.

Biologists have agreed, for conven-

ience, on five steps or phases which cells pass through during the duplication process. It must be remembered that there is no hard and fast line of demarcation between these phases because the process is a continuous one. They merely denote approximate stages.

Interphase. The so-called *"resting" phase,* or *interphase,* is the stage when there is little of no apparent activity in the nucleus. Actually, however, it is during this phase that growth is going on in most cells at a rapid rate and metabolism may in reality be at its peak. The chromosomes at this stage appear as long threads and it is essentially impossible to identify them. The chromonemata (p. 78) are uncoiled, which results in the long thread-like appearance of the chromosomes. Actual duplication of the chromosomes occurs during

FIG. 24-5. Mitosis in the whitefish early embryo.

this stage. The long uncoiled paired chromonemata would have difficulty in becoming sufficiently untangled to be easily separated and passed to the daughter cells. Hence in the stages that follow they contract (coil) to only a fraction of their length to facilitate separation and migration.

Prophase. The first sign that cell division is imminent is the separation of the **centrioles** (not seen in the usual whitefish prep-

arations) and the linear contraction of the chromonemata, resulting in thickened chromosomes that now become dimly visible. This phase is often spoken of as the **early prophase.** The **mid-** and **late-prophase** stages follow in which the coils in the chromonemata become tightened, resulting in discrete, well-defined chromosomes that stain readily, appearing as black strands. The double nature of the chromosomes is clearly indicated at the termination of the prophase, and the centromeres appear as single bodies holding the strands together. The centrioles with their accompanying **asters** have moved toward the opposite poles of the cell, and the nuclear membrane begins to distintegrate.

Metaphase. By the time the nuclear membrane has disappeared, the chromosomes line up at the equatorial plate of the cell. This is called **early metaphase.** The cen-

trioles have reached positions opposite one another and a **spindle** is formed, which in fixed preparations consists of fibers that pass from one centriole to the other. Spindles have been isolated from dividing cells and their composition studied (Fig. 24-8). They are complex structures which make up about 15 per cent of the cytoplasmic proteins.

Once the spindle is fully formed the centromeres divide and separation of the

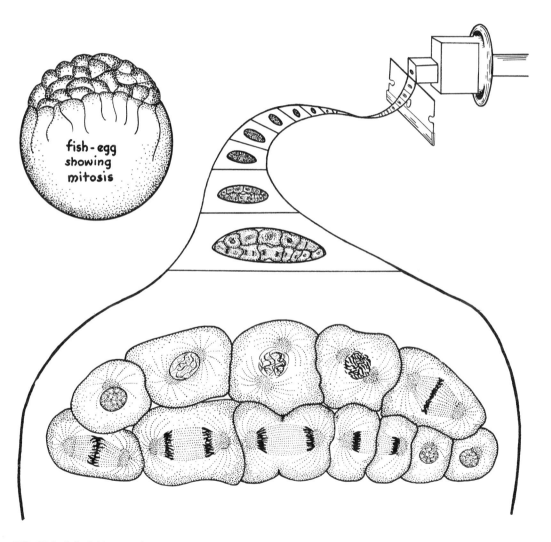

FIG. 24-6. Cell division can best be seen in embryonic tissues such as the early whitefish embryo (upper left). This tissue is killed, dehydrated, and placed in a paraffin block. Then very thin slices (6–8 microns) are cut. These form a ribbon as shown here. When properly stained and mounted on a microscopic slide, the activity going on within the individual cells can be studied.

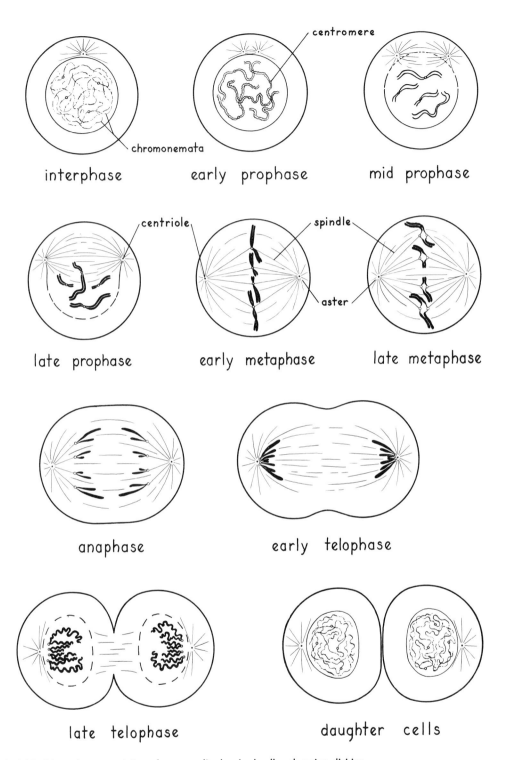

interphase　　　early prophase　　　mid prophase

late prophase　　　early metaphase　　　late metaphase

anaphase　　　early telophase

late telophase　　　daughter cells

FIG. 24-7. Schematic representation of a generalized animal cell undergoing division.

chromosomes begins. Each centromere is attached to a spindle fiber which seems to play some part in subsequent movement of the chromosomes to the poles. The separation of the chromosomes marks the end of metaphase.

Anaphase. This phase, usually relatively brief, includes the movement of the chromosomes to the poles of the spindle. The chromosomes, now known as **daughter chromosomes,** take the form of V's and appear to be "pulled" toward the poles by the spindle fibers. Just what forces are involved in this movement is unknown.

Telophase. The daughter chromosomes now at the poles of the spindle come together, maintaining a parallel arrangement. Shortly, the nuclear membrane appears and the chromonemata begin to uncoil, finally attaining the thread-like appearance seen in the resting cell. All of the stages in nuclear reconstruction reenact, in reverse order, the events seen in prophase. At the same time the cytoplasm and cell membranes cleave forming the daughter cells. Thus the interphase is reached and, following a period of growth, the entire process is repeated in cells that are proliferating. Some cells in the adult body rarely divide whereas others, such as those generating blood cells and spermatozoa, are constantly undergoing multiplication.

Although there are individual variations among animal cells, the process of mitosis is essentially the same in all cells. Many plant cells do not have centrioles and they separate the cytoplasm in a manner different from animal cells, but division of the nuclear elements is the same.

Factors Regulating Mitosis

Cells divide at varying rates in the different tissues of the body, some undergoing mitosis at extremely short intervals whereas others divide only rarely. For example,

sperm cells are produced continuously at a tremendous rate in the mammalian testis, millions every day. Likewise, red blood cells are manufactured at the rate of 10 million per second, meaning that an equal number of mitoses must occur. On the other hand, some cells such as those in the bones and nervous systems are rarely replaced; hence mitoses occur only rarely in these tissues. All of the cells in an embryo are undergoing rapid cell division, but as the organism matures, the tempo gradually slows down. Biologists have been and still are puzzled over the problem as to what controls this rate of cell division.

It is common knowledge that cells in the region of an injury divide more rapidly

FIG. 24-8. These spindles at metaphase have been isolated from sea urchin eggs. Note the complexity of the entire structures.

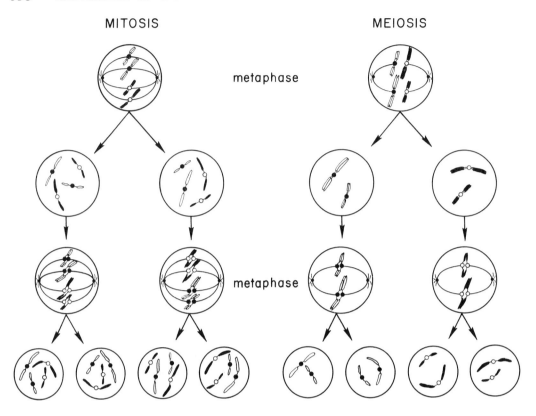

FIG. 24-9. A comparison of mitosis and meiosis in cells with four chromosomes.

than those in the uninjured area. Obviously, the increased rate is essential if the wound is to be closed. Some biologists have been able to demonstrate the presence of a "wound hormone" produced by injured and dead cells which is thought to stimulate mitoses. This. has been demonstrated in plants and it is thought that a similar mechanism may operate in animals.

There is also a purely physical reason why cells must divide when they reach a certain size. If small pieces of cytoplasm of an amoeba are cut away periodically, the cell fails to divide at all. It seems that a certain ratio between the surface area of the nuclear membrane and the amount of cytoplasm must be achieved before division can take place. When there is too much cytoplasm in relation to the surface area of the nucleus, exchange of vital materials

cannot keep pace with the requirements essential to further growth. This may be an important factor in initiating cell division, for by nuclear division the nuclear surface area is greatly increased with no increase in cytoplasm, thus allowing growth to continue.

The significance of mitosis should be apparent when it is recalled that all the cells of our body have arisen by mitosis from the original fertilized egg and that every one of the quadrillions of cells contains the same numbers and kinds of chromosomes and genes that were present in that original cell!

A Special Kind of Mitosis—Meiosis

It has been implied that all cells divide in the manner outlined in the preceding section. There is a very special kind of nuclear division, called **meiosis,** which does not follow this procedure in every detail. Meiosis consists of two nuclear divisions with but one duplication of the chromosomes. Consequently, during meiosis the number of chromosomes is reduced by half. Mitosis and meiosis are compared in Figure 24-9. Note that the end products of the latter consist of four cells with one half the number of chromosomes present in the products of mitosis.

When fertilization occurs the chromosome number doubles. Obviously at some time during the life cycle the number of chromosomes must be halved. If this were not true, the number of chromosomes would double with each generation, which is not the case. It is during meiosis that the number of chromosomes is reduced from the **diploid** number (2N), which is the number found in body cells, to the **haploid** number (N), just one-half the diploid number, which is the number found in the sex cells. As a matter of fact, all body or soma cells contain duplicate sets of chromosomes, one from the paternal parent and one from the maternal parent. Man, for example, has 23 pairs of chromosomes, 46 in all (Fig. 24-10). The germ cells contain one full set, or 23 chromosomes; in other words, only one complete complement of genes or chromosomes, not two sets as in the body cells.

The formation of the **germ cells** (gametes or sex cells), namely, eggs and sperms (Fig. 24-11), is called **gametogenesis—spermatogenesis** for sperms and **oogenesis** for eggs.

Spermatogenesis

The formation of sperm cells takes place in the testis, of course, and varies only in detail among various animals. Let us consider the case of mammalian spermatogenesis.

Sperm have their beginning in the periphery of the **seminiferous tubules** (Fig. 24-12), where the cells are very similar to those of any other body cells, namely, diploid with respect to chromosome number. They undergo successive mitoses to build up their population and move toward the **lumen** (cavity) of the tubule to become mature sperm. It is during this period that their number of chromosomes is reduced to the haploid condition. By following these cells it is possible to determine how this reduction occurs. This is done schematically in Figure 24-11.

Because a great number of sperm cells are produced, the **spermatogonia** undergo many mitotic divisions before launching

FIG. 24-10. These are stained preparations of the 46 chromosomes of man (1). They have been prepared with a fluorescent dye so that they glow in ultraviolet light (2).

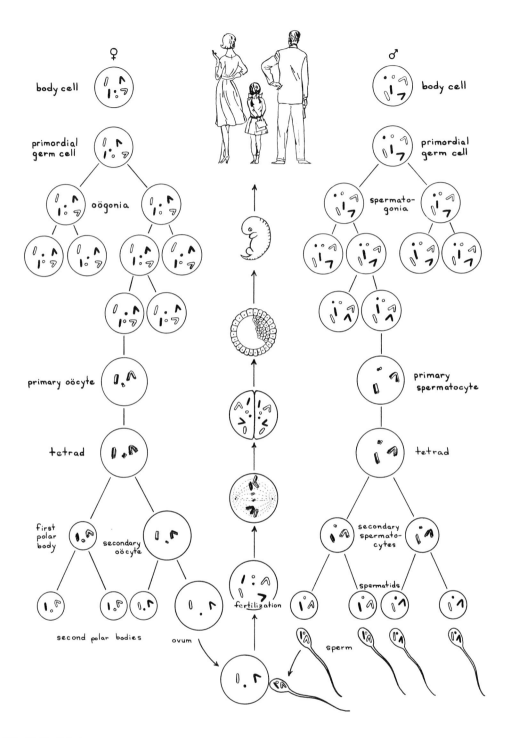

FIG. 24-11. Meiosis.

into the two divisions (meiosis) which precede maturation and the production of mature sperm. At the end of the preliminary division stages, the spermatogonia increase in size and the **homologous chromosomes** pair up. The pairing occurs only between like (homologous) chromosomes, one from the paternal parent and one from the maternal parent. While in this paired condition, each chromosome duplicates itself; thus each chromosome of the pair becomes double. Duplication of DNA occurred at some earlier period, but it is visible only at this time. The association of the four threads is called a **tetrad;** the cells containing them are the **primary spermatocytes.** These nuclei then divide, carrying two of the threads, now called **dyads,** into each daughter cell, or **secondary spermatocyte.** A second division occurs immediately, during which the two threads of the dyads separate so that each daughter cell, now known as a **spermatid,** gets a single thread from each of the original tetrad associations. Each spermatid thus contains only one set of chromosomes instead of two that were present in the spermatogonium; in other words, the spermatid has the haploid number. The spermatid becomes reduced in size, develops a tail, and matures in other ways to become a full-fledged sperm capable of fertilizing an egg (Fig. 24-13).

During this process it will be noted that the maternal and paternal chromosomes (indicated by black and white in Fig. 24-11) may be distributed in several ways so that by the time they reach the spermatid there may be any combination present. There is, however, always a complete set. The mature sperm cell gets only one member of each homologous pair of paternal and maternal chromosomes, never both. This chance distribution of the members of each chromosome pair is very important in the understanding of the mechanics of heredity which we shall study presently.

FIG. 24-12. This is a section of the mammalian testis (rat), showing a seminiferous tubule in detail. Sperm cells begin their development at the outer edges of the tubule and as they mature they move into the cavity. The dark rod-shaped bodies nearest the cavity are mature sperm.

Oogenesis

The process by which eggs are formed varies only slightly from the preceding account for sperm. The principal difference begins when the **primary oocyte** (comparable to the primary spermatocyte) divides. Instead of forming two equal-sized **secondary oocytes,** it produces one large one and one very small one, the latter being known as the **1st polar body.** This discrepancy in size is owing to the fact that virtually all of the cytoplasm goes to one daughter cell. The next division operates on the same principle and results in a single large **ovum** and a **2nd polar body.** Because of their scanty cytoplasm, the polar bodies are nonfunctional and soon disintegrate. The apparent value in this unequal division is to conserve the cytoplasmic contents in order to retain sufficient stored foods for energy during the early stages of embryonic development. This is not necessary for sperms, because once they have contributed their load of chromosomes to the egg in fertilization their job is done. Furthermore, millions of sperm cells are needed to insure fertilization, whereas only comparatively few eggs are necessary to maintain the race.

Eggs vary widely in shape and size

formed. Then some of its cells are set aside to undergo meiosis in the production of gametes, which again unite with others, and so the process continues from generation to generation. We have seen that in the formation of gametes, the chromosomes may be distributed in a variety of ways. The greater the number of chromo-

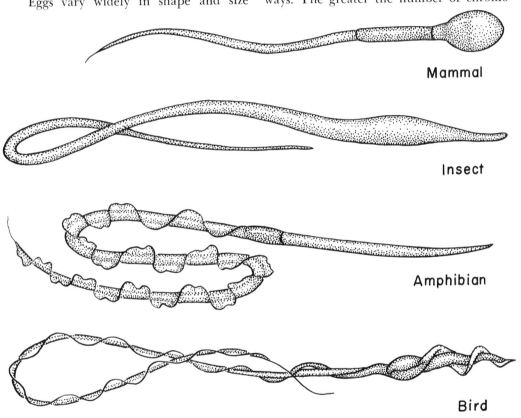

FIG. 24-13. Sperm cells vary widely in shape, as indicated by these sketches.

(Fig. 24-14). The relative size has little to do with the size of the animal that produces it. For example, the eggs of mouse, man and elephant are about the same size, and none is as large as the egg of the humming bird. We learned why this is so in an earlier chapter.

The zygote formed at fertilization thus possesses the full diploid number of chromosomes, and all subsequent divisions are mitotic until the mature individual is

somes (genes), the larger the variety. It is this perennial recombination which accounts for the great variation seen in all living things.

SIGNIFICANCE OF SEXUAL REPRODUCTION

The most obvious fact about sexual reproduction which has come from the discussion of gametogenesis is the great variety of germ cells that can be produced by one individual. A germ cell will receive one single-thread chromosome from each tetrad. The assortment of maternal and paternal chromosome threads to the germ cells is independent for each of the tetrads, so that it is possible that different germ cells may have a different combination of maternal and paternal chromosomes. This is further complicated by the fact that while the chromosomes are paired and in the four-strand stage, they often exchange homologous segments, a phenomenon known as the **crossing-over** (see p. 694). This exchange may occur in several places along the paired threads. Thus the threads which are finally assorted to the germ cells will not all be like the original maternal or paternal chromosome; some will have segments of both. On the average, chromosomes will break and exchange genes in about three places, which means that the original mixing on the basis of chromosome number is increased by 2^3, or 8 times. Let us consider, for a moment, the possibilities in man: there are 23 chromosome pairs in the body cells and, of course, 23 single chromosomes in the germ cells. The possible chromosome combinations then become 2 raised to the 23rd power, or 8,388,-608. If we multiply this figure by 8 we arrive at the number of kinds of germ cells it is possible for one person to produce. Providing it were possible, one couple could become the parents of all of the people in the world and no two of their offspring need be exactly alike.

Because of this wide variability among germ cells, the offspring resulting from their union are different from each other and from either parent. They are new and different individuals, each with its own respective parts assembled in a slightly different manner from any other members of the species. This makes for great variability among species, which is the fundamental reason why evolution has gone on the way it has. Without variation there

would be no way for animals to become better suited to their environment because they would all be exactly alike; hence no one of them would be able to explore a new situation any better than another. This is what happens when **asexual** reproduction is the only means of reproduction. While it is generally confined to the lower animals, it is known to occur among some plants under man's cultivation. The seedless orange trees, for example, are all grown from grafts, so that actually all that is done is to increase the size of the original tree. Since all of the cells carry the same

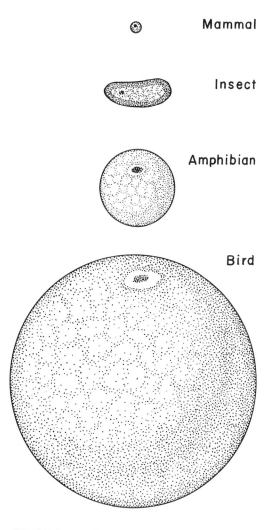

FIG. 24-14. Animals' eggs vary widely in shape and size.

genes, they have no opportunity for variation and must therefore all be exactly alike, barring an occasional mutation. Most of the lower invertebrate animals reproduce asexually as well as sexually. In the former case they likewise have no opportunity for variation. Sexual reproduction evolved very early among animals and is probably largely responsible for subsequent evolution of more complex forms.

SUGGESTED SUPPLEMENTARY READINGS

DeRobertis, E. D. P., Nowinski, W. W., and Saez, F. A., *General Cytology* (Philadelphia, W. B. Saynders Co., 1960).

Mazia, D., "Cell Division," *Scientific American,* 189(2) (August 1953), 53.

Mazia, D., "Mitosis and the Physiology of Cell Division," in J. Brachet, and A. E. Mirsky, eds., *The Cell,* Vol. III (New York, Academic Press, 1961).

Rhoades, M. M., "Meiosis—In the Cell," in J. Brachet, and A. E. Mirsky, eds., *The Cell,* Vol. III (New York, Academic Press, 1961).

Taylor, J. H., "The Duplication of Chromosomes," *Scientific American,* 198(6) (June, 1958), 36.

25
Continuity of the Species

NOW THAT WE UNDERSTAND how cells duplicate and the steps taken in the development of an individual let us discuss the
next problem, namely, the linking of each
generation to the next. From the very beginning, every generation of living things
has been coupled to the preceding through
their genes. It is impressive to note that the
next generation of human beings, nearly
three billion of them, will come from nuclear material that will nearly fill a thimble.
Just how this remarkable material is passed
from one generation to the next is the
subject of *genetics,* the science of heredity.

As sciences go genetics is young indeed,
having gained recognition only during
the present century, although its beginnings
extend back thousands of years.

A common observation, known by man
since earliest times, is that "like begets
like." Children were then and still are expected to look and act like their parents,
usually to the pleasure of both. Probably
early man first attempted to manipulate
this fact in attempts to domesticate plants
and animals. Records indicate that one of
the first attempts was made with the wolf-
like ancestor of the dog. The first associa-

tion was undoubtedly casual, but through selection the animal became more and more the kind of beast that best suited man's personality and habits. Thousands of years of selection were required, intentional or accidental, to produce an animal so well adapted by size, aggressiveness, and behavior to the whims of primitive man, to say nothing of the idealistic requirements of modern man (Fig. 25-1).

Other animals, such as cattle, horses, and sheep, as well as numerous plants, were domesticated later, and in most of them intentional selection for improvement was practiced. This was accomplished simply by applying the rule that "like begets like." Even though we know now that there are certain discrepancies in this "principle," the fact remains that after thousands of years of selection, plants and animals were

gradually molded into the kinds that could best be utilized by man.

It is interesting to note that practically all of the plants and animals capable of domestication were domesticated long before the principles of genetics were known, indeed most of them before writing was established. Very few wild organisms have been domesticated in modern times; all that has been accomplished is improvement of the established types, and in some instances this has been remarkable. For example, modern cattle have become veritable factories for milk and beef production; hens have been known to produce an egg a day for as long as 354 days. An outstanding example among plants is hybrid corn in which the application of the principle of hybrid vigor (p. 683) has resulted in a 30 per cent increase in yield. Even greater accomplishments are anticipated in the future.

HISTORY OF MODERN GENETICS

In spite of the fact that information concerning selective breeding of domestic plants and animals was accumulating throughout the eighteenth century and the first half of the nineteenth, no explanation was given as to how specific characteristics were passed from one generation to the next: Inspired by Darwin's *Origin of Species,* Sir Francis Galton initiated a series of studies on inheritance in about 1859 which resulted in significant conclusions concerning variation within a species. Regarding human inheritance he, like many others, had studied certain complex characters such as height and intelligence and tried to follow them in succeeding generations. The results turned out to be hopelessly complex and he could formulate no generalizations that were meaningful.

This confused situation continued throughout the nineteenth century in spite

FIG. 25-1. Careful selection for thousands of years has produced a wide variety of shapes and sizes in dogs.

of the fact that the basic principles of heredity were discovered and reported by Gregor Mendel in 1865 (Fig. 25-2). This modest Austrian monk, as a result of his efforts, is now known as the "father of genetics." In order to better understand how this remarkable man came by his discovery let us review briefly the story of his life.

Mendel grew up on a small fruit farm where he developed a love for growing plants from his father. He learned how to graft and hybridize plants at an early age. His education included preparatory schooling and two years of college, following which he entered Altbrünn Monastery where he was encouraged to follow his interest in plant hybridization. He carried out his famous pea experiments in the monastery gardens during the years 1856 to 1864, during which time he also attended the University of Vienna where he studied science and mathematics. It was here that he acquired technical skill and an understanding of the mathematical principle of probability which was essential in making his later discoveries. Since Mendel's accomplishments were not recognized during his lifetime, very little information is available concerning his intimate life. Much about how he came to his original concept concerning hereditary mechanisms remains obscure although his interest in living things, his keen intellect, and his devotion to detailed observation contributed to his success in making the revolutionary contribution that bears his name.

Prior to Mendel a great deal of data had been collected but it had very little meaning since it was undigested and therefore incomprehensible. Data were accumulating in other areas of biology that had important bearing on genetics, a science that had not yet been born. The morphology of the cell was being understood and it is highly probable that cytologists would have uncovered Mendel's discoveries through the study of cells, but at a much

FIG. 25-2. Gregor Mendel (1822–1884), working with plants, laid the foundation for modern genetics, although his great work was not recognized by the scientific world until 1900.

later date. During this period sexual reproduction was known at the cellular level, that is, meiosis was deciphered and explained. Being at the heart of recombination this knowledge was an absolute essential before the mechanism involved in hybridization could be understood. Another discipline that was instrumental in solving the mysteries of inheritance patterns came from mathematics. During the early eighteenth century the area of probability became popular, primarily as a result of a need for more information by gamblers and insurance companies concerning predictability. By the beginning of the present century information in these divergent fields was brought to bear upon the problems of heredity and the science of genetics emerged.

Going back to 1865, Mendel presented his work in the form of a short paper before a scientific society of his day. He could hardly be heard above the heated arguments that had been precipitated by Darwin's forceful presentation of the theory of evolution published six years previously, yet in this paper Mendel had portrayed one of the principal keys to evolution. No one understood the significance of this work because he was 35 years ahead of his time. It is not known but undoubtedly Mendel was deeply hurt when he realized that his findings, which to him were fundamental, had been passed over by the scientific world. The significance of his monumental work was not appreciated until 1900, 16 years after Mendel had died, at which time three botanists working in different parts of Europe uncovered the same principles that Mendel had so clearly pointed out many years before. They were DeVries in Holland, Correns in Germany, and Tschermak in Austria. Mendel's paper, which had gathered dust through the years, was republished and only then did this humble man receive the acclaim due him. With this rediscovery of Mendel's Laws the science of genetics was born.

Mendel succeeded where others had failed for several reasons. First he chose to study single characters instead of the whole individual as others had done before him. He was fortunate, also in his selection of material for study, although this may not have been mere chance. Mendel knew a great deal about plants and probably was drawn to those which possessed the characters he wished to study. It is now known that he worked on over twenty different characters of the pea but chose to report only those that were similar and which gave well-defined ratios. The probability of selecting at random seven characters each on a separate chromosome (the pea has seven chromosomes) is highly unlikely; rather Mendel probably selected them because they behaved similarly. This is no discredit to him but is another indication of his appreciation of experimental design. Had his work been accepted in

1865 he would probably have reported his complete work in subsequent publications.

Following his spectacular work with the garden pea Mendel crossed other plants such as different varieties of hawkweeds, but failed to confirm his earlier results. These findings must have shaken his faith to some extent in his work with peas and may have been one of the reasons why he did not press for recognition. He may have felt that the pea was a special case and that what he had learned had little significance as a general principle that could be applied to all organisms. We can now explain the results he obtained with hawkweeds and they in no way detract from his conclusions drawn from his work with peas.

Mendel's choice of the pea as an experimental tool was a good one owing to the purity of the plants for particular characters such as flower color. They always bred true, that is, the offspring retained the character of the adult from generation to generation. Once Mendel had pure breeding strains he could cross them and follow the trait in subsequent generations. This he did by keeping copious notes with actual counts recorded in tabulate form. From these figures his ratios for each experiment stood out strikingly, and they were essentially the same for seven different characters in the pea. This uniformity of these ratios led him to formulate his final conclusions which were consolidated in the famous lecture which he gave in 1865. These were later incorporated by others into what are now known as Mendel's Laws.

During the first ten years of the twentieth century the science of genetics became firmly established. Some of the great biologists of this period, already deep in genetic problems, were stimulated to apply Mendel's ratios to other plants and animals. Among these men was the Englishman William Bateson (1861–1926), who immediately set about to test Mendel's Laws on plants other than the pea, as well as on poultry and other animals. The full impact of Mendel's discoveries became known when Bateson and others found that the ratios applied to the organisms they worked with, and his was, therefore, a general principle for all organisms, a concept which Mendel himself believed.

By 1906 the new science had received the name of **genetics** from Bateson and continued to grow in recognition up to the present. Organisms from viruses to mammals are being used in a large variety of experiments including those concerned with the molecular nature of the gene to those concerned with the inheritance pat-

plants of Mendel's original experiments.

If guinea pigs of the same color (pure strains) are crossed with one another, as, for example, a pure-breeding black with a pure-breeding white, the offspring will all be black (Fig. 25-3). From this cross one outstanding fact is observed, namely, that black is **dominant,** white **recessive.** This means that when two such characters are brought together in the production of a hybrid, one character will completely mask the other. In the above case, the factor for black hair completely dominates the factor for no color, or white. Consequently, all of the offspring are black.

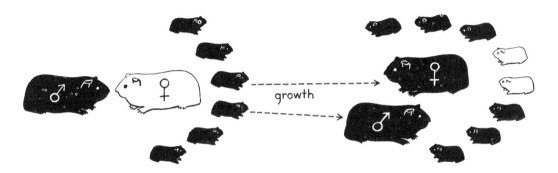

FIG. 25-3. Mendel's first law—segregation—can be shown by breeding guinea pigs as outlined here. Black and white animals (parents) give rise to only black pigs in the F₁ generation. When these are crossed the black and white hair color segregates out so that the ratio is three black pigs to one white one in the F₂ generation.

tern of cancer in man. The information coming from laboratories all over the world has great significance not only because of its practical importance but also because it contributes to our understanding of the processes of nature.

MENDEL'S LAWS

First Law—Segregation

Mendel worked primarily with plants, but what he learned in plants has since been found to be equally true of animals. We will therefore employ familiar animals to describe his discoveries rather than the

The hybrid is known as the **first filial** or F_1 **generation.** In order to determine whether or not the white is completely lost in the F_1 pigs, they can be bred together, producing another generation, the F_2 (**second filial**). When many crosses are made, so there are large numbers of offspring, about three-fourths will be black and one-fourth white. This is called the 3:1 ratio which Mendel was able to obtain so many times with his plants. From this experiment it is obvious that the character for white was not really lost in the F_1 generation. It was merely temporarily hidden or latent, because when the hybrids were crossed the character for white **reappeared** unchanged and in a definite ratio. This means that the character was a **unit** and remained as a unit, even though it was unable to express itself when in the presence of the dominant character. This is Mendel's **Law of Segregation.**

Second Law—Independent Assortment

The above crosses involve only one character, namely, color of the skin coat. What would happen if two characters are followed through two generations? Will the

whorls in various places on the body, giving the animal a roughened appearance. The character is easily seen and is dominant over smooth. When a **rough black** guinea pig is crossed with a **smooth white** one, all of the hybrids (F_1) are **rough black.** When these are inbred new combinations are seen. There are **nine** rough black, **three** rough white, **three** smooth black, and **one** smooth white. This is called the 9:3:3:1 ratio. The essential fact obtained from this experiment is that each of the two characters retains its identity absolutely **inde-**

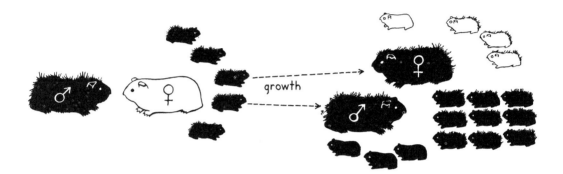

FIG. 25-4. Mendel's second law—independent assortment—can also be demonstrated with guinea pigs. In a crossing of a black rough pig with a white smooth one, the F_1 generation consists of only black rough pigs. If any two of these pigs are crossed, both characters (coat color and texture) reappear, but in different combinations. There will be 9 black rough, 3 black smooth, 3 white rough, and only one white smooth. From this it can be deduced that the characters are independent units.

characters again be lost, will new combinations be formed, or what will happen?

There are thousands of pairs of contrasting characters in any animal, but by selecting any two, preferably each pair that demonstrate a striking dominant and recessive condition, it should be possible to determine the fate of the characters as they pass from one generation to the next. Employing guinea pigs again we may select another pair of characters in addition to black and white color, such as **rough** and **smooth** coats (Fig. 25-4). Ordinarily the coats are smooth, with all of the hairs pointed in one direction. However, there is a breed in which the hair grows in

pendent of the other. They are all combined in the F_1, though only the dominant ones, namely, rough and black, are visible. In the F_2 each character went its own way independent of the other and showed up in the offspring in new combinations that were not present in either parents or grandparents, that is, rough white and smooth black. This is the **Law of Independent Assortment.**

The significance of Mendel's work is difficult to estimate because it was the starting point from which geneticists were able to delve into the more precise nature of the mechanism of inheritance. Let us now view these discoveries in the light of information that has come to us since Mendel's time, for we now understand what he did not know, namely, what goes on within the cell that is responsible for these ratios. He knew nothing about genes but his theoretical "units" behaved as genes do.

GENE COMBINATIONS

As was learned in an earlier chapter, each body cell contains a pair of genes for each trait, a **paternal** gene from the father and a **maternal** gene from the mother. The genes lie in the same position in homologous chromosomes and these points on the chromosomes are called **loci** (singular— *locus*). At the time of meiosis they separate and are distributed to the sex cells, but upon fertilization the pair is restored once more. Obviously, if the gene in each of the homologous chromosomes carries the potentialities for producing the identical trait in the offspring, there is no evidence of their existence. It is only when the genes produce opposite effects that the mechanics of inheritance can be studied. Two such genes that produce the contrasting traits are called **alleles,** and they are always inherited in such a way that the offspring can possess one but not both of them. For example, the gene that controls color in guinea pigs is located at one locus on the chromosome and it may possess the ability to produce black coat or brown coat in the offspring, but it cannot produce both because only the one gene can exist in one locus. There may be genes that alter the hair in other ways such as producing a rough coat, but these genes would occupy other loci on the same or other chromosomes and would therefore have no effect on those that produce color. Note that although the genes produce the effect, they are not colored themselves nor do they carry the actual trait in any way except that the production of the trait is bound up in the configuration of DNA (p. 646).

When the homologous genes are alike, the stock is said to be "pure" or, better, **homozygous;** that is, it always breeds true by showing only the one character. If, on the other hand, it carries a gene for one trait in one of its chromosomes and a gene for a contrasting trait in the homologous chromosome the individual is said to be **heterozygous** or **hybrid.** This is best illustrated by the use of letters as symbols for genes. For example, a homozygous black guinea pig may be represented thus, WW; likewise, a homozygous white pig may be represented thus, ww. By convention, the first letter of the trait that has appeared most recently in evolution is used. In guinea pigs, colored pigs probably preceded white ones, therefore the letter w is employed. Capital letters indicate the condition of one gene whereas lower case letters represent its allele or contrasting trait. An animal carrying both genes, that is, a heterozygote, would be represented by the letters Ww. With this scheme it is a simple matter to follow the genes from one generation to the next.

It is convenient to designate an individual both in respect to its appearance and its genetic constitution. The appearance of an individual with respect to a specific trait is known as its **phenotype,** and its genetic constitution as its **genotype.** The F_1 hybrid in the crosses mentioned above are phenotypically black but genotypically Ww. Pigs that are Ww or WW are phenotypically alike, that is, they are both black, but genotypically different because their genes are not the same.

In observing the ratios in actual practice one might think that they are not very precise. For example, in one litter of guinea pigs as a result of a mating between the F_1 hybrids in the above experiment there may be nearly all combinations of the expected 3:1 ratio. If only four pigs were born they may all be black or they may all be white, although the latter possibility is very remote. It is more probable that there would be some combination of black and white, two of each color or even the expected 3:1 ratio. If, on the other hand, the litters of many such matings were used, say 1,000 offspring, the 3:1 ratio would be approximated very closely. This simply means that all genetic ratios follow the laws of probability, and in small samples these laws, while operative, are not very reliable. In the above cross there are always three chances out of every four that the pigs will be black and only one chance that they will be white. Likewise, in the matings of heterozygous brown-eyed people, each child has three chances of being brown-eyed and only one of being blue-eyed, and this holds true no matter how many children there are in the family. If there are three brown-eyed children in a family and a fourth one is expected, there is no more likelihood that he will be blue-eyed than there was for any of the other children. It must be remembered that at every union of the egg and sperm the chances are three to one for brown eyes no matter what previous unions have produced.

With this information, let us study various crosses in order to understand how they work out in actual practice.

A Simple Monohybrid Cross

In tracing through the simple Mendelian ratios we shall use the same organism that Morgan first employed because much more is known about the genetics of *Drosophila melanogaster* than any other animal. This tiny fly possesses four different chromosomes, all of which have been partially mapped (p. 694). By the use of X-rays hundreds of gene changes (mutations) have been produced, so that there are a great number of alleles, many of which have been investigated. Through the study of hundreds of thousands of generations of this tiny animal has come most of our knowledge of animal genetics.

In Drosophila cultures, occasionally a fly will appear with very much reduced wings, called vestigial wings (Fig. 25-5). If this individual is crossed with a normal fly, what might we expect in the offspring? First let us examine the nature of the germ cells of these two flies, assuming that the female is normal-winged and the male has vestigial wings. In this cross it makes no difference which sex has vestigial or normal wings. During meiosis in the male each sperm will receive a single gene, v, for vestigial wings because it is homozygous; likewise, each egg produced by the female will contain a gene, V, for normal wings. The flies resulting from the union of these eggs and sperms will be heterozygous (Vv) and normal-winged (Fig. 25-5), because normal wing is dominant. Without making this cross we have no way of knowing which of these two traits is dominant. If these F_1 hybrids are crossed with one another (inbred), we already know the ratio will be 3 normal to 1 vestigial-winged flies. But why?

During meiosis of both male and female hybrids, the two alleles are distributed to the sperm and eggs in a random manner. Half of the germ cells of each will contain a gene for vestigial wing and half for normal wing. Upon fertilization these unite according to the laws of chance, and since there are four possibilities, we would expect them to occur in equal numbers for each combination. There is no special attraction between eggs and sperm of different or the same kind of gene. One-fourth of the offspring should be homozygous for normal wing (VV), one-fourth should be homozygous for vestigial wing (vv) and the remaining one-half should possess both genes, that is, they should be heterozygous (Vv), and since normal is dominant, they will all have normal wings just like the parents. It does not matter whether we designate the genes as one-fourth Vv and one-fourth vV, since the end result is one-half heterozygotes Vv, the order of the

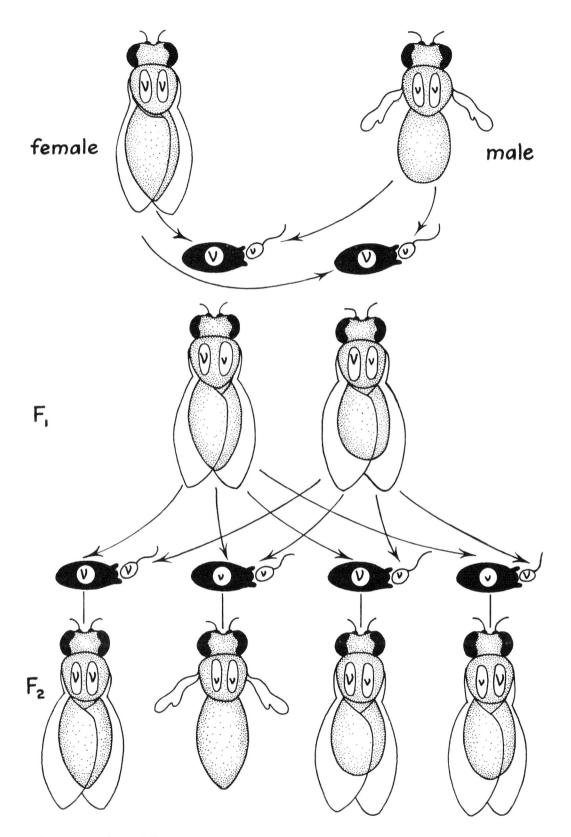

FIG. 25-5. A simple monohybrid cross in Drosophila shows the behavior of the genes.

TABLE 1

MALE			FEMALE
Parents:			
Normal wings	$VV \times vv$		Vestigial wings
One kind of sperm	V v		One kind of egg
F₁ Generation:	Vv		Normal wings (Heterozygotes)
Crossing two hybrids	$Vv \times Vv$		
Two kinds of sperm	$V \& v$ $V \& v$		Two kinds of eggs

genes making no difference in the end result. See Table 1, above.

These germ cells unite at random. This can best be shown by employing the "checkerboard" or Punnett square, named after the British geneticist who first used it.

F₂ Generation:

Sperm

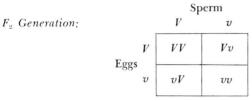

	V	v
V	VV	Vv
v	vV	vv

Eggs

Phenotypic ratio = 3 normal wings : 1 vestigial wing (3:1)

Genotypic ratio = 1 homozygous normal wing
2 heterozygous normal wing
1 vestigial wing (1:2:1)

Back Crosses

It is sometimes important to know the genetic constitution of animals showing the dominant trait but suspected of being heterozygotes. This is particularly true in the breeding of livestock. In the above F₂ flies, three-fourths of them are normal-winged, but the question arises as to which of these are heterozygous and which are homozygous. By mating each of them with the homozygous recessive grandparent this can be told. This kind of cross is known as a *back cross* or *test cross*. If the normal-winged fly is heterozygous the offspring will be half normal and half vestigial-winged, but if it is homozygous the offspring will be normal-winged. This is made clear as follows:

If the fly is heterozygous for vestigial wings (Vv) the cross will be:

$Vv \times vv$ (recessive)

Two kinds of gametes	$V \& v$ v	One kind of gamete
Possible offspring	Vv vv	
Ratio	1 : 1	

In other words, one-half of the offspring would show the recessive trait.

If the fly is homozygous for the dominant trait (VV) the cross will be:

$VV \times vv$ (recessive)

| One kind of gamete | V v | One kind of gamete |
| Possible offspring | Vv | |

All offspring would show the dominant trait.

A study of the inheritance of the abnormality, albinism, in man will also demonstrate this type of inheritance. An albino is lacking a gene to produce pigmentation in the skin, hair, and even in the eyes. This is inherited as a recessive, hence it must be homozygous (aa) to appear. If, then, a normal man (AA) marries an albino woman (aa), their offspring will be normal, although heterozygous for albinism (Fig. 25-6). If this offspring later marries an albino, his children will have a one-to-one chance of being albino, which is similar to a typical test cross and definitely establishes him as heterozygous. If, however, he marries another heterozygote like himself, their children will have one chance in four of being an albino. This is simply an F₂ generation of a monohybrid cross. If he marries a normal person, that is, a homozygote for normal pigmentation

albino
aa

egg a

normal
AA

A sperm

heterozygous
Aa

If he marries an
albino or heterozygote
his offspring will be

albino   aa

Aa   heterozygous

Aa   Aa   aa   aa
1:1

AA   Aa   aA   aa
3:1

FIG. 25-6. Albinism in humans is recessive and appears only when homozygous. The manner in which it is inherited is indicated here.

(*AA*), all of their offspring will be normal (not shown in Fig. 25-6).

Such test crosses have proven of great value in the establishment of "pure" breeds of domestic animals such as cattle for beef or milk production and chickens for egg laying. Rather than pick out the best phenotypes as was the custom for centuries, breeders now make such test crosses until they establish the genotype for a particular trait. Animals possessing this trait are then used as breeding stock. This has been particularly profitable to farmers who wish to build up their herds in respect to milk production. It is possible through recent techniques in artificial insemination to fertilize thousands of cows with sperm from a single bull that is known to produce offspring with high milk-giving qualities. With the use of **progeny selection,** the output of cows is increasing each year until today some record cattle have produced as much as 19,000 quarts of milk a year. This is a far cry from unselected cows which give no more than 350 quarts in a year!

Dihybrid Cross

So far, we have explained what happens when only one pair of contrasting genes is considered. Now let us attempt to explain what Mendel did not know when he crossed two pairs of contrasting characters. The F_1 generations of such crosses are called **dihybrids.** It sometimes is essential for geneticists to follow three and four or more characters simultaneously; this becomes increasingly complex with each added character. We shall confine our attention to the two-character cross and leave the others for advanced books in genetics.

Using normal and vestigial wings in Drosophila again, we can also follow body color. Ebony or dark-colored individuals occasionally occur in stocks of the normal gray-bodied wild type, and these dark individuals are recessive to the gray-bodied

wild type (Fig. 25-7). By crossing a gray vestigial female with an ebony normal-winged male the F_1 offspring are all gray and normal-winged. Note that each of the parents was recessive and dominant for different traits. We could as well have crossed a gray normal-winged individual with an ebony vestigial fly and obtained the same normal-appearing heterozygous offspring. The sexes could also have been switched and it would have made no difference in the outcome. When these two hybrids are crossed, 16 combinations are possible in the F_2 generation. To follow these possible combinations it is convenient to employ the Punnett square again (Fig. 25-7).

Each of the hybrids can produce four different kinds of gametes during meiosis, each bearing the two different genes. These genes must necessarily be located on different chromosomes, for if they were on the same chromosomes the typical ratios would not occur, for reasons that we shall discuss a little later (linkage, see p. 689). By arranging the four different kinds of sperm along the top of the checkerboard and the eggs along the left side and placing in each square the gene combinations that result from the union of those particular eggs and sperm, the 16 possible combinations become obvious. Remembering which are dominant and which recessive, it is clear that there will be 9 gray normal, 3 gray vestigial, 3 ebony normal, and 1 ebony vestigial. This is the 9:3:3:1 ratio that Mendel verified many times with plants. We see here an explanation for both genotypes and phenotypes. The heterozygotes can be checked for their genes by employing test or back crosses just as was done for the single-pair genes. If, for example, a gray-bodied, long-winged heterozygote (*VvEe*) is crossed with a double recessive (*vvee*) the offspring will fall into four groups: ¼ long gray, ¼ vestigial gray, ¼ long ebony, and ¼ vestigial ebony. This is portrayed in Table 2.

FIG. 25-7. A schematic representation of the gene behavior in a typical dihybrid cross using Drosophila.

TABLE 2

Long gray *VvEe* × *vvee* Vestigial ebony

Four kinds of eggs: *VE, Ve, vE, ve*				*ve*	Only one kind of sperm
Test cross	¼ *VvEe,*	¼ *Vvee,*	¼ *vvEe,*	¼ *vvee*	
	(long,	(long,	(vest.,	(vest.,	
	gray)	ebony)	gray)	ebony)	
Ratio:	1 :	1 :	1 :	1	

A test cross to the dominant parent would yield all long gray offspring and would tell nothing about the genotypes.

INTERACTION OF GENES

Up to this point we have attempted to explain Mendel's observations and the explanation has been essentially simple. With the passing of time, a great many genetic variations have been noted that cannot be explained so simply. Several new principles have been discovered which are based on the interaction of alleles as well as genes occupying different loci on the same or other chromosomes. With the addition of these new principles, genetics has become an exceedingly complex science.

Blending or Incomplete Dominance

Occasionally a gene does not demonstrate complete dominance, so that the heterozygote shows a mixing or **blending** of the dominant and recessive traits. This may be due to a cumulative effect where the recessive allele is negative and the dominant allele manifests itself according to whether or not it is single or double. The heterozygote would then show half the effect that the dominant homozygote would. For example, in hair color in cattle, a red bull (*WW*) may be mated to a white cow (*ww*) and the hybrid (*Ww*) will be roan, which is a mixture of red and white (Fig. 25-8). Actually the hairs are still red or white, but they both appear, thus giving the coat its roan color. The appearance of one dominant red gene produces only half as many red hairs as the two genes will produce.

When the hybrids are mated (*Ww* × *Ww*), the F₂ generation shows a ratio of 1 red, 2 roans, and 1 white. In other words, the genotypes and phenotypes are identical. In such matings it become impossible to get a pure breeding roan stock, because reds and whites will continue to show up in future progeny no matter what selecting procedures are employed.

MULTIPLE GENE INHERITANCE

So far we have been considering characters that are clearly defined, where the phenotypes are sharply set off by color or some other trait. But there are a great many characters which, instead of demonstrating clear-cut differences, show continuous variation from the two extremes; this is particularly true of such human traits as skin color, height, weight, special abilities, and intelligence. In cross-matings between individuals possessing the two extremes of these traits, children do not resemble one parent or the other but are intermediate between the two. This is like blending inheritance in which more than one pair of genes is involved. This means that several genes, known as **multiple genes** or **factors,** influence one trait and their ultimate effect depends on additive action. This can be illustrated by a consideration of skin color in humans, which is the best-known example of this type of inheritance.

In certain parts of the world where there is no "color line," marriages between Negroes and whites are common, and such practice has afforded geneticists sufficient

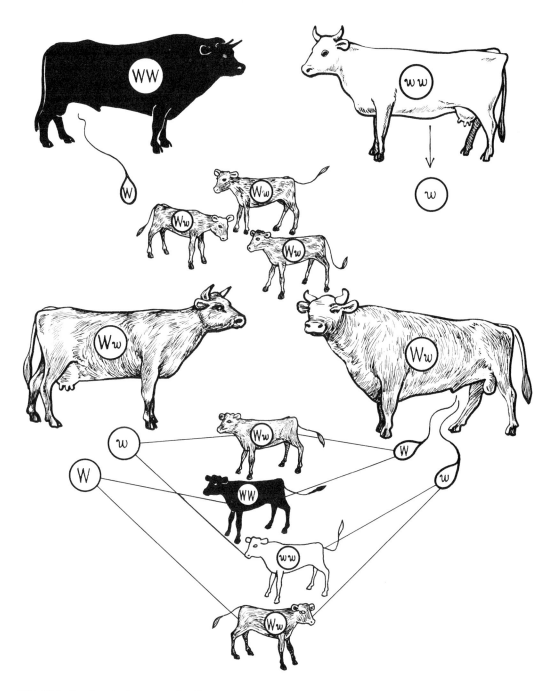

FIG. 25-8. Blending dominance can be illustrated with red and white cattle. Here the genotype can be distinguished by simply observing the coat color.

information about the inheritance of skin pigmentation to understand it genetically. It is known that two pairs of genes on separate chromosomes are involved. These may be called *Aa* and *Bb* where *A* and *B* are responsible for pigmentation. In the F_1 generation resulting from a mating between a homozygous Negro (*AABB*) and a homozygous white (*aabb*) we would expect the hybrid (*AaBb*) to be either all black if the genes for pigmentation were completely dominant or half black, **mulatto,** if blending occurred. The latter proves to be the case. The genes for pigmentation show incomplete dominance and the offspring are dark-skinned, approximately intermediate between the white and black parents. This resembles exactly what one would expect in a single gene pair trait. The double gene-pair proof comes when two mulattoes mate (*AaBb* × *AaBb*). If there were but a single gene pair, the typical 1 white : 2 mulatto : 1 black ratio would be expected, but instead an entirely new ratio appears, that is, 1 black : 4 dark brown : 6 mulatto : 4 light brown : 1 white. Since there are sixteen possibilities, there must have been four genetically different sperm and four genetically different eggs, or two pairs of genes, each located in different chromosomes. This is simply the F_2 generation of a dihybrid cross. Why, then, should this peculiar ratio result instead of the typical 9:3:3:1?

If we assume that the genes *A* and *B* influence the production of equal amounts of pigmentation even though located on different chromosomes, and that blending occurs between each with its recessive, *a* and *b*, then the 1:4:6:4:1 ratio is exactly as one would expect. Moreover, the intensity of the skin pigmentation, that is, the phenotype, would give a clue as to the genetic constitution or genotype of an individual. The darker the skin, the more capital letters would appear in the genic constitution. For example, a full Negro would have the genetic formula of *AABB;* a dark brown Negro would be *AABb* or *AaBB;* a mulatto would, of course, have one of each gene, *AaBb.* However, it would be impossible to tell whether the formula was *AAbb, AaBb* or *aaBB,* since each dominant gene has the same influence in producing pigmentation. The light brown would have but one dominant gene, *Aabb* or *aaBb,* whereas the white would be double recessive (*aabb*), naturally. Thus, in this F_2 generation there would be one person resembling each of the grandparents and all others would be graded in respect to pigmentation.

Can such information be of assistance in predicting what one might expect in offspring of matings where the skin pigmentation varied in the two parents? Obviously matings between the double recessive white and a person with any degree of pigmentation will produce offspring lighter than the dark parent. Matings between individuals carrying only one gene for pigmentation and appearing as light as many non-Negroes *may* produce children darker than either parent. On the other hand, they have an equal (1:4) chance of producing children with no genetic trace of pigmentation. Such white children are double recessives (*aabb*) and therefore can never transmit pigmentation to their offspring although other Negro characteristics may appear.

Normal Frequency and Multiple Genes

The character of skin color involving two gene pairs in man is a relatively simple case of multiple genes. As a rule such characters involve many more gene pairs, as, for example, height in man, where ten or more are influential. With three gene pairs influencing one trait, the F_2 comes out in the ratio 1:6:15:20:15:6:1. With each added gene pair the shape of the distribution approximates more and more closely a normal bell-shaped frequency curve (Fig. 25-9). When ten gene pairs influence a

#DOSE	0	1	2	3	4
RATIO	1	4	6	4	1

FIG. 25-9. Many gene pairs are involved in the control of height in humans. Three generations are represented here where only two gene pairs are considered, leaving space for any number of others to be added. The tall (dominant) and short (recessive) grandparents produced heterozygous children of average height. Crossing of two such heterozygotes results in offspring of a whole range of heights, which turns out to be a normal curve in the grandchildren (F2). The number of dominant genes received by each individual (dose) and the number of individuals in each category (ratio) appear at the bottom.

single trait, the distribution coincides with the normal distribution curve. In other words, ten gene pairs are sufficient to produce a normal population in respect to one trait whether it be height, weight, length of neck, or degree of intelligence. If one measures the height of 10,000 adult white males in America, he would find a range from about 55 to 85 inches with an average falling around 68. There would be very few as short as 55 inches and very few as tall as 85 inches but a great many around the average of 68 inches. By plotting the number of people at each height against inches, a normal distribution curve results (Fig. 25-9). This is exactly what

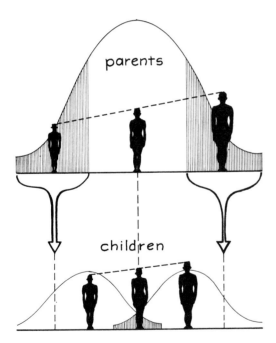

FIG. 25-10. Height in a population of humans shows a normal bell-shaped frequency curve as shown in the upper figure. There are a few about 55 inches tall and a few about 85 inches tall; most people are between these extremes, the average being about 68 inches. When these heights are plotted against numbers, a bell-shaped curve results, which is what is expected when ten gene pairs are involved.

The lower portion of the figure shows how Galton's law of filial regression operates. Children of short and tall parents are never as short or as tall as their parents. They tend toward the average height of the population.

is obtained when the distribution is computed for height on the basis of ten gene pairs being involved.

Quantitative Studies of Populations

Long before Mendel's Laws were known, some effort was made to understand inheritance by a careful analysis of a single trait in large populations. The most outstanding investigator in this field was Sir Francis Galton of England, referred to earlier, who studied the inheritance of many traits of British people, including such intangible ones as intelligence. He discovered that high intelligence seems to "run in families," as shown by the frequency that names of members of famous families appeared in the British "Who's Who." Such traits as height, which, as we have seen, is inherited through multiple genes, led him to formulate his **filial regression law.** This law merely states that offspring of tall or short parents, while taller or shorter, respectively, than the average British subject, are still not as tall or as short as their parents. This means that at the extremes of height offspring tend to regress toward the average (Fig. 25-10).

Although Galton's studies contributed virtually nothing to the mechanics of inheritance, they did give later workers, not only in biology but also in sociology, economics, and other fields, a tool by which a quantitative description of a naturally or artificially occurring series of variables could be stated. It has been used extensively in biology in determining a normal population in respect to one or more traits. This is important to animal breeders who are trying to improve their stock with respect to a particular character, such as egg laying in chickens. By carefully selecting for breeding stock those birds that produce the greatest number of eggs, the whole population can gradually be improved along that line. This means a selection toward all dominant or all recessive genes. When the stock becomes homozygous for a particular trait there is nothing more to be gained by further selection. One needs only to inbreed and keep the desired qualities which have thus been attained.

Hybrid Vigor or Heterosis

One of the strange and unexplained outcomes of multiple gene inheritance is that the hybrid resulting from two parents with contrasting traits is frequently more vigorous, bigger, and apparently better in every way than either parent. This condition is known as **heterosis** or **hybrid vigor**. This observation has been made on a great many animals. The mule, which is a result of a mating between a jack and a mare, is notorious for its strength and endurance as well as its stubbornness (Fig. 25-11). Every farmer is familiar with the value of hybrid corn, which demonstrates heterosis very markedly. Some striking cases of heterosis among human beings have occurred where two distinctly different races have crossed. The most celebrated instance is that of Captain Christian and his fellow mutineers of the *Bounty* who took native Polynesian women from Tahiti and settled on tiny Pitcairn Island. The first generation of children were more vigorous, taller, and more fertile than either the white or the Polynesian stock from which the parents came. Incidentally, this is also one of the few cases in human history where a nearly perfect inbreeding experiment was carried on. Studies of half-breed Indians, as well as hybrids from Hottentot and Boer crosses, have likewise revealed heterosis to a marked degree, although the condition does not seem to be evident on certain black-white crosses.

The second generation following the original crosses usually results in a gradual loss of the early hybrid vigor, and the offspring in succeeding generations slowly return to an intermediate type. This might be explained by considering that each member of the first cross possesses certain

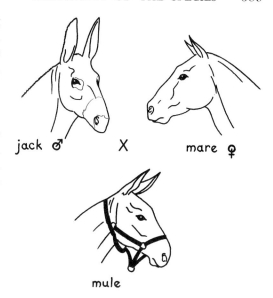

jack ♂   X   mare ♀

mule

FIG. 25-11. Cross-breeding of a jack and a mare results in a mule which is usually sterile. The reciprocal cross (female burro with a stallion) results in a more horse-like hybrid, the hinny.

dominant genes for desirable traits which were lacking in the mate. When crossed, a now full complement of dominants would produce their desirable effects, thus producing the vigorous offspring. In subsequent hybrid matings the dominant genes would segregate out, as one might expect, and eventually the recessives would once more reduce most of the race to the condition of the original parental stock.

New Phenotypes Resulting from Gene Interaction

Sometimes two pairs of genes interact, so that the expected 9:3:3:1 ratio in the F_2 is significantly altered.

Occasionally when two dominant genes interact a new phenotype is produced. The classical case of this interaction occurs among combs in chickens. Three kinds of combs are well known; **single, pea,** and **rose** (Fig. 25-12). Both pea and rose are dominant to single. What happens when pea and rose, two dominants, are crossed?

The result is a new kind of comb, called **walnut!** This demonstrates the combined action of two dominant genes, namely, that each supplements the other and the result is a comb different from that each would produce alone. The proof of this conclusion can be shown merely by crossing two walnut-combed animals. The offspring appear in the ratio of 9 walnut : 3 rose : 3 pea : 1 single, which means that wherever the genes for rose and pea come together their supplementary action produces a walnut comb. This type of gene action is different from blending because the genes are located on different loci on the different chromosomes and are therefore not alleles. Moreover, it is possible to produce a pure breed of walnut-combed chickens simply by making test crosses with the double recessive single comb to establish homozygous genes. Once this is done, the mating of two homozygous birds will result in all walnut-combed offspring and the pure breed is established. You will remember that this procedure is impossible with those showing incomplete dominance. Another slight variation in this type of gene interaction can be demonstrated in guinea pigs. Black coat (BB) is dominant to brown coat (bb). In addition to these genes there is a third gene (C) which is essential in order that the color appear at all. A double recessive (cc) is an albino. If a brown guinea pig ($CCbb$) is mated with an albino ($ccBB$), the offspring will all be black ($CcBb$) which might seem surprising until the genes are examined. Whenever the gene for color (C) is in combination with the gene (B), the phenotype will be black, but if it occurs only with the recessive (c) no color appears. If two of these F_1 pigs are mated, the F_2 generation will have the ratio of 9 black, 3 brown, and 4 albino. Here we see two independent gene pairs interacting in such a way that one dominant will produce its effect with or without the other. The second dominant, however, can produce its effect only in the presence of the first.

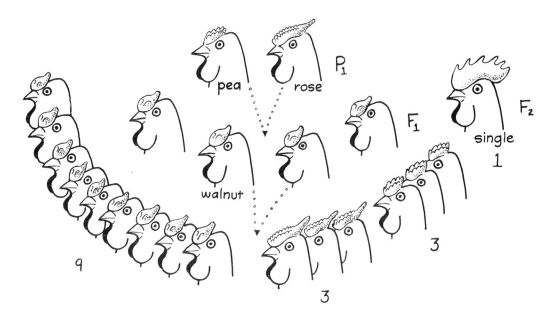

FIG. 25-12. The inheritance of combs in fowls is due to two dominant interacting or supplementary genes. In a cross between pea- and rose-combed animals a new type of comb, walnut, is produced. Crossing walnut-combed fowls gives the typical 9:3:3:1 two gene ratio, but the interaction of the genes show a distribution of comb types as shown here. The double recessive comes out to be a fourth kind, single comb.

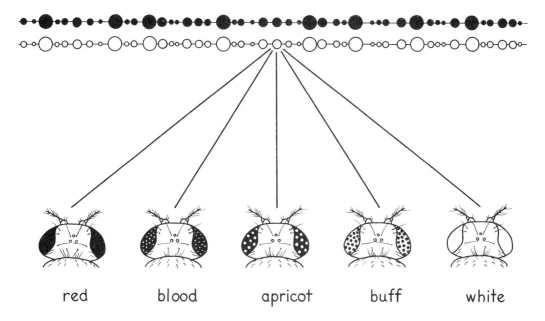

FIG. 25-13. A schematic representation of five of the fourteen alleles for eye color in *Drosophila*. The gene locus on the X-chromosome is indicated at the top of the drawing and the five phenotypes below.

Multiple Alleles

It was pointed out earlier that several unlike genes may occupy the same locus in a chromosome but not at one time. These are called **multiple alleles.** By the use of X-rays, hundreds of multiple alleles have been produced in Drosophila, so that for one locus, eye color for example, there are fourteen known alleles, all different (Fig. 25-13). Their influence on eye-color production ranges from dark red to white with all shades in between. Coat color in rabbits likewise is controlled by multiple alleles. There is a gene (C) which controls coat color, whereas the homozygous genes (cc) cause no color or albinism. Two alleles, (c^{ch}) and (c^h), when homozygous, produce "Chinchilla" and "Himalayan," respectively. The former is steel gray, while the latter is white all over except the tips of the ears, toes, tail, and nose (Fig. 25-29). When arranged in a series, C, c^{ch}, c^h, c, each gene is dominant to those following it and recessive to all of those preceding it. For example, a rabbit with the genes $c^{ch}c$ is a "Chinchilla," one with $c^h c^{ch}$ is also "Chinchilla," whereas one with genes $c^h c$ is "Himalayan."

One of the best-known characteristics in man that is inherited by multiple alleles is the A, B, AB, and O blood groups which we discussed in Chapter 20 (see p. 575). Three alleles are responsible for the various groups: genes A, A^B, and a, of which the first two are dominant to the last. Gene A controls formation of antigen A (agglutinogen); gene A^B controls the formation of antigen B; and gene a is without effect in that it causes no antigen formation. Neither A nor A^B is dominant to the other, so when both are present in homologous chromosomes the blood group AB results. Since these genes are inherited in a definite fashion, the knowledge of blood types has some value in addition to that needed in transfusions. In cases of questionable paternity the knowledge of blood types can be used and may rule out certain males as possible fathers of a child. It cannot be employed to determine whether a certain man *is* the father but only that he *could be*. The manner in which this operates can be seen from a consideration of all of the genotypes:

Blood Group	Genotype
A	*Aa* or *AA*
B	*A^Ba* or *A^BA^B*
AB	*AA^B*
O	*aa*

A child with blood group A (*Aa* or *AA*), for example, and a mother with Group B (*A^Ba* or *A^BA^B*) must have a father with group A or AB. A male with group O or B could not possibly be the father of such a child. Do you see why?

The Rh blood antigen discussed earlier (p. 577) was thought for a long time to be simple. It was postulated that a single pair of alleles, *R* and *r,* accounted for the difference between Rh-positive and Rh-negative blood and these were inherited in Mendelian fashion. However, as more antisera were studied additional genes were needed to account for the complex inheritance patterns. Eight alleles and even more have been included by some investigators, although others believe three pairs of linked genes (p. 690) explain the results. More recently, a new hypothesis, based on a compound locus (p. 698), is being investigated. As yet not enough evidence is available to obtain a clear answer to this perplexing problem.

Inheritance of Sex

The obvious fact that sexes appear in the ratio of 1:1 meant nothing until geneticists noted that the cross of a hybrid (*Ww*) and its double recessive (*ww*) was also a 1:1 ratio, which fact suggested the possibility that sex might likewise be determined genetically. Cytological evidence before 1900 had shown that some of the sperm cells of certain insects such as the firefly had a very tiny chromosome, whereas the other sperm cells had a large one in place of the small one. As early as 1902, McClung in this country suggested that this difference might control sex and for the next 20 years the problem was avidly pursued until his conjecture was generally accepted as true. This meant, then, that there are two kinds of chromosomes in every cell: the **sex chromosomes** which determine the sex, and the **autosomes** which include all of the remaining chromosomes. The female is distinguished by having two sex chromosomes, called **X chromosomes,** while the male has only one of these plus a second very much smaller chromosome, the **Y chromosome.** Therefore, a human female has 22 pairs of autosomes and one pair of X chromosomes in every body cell, and the male has 22 pairs of autosomes plus one X chromosome and one Y chromosome. This situation exists in most animals, although there are some notable exceptions (Fig. 25-14). In some insects and birds the arrangement is reversed. Interestingly the sex in bees is determined by whether or not the individual is haploid (males) or diploid (females).

At meiosis two kinds of sperm are produced, both containing the autosomes plus either an *X* or a *Y* chromosome (Fig. 25-15). Upon fertilization the egg, which contains only a single *X,* may receive either a sperm containing an *X* or one with a *Y.* In the former case the offspring will be female (*XX*) and in the latter, male (*XY*). Since fertilization occurs at random, there is a 50–50 chance of either kind of sperm fertilizing the egg, hence the equal numbers of both sexes. In other words, the male is heterozygous for sex, the female homozygous. It would seem that sex determination is a very simple matter, but experimental work over a long period of time has brought to light certain conditions which indicate that the process is, unfortunately, not as simple as was once thought.

FIG. 25-14. Sex determination varies in different animals. Many insects, such as the grasshopper, have no Y chromosome; males have one X and females two X chromosomes. The drone bee is produced from an unfertilized egg, therefore requires no meiosis to produce haploid gametes. Males are haploid and females are diploid. In chickens, as in all birds, the female produces two kinds of eggs (Z and W) which determines the sex. The opposite situation exists in most animals, man included, where two kinds of gametes (X and Y) occur in the male. The fertilized egg containing Y chromosomes is male.

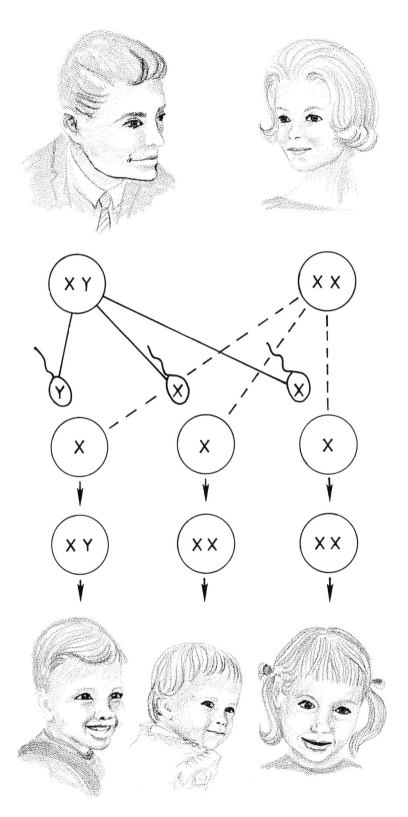

FIG. 25-15. Sex is determined in animals at fertilization, depending on the genetic composition of the sperm which enters the egg. In humans if it contains an X chromosome the offspring will be female; if it contains a Y chromosome the offspring will be male.

Genic Balance and Sex Determination

One of the first experiments that extends the theory of sex determination by the X and Y chromosomes was the appearance in about 1922 of a fly in Dr. Calvin Bridges' cultures at Columbia University which possessed three sets of autosomes (9 chromosomes instead of only 6) and 2 X chromosomes. According to the theory, this fly should have been a female, but actually it was an intermediate between male and female, or an *intersex*. Apparently the presence of an extra set of autosomes upset the "genic balance" in such a way that the two X chromosomes could not completely control the situation in order to produce a female. This and subsequent experiments made it clear that other genes scattered throughout the autosomes were also influential in determining the sex. The distribution of the genes in the autosomes and X chromosomes seemed to be the deciding factor, as indicated in Table 3.

ovary was destroyed because it received male hormone from an activated residual testis. Certainly the genetic balance was not changed. What actually did happen is another unsolved riddle in biology.

Sex Linkage

In addition to carrying genes for sex the X chromosomes also contain other genes that have nothing to do with sex, such as those that control eye color in Drosophila. The Y chromosome is virtually without genes, that is, it seems to be a genetic blank, and at least some insects (*Anasa*— the squash bug) do not have it at all and apparently get along satisfactorily. Since the X chromosome carries certain genes that control traits besides sex, it follows that those genes will be tied in some peculiar fashion to the sex, in other words, they will be **sex-linked.** In man the genes responsible for **red-green color blindness** and the blood abnormality, **hemophilia,** are carried on the X chromosome, so that one

TABLE 3

2 A (autosomes) plus 1 X	=	Normal male characters
2 A " 2 X	=	Normal female characters
3 A " 1 X	=	Over-developed male characters
2 A " 3 X	=	Over-developed female characters
3 A " 2 X	=	Intersex

From these experiments it is evident that the X chromosomes carry a preponderance of genes for femaleness while the autosomes contain a preponderance of genes for maleness; how much "maleness" or how much "femaleness" the offspring exhibits is determined by how great a dose of either one or the other it receives. If the dose is intermediate, the offspring displays the external characteristics about evenly divided.

This revised view of sex determination does not explain all of the observed facts. Earlier (p. 491) we saw that the sex of a hen chicken could be reversed when the

might expect these anomalies to be associated with sex. This is definitely true and has been recognized for centuries, particularly with respect to hemophilia. Because this condition has occurred in royal families whose histories are well known, it was learned very early that the dread disease passed from mothers to sons but never from fathers to sons. For example, Queen Victoria of England apparently carried the defective gene because she herself did not have the disease but transmitted it to one of her sons and through two of her daughters to succeeding generations so that it has occurred again and again in her male descendants, particularly in the Russian and Spanish royal families.

This great enigma in man's inheritance remained a mystery until a mutation producing white eye color occurred in some of T. H. Morgan's fly cultures. When the inheritance of this trait was worked out it paralleled the transmission of hemophilia in man. From this white-eyed stock of Drosophila, Morgan was able to show that the gene for eye color was located on the X chromosome and that its inheritance was definitely linked with this chromosome and consequently with sex. As a result of many experiments, it has been found that the inheritance of this sex-linked trait follows a specific pattern (Fig. 25-16). The gene for white eye color is recessive and is therefore obvious only when homozygous. Since the male has but one X chromosome, white eyes will appear whenever a single X chromosome carrying a defective gene is a part of the genetic make-up of the male fly.

In a cross between a white-eyed female, whose X chromosomes must each carry the defect, and a normal red-eyed male, all of the female offspring will be red-eyed, although they will be heterozygous, and all of the males will be white-eyed because their one X chromosome carries the gene which induces this defect (Fig. 25-16). When these F_1 flies are allowed to interbreed, the effect of the linked condition is further demonstrated. The female can produce two kinds of eggs, one-half containing an X chromosome with a normal gene and one-half bearing a defective gene. The male produces two kinds of sperm as usual, that is, half containing an X and half a Y chromosome. The sperm containing the X chromosome, however, carries the defective gene (w). Random fertilization will result in half of the female offspring being homozygous and therefore white-eyed; the other half will be red-eyed but heterozygous. Half of the males will be white-eyed and half red-eyed because the eggs from which they came contained one-half defective and one-half normal genes for eye color. The Y chromosome, of course, plays no part except in determining the sex. Therefore, the ratio is 1:1 for each of the sexes and also for the entire F_2 generation.

The explanation of sex-linked genes in Drosophila suffices for hemophilia and red-green color blindness in man. For example, in the latter instance, if a woman heterozygous for color blindness marries a normal-visioned man, all of the daughters of this combination will have normal vision but half of the sons will be color blind (Fig. 25-17). One-half of the daughters, however, will be heterozygous for the defect, whereas the normal sons will show no trace of the anomaly and therefore will never transmit it to their children. The heterozygous daughters can have color-blind sons while the homozygous daughters will never pass the trait on to either sons or daughters. Obviously, this type of **criss-cross** inheritance explains the early observation concerning hemophilia in royal families. Many other organisms, both plants and animals, exhibit this type of inheritance.

Characters other than the sex organs are controlled by genes on the autosomes but, even so, they are definitely associated with the sex. Their effect is probably on the production of hormones which in turn control the appearance or absence of the trait. Such traits are said to be **sex-limited** because they do not follow the pattern of sex-linked genes. The presence of horns in one sex of certain animals and not in the other is controlled by such autosomal genes.

Linkage and Crossing-Over

During the early studies of Mendelian inheritance it was soon discovered that there were more traits than chromosomes, and this fact led workers to conclude that more than one gene existed on each chromosome. If this were true, then what happens

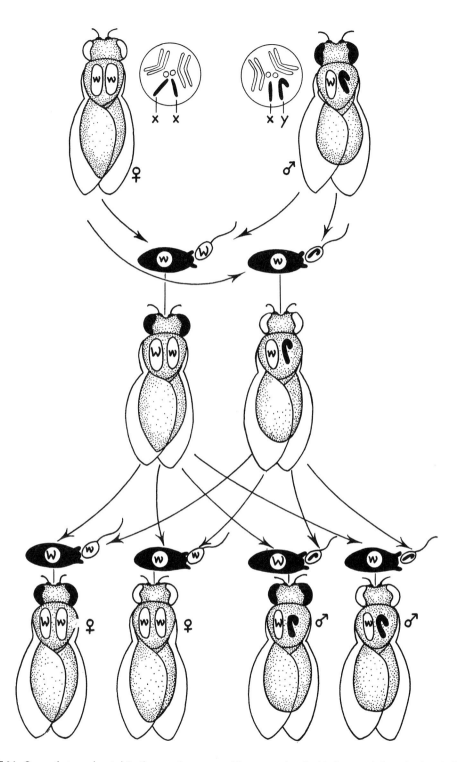

FIG. 25-16. Genes that are located in the sex chromosome (X) are associated with the sex of the animal, as indicated here in Drosophila. The gene for eye color (white) is located on the X chromosome and behaves in the manner shown here.

during meiosis? As long as the genes are on separate chromosomes the ideal ratios of Mendel come out beautifully, but if they are located on the same chromosome, the ratios are different, though quite exact. Morgan and his students showed that traits entering a cross often stayed together in subsequent generations, which proved that they were linked together on the same chromosome. Therefore, genes located on the same chromosome are said to be **linked.**

There should be as many linkage groups as there are chromosomes, which proves to be the case in those plants and animals where sufficient information is available. *Drosophila,* for example, has four pairs of chromosomes and four linkage groups. Moreover, the linkage groups even approximate the chromosomes in size. There is a small pair of chromosomes and a small linkage group, a middle-sized pair and a middle-sized linkage group, and there

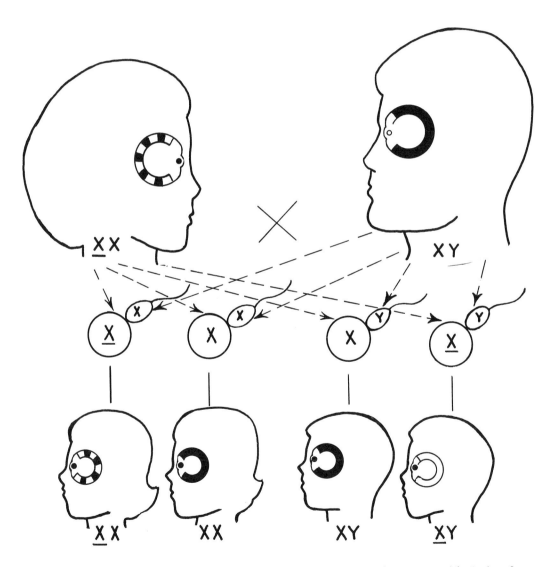

FIG. 25-17. Color blindness is sex-linked in man and is inherited, as white eye color is in Drosophila. In these figures the solid black retina indicates normal vision, the broken retina represents the heterozygous condition in the female, and the white retina indicates red-green color blindness.

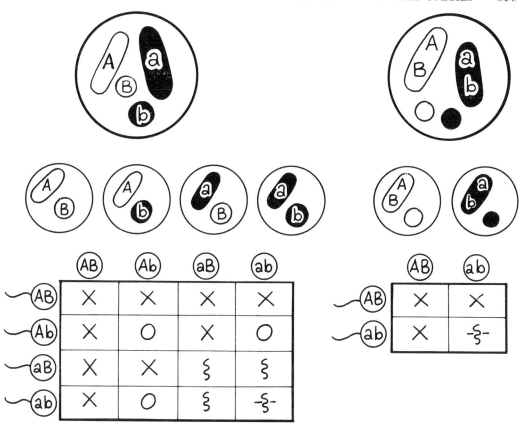

FIG. 25-18. Genes that are located on separate chromosomes give the typical Mendelian ratios, as in the case of four genes located on four different chromosomes on the left above. The typical 9:3:3:1 ratio results in the F_2. If the dominant genes are located on one chromosome and the recessives on another, they will behave as single genes as shown in the figures to the right.

are two pairs of large chromosomes and likewise two large linkage groups. These facts, together with information that is to follow, certainly identify genes with chromosomes.

Linked genes respond in a manner similar to single gene inheritance. For example, if genes A and B are linked in one chromosome (Fig. 25-18) and their homologous recessives, a and b, are linked on the homologous chromosome, they segregate in the formation of germ cells as if they were single genes and the subsequent typical one-gene ratio will result. Whereas if the genes were located on separate chromosomes, the typical 9:3:3:1 ratio would follow. Such linkages obviously decrease the possible number of combinations and thus definitely limit variation.

Strangely enough, genes once linked do not always remain so. During meiosis, you will recall, the homologous chromosomes come together and wind about one another just before the tetrads are formed. You will also recall that the homologous genes lie opposite each other, that is, those for the same trait are drawn together by some mutual attraction. During early prophase, sequences of genes in the chromosome break and exchange places with their homologous counterparts so that when the chromosomes separate during subsequent meiotic divisions, groups of genes from one chromosome become a part of the other chromosome in some such manner as indicated in Figure 25-19. The resulting chromosomes, containing a mixture of maternal and paternal genes, seem to heal perfectly because for the most part they contain their full complement of genes. This process of **crossing-over,** as it is called, operates purely fortuitously, so that in it we see another opportunity for a further juggling of the genes, compensating in part for the limitations placed upon variation through linkage.

Crossing-over, together with the other methods of mixing genes during meiosis, accounts for the vast array of combinations that are possible in offspring, particularly in organisms where the chromosomes are numerous. Consider the case of man, with 23 pairs of chromosomes. If each of the maternal set could be designated *A, B, C,* and so on, up to 23 and likewise each of the paternal set labeled *A', B', C'* up to 23, following meiosis some sperm may have a majority of their genes from one parent or the other, but most of them will contain a well-mixed set. The number of possible combinations that every couple is capable of producing is tremendous.

Chromosome Maps

The troublesome ratios that resulted from crossing-over were a blessing in disguise

FIG. 25-20. Chromosome maps are based on cross-over percentages. See text for explanation.

because they made possible the ultimate construction of chromosome maps. Sturtevant, in 1913, reasoned that crossing-over should occur more frequently between genes that lie farther apart in chromosomes than between those lying close to one another. For example, in Figure 25-19 there would be a greater chance for crossing-over to occur between genes A and G than between A and B, owing to the distance between them. The frequency of crossing-over can be taken then as a criterion of the distance between genes. Let us see how this provides information in chromosome mapping.

If genes are arranged in a linear fashion on the chromosome then let us suppose that the frequency of crossing-over between A and B is 10 per cent and between B and C is 5 per cent. This means that B and C are one half as far apart as is A and B. This does not tell us the relative positions of these genes—that is, are they arranged A, B, C, or A, C, B? The answer to this question can be determined by obtaining the percentage of crossing-over between A and C. If this turns out to be 15 per cent, the linear arrangement is A, B, C; if, on the other hand, it is 5 per cent, the sequence is A, C, B. These two possibilities are given in Figure 25-20.

Hundreds of genes in *Drosophila* have been mapped in this manner, a few of which

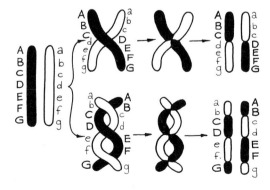

FIG. 25-19. Homologous genes have a tendency to exchange places during synapsis in some such manner as shown here.

are indicated in Figure 25-21. The chromosomes of other organisms have been mapped but owing to the laborious nature of this type of research, the number is small. A small beginning has been made with human chromosomes but, owing to man's inadequacy as an experimental animal, the progress has been exceedingly slow. The information that is now available has come, of course, from a study of defective genes in populations and from family pedi-

a term we have used from time to time without explanation.

Gene mutations can be detected only when they produce visible changes in the organism, and since most mutations are recessive, they only become effective when homozygous. A great many mutations may occur but because they are recessive they remain hidden in heterozygotes, perhaps for many hundreds of generations. Eventually, by pure chance, they will show up,

FIG. 25-21. The linear arrangement of the genes on the chromosomes has been worked out for a few animals, among them Drosophila. This has been accomplished in two ways, one by employing cross-over technics, and the other by actual observation, the latter method being possible only because of the tremendous (1,000 to 2,000 times normal) size of the chromosomes in the salivary gland cells. A portion of the left end of the X-chromosome is shown here with a few genes indicated as to observable position on the chromosome and as computed by cross-over studies.

grees. If and when man's chromosomes are mapped, the information may be important in the control of certain hereditary diseases.

MUTATIONS: ALTERATION OF GENE STRUCTURE

We already have learned that genes (DNA's) are subject to change, as are all molecules. This may occur spontaneously or be produced artificially as a result of physical forces from the outside. When DNA changes, its properties change correspondingly; such changes are called **mutations,**

which probably accounts for the apparent spontaneous occurrence of anomalies in many plants and animals, including man. Strange as it may seem, most mutations are harmful to the species and soon after they appear are eliminated, because the animals possessing them are not as well fitted to cope with their environment as the unchanged type. Through centuries of selection the unchanged type probably already possesses the best possible combinations of genes to fit it for its particular environment, so that any change that might be made is more likely to result in an organism less suited for survival.

Undoubtedly gene mutations occur in

the soma cells, but when they do, there is no effect on subsequent generations because the mutation is not passed on to the offspring unless the change occurs in the sex cells. Aside from the results in the individual possessing them, somatic mutations are of no importance in evolution.

Occasionally a mutation may reverse itself, that is, mutate back to its original condition. Such **back mutations,** as they are called, rarely occur, but when they do the resulting organism is apparently in no way different from the original stock. Such reverse actions might well be expected in the light of similar actions in protein molecules. Similarly, certain mutations seem to occur again and again in a stock of animals. This might mean that under certain environmental conditions genes are receptive to change, and such changes are more likely to occur when these conditions are met. Moreover, similar mutations have been known to occur in closely related species of organisms under similar conditions. Such mutations are referred to as **parallel mutations.**

Mutation Rate

Obviously, genes must be very stable molecules, because if they were not it would be difficult to understand how a species could maintain itself for any great length of time. If changes occurred readily in response to minor alterations in the environment, the race would be very unstable. Under normal conditions, mutations of the same gene occur in Drosophila cultures about once in every million individuals. Even then, some genes mutate more frequently than others; indeed, some have never been known to mutate. Since mutations are the tools with which the geneticist works, it is understandable that in the early days of modern genetics a continued effort was made to find some means of bringing about these gene changes artificially. For a long time the work was fruitless until Muller, a Nobel prize winner in

1946, found that by exposing fruit flies to a blast of X-rays just short of the lethal dose he was able to increase the normal mutation rate 150 times. Apparently the particles were able to penetrate to the genes in the sex cells and bring about a change in the structure of their DNA. Many of the mutations that appeared in Muller's cultures were no different from those appearing spontaneously. They were also recessive and usually harmful or lethal. Here, then, was a technique of bringing about gene changes artificially, which was a boon to genetic research. Other radiations such as ultraviolet and radium as well as certain chemicals have since been successfully employed. Even high temperatures may be effective if used at particular times in the life cycle of the animal.

CHROMOSOME ALTERATIONS

Mutation refers to changes within the gene itself, that is, chemical changes of the DNA. Not all changes in hereditary pattern are due to such changes—some are caused by a physical change in the chromosome itself. For example, during meiosis a small segment of a chromosome may break off and become lost, thus rendering that chromosome short in those genes that were contained in the missing fragment. This kind of alteration is called **deletion.** Such gametes, deficient in certain genes, often cannot function at all or if they do the resulting offspring may be deficient in certain visible traits. Occasionally a broken fragment becomes attached to another chromosome where it does not belong, thus duplicating certain genes in such a gamete. This condition is referred to as **duplication.** The duplicate set of genes may have the effect of exaggerating that particular trait in the offspring. It has been possible in some instances actually to verify these breaks by examining the chromosomes under a microscope. When this has been successful, gene locations on chromosome maps have been definitely ascertained.

Another peculiar aberration that sometimes occurs among chromosomes is **inversion,** a condition that results when a chromosome breaks in two places, the fragment rotates through 180 degrees, and then the broken ends fuse to the chromosome in reverse order. There is no loss of genes; they are merely no longer in the normal position. Since all of the genes are present, the offspring are usually normal. However, in gamete formation, trouble is encountered during pairing of the homologous chromosomes, producing loops and possibly fragments which can be seen under the microscope. Crossing-over is interfered with and considerable sterility sometimes results, particularly in plants.

Variations in Chromosome Number

One might expect that occasionally during meiosis the number of chromosomes going to the gametes might vary in number. This happens when a pair of homologous chromosomes fails to separate at reduction division. One gamete will then have one extra chromosome (*n* plus 1) while another will be short one (*n* minus 1). If fertilization occurs with normal gametes, one offspring will possess an extra chromosome in each cell while another will be short one. The latter probably will not develop whereas the former may show variations in the resulting trait because the genes are doubled. There have been many cases of **heteroploidy,** as this condition is called.

This phenomenon of extra chromosomes includes the addition of complete sets, so that gametes possess a diploid instead of the usual haploid number, and in some cases (particularly in plants where the phenomenon is better known) even 3, 4, and 5 extra sets. Organisms possessing more than the diploid number are called **polyploids.** They may be larger and more vigorous than the usual diploid, hence poly-

ploids have found a definite market in the plant world. Polyploid flowers are usually larger and more beautiful than the normal ones. Leaves of polyploid tobacco plants are much larger. Efforts to induce polyploidy artificially have been successful. The drug **colchicine** or **camphor** prevents division of the cells but does not interfere with the dividing of chromosomes; hence, the gametes possess the diploid number of chromosomes instead of the normal haploid number. Upon fertilization, the resulting offspring then have a double set of chromosomes, that is, they are **tetraploid. Triploids** will result from the union of a diploid gamete with a haploid gamete. Experimental breeding of these various polyploids has resulted in the introduction of new strains of plants that have proven very valuable in increasing our food output. Very little is known about polyploidy in animals probably because it occurs so infrequently.

GENES AND THEIR ACTION

In our discussion of the cell many chapters ago (p. 78) we described our present view regarding the physical and chemical nature of the gene. Let us now return to the structure of the gene and consider it in the light of modern genetics. But first let us take a brief look at the evolution of our thinking regarding genes based on the work of some very remarkable men.

The earliest workers in the field of genetics concentrated on the nuclei of sex cells for the explanation of inheritance. In 1902, W. S. Sutton and C. E. McClung in this country, and Theodore Boveri in Germany, decided that **hereditary factors** within the chromosomes were responsible for heredity. In 1911, another American, Thomas Hunt Morgan, whom we have referred to earlier, conceived the idea of unit particles lying in a linear fashion on the chromosomes. His convictions were based on cytological evidence. Whenever he noted irregular behavior in the inheritance of certain traits in his Drosophila cultures he also observed irregularities in their chromosomes and, conversely, any deviation in the chromosome pattern was reflected in abnormal flies. From this and other information Morgan and his associates were able to construct chromosome maps.

Attempts to distinguish the parts of the chromosome were undertaken by early cytologists. Balbiani in 1881 described the large bodies in the salivary gland cells of certain flies which since have been identified as giant chromosomes, although at that time he was not interested in the mechanics of inheritance. In recent years these chromosomes have been studied carefully with both light and electron microscopes and while there is still some disagreement as to the interpretation of what is seen, all agree that they are composed of a series of dark bands alternating with clear zones (Fig. 25-22). The dark bands contain DNA and are therefore known to be the location of the genes. The bands are remarkably constant in their location and number in the cells of any particular species. Because of their great size they are extremely useful in studying aberrations which are associated with abnormalities in body structure and function. There are over 4,000 bands in the four chromosomes of Drosophila, each of which represents one or more genes.

FIG. 25-22. The chromosomes from the salivary glands of Drosophila are extremely large and for that reason show their constitution. Note the black discs arranged on a non-staining strand. The genes are thought to correspond to the position of the discs.

With the newer knowledge about gene action it has become necessary to revise our ideas about the definition of the gene. This evolution in our thinking has come about as a result of more and more critical experiments, particularly with Drosophila and microorganisms. The gene has been described from three different points of view: (1) a unit that segregates and recombines, (2) the smallest unit that has the capacity to mutate, and (3) a genetic unit of function. These three categories have been designated respectively, **recon, muton,** and **cistron** for convenience. These terms were devised by bacterial and viral geneticists but have since been taken over by other geneticists as useful terms. The recon is the smallest, having about 0.01 of a cross-over unit. The muton is two or three times larger than the recon and represents the smallest area required to alter a function. The largest is the cistron which represents two to four cross-over units. In the following discussion the gene will be considered from these various aspects.

Compound Loci. Since it is impossible to see the gene there is no present cytological method that will separate it into its parts.

Hence biochemical and genetic tests must be relied upon to detect the physical dimensions of the gene. Highly refined techniques have been devised to detect crossing over of small sections of the chromosome. With this technique some areas of *Drosophila* chromosomes have been shown to be divided into several parts. These subdivisions are now considered to be genetic units which lie very close to one another and affect a single character. Ordinarily they stay together during recombination but sometimes they separate producing combination effects. A number of loci which were once considered to be single genes have been found to consist of more than one unit or recon.

The first inkling that the gene might be a compound unit came when, over 20 years ago, C. P. Oliver crossed *Drosophila* with lozenge eyes and found in the progeny a few wild-type red-eyed flies which were not supposed to be there. The parents carried the genes lz^g and lz^s which were thought to be alleles occupying exactly the same locus on the chromosome pairs, that is $\frac{lz^g}{lz^s}$. All of the progeny were expected to be lozenge-eyed; instead a few red-eyed flies appeared. This was explained by speculating that the two genes were not located in exactly the same position on the chromosomes, but slightly to one side of one another thus, $\frac{lz^g\ +}{+\ lz^s}$. It then had to be assumed that crossing over occurred which would place the two alleles side by side on the same chromosome, $\frac{lz^g\ lz^s}{+\ +}$, each being heterozygous to the wild type. This, of course, would explain the red-eyed flies.

The lozenge-locus was further investigated by other workers who showed that at least three recons (lz^{BS}, lz^{46}, lz^g) existed which could be separated by crossing over. These are shown in Figure 25-23 where the phenotypes are indicated. This locus, which was once thought to be occupied by a single gene is now known to consist of several

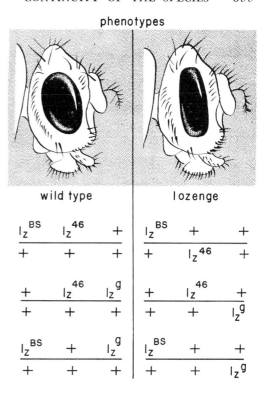

phenotypes

| wild type | lozenge |

lz^{BS}	lz^{46}	+	lz^{BS}	+	+
+	+	+	+	lz^{46}	+
+	lz^{46}	lz^g	+	lz^{46}	+
+	+	+	+	+	lz^g
lz^{BS}	+	lz^g	lz^{BS}	+	+
+	+	+	+	+	lz^g

FIG. 25-23. Lozenge eye in *Drosophila* has been shown to be controlled by three recons rather than one gene as was once thought. Wild type appears when the recons are arranged as on the left, lozenge when they are arranged as on the right.

recons, and is identified as a **compound locus.** Several other examples of compound loci have been demonstrated in *Drosophila*. In the white-eye cistron, as many as five sites have been identified.

Compound loci have also been identified in lower organisms, particularly bacteria and molds. Indeed, these organisms lend themselves to this type of research owing to the fact that large numbers of organisms are easily obtained, and selective media make the identification of mutants relatively easy. By subjecting the common baker's mold, *Neurospora* to high energy radiations, great numbers of biochemical mutants have become available for study. From these studies further evidence for compound loci has emerged. This is called **complementation.** It has been demon-

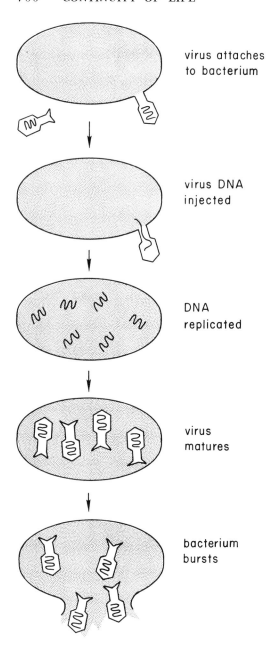

virus attaches
to bacterium

virus DNA
injected

DNA
replicated

virus
matures

bacterium
bursts

FIG. 25-24. This series of sketches shows how a virus infects the bacterium and replicates its own DNA from materials supplied by the host. When two mutated viruses infect a bacterium, recombination may occur.

strated that mutants within a given locus or cistron will complement each other and produce wild types. This is possible without observing recombination. The test involves the mating of different mutant types and observing the phenotypes in the zygote. The resulting data suggest the presence of compound loci. For example, the final step in tryptophane synthesis is controlled by the cistron, *Td,* which is composed of several subunits arranged linearly.

Perhaps the most sophisticated analyses of compound loci are those carried out with the viruses infecting bacteria, called **bacteriophages.** The most celebrated virus in this respect is the T_4 bacteriophage which infects the colon bacillus, *Escherichia coli.* This virus has a "head" which contains a single long strand of DNA (molecule), and a tail which is used in attaching to the bacterial cell wall prior to infection (Fig. 25-24). Once attached the DNA molecule is "injected" into the bacterium where it controls the reorganization of the cell machinery to produce 100 or more identical copies of the virus. This is a complex process because each copy consists of six proteins in addition to the DNA. The entire operation is under the control of the original virus DNA molecule. During this process errors are occasionally made (mutations) and these are the tools the geneticist uses to investigate the gene.

The existence of compound loci in the virus gene came from a study of the so-called rII mutant. When it invades bacteria, spread in a thin layer over an agar plate, a specific type of plaque (clear space) is formed which can be easily identified. Other mutants produce different types of plaques. The mutant rII can be divided into two different cistrons, called rIIA and rIIB, each producing plaques unlike rII. However, when both rIIA and rIIB infect the host bacterium simultaneously, recombination occurs and the resulting phages produce rII plaques. The two subunits complement each other and the region can be identified as a compound locus.

The rII cistron continues to be investigated by S. Benzer and his collaborators and the outcome is approaching a rather complete analysis of this one region of the DNA molecule. They have found some 80 segments occupying the rII region, all of which are apparently able to cross over among themselves as well as complement each other.

tional aspects of the unit and then the more precise terms must be used.

GENES AND ENZYMES

In the past genes were designated by the effect they produced as expressed in the altered phenotypes. Today we are learning what they do chemically and this field has come to be known as **biochemical genetics.** We still rely on phenotypic expression although in a few cases it has been possible

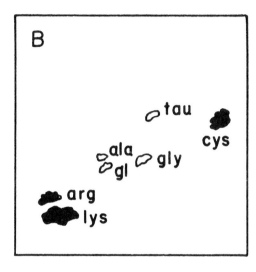

FIG. 25-25. Chromatographs of the urine from a normal person (A) and one suffering from cystinuria (B). Note that in the latter three amino acids (black) appear which are not found in normal urine. See text for further explanation.

From these analyses we have genetic units of different sizes. The smallest are the mutons and recons; the next in size are the two cistrons, A and B, and lastly the largest unit the rII region which includes both cistrons. One may well ask, which of these may be defined as the gene? The earlier definition of the gene could apply equally well to all of them. And it will make little difference if one is referring to the higher level of integration where no discrepancy exists between the units referred to. It only becomes important when the work involves the more specific opera-

to identify the chemical steps involved. One example of an error in metabolism may be taken from man.

Today very small amounts of various chemicals can be identified by paper chromatography, a simple process employing the principle that various molecules move through paper at different rates and thus can be separated. The mixture of molecules is placed in one corner of a large piece of filter paper which is then dipped in special solvents. The solvents move over the unknown molecules by absorption and carry them at different rates, ultimately depositing them in isolated spots which can then be visualized by chemical reagents. Employing this technique urine samples of many people, both normal and abnormal, have been examined. Most normal individuals excrete only six amino acids (Fig. 25-25). One type of abnormality, called **cystinuria,** is identified by the excretion of large amounts of the amino acid, **cystine,** as well as arginine and lysine, none of which is excreted by the normal person. While some people possessing this abnormality show no symptoms, others form cystine-containing kidney stones which often cause damage to the kidney. This abnormality is due to a recessive gene which is observed in the individual only when it is homozygous.

Most of our information about biochemical genetics, however, has come from the study of viruses, bacteria, and molds, some of which has been transposed and applied to long known aberrations in higher animals.

Since we know that chemical reactions in organisms are under enzyme control, and that genes are responsible for enzyme production, then there must be some connection between the genes and chemical reactions. A great deal of knowledge has been gained in this regard by a study of *Neurospora,* initiated by two American workers, G. W. Beadle and E. L. Tatum who received a Nobel Prize in 1959 for their efforts. They found that this mold normally thrives on sugar, ammonia, salts, and one vitamin, biotin. It is able to synthesize all other compounds essential in the manufacture of its protoplasm. By showering the spores of this mold with X-rays the workers produced a large number of strains that required more than the minimal diet. The genes mutated so that they could no longer control the production of a certain nutrient, say an amino acid or a vitamin, and therefore required that substance in their diet. These men were able to demonstrate, by employing a large number of strains of the

mold, that each step in the production of a nutrient is controlled by a single enzyme and that this enzyme is controlled by a single gene. Therefore, there is a one-to-one relationship between the gene, the enzyme and the ultimate chemical reaction. More recently this idea has been refined to mean that one cistron is responsible for one polypeptide. This generalization has added much to our knowledge of gene action.

Let us see how this information can be utilized in explaining coloring in higher animals including man. The pigment that is responsible for brown, gray, and black coloring is melanin. The degree of coloring depends on the quantity of melanin and this is controlled by genes. Negroes possess genes that provide large amounts of melanin, whereas white people have genes that produce less melanin. The distribution of pigment to the eyes is controlled by separate genes, and the various coloring of the iris of the eyes is dependent on the quantity of brown pigment present. Blue eyes have no pigment and the color is caused by the physical properties of the iris itself. Brown or black eyes contain sufficient pigment to completely obscure the natural blue.

One of the best known examples of the relation between a gene and a specific character is pigment formation in man. The complete absence of pigmentation results in albinism in which the skin, eyes, and hair are devoid of coloring. The eyes are very light blue or pink owing to the appearance of the blood vessels within the eyeball which can be seen through the iris. This condition appears when the single gene (*a*) is in the homozygous condition (Fig. 25-6). The heterozygous individual (*Aa*) does not show the trait nor, of course, does the homozygous normal (*AA*). The series of chemical reactions that lead to pigmentation are well known.

The chain of reactions that produces melanin begins with the essential amino acid, phenylalanine, which is oxidized to another amino acid, tyrosine, under the

FIG. 25-26. This series of biochemical reactions demonstrates what happens when certain enzymes are absent or defective. Each enzyme is presumed to be gene-controlled. If the gene does not function properly, the enzyme is not formed, and the reaction stops at that part of the sequence. The diseases resulting from these blocks are shown in the boxes. See text for further explanation.

control of a specific enzyme (Fig. 25-26). This compound is further oxidized to dihydroxyphenylalanine (dopa) under the influence of a second enzyme. Two more steps are involved, each controlled by enzymes, which convert dopa to melanin, the end product. Obviously, one or more blocks in this series of reactions prevent the formation of melanin which would then appear as albinism in the organism. It is now known that the gene *a* can prevent the oxidation of dopa, providing it exists

on both chromosomes, that is, homozygous. In such individuals dopa accumulates because there is no enzyme for oxidizing it to melanin; hence they are albinos. Albinism can be explained by this genetic aberration in all organisms, from mice to men. An obvious cure for the defect would be to supply the enzyme exogenously. Some progress has been made in this direction with *Neurospora* but so far, there has been no method discovered by which an enzyme can be introduced into a cell in a metazoan animal. It seems that the enzyme must be built by the cell itself in order to be effective. Further research may overcome this obstacle.

Another hereditary human abnormality can also be explained by a block in the metabolism of phenylalanine. This disease is called **alcaptonuria,** which is characterized by the urine turning black upon standing. Another symptom is the darkening of cartilage which can be seen in the ear, elbow, and wrist. The blackening of the urine is caused by the presence of **alcapton** or **homogentisic acid** which in normal people is converted to acetoacetic and fumaric acids and then to carbon dioxide and water (Fig. 25-26). Alcaptonurics apparently lack genes which produce the enzymes responsible for these conversions. The amount of alcapton that appears in the urine can be controlled by the amount of phenylalanine in the diet, which is not the case in normal people.

A far more serious disease in humans, called **phenylketonuria,** is caused by another block in the normal metabolism of phenylalanine. People suffering from this disease excrete large quantities of phenylpyruvic acid in their urine and, what is worse, are seriously retarded mentally. The amount of the acid in the urine is proportional to the amount of phenylalanine in the diet, which, again, is not the case in normal people. Normally phenylalanine is converted to tyrosine but in phenylketonurics the enzyme responsible for making the conversion fails to function; hence a block occurs and phenylpyruvic acid accumulates and is excreted in the urine (Fig. 25-26). Again a single recessive defective gene is responsible for the block. Normal people possess the genes to convert phenylalanine to tyrosine and tyrosine into p-hydroxyphenylpyruvic acid which can also be produced from phenylpyruvic acid. Phenylketonuria results when the block occurs between phenylalanine and tyrosine. It will be noted that this occurs much earlier in phenylalanine metabolism than the block which is responsible for alcaptonuria and it has far more profound effects. It seems that the earlier in the chemical series a block occurs, the more drastically the person is affected. Another associated trait is the blond complexion of all phenylketonurics. This is caused by the failure of the production of the normal amount of tyrosine which is a precursor to melanin formation.

The gene control of metabolism is well illustrated by this series of steps in phenylalanine metabolism. Clearly the phenotypes are markedly different; yet the chemical processes involved are very closely related. They proceed in a stepwise manner, each controlled by an enzyme and each enzyme is produced under the influence of a gene. Blocks in other parts of this chain of reactions would probably cause other defects that would be expressed phenotypically. While this is one of the best known series of reactions, it is generally believed that most, if not all, proceed in somewhat the same fashion.

Complex Consequences of a Single Gene Defect

Defective genes have one primary effect which is usually very obvious. However, there are often many other minor abnormalities which result indirectly from the primary defect. This is well illustrated in chickens where, owing to a single abnormally functioning gene, the trait called *frizzle* appears. Such chickens possess brittle, curly feathers which are few in number. Chickens with this trait are easily distinguished from normals (Fig. 25-27). In addition to this primary trait they possess a whole galaxy of other abnormalities which result from the primary defect. They lay few eggs and the number of chicks hatching is low and those that do hatch have a high mortality rate. The young, as well as the adults, have high metabolic rates although they are less active than normal chickens. They consume large quantities of food, their hearts are larger and beat faster, the spleen is enlarged, and all of the digestive organs are unusually enlarged, presumably owing to their large food consumption. All of these characters are associated with the defect in feather formation. Because the insulation from temperature change cannot be regulated in the frizzy chicken its organs have become overdeveloped to take care of the body needs. Under normal temperature fluctuations these chickens fare poorly, but when the temperature is uniformly high, they survive better than normal chickens.

FIG. 25-27. The frizzled chicken on the left has defective feathers, a gene-controlled abnormality. Owing to a lack of insulation, rather profound physiological and morphological abnormalities appear in these animals.

Another example of the profound effects of what appears to be a simple abnormality can be drawn from the study of human blood. When the red blood cells of certain people are placed under reduced oxygen conditions, they send out projections which give them a characteristic shape; the phenomenon is called "sickling" (Fig. 25-28). This condition is caused by a single gene and when it exists in the heterozygous condition (Ss) the person suffers no ill effects. However, when a person carries both recessive genes (ss), a number of serious abnormalities appear which together have been called "sickle-cell disease." These defects include severe anemia, poor

body development, and paralysis, all of which apparently result from the sickling condition of the red cells in the blood vessels. The red cells do not sickle in heterozygotes; consequently such people appear normal.

In sickle-cell disease the hemoglobin molecules are chemically different from those in normal blood, and this difference was first noted by observing that the electric charge on the two hemoglobins was not the same. Further analysis demonstrated that the two hemoglobins differ by one amino acid out of about 500. One of the glutamic acid molecules in normal hemoglobin is replaced by the amino acid, lysine, in exactly the same place in the sickle-cell hemoglobin. Lysine has a charge opposite to that of glutamic acid, which accounts for the difference in electrophoretic patterns in the two hemoglobins (Fig. 25-

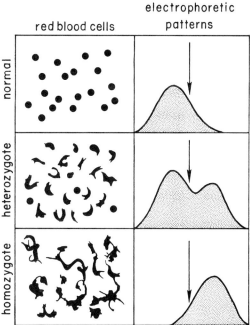

FIG. 25-28. Sickle-cell anemia is an abnormality of the red blood cells, as shown at the left. It is gene-controlled; the heterozygous condition is harmless, but homozygotes are seriously ill. The electrophoretic pattern on the right indicates that the hemoglobins are slightly different, owing to the substitution of one amino acid for another.

28). At present there seems to be no other difference in the two hemoglobins. One would guess that so slight a change would have little, if any, difference in the large hemoglobin molecule. Quite the contrary is true when one observes a person suffering from sickle-cell disease.

A single gene controls the substitution of lysine for glutamic acid in the hemoglobin molecule, and this simple switch of one amino acid for another has far-reaching effects in the victim of sickle-cell disease. Their anemia weakens them physically and retards them mentally; the clumping of the cells in the blood vessels brings on heart failure, paralysis, and kidney obstruction. Thus we see a whole chain of events brought about by one small genetic change at the molecular level. Undoubtedly other abnormalities of genetic origin will be explained in this manner as we gain more information about disease at the molecular level.

An interesting outcome of this abnormality has been observed in parts of the world, such as Africa, where malaria is common in the population. Those persons who are heterozygous for sickle-cell disease are more resistant to malaria than are normals. Just why this is so is not known. For this reason they have a selective advantage and the percentage of the population carrying the gene for sickle-cell anemia is higher in regions where malaria is common than in other parts of the world where the disease does not exist. Therefore, a trait, which may under some conditions be deleterious to a race, actually is beneficial under other conditions.

HEREDITY AND ENVIRONMENT

The age-old question of which is more important, heredity or environment, stimulates the most passionate arguments among people in various walks of life, from educator to the man on the street. What are the best unbiased answers to the questions rising from such discussions that have come to light so far?

One should first be concerned with the problem of what is really inherited. Is a child unmusical because his parents have no musical skills or is he unintelligent because his parents possess a low order of intelligence? Is a starved child short and underdeveloped because his parents are likewise starved and poorly developed? A careful examination of some data should give us an inkling of the answer to these questions. A child placed in an environment in which every opportunity is afforded him to study music as well as other cultural subjects may show unusual artistic talents and intellectual achievements even though he might not appear to have inherited such ability. Likewise, well-fed children of starved, stunted parents often exceed them in height and physical vigor by a considerable margin, as has been demonstrated so many times when children of immigrants are larger and more robust than their parents, who matured on inadequate diets. In these instances was it the environment or was it heredity that played the more important part?

It is clear that the children inherited a set of genes which provided the **capacity** to reach these goals. The environment was merely the factor which determined whether or not the genes would be given a full opportunity to express themselves. Without the substantial set of genes in the first place, no amount of encouragement from a satisfactory environment would have brought them to heights beyond the basic design established by the genes. Of course, the desired goal in any society is to give the genes in each person ample opportunity to express themselves to their greatest capacity. Therefore, while good genes are essential for good stock, they are not enough. Good genes in a good environment is the ideal goal.

There is experimental evidence to

demonstrate further the intricate relationship between environment and heredity. In studying the life span in fruit flies, Raymond Pearl found that in a closed milk bottle the vestigial-winged forms lived only half as long as the wild type. If he increased the number of flies of the wild type he cut their lifetime to that of the vestigial-winged flies. If both types were starved they lived about the same length of time. Certainly the environment limited the capacity of the genes. Similarly in "Himalayan" rabbits (Fig. 25-29) the environment is important in determining the coat color pattern. The intense black fur that occurs at the tips of the ears, paws, and tail is controlled by temperature. These tips being the coolest parts of the animal, the lowered temperature induces the formation of heavy pigmentation. If the hair is removed from a portion of the body that is white and this region kept cool, the hair that grows in is black. If the rabbit is chilled in a refrigerator, it will become totally black; conversely, if it is warmed up to a relatively high temperature it becomes totally white. It is quite obvious in these cases that the genes lay the pattern for capacity, whereas the environment determines whether or not that full capacity will be realized.

The close interaction of these two forces, environment and heredity, can be still further emphasized by following through the development of an organism, say a human being, from fertilized egg to young adult (Fig. 25-30). Beginning with the fertilized ovum, we have a cell consisting of cytoplasm, controlled by the genes (G) and surrounded by an environment. Very soon, as cleavage starts, the surrounding environment (E) contributes to the cytoplasm, thereby changing it slightly. Moreover, the immediate community of cells has its effect upon the cytoplasm of each of the other cells. The cytoplasm is therefore influenced from within by the genes (G) and from without by the environment (E), even at this early stage. As development proceeds, the cytoplasm of the many different cells continues to be influenced by surrounding cells, yet the genic constitution remains essentially the same in all of them. All of this brings about the development of organ systems, and ultimately the full-fledged fetus, but in each step the genes control the cytoplasm which, in turn, is influenced by surrounding cells (organizers) so that the cells are channelled into a pattern directed toward the final organized individual. Another environmental factor that is influential is the nourishment (N) received by the fetus from the uterine wall. If food, as well as oxygen and hormones, that comes to it from the placenta is deficient in any respect, the fetus is directly affected, perhaps to a point where normal development

FIG. 25-29. The normal Himalayan rabbit has black extremities (top). If it is placed in an incubator at elevated temperatures, the black areas become lighter (left). If its ears and feet are clothed and an ice pack placed over a shaved area on its back for some period of time (right), the new hair will be white on the feet and ears, and a black patch will appear on the back (bottom). From this we can conclude that environment does influence the expression of genes.

FIG. 25-30. The individual is a result of two forces, one due to the inherited genes and the other to the surrounding environment which begins with the zygote and continues throughout the life of the individual. The various steps sketched here are explained in the text.

is impossible. This is a very important environmental aspect of development. The genes strive toward the production of a normal offspring, but they can accomplish this end only if the environment is adequate.

When the child is born, another factor, the psychological factor (P), enters the picture. All of the other factors still operate, and the addition of this new factor definitely controls further mental development and probably physical development as well. Lastly, as the child matures, the social factors (S) become more and more a dominant part of his environment. The genes are still at work and will continue to be throughout life but the environment

has a marked molding effect on their action. Thus, we see that it is impossible to have heredity without environment and vice versa. The two forces work hand in hand to produce a normal, well-adjusted individual.

The occasional appearance of two offspring as a result of one fertilized egg (identical or monozygotic twins) has provided almost perfect material for the study of the relative effects of environment and heredity (Fig. 25-31). Monozygotic twins have the same sets of genes, so that if heredity were solely responsible for all of their characters they should be exactly alike. A study of a large number of identical twins by Newman and others has

fertilization in oviduct

identical

fraternal

tical twins reared apart were over 90 per cent alike in height, nearly 90 per cent alike in weight, but only about 70 per cent alike in intelligence as measured by standard I.Q. (intelligence quotient) tests. Identical twins reared together had about the same scores for height and weight but were also nearly 90 per cent alike in regard to intelligence. Two-egg twins (Fig. 25-31) of the same sex were only about 65 per cent alike in all of these traits. When one monozygotic twin is bright, the other is also, but when their educations vary considerably their I.Q.'s also vary correspondingly. Better schooling definitely raises the

FIG. 25-32. A pair of identical or monozygotic female twins who happen to be albinos as well. They are the result of a single zygote, hence their likeness. They are alike physically, mentally, and even emotionally. Studies of such genetically identical individuals has added much to our knowledge concerning the relative importance of heredity and environment.

FIG. 25-31. Identical or monozygotic twins are a result of a single fertilized egg, therefore they are genetically alike, as shown in the upper figure. Fraternal twins are a result of two zygotes and may be as genetically different as any other members of the family. Furthermore, each developing fetus has its own placenta, whereas this is usually not the case with monozygotic twins.

shown that they are indeed remarkably, almost unbelievably, alike (Fig. 25-32). Such traits as height, weight, general appearance, fingerprints, and tooth formation show very close similarity as might be expected, but when such intangible traits as susceptibility to disease (both organic and infectious), food preferences, and even attitudes of mind show marked correlations it seems quite incredible. Intelligence tests usually show that they vary no more than either individual might on two different tests. With such material as this, it should be possible to learn some interesting facts about the effects of environment.

Newman found in his studies that iden-

FIG. 25-33. Lobed and non-lobed ears (upper), as well as fused toes (lower), are inherited in a definite fashion.

I.Q. rating. However, under similar cultural environments identical twins, although reared apart, differed only 5 points in their I.Q. ratings. This is within the normal variation that might be expected from day to day with the same person. From these studies, environment seems to have a considerable influence on intelligence as it is measured with I.Q. tests, although this may not be a valid measure of true intelligence. On the other hand, in regard to such physical traits as height and weight, the inherited genes are strikingly more important.

Fortunately, because of the stability of genes, the environment has little or no effect upon them. Excellent genes may be carried along for many generations in starved, poorly developed bodies, but as soon as the environment becomes completely adequate they express their full capacity by producing a vigorous, healthy body. In a world that has always suffered periods of famine intermingled with times of abundance, only stable genes could have made possible a race that has been able to survive up to the present.

HUMAN HEREDITY

Human beings, like all species of animals, show wide variations in height, weight, eye color, hair color, skin color, facial configuration, mental ability, and many other traits (Fig. 25-33). Within limits, these variations are highly desirable because they allow evolution to take place. However, at the extremes of each one there are usually either mildly or highly undesirable conditions which do not permit the individual possessing them an equal chance with others to become a self-sustaining member of his own social group. Some defects such as albinism render the individual only slightly more handicapped than his normal fellows. Most of us are pretty apt to agree, however, that a combination of genes that produces idiots, blindness, or deafness is undesirable. Although we are concerned with the inheritance of defects in order to breed them out of our people, we should be even more concerned with the positive approach, that is, retaining the quality of our present stock and improving it where possible. Let us now consider what is known about some of the common human defects and later some of the problems involved in improving the human race.

Some Congenital Defects

We have previously discussed the slight defects of color blindness (p. 692) and albinism (p. 674), as well as the more serious anomaly, hemophilia (p. 570). Some others are listed in Table 4 (see also Fig. 25-34).

Ichthyosis, sometimes called fish-skin disease, is a congenital disease. Those suffering from this malady have dark skin, ¾-inch thick, which is cracked in such a way that it resembles scales, hence the name, fish skin. It occurs over the entire body except the palms of the hands and the soles of the feet. It is fatal, the child dying shortly after birth. The disease was seen for the first time in England in 1731 where it appeared in the son of a laborer. Another type of ichthyosis (nonlethal) has been traced through five generations and has successively appeared in the sons but never in the daughters. Furthermore, the daughters never transmit it to their offspring, which definitely places the responsible gene for the trait in the Y chromosome. This is one of very few cases where a gene has been definitely located in the Y chromosome in man.

A type of blindness caused by the clouding, or fogging, of part of the transparent portions of the eye is called cataract. Pedigrees of families in which this disease occurs bear out the contention that the trait is carried by a dominant gene, although it usually appears in the heter-

TABLE 4

Disease	Condition	Type of Gene
Congenital cataract	Opaque growths in eye	Dominant
High-grade myopia	Extreme nearsightedness	Recessive
Astigmatism	Irregularity of cornea	Dominant
Polydactylism	Extra digits	Dominant
Lobster-claw	Split hand and foot	Dominant
Achondroplasia	Short appendages	Dominant
Diabetes mellitus	Improper sugar balance	Not clear
Amaurotic idiocy	Degeneration of nervous system	Recessive
Deafness	Atrophy of auditory nerve	Dominant
Harelip and cleft palate	Malformed lip and palate	Recessive
Allergy	Allergy	Recessive
Epilepsy	Convulsive seizures	Dominant
Congenital hemolytic jaundice	Increased red cell fragility	Dominant
Pernicious anemia	Blood deficiency	Dominant
Schizophrenia	Split personality	Recessive
Sickle-cell anemia	Abnormal red blood cells	Recessive

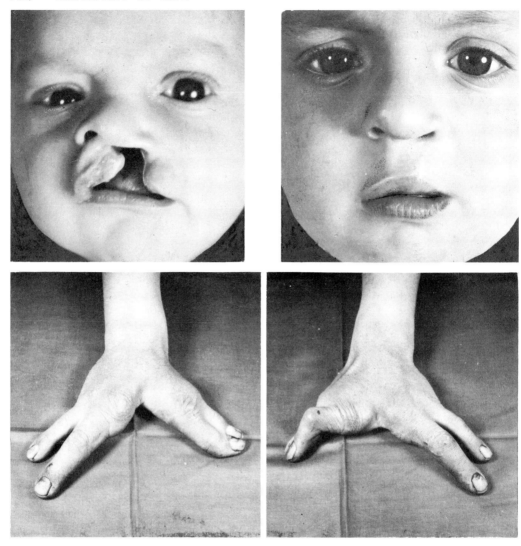

FIG. 25-34. There are a great many human anomalies that have been traced to a genetic origin. Certain types of hare-lip are inherited. One of the common types is shown here (upper left). Modern surgery has worked wonders in repairing these unfortunate abnormalities (upper right).

Many deformities of the hands and feet are inherited. Here are two cases of "split-hand" (lower). This trait is usually dominant and occurs once in about 90,000 births. More often than not the gene responsible for this abnormality is also responsible for others. Both of these cases were abnormal in other respects.

ozygous condition. That is to say, a parent may have the disease but usually only certain of his children, regardless of sex, will show it, indicating that the parent must have been heterozygous. Had he been homozygous for the trait, all of his children would have the defect. Cataract is also acquired by excessive exposure to heat, radia-tions, and contusions, but in these cases heredity, of course, is not involved.

Aside from obvious physical defects there are hereditary traits that affect the nervous system and alter the mental behavior of the individual very radically. There is no doubt that many mental ill-nesses, like physical defects, are gene-controlled, so that a careful study of them should yield some valuable information to aid in guiding our future actions.

One kind of nervous disorder, called **microcephalic idiocy,** is inherited as a recessive. It usually springs up in families of normal parents, as one might expect. However, a large proportion of the children resulting from the marriage of an idiot to a normal person would be idiots. Fortunately such marriages are rare and the line usually dies with the defective person.

Another very serious congenital disease is **Huntington's chorea,** in which there is a marked degeneration of brain tissue, resulting in poor muscular coordination, twitching, and jerking movement. In addition, there are other associated defects which contribute to produce socially and mentally deranged individuals. The most unfortunate part is that the disability does not become apparent until middle life (25-55 years of age) after most, if not all, of the children have been born. Thus the trait is passed on to the next generation before it is recognized in the parent. Cases of the disease in this country have been traced back to three brothers who arrived here from England in 1630. The malady has shown up hundreds of times in the several thousand descendants of these men, and studies have revealed that about one-half of the children of afflicted persons develop the disease some time after they are 25 years old. A person who knows that he might develop it or pass it on to others is under terrific mental strain, which in itself is often sufficient to bring on nervous disorders. Some recent studies indicate that electroencephalographic patterns can identify these people during adolescence.

MEDICAL GENETICS

From such studies as those indicated above, the medical profession seems to have found some information of real clinical value. Data accumulated by the pure geneticists for the past fifty years are just now reaching a point in development where some practical use can be made of them by physicians. This has resulted in the young flourishing science of **medical genetics,** which is not to be confused with **eugenics** (see later), a subject that has enlisted the active participation of people outside the field of medicine.

Professor L. H. Snyder has cited many illustrations of the use of genetics in the diagnosis, prognosis, and even prevention of a wide variety of diseases. For example, in attempting to diagnose what was causing a patient to vomit blood, the doctors decided it must be one of two things, ulcers or liver disease. Elaborate laboratory tests revealed that neither of these seemed to be the cause. One of the physicians recalled that the father of the patient had shown a tendency to bleed due to the fragility of his capillaries in local lesions. Because this condition is controlled by a dominant gene, the likelihood of a similar condition appearing in the son was good. By an exploratory examination of the stomach the suspected diagnosis was verified, the region of capillaries giving the trouble was removed and the case was cured. Here a knowledge of genetics was very helpful in solving a problem which probably would have continued to be a mystery to the physician and a source of discomfort to the patient.

Of equal and perhaps greater importance is the use of genetics in the realm of prognosis. Young married people or those about to be married often wish to know what the probabilities are for them to have normal children. This is particularly important to those who have some so-called "taint" or "skeleton in the closet" in their family. Sometimes advice is sought for on the positive side, that is, they wish to know what the chances are for them to transmit certain talents to their offspring. One case will illustrate the importance of such information. In a family of five children, two boys were severely crippled by serious muscular disease; the others, two girls and a boy, were normal. The problem that concerned the parent was the chance of this disease appearing in the next generation. After careful analysis of the situation it was evident that the gene causing the difficulty was sex-linked. Therefore the father must have had a normal X chromosome (AY) while the mother must have carried the defect in one of her X chromosomes (Aa).

The boys showing the affliction must accordingly have been aY, whereas the normal son was like his father (AY) and the daughters might or might not have had the defective gene (Aa or AA). The normal son would, of course, be unable to transmit the defect to his children. The daughters, on the other hand, had an even chance of picking up the defective gene from their mother. Such information is highly valuable to intelligent people because they can make their decisions in the full light of scientific fact rather than blind faith. The field of medical genetics is just beginning and cannot fail to become eventually a most fruitful part of medical science.

EUGENICS

Eugenics is the study of race improvement or the "science of being well born." Since planned matings are not possible in humans, scientists who are interested in eugenics are forced to collect and analyze family histories in an effort to account for our status now and to predict what is likely to happen to us genetically in the future. It is relatively easy to collect vast amounts of data regarding family histories, and certain trends seem to be indicated, some of which are disconcerting. Some authorities estimate (Fig. 25-35) that by the year 2000 the percentage of the population with an I.Q. of 115 or better will have been reduced from the current 12 per cent to 7 per cent, and the present 2 per cent below 70 (moron, etc., group) will have doubled. The situation may not be quite as grave as these figures would indicate, because we know that some of the progeny of the more intelligent will have lower I.Q.'s than their parents and some of the children from the less able group will be brighter than their parents. Even though there might be only a small loss in our intellectual heritage, it would seem that every effort should be made to combat this downward trend. What, if anything, can be done about it?

Suppose we could breed the ideal race of men, what would we breed toward? What kind of man do we want? What are the desirable traits and who is to be the judge? These are difficult questions for which no scientist and only a highly conceited layman would have an immediate answer. Every sane person, however, would have an immediate positive response to the question of preventing the continual pro-

FIG. 25-35. There is substantial evidence that our intelligence, as measured by I.Q. tests, is steadily dropping with each generation. When these figures are projected to the year 2000, the shift in intelligence may reach the levels indicated in the above figures.

duction of defectives such as microcephalic idiots. At this end, common agreement can be attained, because such defectives bring misery to everyone who is in any way associated with them. Fortunately, very few of the hopelessly defective individuals reproduce.

Present Dysgenic Practices

Instead of improving our people genetically it would appear that the operating forces in our modern civilization are doing just the opposite. Our way of life has vastly improved in the past two hundred years, but paralleled with it is this insidious decline in our genetic heritage. The features that have made our lives more safe and pleasant and have been responsible for our tremendous increase in numbers have simultaneously introduced factors that interfere with the agencies of natural selection, which through the ages have tended toward the building of a sturdy body and mind in a very demanding environment. When that point was reached, it seems that decline has followed. Modern man has interfered with natural selection in several very important ways which are only now showing their effects.

Birth rates compared to death rates readily reveal whether a population is increasing or decreasing. Whether the number of people in a population such as we have in America is increasing or decreasing is not as important as the more serious problem of what groups are reproducing the population. Are the qualities that we agree are desirable being perpetuated or are they gradually being sacrificed for less desirable qualities? The picture is not as comforting as we wish it were.

One of the potent forces bringing a shift in the quality of people is the difference in the rates at which children are born to groups of various abilities. If different groups reproduce at different rates, as we know they do, the over-all reproductive rate of a country is a composite of all of these groups. For example, if one group reproduces at a rate 20 per cent higher than the native stock, there will be a gradual replacement of the native stock by the faster multiplying groups. This is important only if there is a concomitant dropping in the quality of the people as a whole.

During colonial days in America, the families of the more prosperous citizens were larger than those of the less able. Statistics taken from an early study of New England showed that the upper quarter of the more successful families had on the average one more child than the lower two-thirds (that is, 7.2 to 6.2). The years since this period have seen a gradual decline in the more able group. Thus today persons belonging to the professions and business class are not replacing themselves by 15 to 25 per cent. The largest families occur in people in the lowest occupational levels. In other words, there is an inverse relationship between occupational level and size of families. The birth rate among unskilled laborers is almost double that of men in business or professions. Likewise, there is an inverse relationship between intelligence and the size of family. A study made by Lentz over 25 years ago demonstrates a trend that is no different today. He found that children with an I.Q. of 150 or over came from families with 2.2 children, whereas those with I.Q.'s of 70 to 79 averaged 5.3 children per family. The family sizes increased with each succeeding declining I.Q. In such a situation, the families with high intelligence were not replacing themselves while those in the lower brackets were more than doing the job. If the present trends continue, within three generations a great proportion of the population will come from the less intelligent class, resulting in a continued drop in general intelligence of the population as a whole. It has been estimated that the I.Q. is dropping in the United States at the rate of one point each generation and in England at the alarming rate of 3 points each generation. Bertrand Russell predicted that for the next few hundred years each generation will become more stupid than its predecessor. It is questionable whether or not a nation depending on an intelligent population can survive such inroads on the prime factor responsible for its existence.

Modern medicine, while certainly alleviating the miseries of mankind during the past two hundred years, has also prolonged the lives of many and saved the lives of a multitude of others who, in the normal course of events would never have survived. The genes responsible for these weaknesses would have been kept to a low frequency under natural selection, but with the intervention of modern medicine they have been saved to be perpetuated and thus increased in subsequent generations. Let us hasten to point out that saving these lives from a humanitarian point of view can only be praised, but in the eyes of the geneticist it simply means that one of the most potent factors in building a strong race is prevented from functioning. The results could lead to inferior stock.

Another dysgenic factor in our present civilization is modern warfare. In centuries past the strongest, cleverest, and most intelligent men went into battle and the best of these survived to come home and become the fathers of the next generation. This was natural selection at work. Since the advent of gunpowder and subsequent deadly weapons, the strong and able are cut down equally with the less well endowed. Indeed, it is said that taller men are more apt to be hit first because they constitute a larger target. In the past it is believed this has had a tendency to reduce the stature of large groups of people. Furthermore, in all wars the best equipped both physically and mentally are selected for duty first, thus eliminating many of them from the opportunities of becoming parents. To be sure, there is always a sudden burst in the numbers of babies sired during and following wars, but it is unlikely that this alters the over-all genetic constitution of the race. Too much of this increase is accounted for by the physically and mentally unfit that are left at home. The military can hardly be blamed for wanting the best men they can get to man the complicated instruments of modern warfare, but these same men are also the best stock we have and their chances of becoming the parents of the next generation are much reduced when in service as compared to life at home. For the past several hundred years, then, we have been following a policy that is definitely contrary to natural selection and undoubtedly has had its influence in reducing the quality, not the quantity, of our stock.

A physical force that has very recently been introduced into our lives, and one that is thought by some geneticists to be important in changing our genes, is the vast array of radiations that are being artificially produced and permitted to bombard our bodies. The most spectacular of these, of course, come from atomic and hydrogen bombs, and much has been written about the effects of these radiations on plant and animal life in the vicinity of the blasts. Instruments all over the world keep track of the fallout resulting from hydrogen bomb tests and information is accumulating on the effects of these radiations on living things. Concern is registered by some people and predictions have been made that genes, even human genes, are being damaged. Very little attention is given to another source of radiation that millions of people in countries where modern medicine flourishes are being exposed to every day. X-rays are used routinely for diagnosis with little thought given to any possible damage that might result. We know that X-rays, as well as other radiations, are very effective in increasing gene mutation rates and that the mutated genes result in changes in the progeny that are nearly always less desirable than the normal. It is true that mutations occur spontaneously and probably always have, but in modern civilized societies we have altered the environment so that not only is the rate of mutations stepped up but modern medicine has made it possible to preserve these changes for longer periods of time in people who, at an earlier period of our history, would not have survived. Moreover, the mutated genes are inherited so that succeeding generations will possess them and thus the number of abnormal traits gradually increases with time. Obviously this could result in catastrophe if nothing is done about it.

From the foregoing discussion it would seem that while our present civilization has brought us a higher standard of living, at least in America, it has likewise introduced several factors that tend to drag the body and mind of man to ever lower levels. Is there no way out of this dilemma? Can we have a high standard of living without losing our genic heritage? It would certainly seem that we should have sufficient intelligence to apply some of our knowledge of human genetics to our own situation and curb the disastrous decline that seems to be upon us.

Possible Solutions

Many thinking people have faced this problem and there is some concerted effort, feeble though it is at present, to halt this tide of ever increasing defectives and the dilution of our precious germ plasm that has taken millions of years to produce. The problem is extremely difficult because of our incomplete knowledge of human inheritance. Even more difficult is the problem of convincing people that something should be done about it.

To stem the tide of defectives, sterilization is being practiced in 27 states in the United States and many countries in Europe. By February, 1935, Germany had sterilized about 200,000 hereditary defectives, perhaps the most ambitious program in the world. Our first sterilization law was passed in 1907 (Indiana), and by the end of 1948, 49,207, of which 19,042 were in California, had been sterilized. These are primarily feeble-minded and insane patients who have been committed to institutions. Just what effect does sterilization have in reducing the number of defectives in future generations? It has very little, unfortunately. It is estimated that most defects which are carried as recessives would probably require 2,000 years to reduce their numbers by 50 per cent, employing the most rigid sterilization laws. (See Hardy-Weinberg Law, p. 755).

Isolation and sterilization will have little influence on the ominous drop in general intelligence brought on by differential birth rates. Birth-control measures have been gaining a foothold in recent years and seem to be providing a partial answer to the problem. Such organizations as the Planned Parenthood Leagues emphasize both the negative and positive side of the problem, that is, they are as much, if not more, interested in encouraging larger families among certain groups as they are in lending a hand in helping the less fortunately endowed to reduce the number of births. Workers in birth-control clinics are well aware that people in all walks of life are very much interested in spacing their children so that they bring into the world only the number they can adequately care for. People in the lower income groups, for example, have shown over and over again that their large families are due more to ignorance than desire on the part of the parents. Birth-control information is eagerly received by these groups and practiced to a point where beneficial effects are already clearly observable. On the positive side, the dissemination of birth-control information has had little effect, mainly because those people who should have more children also have the information and have been practicing contraception anyway. A thinking couple of moderate means, even though they may desire to do so, will hesitate to bring a large family into the world when they know that to rear each child will be costly.

Is there any way, then, to reverse the present dysgenic trends that are threatening the civilized nations of the world? The most comprehensive studies of this problem has been made by the Scandinavian countries where they have settled on a solution which seems to have more merit than any others. They argue that since the nation's people is its prime asset, the burden of providing a continuing stream of high-grade protoplasm is the responsibility of everyone. Therefore, all should share in the care and education of all children. Consequently, the burden of educating and feeding during the maturing years falls upon the state. This has encouraged the rearing of larger families in the upper and middle classes and has been no stimulus to the lower classes. The present movement in the United States toward federally supported scholarships to young people who can profit by a higher education should also have gratifying results in the years to come. This has been an outgrowth of the G.I. Bill of Rights, which was one of the finest things that came out of World War II. It made possible the continued education of those who could profit by it even though they were in many cases beyond the normal college age level. An even more encouraging side of this picture is the fact that many or most of them were able to have families while they were gaining a higher education. This meant that large numbers of our population were rearing their families at the time when they should be and not postponing it, as is so often the case, and thus cutting down the reproductive years. Support of this kind undoubtedly will have substantial eugenic effects in future generations and should be heartily endorsed by everyone.

SUGGESTED SUPPLEMENTARY READINGS

BEADLE, G. W., "Structure of the Genetic Material and the Concept of the Gene," in W. H. Johnson, and W. C. Steere, eds., *This Is Life* (New York, Holt, Rinehart and Winston, Inc., 1962).

BENZER, S., "The Fine Structure of the Gene," *Scientific American,* 206(1) (January, 1962), 70.

GARDNER, E. J., *Principles of Human Genetics* (New York, John Wiley & Sons, Inc., 1960).

MULLER, H. J., "Radiation and Human Mutation," *Scientific American,* 193(5) (November, 1955), 58.

NEWMAN, H. H., *Multiple Human Births* (New York, Doubleday, Doran and Co., 1940).

OSBORN, F., *Preface to Eugenics* (New York, Harper and Bros., 1951).

STANBURY, J. B., WYNGARDEN, J. B., and FREDERICKSON, D. S., eds., *The Metabolic Basis of Inherited Disease* (New York, Blakiston Division, McGraw-Hill Book Co., 1960).

STERN, C., *Principles of Human Genetics* (San Francisco, W. H. Freeman & Co., 1960).

WOLSTENHOLME, G. E. W. and O'CONNER, C. M., eds., *The Biochemistry of Human Genetics* (Ciba Foundation Symposium, Boston, Little, Brown & Co., 1959).

PART VIII

Organic Evolution

26

Evolution—Past and Present

THROUGHOUT THIS BOOK constant reference has been made to the gradually increasing complexity of life from protozoa to mammals; in fact, the underlying theme is this basic concept of change from simple to complex. The word *evolution,* in its broad sense, means unrolling or unfolding and, used in terms of the living world, simply implies that all plants and animals alive today have descended by slight modifications from simpler preexisting forms. Our discussion of the various animal groups has been based on this idea and, even though we have accepted it as a basis for

our thinking, let us now return to the story of the rise of animal life to examine the theory of organic evolution as a logical explanation of what has taken place.

EVIDENCE FROM ANCIENT ANIMAL LIFE

Geologic Time

In tracing life from the beginning, the course of events has afforded us a convenient way of reckoning time. The earth's thin crust has provided "clocks" that tell time in millions of years. Geologists are becoming more and more adept at reading these clocks, although a reading with an error of a few millions of years one way or the other is still considered satisfactory. Even though the exact times may not be accurate, the sequence of events and the orders of magnitude of each event are correct. By reading these geologic time clocks it is possible to approximate dates of the origin of various forms of animal and plant life.

One of the most accurate methods of reading time which has recently come into prominence employs radioactivity. Radioactive elements disintegrate at a remarkably uniform rate, extending over millions of years in some elements. Uranium, for example, decays or disintegrates at an extremely slow rate into a special kind of lead (atomic weight 206 as compared to 207.2, the average atomic weight of ordinary lead) and helium gas. It requires 2 billion years for one-quarter of a sample of uranium to decompose into these constituents. In determining time by this method, a rock containing a mineral impregnated with uranium is analyzed for its lead content. Since the mineral was incorporated into the rock when it was formed, the relative proportions of lead and uranium would be an indication of the age of the rock. If one-fourth of the uranium had been converted to lead, the rock would be 2 billion years old. It is from such data as these and others that the earth is thought to be at least 4 billion years old.

In the study of animals that have lived in past ages it is more convenient to use terms which denote sequence of animal life rather than numbers of years. The entire history of the earth's crust is divided into **eras, periods,** and **epochs,** each succeeding one being a subdivision of a previous one, as shown in Figure 26-1. Although the dates are only approximate and may vary one to several million years either way,

the sequence of events is rather well established. For example, it is quite certain that the Permian Period precedes the Triassic and follows the Pennsylvanian. Moreover, the relative lengths of the periods are rather well known. Such information is helpful in understanding the relative success of animals as well as the rates at which evolution occurred.

How Fossils Are Formed and Preserved

Under very special conditions parts or even whole animals have been preserved in many different ways. From these remains we can learn not only something about their anatomical features but also how they lived. It must be remembered that fossilization occurs only under ideal conditions and that only a very small fraction of the animals existing at any one time died under these conditions. Most of them, of course, disintegrated completely, just as they do today, leaving no clue to anyone in the future that they had ever lived. There are many ways in which fossils are formed, some of which we shall consider.

The ideal fossil is the whole animal preserved intact so that its entire anatomy can be studied in detail. This has occurred in the case of insects of the Oligocene, when they became embedded in the sticky pitch of the coniferous trees of that period. These animals show bodily structures in the finest detail. Even scales on the wings of butterflies are as perfectly preserved as if they had lived only yesterday. In certain cold regions such as Siberia the woolly mammoths (Fig. 26-2) often fell into crevasses in the ice where they were quickly frozen and thus preserved—flesh, skin, and all—for at least 20,000 years.

Animals that have fallen into petroleum surface deposits have been preserved in their entirety, although more frequently the flesh disintegrates, leaving only the bones in perfect condition. The most famous case is that of the La Brea tar pits in

DOMINANT ANIMAL LIFE	MILLIONS OF YEARS	EPOCHS	PERIODS	ERAS
MAMMALS	025	recent	QUATERNARY	CENOZOIC
	1	pleistocene		
	11	pliocene	TERTIARY	
	16	miocene		
	11	oliqocene		
	19	eocene		
	17	paleocene		
REPTILES	130		CRETACEOUS	MESOZOIC
			JURASSIC	
			TRIASSIC	
AMPHIBIANS	75		PERMIAN	PALEOZOIC
			PENNSYLVANIAN	
			MISSISSIPPIAN	
FISHES	80		DEVONIAN	
			SILURIAN	
INVERTEBRATES	145		ORDOVICIAN	
			CAMBRIAN	
FIRST LIFE	1500		PRECAMBRIAN	PROTEROZOIC
FORMATION OF EARTH'S CRUST	?			ARCHEOZOIC

FIG. 26-1. Geologic time is represented here both in approximate numbers of years and in terms that denote se-
qence of animal life. Representative animal types are also shown in the approximate periods they lived.

FIG. 26-2. A restoration of a herd of American mammoths that lived in Michigan as recently as 15,000 years ago.

Los Angeles where elephants, antelopes, bears, lions, horses, and the famous saber-tooth tigers (Fig. 26-3) have been found in great abundance. Apparently the animals became bogged down in the viscous tar and were attacked by predators which also met the same fate; hence, the rich fossil find in this one locality. The efforts of man to preserve his own kind by various means has been reasonably successful in that mummies have been found dating back 6,000 years.

FIG. 26-3. A reconstructed skeleton of a saber-tooth tiger taken from the La Brea tar pits in Los Angeles. These are the actual bones which have been preserved by the action of tar. Note the large canine teeth which undoubtedly made this big cat one of the more formidable animals of its day.

The hard parts of animals become fossilized very readily, as attested by the large numbers found in various parts of the world. Such parts as shells and other exoskeletons of invertebrates (Fig. 26-4) and the endoskeletons of vertebrates are most commonly preserved. Here again ideal conditions must prevail if the fossil is to form. The animal must be buried shortly after death, usually by the sinking of its body into the soft mud bottom of a stream or other body of water, and then be quickly covered by silt which subsequently becomes rock by the cementing action of minerals in the water (Fig. 26-5). Thus the original shape of the animal is maintained even though the organic parts completely disappear at some later time. Ground water containing carbonic acid dissolves away the shell, leaving a **mold** which is later filled with minerals that precipitate out as the ground water seeps through. The **cast** that is formed is an almost perfect replica of the original shell or other hard part. More commonly the replacement is

accomplished a little at a time: the most soluble parts are filled in first, the least soluble portions last. This type of replacement often reveals the minute detailed internal anatomy and is referred to as **petrifaction.**

Animal products such as eggs and excrement have been fossilized, and even tracks have been preserved in great abundance in certain localities, including the southwest part of this country (Fig. 15-32). Such impressions as tracks were made in soft mud which later dried sufficiently hard to withstand subsequent rains, and were finally filled with new material. Both the old and new deposits became rock and thus the tracks were preserved. Today when these strata are split open, the tracks are as distinct as when they were first made. Raindrops have also been preserved in this way. Such findings have been invaluable in determining the habits of these ancient animals. Tracks, for example, reveal whether the animal walked on all fours or hopped on its two hind legs. This

FIG. 26-4. Invertebrates with rigid outer coverings were fossilized in great numbers. Here are two examples. The ancient spider (left) was found in coal from southern France. It lived 300 million years ago. The insect (right) is embedded in its entirety in amber. Note how closely it resembles modern hymenopterans.

information, together with the fossil remains of the animal itself, gives a rather full picture of animal life in the past.

Ancient Animal Life

We have concrete evidence that life took hold in earnest only during the last billion years of earth history. As was pointed out at the beginning of this book, millions of years were required to produce the first living thing, but once it was formed evolution went forward at a rapid pace. It probably took longer to produce the first simple

appear almost spontaneously and simultaneously in a large variety of forms. Assuming that they did, all groups would very shortly acquire the character or perish, in accordance with the law of selection. This might conceivably account for the sudden appearance of the ancestors of all modern phyla in this very early period of geologic history.

Most, if not all, of the major phyla have left fossil remains in the Cambrian, which lasted 60 million to 90 million years, certainly a sufficiently long period of time

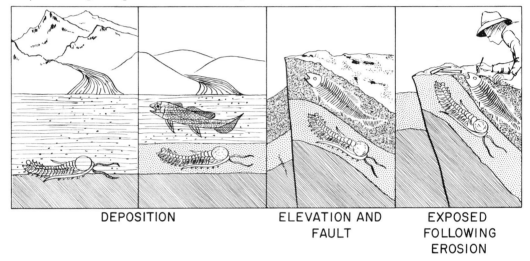

DEPOSITION   ELEVATION AND   EXPOSED
                      FAULT   FOLLOWING
                                        EROSION

FIG. 26-5. The hard parts of ancient animals become fossils as indicated.

cell than it has taken to evolve man from that first cell. Evidence of living things appears for the first time in the Cambrian rocks and, strange as it may seem, occurs here in great abundance. This must mean that once evolution started it went forth with a burst of speed from the very beginning, because fossils are found in all periods following the Cambrian. There is very little proof that animals lived in pre-Cambrian times, although had they possessed soft body parts which do not fossilize they could have lived and died without leaving recognizable imprints in the rocks. It seems incredible, however, that hard parts would

to allow for the evolution of such a large variety of forms. Each of the principal phyla represents a distinct level of anatomical organization which had its beginnings then. Apparently by happy coincidence, specific anatomical and physiological characteristics appeared that possessed great evolutionary potentialities. These became evident in the diversification of species within each phylum that followed. The course that each has taken from the Cambrian up to the present is portrayed in Figure 26-6 in graphic form. It will be seen that each of the principal phyla today started in the Cambrian and through the

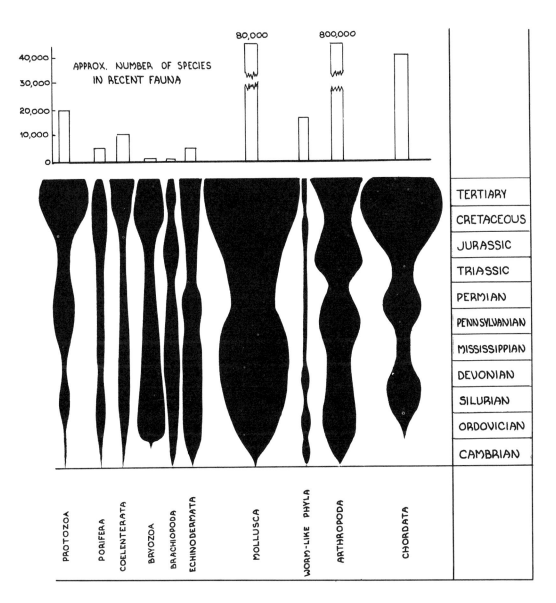

FIG. 26-6. The historical record of life is here shown in graphic form. The various phyla extend from the Cambrian or Ordovician up to the present, and the width of the black pathway indicates the relative numbers of genera in each phylum over this period of time. The upper figure represents the variety of species in each phylum in fauna of the present time.

subsequent periods has had its "ups and downs." Moreover, in the past geologic periods the relative proportions of the various groups differ from those of today (Figs. 26-7, 26-8). The most striking fact that

emerges from this observation is that all of the original phyla have living representatives today and that all of them are more numerous than in Cambrian times. Not only are there more individuals, but there

FIG. 26-7. This is a reconstruction of a Devonian coral reef that existed in the region of Rochester, New York. Note the great variety of form and structure of these ancient coelenterates. In the foreground on the right is a huge trilobite, a distant relative of the crustacea. In the middle foreground are two cephalopod mollusks, one in a straight cone-like shell and the other in a segmented coiled shell. All of these species are extinct today.

is also a much greater variety of species. This is one of the remarkable outcomes of organic evolution—more and more animals with greater and greater diversity of form and structure. To say it another way, there is a never-ending trend toward producing more and more protoplasm organized in more and more different ways.

With the phyla well established in the Cambrian, let us follow the history of one, the Chordata, during the ensuing periods and note some of its ramifications in establishing subgroups. In this brief survey we should gain some understanding of how evolution has gone on in the past, which will prepare us for the next chapter where we shall consider how it is going on today.

The Story of Vertebrates

The vertebrates, both past and present, constitute the most important animals in the phylum Chordata. Since the prochordates have left no fossil remains, we are forced to ignore them and study the history of the vertebrates alone.

The Chordates undoubtedly had their beginnings in the late Cambrian because they are well established as vertebrates in the Ordovician, well on their way toward becoming the most important of all groups of animals (Fig. 26-9). There are eight classes represented, of which four are swimmers and four possess legs adapted to movement over solid surfaces. Of the classes of swimmers, all but the placoderms have living representatives today. The jawless fishes (cyclostomes) had rather modest beginnings and all but died out in the late Devonian. In recent times they have shown signs of increasing in numbers and varieties, as indicated by considerable numbers in the oceans. Some have also invaded fresh water. The placoderms had the first true jaws which were hinged to the skull, a feature that was retained in all subsequent forms. They also possessed heavy bony skeletons. Both the cartilaginous and bony fishes were offshoots from the placoderms, the former sacrificing bone for cartilage and the latter retaining the bone. Today we have both represented: the cartilaginous fishes in the sharks and rays, and the more successful bony fishes which abound in all waters of the globe. The cartilaginous fishes have held their own rather well through this long geologic time while the bony fishes have increased at a tremendous rate, particularly since the Permian.

The most primitive land-dwellers, the amphibians, arose from the bony fishes some time during the Devonian, reaching a peak which they maintained through the Pennsylvanian and Permian, but then suddenly lost ground probably because their chief competitors, the great reptiles, became the dominant land life. With the passing of the great dinosaurs, the amphibians made a slight comeback which they have maintained up to the present. The reptiles came from the amphibians in the Pennsylvanian and very soon reached a peak which they continued to hold, with a setback during the Triassic, until the end of the Mesozoic (beginning of the Tertiary), when all of the large dinosaurs suddenly disappeared leaving only remnants which have continued on to the present. The reptiles have been the most

FIG. 26-8. This is a reconstruction of the ocean floor during the Cretaceous Period in the reign of Tennessee (U.S.), showing the abundance of invertebrate life. Although none of these species is alive today, it is not difficult to recognize them as mollusks. The two squid-like forms in the upper right are very similar to our present-day forms. The large coiled ammonite in the lower right is very much like the chambered nautilus of today. The numerous cephalopods with shells resembling cones are all extinct in any form. Our present-day clams and snails seem to be well represented on the floor of this ancient ocean.

successful of all animals living in the past and it is problematical whether any group in the future will reach such peaks as they did.

Both the mammals and birds were derived from the reptiles some time during the Triassic but good records are available only of the early Tertiary. Both started out very slowly, while the great reptiles ruled the earth. With the decline of these beasts, both the birds and mammals came into their own, increasing in numbers and variety at a tremendous rate. One can imagine that through the Triassic and Jurassic small birds and mammals occupied the secluded niches in the environment, keeping well out of the way of the numerous reptiles. All the while their bodies were evolving to a stage where, when the opportunity for survival improved, they were ready to set forth on the road that led them to the dominant position among present-day animals. Certainly the mammals have become the most diversified of all animals, whereas the birds have clung pretty much to a common pattern that seems to serve them well for life involving flight. Mammals reached their peaks in the Tertiary and have since shown a steady decline in numbers of species even though man, a member of this group, is considered to be the dominant form of life on earth today.

All of the evidence from studies of ancient life confirms and elaborates the theory that living things today descended from similar but different forms living in past ages. In other words, paleontological studies confirm and extend the theory of evolution as accepted by all scientists and most others today. Let us continue our search for facts supporting this or any other theory by examining evidence that appears in our living world of today.

EVIDENCE FROM RECORDS OF LIVING ANIMALS

We have seen that paleontology lends substantial support to the theory of evolution, but what about the living world of today?

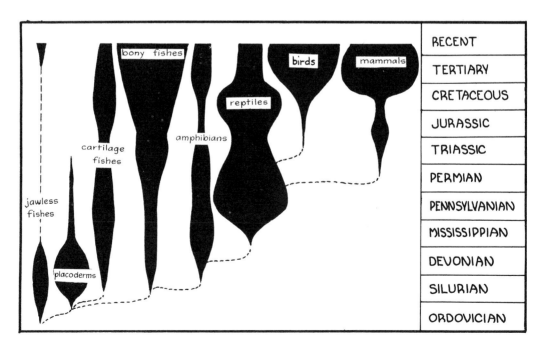

FIG. 26-9. The historical record of the vertebrates; the width of the black pathways indicates the relative variety of known forms in the various vertebrate classes.

MAN

DOG

BIRD

FISH

FIG. 26-10. The early embryos of all vertebrates are very similar during some stages of their development.

Can we find additional evidence among the animals around us to add to the bulwark already substantiated? Zoologists have been busy for the past 150 years adding vast stores of information to this end, and today we find supporting evidence from many branches of the biological sciences. Indeed, so much has been accumulated that it is questionable whether evolution should be referred to any longer as a **theory.** It is rather a clearly established fact. Some of the evidence which has afforded proof we shall consider briefly.

From Embryology

As early as 1821 Meckel had noted that embryos of higher animals passed through successive stages which resembled more or less completely the lower animals. Haeckel in 1866 summed up the evidence that had accumulated at this time in his statement, "Ontogeny (the development of an individual) is a brief and rapid recapitulation of the phylogeny," and assigned to this formula the imposing name of the Biogenetic Law. He claimed that animals recapitulate in their early embryological stages the phylogenetic history of the race, which we have already seen in various animals. Haeckel's all-inclusive statement has since been attacked from many sources and today stands only in its skeleton form. Although there is definite resemblance between the embryos of related species (Fig. 26-10), they are not as clear-cut and absolute as was once thought, and this is as one might expect. Since evolution has come about by a series of many small changes (micromutations) in the genic constitution of a species, it might be expected that gene changes would occur affecting all stages of the individual, that is, gene changes might affect the embryo itself so that "short cuts" could be taken in producing a certain organ system, for example. Similarly, structures which no longer serve a purpose in the adult animal might be retained simply because they were not "in the way" during the course of development and because no specific gene change occurred that ruled them out. Therefore, one might expect numerous remnants lingering on in the bodies of some animals but not in others, even closely related species. This is exactly what we observe.

In spite of some important omissions, the parallelism between the developing individual (ontogeny) and the phylogenetic sequence of animals (phylogeny) is remarkable and certainly lends support to the theory of evolution. Both the fertilized egg and single-celled protozoa exist as individual cells, the former destined to become something more complex, whereas the latter never rises above the one-celled condition (Fig. 26-11). Colonial protozoa (for example, *Volvox*) resemble the blastula, and the gastrula parallels the two-layered coelenterates (for example, *Hydra*). Subsequent stages of higher embryos

become worm-like tubes reminiscent of the annelids (for example, *Nereis*). Organ systems are formed in a primitive stage and function in primitive forms, while in higher forms they are laid down only in basic design, to become something far more complex at a later time. From this point on, the embryo undergoes further changes which take it farther and farther up the line of animal development. Early embryos from fish to man follow similar pathways, each dropping out in its appropriate place along the line—the fish first, man last.

Obviously, from what we have already said, the higher embryos will possess features that are functional in the adults of the lower forms. For example, the human embryo has a set of folds in the neck region in the fourth and fifth week of life. The fish embryo in a comparable stage of development possesses a similar set of folds; and, in fact, the embryos resemble one another so closely at this early stage that it is difficult to distinguish one from the other (Fig. 26-10). In the fish the folds give support to functional gills in the adult, whereas in the human they undergo a whole series of modifications, ultimately becoming a part of the hearing and sound-making apparatus as well as a part of the upper breathing tract (Fig. 26-12). We are reminded once again of the fact that, in the long evolutionary history of animals, structures which no longer find a use in the body often take over new tasks and by slight or great modifications become adapted to the new function.

There are many other features that appear in the developing human embryo that are tell-tale evidence of our lowly origin. For instance, a well-developed tail (Fig. 26-16) makes its appearance in the first few weeks of life but soon vanishes without performing any function other than to indicate to us that man came from stock which once possessed a tail. We have already noted the presence of a yolk sac which could hardly have a function since

ONTOGENY

PHYLOGENY

SINGLE CELLS

MANY CELLS

TWO LAYERS

THREE LAYERS
COELOM
SEGMENTATION
ORGAN SYSTEMS

DORSAL NERVE CORD
NOTOCHORD
GILL SLITS

yolk sac

FIG. 26-11. The Biogenetic Law can be demonstrated by comparing the embryonic stages in the development of a complex animal, such as a vertebrate, and adult representatives of certain of the phyla. Each higher form re-enacts the long history of the race in its own embryology.

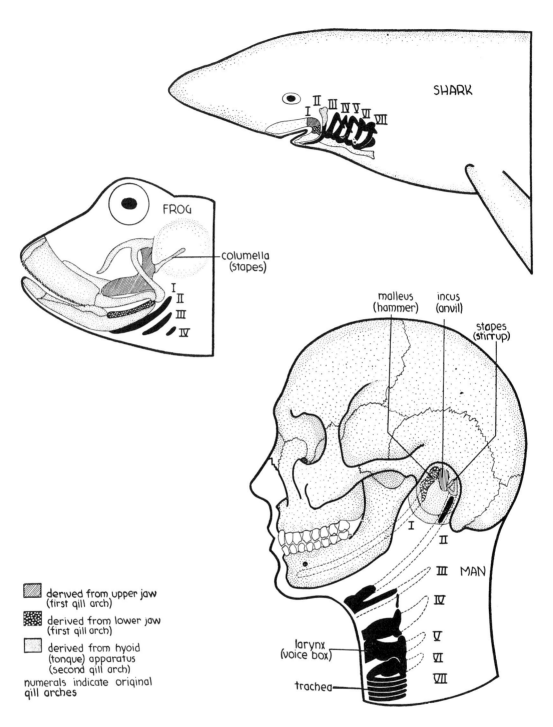

SHARK

FROG

columella
(stapes)

malleus
(hammer)

incus
(anvil)

stapes
(stirrup)

MAN

larynx
(voice box)

trachea

derived from upper jaw
(first gill arch)

derived from lower jaw
(first gill arch)

derived from hyoid
(tongue) apparatus
(second gill arch)

numerals indicate original
gill arches

FIG. 26-12. The history of the visceral arches indicates that many changes took place between the shark and man, yet evidences of the transition are clearly present. In the shark the arches gave support to the gills used in breathing water. In the frog the beginnings of the sound-making apparatus have developed and the sound-receiving apparatus has been further perfected. A portion of the hyoid (II) has become the columella, a forerunner of the stapes in the mammalian ear. The frog has also made use of the remaining gill arches in the formation of the laryngeal apparatus for the purpose of making sound.

In the mammal the sound-receiving and sound-making apparatuses have developed to a high degree of perfection, but the origins of the ear bones and the larynx are still evident.

it is devoid of yolk (food) and is not needed because nourishment is provided by the placenta. Here again it tells us that some time far back in evolutionary history our ancestors were egg-laying animals in which the embryos did receive their nourishment from a yolk sac. The human embryo, in the fifth month, develops a coat of hair called the **lanugo,** which is shed before birth, usually in the eighth month of gestation. Such hair could not possibly perform any conceivable function but does lead us to believe that at one point in our evolution we possessed a coat of hair as adults, extending back, probably, to some common ancestor of both man and apes.

FIG. 26-13. The appendages of the vertebrates are homologous, as shown by comparing the skeletons of these three. It would be difficult to explain these similarities on any other basis than organic evolution.

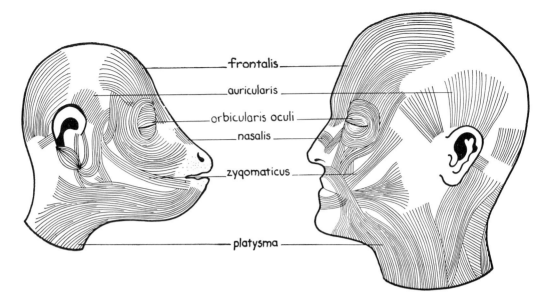

FIG. 26-14. Vestigial structures such as ear muscles in man (auricularis) are similar to those in the monkey. In the latter they have some function in moving the ears which perhaps aids in directing the sound into the ear; in man they are vestigial and serve no purpose, yet they persist.

The entire study of both invertebrate and vertebrate embryos supports the theory of evolution; no other explanation serves so well.

From Comparative Anatomy

One of the most striking observations that impresses anyone who studies a large variety of vertebrates is the fundamental likeness of the body architecture. The similarities are evident no matter what system is examined—appendages, muscles, digestive systems, circulatory systems, or any other. By comparing the appendicular skeletons of the horse, man and the frog (Fig. 26-13) it is obvious that the bones are similar, varying only in emphasis of specific parts of certain bones. In the horse, the forelegs are extended by elongating the equivalents of the wrist and hand bones of the frog and man. This provides the horse with an appendage well adapted for traveling at high speeds over soft turf. The same bones modified in different ways have given man a maneuverable appendage which is handsomely adapted to the kind of life he leads. Consider how much of our surroundings are designed for manipulation with the hand! An appendage not greatly different from that of man serves the frog satisfactorily in its way of life. Similarly, the hind appendages have been modified to perform specific jobs. The important point to note here is that the fundamental plan is the same; that is, the appendages are **homologous,** which means that they must have had a common origin. It would be difficult to explain their likenesses on any other basis.

A study of the muscles in any two vertebrates, will reveal the same sort of homologies noted in the skeletons. The large, major muscles in both animals are similar, most of them performing the same function in both. They vary only in size due to use, which is reflected in the activity of the animal. The cat walks on all fours and therefore uses its front appendages primarily for locomotion, whereas man puts his homologous appendages to quite a different use. Facial muscles of both man and monkey are likewise similar, although we have more of them and consequently can register more emotions in our faces (Fig. 26-14). The digital tips of a bird, a man, and a horse, referred to earlier (Fig. 16-2), can be compared in the same way. Other examples were mentioned earlier in the discussion of the origin of scales, teeth, and feathers (see p. 422). All of these comparable structures, with modifications in various species in response to function, and many more support the thesis of common origin. Common origin implies evolution.

From Vestigial Structures

Many animals possess structures which are vestiges of some past functional organ. The appendix in man is such a structure. It apparently performed some function when man's diet was not quite what it is today. Perhaps at one time he was more of an herbivore. In any case, it is no longer needed, as is attested by continued health after its removal. Indeed, failure to remove an infected appendix may mean death in man.

Another human vestigial structure is the ear muscle. Man possesses a complete set of muscles, similar to those in other primates, for moving the ears in all directions (Fig. 26-14). However, it is only with extreme difficulty that he can move his auditory appendages and even then the movement is ineffective in improving his hearing. Man also possesses a rudimentary tail together with a complete set of muscles for wagging it in all directions. These are even more useless than the ear muscles; yet they have persisted for thousands of generations. Since there is wide variation in the number of segments in the tail (coccyx) one might believe that it is disappearing, and this is probably true. A similar situation exists with the last set of molars (wisdom teeth). Perhaps a few thousand generations hence people may be born without wisdom teeth, an appendix, or a tail.

Vestigial structures in other animals often tell us something about their life history. The porpoise, for example, has a tiny pelvic girdle (Fig. 26-15) buried deep in its hip region where it could not possibly perform any function whatever, yet it is faithfully produced in the body of every porpoise. This vestige supports other evidence that this animal was a four-footed land animal at one time in the far distant past. Similarly, the python possesses a rudimentary pelvic girdle (Fig. 26-15), whereas all other snakes are without appendages of any sort. This vestige indicates that snakes had four-footed ancestors in the dim, distant past.

Anomalies in development occasionally occur which give some hint as to the history of certain structures. They are caused by the retention of embryonic structures in the adult and are called **atavisms** or **reversions.** For example, it is not uncommon for a child to be born with a well-developed external tail, reminiscent of a similar structure in the embryo (Fig. 26-16).

FIG. 26-15. Structures that performed a function at one time in an animal's history often continue to appear although today they are useless structures. Two good examples are the posterior appendage bones in porpoises (whales as well) and the remnants of similar appendages remaining in the python. Porpoises have no use for the bones, yet they always appear in every animal. The observable external remnant of posterior appendages occurs only in a few snakes but indicates that the ancestors of present-day snakes had legs.

FIG. 26-16. Occasionally an embryonic structure persists in the adult, such as a well-developed tail or numerous nipples in humans. These structures are found in relatives of man and may have existed in his ancestors. The only feasible explanation is that of common origins.

On very rare occasions rudimentary gill slits occur in the neck region (Fig. 26-17). Sometimes, additional nipples occur along lateral lines that coincide with the milk ridge in the embryo. In animals with multiple births this arrangement of the mammary glands is customary. Such "mistakes" in development throw light on the history of the body.

From Comparative Physiology and Biochemistry

The very fact that all animals possess essentially the same elements and chemical compounds would indicate a common origin.

Even protoplasm is very similar among all animals. The various enzymes that are found in the digestive tract of man can be identified in other animals, even down to the protozoa. Other intracellular and extracellular enzymes can likewise be identified in all animals which have so far been studied. It appears reasonable to assume, then, that the chemical constitution of two closely related species is more nearly alike than that of two distantly related species. Appropriate immunological and biochemical tests of the various fluids and tissues of a large variety of animals have shown this to be the case. Blood is most commonly studied because it is most readily obtained and most easily handled in the laboratory. By utilizing the antigen-antibody technique described earlier (p. 572), it has been possible to verify the relationships between many animals. It is gratifying to note that the relationships established by these blood tests corroborate those established by our system of classification based on homologous structures. For example, it is possible to show that among invertebrates *Limulus* is more closely related to the scorpions than any other invertebrates, and among vertebrates that seals and sea lions are more closely related to one another than to other mammals. Man's nearest kin among the primates has been shown to be the great apes and his most distant the lemur. The uniformity of birds has been verified by blood tests because they all give strong reactions with sera containing antibodies for the domestic fowl. Paleontologists have long contended that birds evolved from the line that gave rise to turtles and crocodiles rather than the snake-lizard line, and blood tests have confirmed their findings.

Another interesting evidence for evolution comes from a study of the salt content of the ancient and modern seas as compared with that of body fluids of ancient and modern animals (Fig. 26-18). It is known that the salt content of the seas has steadily increased through the ages. Freezing-point depression studies are a convenient method of determining indirectly the number of particles in a fluid, hence the osmotic pressure; for the greater the number of particles, the higher the osmotic pressure and the greater the freezing point is depressed. Such studies show that the fluids (blood) of modern animals have about the same freezing-point depression as that estimated for the ancient seas (0.55°C). It is generally agreed that the most ancient vertebrates did live in the ancient seas but migrated into fresh water where they gave rise to modern fish, includ-

ing sharks, and all land vertebrates (amphibians, reptiles, birds, and mammals). The freezing-point depression of all of these, except the sharks, is approximately that of the ancient seas. The sharks and their relatives, as well as many bony fishes, migrated into the seas where they were forced to compensate for the gradual increase in hypertonicity of sea water as millions of years passed. The sharks retained urea in their blood until the osmotic pressure balanced that of the sea water. Some teleosts retained the low osmotic pressure but counteracted the high salt concentration of the sea by modifying their kidneys and excreting excess salt at their gills (p. 598). Some other teleosts were able to migrate readily between fresh and salt water and their blood has a freezing-point depression approximately intermediate between the sharks' and land forms'. The marine mammals, such as the whales and porpoises, retained the freezing-point depression of their land ancestors and are quite at home in the sea. Being air breathers, water does not come

FIG. 26-17. Rarely, remnants of gill arches persist after birth, as shown in this photograph. Note the three rudimentary gill slits in the neck region.

FIG. 26-18. By studying freezing-point depressions (indicated here by the numbers) of modern seas and the blood of modern animals and comparing these with indirect evidence for similar data on ancient seas and primitive animals, it has been possible to trace animals from the sea onto land. For an explanation see text.

in contact with permeable membranes, hence they are not bothered by the hypertonicity of the sea any more than man is when he takes a swim in the ocean.

This striking physiological evidence corroborates the course followed by animals from water to land as determined by other studies. All physiological and biochemical data that have been carefully examined supplement those gathered from other disciplines supporting the theory of evolution. Many other substances present in the bodies of higher animals can be traced to their origins in lower forms, which certainly lends support to the thesis that they have a common origin. It would be difficult to explain them any other way.

From Animal Distribution

There are many places on the earth's surface that are idyllic spots for a large variety of animals, yet none occupies these regions. If animals were created simultaneously, why are not all of the favorable places in the world occupied by those that are fitted for such environments? Only in the light of evolution, both physical and organic, can a satisfactory answer be found for this situation.

Interplay of two evolutions, one of the earth itself, the other of the animals and plants upon it, has taken place. The young earth changed violently at first, gradually quieting down as it grew older and finally becoming inhabited with living things. Once life originated and new species began to appear, any subsequent alterations of the earth's surface or climate drastically affected the life then existing. Such changes as the rise and fall of large areas of the earth's surface and sharp climatic shifts were most important in determining not only the animals that survived but also the direction evolution took in any given locality.

Although there seems to be some question about the movement of entire continents (continental drift), there is no doubt about the fact that there have been many "ups and downs" within the various continents themselves. The presence of fossil remains of sea animals on the top of mountains is unequivocal evidence that these regions were at the bottom of some ancient ocean. Great sections located in mid-continental North America abound in marine fossils, though these areas are over a thousand miles from the sea today. The rising and falling of these areas has occurred again and again in certain regions, and geologists can tell us how many times and approximately when this has happened. There is no doubt that such striking dislocations of great areas had a profound effect on animal life, and we know the history of some of these effects.

Coincident with these shifts in the surface of the earth, the climate changed dramatically from one extreme to another and back again. The great coal deposits in the northern sections of the globe are a result of luxuriant plant growth in some ancient period, which is substantial proof that such regions were tropical during these times. Areas that once received a tremendous rainfall later became dry plains. This transition can be observed today by flying over large regions of the North Central United States. It is possible to see the outlines of ancient lakes that are now forest lands and old forest lands that have become grass-

lands. All of these changes have come about because of the gradual trend toward a more arid climate. The sudden appearance of a mountain range must have had a profound effect on the amount of precipitation that fell in surrounding regions, which in turn altered both plant and animal life. Undoubtedly the success of a species depends a great deal upon the coincidence of gene mutations with changes in the climate and topography of the region. The proper timing of genetic changes in the animal with climatic and environmental changes might mean the success or failure of a species. These constant shifts in climate and topography have influenced the evolution of animals to a marked degree.

Closely related species of animals are usually found in adjacent **ranges** (region occupied by a species), just as one might expect. If they had split off from one another only recently, they would not be separated by very great distances, and more than likely some barrier would exist between them such as a mountain, canyon, or body of water, which may have been responsible for the new species in the first place. The more recent the separation of two species the more closely related they are, and the more ancient the separation the greater the differences between them. The greater differences constitute genera, families, orders, classes, and phyla. When great land masses are separated for millions of years one would expect the entire fauna to be quite different on each of them. Such is found to be the case when, for example, the animals in Australia and in the continent of Asia are compared. The explanation of the occurrence of primitive animals in Australia has direct bearing on the history of this large land mass.

Most of the earth's land is located in the northern hemisphere. It was all connected at one time when there was a land bridge across Bering Strait. Therefore, animals originating in any part of this great land mass could have migrated to any other part during this period. It is thought that mammals originated in these northern continents and spread in all directions. The frigid barrier to the north encouraged southward migrations of primitive mammals during the Mesozoic when the three great land masses to the south (Africa, South America, and Australia) were connected at various times to the continents of the northern hemisphere. Australia was bridged through the Malay Archipelago and the two Americas were connected through Central America, just as they are today, although during early Tertiary times there was no land bridge at this point and the two continents were separated. Evidence for this is substantiated by the fact that marine life in the Atlantic and Pacific oceans in this region is very similar yet sufficiently different to be accounted for only by the formation of a relatively recent land barrier which separated the two oceans.

The primitive mammals, which probably resembled our present-day monotremes and marsupials, spread over these land bridges to Africa, South America, and Australia. Later the placental mammals evolved in the northern continents and, because of their superior ability to cope with the environment, were able to drive out or destroy all of the primitive mammals in these northern areas. However, before the placental mammals made their way too far south, the sinking of the land connection between North and South America below the surface of the oceans prevented them from getting into the southern continent. Likewise, the land connections between Asia and Australia and to a lesser extent between Europe and Africa gave way, thus cutting off the possibilities of further migrations southward. The primitive mammals were thus isolated from their more aggressive relatives and were able to survive up to the present. For that reason we see not only primitive mammals but also other primitive groups of animals ranging from insects to birds in the southern continents.

The fact that primitive mammals could not withstand the onslaught of their more recent placental relatives has been demonstrated within historical times. Rabbits introduced into Australia multiplied so rapidly that they soon outstripped the local marsupials at a tremendous pace. They are well under control today, however, owing to man's ingenuity. A disease, fatal to rabbits, was introduced which has kept them in reasonable numbers for the past several years. One interesting exception to this apparent superiority of northern fauna is the case of the opossum (Fig. 26-19). This marsupial made its way back north over the recent land bridge between the two Americas and it has competed rather successfully there with its aggressive descendants.

Another interesting case of animal distribution which can be explained in no other logical way than by evolution is the occurrence in widely separated parts of the world of animals that are morphologically similar yet geographically far apart. For example, the camel family is represented by the true camels in Asia and Africa and by the llama and its relatives in South America. How can one explain the existence of these closely related animals in areas so far distant today? To account for this one can consult the fossil records. It has been found that the ancestor of these two species roamed over not only their present habitats but also Europe and North America, which lie between them. Apparently, relatives of the present living members of the camel family died out in the intervening regions. Similarly, the only alligators in the world exist in southeastern United States and the Yangtse River in China. Fossil alligators have been found in North America and Europe, which accounts, then, for the present location of living alligators. Just why they died out over the large intermediate areas is conjectural.

The theory of evolution is the most logical explanation for the distribution of animals over the earth. We may rest assured that if and when a better explanation presents itself scientists will be the first to recognize and accept it.

RATES OF EVOLUTION

From the foregoing discussion it is obvious that evolution has gone on at different rates at different times, bringing about radical changes in some groups whereas in others little or no change at all has occurred over millions of years. For example, the chambered nautilus (Fig. 26-20) evolved rapidly to a certain point after which, for the past 75 million years, it has not changed. During the same period of time the horse has come all the way from a many-toed, shy little animal to the huge beast we see today. The nautilus evolved very rapidly from Silurian times, reaching a peak in the Jurassic and then coming to a standstill in the Tertiary with no change from that point up to the present. All of its relatives died out in this early period and it was only by some peculiar circumstance that this "living fossil" has survived to the present time. The horse, on the other hand, has shown a progressive change up to the present and is still changing (Fig. 27-5).

Even if the whole animal seems to have evolved steadily, a careful examination of its various structural aspects shows that it has undergone change at varying

FIG. 26-19. The opossum is the oldest living mammal, having originated in the Cretaceous and maintained itself unchanged up to the present time. Note the hand-like front appendage in this young specimen.

FIG. 26-20. The chambered nautilus is a "living fossil." The group to which it belongs was dominant during Paleozoic times. Note the elaborate exterior configurations (above) and the chambers in the sectioned specimen (below).

sudden pauses for reasons which we do not know at present and may never know.

Another way of studying the rates of evolution is to determine the number of different kinds of animals produced, that is, the number of new species, new genera, and even larger categories that came into existence in a specified period of time. Using as factors the number of genera of animals in a family and the length of time known, it is possible to compute how many years are required to produce a new genus. This has been done for the familiar horse lineage and it has been estimated that a new genus appeared about every 7,500,000 years. Estimates for other hoofed mammals seem to be about the same during that period, although this generalization does not hold for all animals, even mammals. The opossum, for example, has changed very little if any since the Cretaceous, over 80 million years ago, and at that time it was the most advanced of all animals. This is certainly substantial evidence that some animals have evolved much more rapidly than others, and also that the rate may vary greatly at different times within a small group of animals.

Considerable data, brought together by G. G. Simpson, show the rate at which genera have originated in several groups of animals from the Cambrian to the Tertiary (Fig. 26-21). The amphibians start producing new genera at a slow rate during Devonian times and then build up to a peak in the Pennsylvanian. The rate drops off until it reaches its lowest numbers in the Jurassic and Cretaceous, gradually coming back in the Tertiary. The reptiles produce new genera at a tremendous rate from their very beginnings in the Pennsylvanian reaching a sharp peak in the Permian, followed by a sharp decline in the Triassic and levelling off from that point on to the present. Mammals, starting in the Jurassic, show first a decline and then a sudden and continuing burst of speed in the production of new genera that has been main-

rates. For instance, among the early Pliocene horses some show marked changes in both teeth and feet over the ancestral Miocene horse, others show changes in teeth but not feet, and still others show no change in feet or teeth. This indicates that the teeth and feet have changed at different rates and at different times in the various groups of horses. Similar instances can be found in other groups of animals. It is apparent that structural evolution has gone ahead erratically with bursts of speed and tained up to recent times. Only within the past 10 million years have there been any signs that indicate the peak has been reached and passed.

An interesting feature of the rates at which new genera are produced in verte- brate groups is that each has a peak fol- lowed by a decline. Starting with the jaw- less fishes, which are the lowest in numbers of new genera and the first to appear in geologic time, each succeeding peak is higher than the preceding, that of the am-

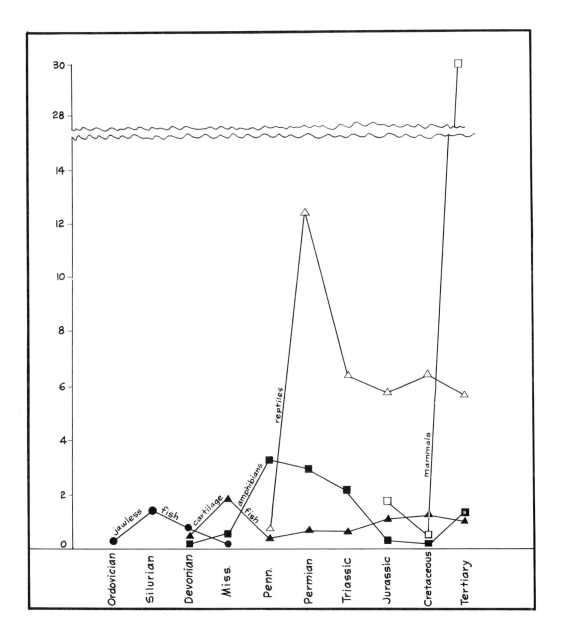

FIG. 26-21. Rates of evolution in several classes of vertebrates are shown from Ordovician to Tertiary. The curves indicate the number of new genera that appeared in each one million year period. The numbers to the left represent the number of new genera.

phibians being higher than the jawless and cartilaginous fishes, that of the reptiles being higher than the amphibians, and that of the last, the mammals, being the highest of all. If the mammals have passed their peak in the production of new genera, perhaps they are on their way out. In that event, if historical evolution repeats itself, there must be some other group of animals coming up. Careful studies may make it possible to predict which group will succeed us as the dominant animals on the earth. We may even be able to do something about it!

SUGGESTED SUPPLEMENTARY READINGS

BERRILL, N. J., *The Origin of Vertebrates* (London, Oxford University Press, 1955).

COLBERT, E. H., *Evolution of the Vertebrates* (New York, John Wiley & Sons, Inc., 1955).

DODSON, E. O., *Evolution: Process and Product* (New York, Reinhold Pub. Corp., 1960).

GLAESSNER, M. F., "Pre-cambrian Animals," *Scientific American*, 204(3) (March, 1961), 72.

WALD, G., "Biochemical Evolution," in E. S. G. Barron, ed., *Trends in Physiology and Biochemistry* (New York, Academic Press, 1952).

27

Theories and Mechanism of Evolution

The question as to *how* the present colossal array of living things came about has puzzled man from the dawn of human intelligence. Civilizations of all kinds have pondered the problem and have come up with some sort of answer which usually has been incorporated into their philosophy and religion. The most gratifying answer was a simple one, and to the western mind special creation as portrayed in the Book of Genesis was also the most satisfactory. The idea that all living things were created for a purpose which they now fulfill left little room for argument and was satisfac-

tory for large segments of the populations of the civilized world until about 100 years ago. The belief that the earth was much older than the allotted 6,000 years ascribed by Christians did not obtain a secure foothold until geologists began to unearth very convincing evidence confirming the antiquity of the earth. Once the earth was shown to be very old, the history of life on it became an immediate and a very important problem. The constant discoveries of fossil remains of plants and animals led to the concept that life on the earth was likewise very ancient, much older than anyone had imagined. With this start, the whole matter of the origin of living things, both past and present, became a problem demanding careful scientific analysis. Several theories have been advanced, the more important of which we shall consider after a brief historical background.

HISTORICAL BACKGROUND

Rudiments of the theory of organic evolution can be found in writings of the early Greeks, especially Anaximander (588–524 B.C.), Empedocles (495–435 B.C.), and Aristotle (384–322 B.C.). Of these, Aristotle overshadowed all others because of his command of natural history of the world of his day. He, like others of his time, believed that living things progressed from simple to more complex forms, reaching the pinnacle in man. In this sense his writings had the germ of the evolution idea, but beyond that they showed little advance over primitive mysticism. Unfortunately, Aristotle's ideas were proclaimed as dogma by the church during the Middle Ages hence the possibility of scientific reasoning was impeded for many centuries. His tenet was idealistic in that he claimed each animal was specially created in its present form. Since that fitted perfectly into the doctrines of the churches there was no quarrel at this early period. Historical geology had not yet been born, so there could be no conflict from that quarter. It was only when fossils were unearthed and needed explaining that serious clashes occurred between those adhering to special-creation dogma and those willing to accept historical facts of organic descent.

Certainly during the long period between Aristotle and the Renaissance there must have been some brave souls who entertained *sub rosa* ideas concerning the historical hypothesis, but because of the dominance of the special-creation doctrine they are unknown to us. By the seventeenth century social sanctions relaxed somewhat, and it was then that historical descent gradually became a topic for open discussion. Some of the men who were bold enough to speak and write their thoughts were Hooke (1635–1703) and Ray (1627–1705) of England, de Maillet (1645–1738) and Buffon (1707–1788) of France, and finally Erasmus Darwin (1731–1802) of England, the grandfather of Charles Darwin, of whom we shall hear much more later. While all of these men considered evolution as the most likely explanation of animal life on earth, they did not succeed in establishing this principle to any appreciable extent because of the scanty facts they were able to muster in support of their thesis. Furthermore, opposition from theologians carried such staggering weight that the world gave scant attention to the struggling historical hypothesis. But the seed had been sown, and it could not help but gather support as more and more knowledge of the natural world accumulated. Moreover, as those who proclaimed evolution began adding theories as to how evolution occurred, more attention and often more support were given to the budding principle.

Among the outstanding men of this period who pushed the doctrine of evolution farther than most was Lamarck (1744–1829), a French biologist, who not only accepted the theory of evolution as an explanation of the existence of all living things but also proposed a theory which seemed to explain evolution very well. Lamarck was a vitalist, as were the majority of eighteenth century biologists. He believed that all living things are endowed with a vital force, distinguished from a physical force, that controls the function of all their parts and ultimately makes it possible for them to inhabit the environment where they now reside. Furthermore, he believed that any traits acquired in the lifetime of an organism were transmitted to succeeding generations. Any such acquired traits could be enhanced or depressed by "use and disuse," and the more an organ or part was used the better suited it became to do the job. Such acquired advantages would then be passed on to the offspring. He used the now classical example of the giraffe's neck, in which he assumed that the ancestor of this animal possessed a short neck but because it began browsing on tree leaves and twigs a long neck was particularly advantageous in survival. Hence the continuous stretching of the neck brought about a longer neck, and this trait was then passed on to the offspring whose necks would thus be longer. This is a captivating idea and was readily acclaimed by many as the ideal answer to the question of how evolution occurred.

Lamarck's theory was the outcome of much thought about the problems that had to be solved, namely, random and oriented evolution. He knew that a general theory, if it were tenable, had to explain both. In addition, the great problem of adaptation had to occupy the center of the stage in any explanation, because it was at that time and for many years later the most difficult to interpret. His theory encompassed these features in a manner that would be completely satisfactory if his major premise could be borne out by fact. It has been thoroughly established that acquired characters cannot be transmitted because they do not influence the genes which are the only means of transmission from one generation to the next. Any traits acquired in the lifetime of an individual influence only his soma cells and have no effect on the germ cells. Thus the very heart of Lamarck's theory is faulty. Since genetics has firmly established this fact, his theory has no following among modern biologists. In spite of Lamarck's failure, his ideas were important during this early period in stimulating others to propose other theories from which the correct one finally emerged.

Although interested in natural history

FIG. 27-1. Charles Darwin in his later years. He was born February 12, 1809, the same day as a famous American, and died in the year 1882.

as a child, Charles Darwin's (Fig. 27-1) college training was in medicine and theology. Neither of these professions suited his taste, so when the famous naturalist, Professor Henslow, suggested that he might go on the ship *Beagle* for a five-year cruise around the world, Darwin grasped the opportunity to continue his earlier studies of geology and biology. The British Navy needed maps and charts of Great Britain's oceanic island possessions, as well as some knowledge of their geology and natural history. The trip took him to the east and west coasts of South America, to Ecuador and west to the Galapagos Islands. It was while he was making a comparison of the flora and fauna of these islands, together with their geology, with that of South America that he became convinced that living things were not static nor specially created as he had thought up to this time, but rather that they were undergoing constant change and that this change was intricately linked with the movements of the earth's surface. This extensive cruise gave him a rare opportunity to study animals and plants in different parts of the world where he could see various relationships. It is interesting to note that Darwin left England a devout special creationist and returned, after five years of direct field study of natural history, with very little reference to the works of others, a confirmed evolutionist.

During the trip he gathered voluminous notes which, when assembled back in England in the course of the next twenty years, so thoroughly convinced the world of the validity of evolution that it has never been seriously questioned since. This one effort alone placed Darwin head and shoulders above his contemporaries or predecessors. Not satisfied with this accomplishment, he sought an explanation for evolution which eventually was resolved in his theory of natural selection.

Alfred Russell Wallace, a friend of Darwin's, working over the flora and fauna of the Malay Peninsula and the East Indies, hit upon an explanation of evolution which was in essence identical with Darwin's theory of natural selection. He conveyed his ideas to Darwin in the form of a letter. This occurred in the year 1858 after Darwin had completed his data and was about to consider publishing his findings. Rather than rush into print to obtain priority, Darwin presented a short draft of his work simultaneously with that of Wallace before the Linnean Society in London. The following year, 1859, he published his classical work, *On the Origin of Species by Means of Natural Selection,* in which he formulated his theory backed up by abundant evidence. Even though both men had

arrived at similar explanations of evolution, the credit has gone to Darwin, as it justly should.

Darwin's book convinced the scientific world of the soundness of evolution, and his theory of natural selection provided food for thought for those interested in how it came about. Because the book was written in a manner comprehensible to laymen and because it was staunchly defended by such eminent biologists as T. H. Huxley, the theory of evolution came to be generally accepted by the intelligent world. Natural selection as an explanation as to how evolution came about was immediately attacked by scientists and has continued to be under fire up to the present, although today it is generally accepted, with modifications, as the most tenable of the explanations advanced thus far.

THE THEORY OF NATURAL SELECTION

Both Darwin and Wallace had been stimulated by Robert Malthus (1766–1834) for the central theme which culminated in the theory of natural selection. Malthus had written his "Essay on Population" in 1798 in which he argued that since human beings reproduce at a rate far outstripping the food supply, there must be positive checks such as wars, disease, and famines to keep them from overrunning the world. This by its very nature involves a "struggle for existence." Darwin seized upon this phrase as a possible explanation for the origin of new species which is the heart of evolution. He reasoned that favorable traits would be preserved and unfavorable ones would be destroyed, thus paving the way for the origin of new species. With this kernel as a start, Darwin, as well as Wallace, developed the theory of natural selection.

In essence, Darwin's theory of evolution or origin of species through natural selection involves the following steps in reasoning which are borne out by fact.

First, he considered variation an innate property of protoplasm because he encountered it in all groups of plants and animals (Fig. 27-2). Any species of living thing varies widely, a fact that he could not account for but for which we have since found an explanation, to be considered presently. This variation within a species provides raw material with which evolution can proceed. Without it there could be no evolution.

Second, since each organism produces many more offspring than can possibly survive and yet populations remain fairly con-

stant, there must be a continual "struggle for existence" within and between groups as well as with the environment; those best suited to survive under the existing conditions prevail. This could be a passive struggle, such as that engaged in by plants and animals resisting the desiccation of desert regions; or it could be extremely active, as in predation. In any case, only the most fit would survive, and for this Darwin used the phrase, "survival of the fittest," suggested to him by Herbert Spencer. Thus the struggle for existence has a selective effect in removing the unfit and preserving the fit. Moreover, since only the

FIG. 27-2. A series of pelts of the striped skunk (*Mephitis*). These are all of the same species, yet they show wide variation in regard to the white-stripe pattern.

most fit survive, they alone can perpetuate the traits that made them best suited and hence pass them on to their offspring.

Modern Interpretation

The theory of natural selection as an explanation of evolution has stood the test of time although it must be interpreted in the light of discoveries made in the past century. Information has come from cytology, genetics, and many other sources, all of which have contributed to our understanding of how evolution takes place. The modern, or so-called **Neo-Darwinian** view includes five principle factors which are responsible for evolutionary change. First, variation can now be explained by **mutation,** and mutated genes recombine during sexual reproduction; second, **natural selection** promotes favored traits and eliminates undesirable ones; third, chance, or **genetic drift,** is effective in survival; fourth, **geographical** and **genetic isolation** are responsible for the origin of new varieties; and fifth, sexually mature larvae (**neotony**) contribute significantly to evolutionary change. Let us consider each of these.

Mutation. The science of genetics has made it possible to understand variation, something Darwin recognized but could not explain. Variations provide the raw material with which natural selection operates, hence were the heart of Darwin's theory. We know now that variation results from gene or chromosomal changes collectively called **mutations.** Any variations due to environmental changes during the life of the individual, in the embryo or later, have no effect on the genes, hence are of no significance in evolution. Mutations may involve only a single gene (micromutations), which is the most usual, or they may include a group of genes (macromutations), which accounts for sudden large changes such as short legs in sheep or extra toes in cats. Most biologists believe that species have

originated from the accumulation of a great many micromutations rather than by one or more macromutations. Accordingly, it is doubtful that a full-blown species ever appears in one generation, it is more likely that many tiny, almost imperceptible, mutations occur and by the process of natural selection accumulate until a new species appears.

The first careful records made of mutations were those of the Dutch botanist, Hugo DeVries, who described them in the evening primrose. In fact, DeVries named these sudden and spontaneously occurring changes mutations, a term which today applies to any alteration in the genic composition of an organism. DeVries thought that evolution occurred as a result of mutations and not by natural selection. Now we know that mutations provide the basis for the operation of natural selection. In other words, both mutations and natural selection are essential for evolution.

Mutations have been noted in a large number of plants and animals under experimental conditions and they are undoubtedly occurring continuously among organisms in their natural habitats (Figs. 25-33, 27-3). Over a thousand mutations have been recorded for Drosophila alone. A great many gene changes probably go unnoticed which, in nature, might have considerable survival value. For example, a mutation might occur in an animal living in a region where some element in the diet was becoming deficient, which would so affect the enzyme systems of the animal that it could get along on a minimum amount of the element. Such a mutation might show no visible difference in the animal itself and yet be most important in survival. Animals with the favorable gene would be more apt to live to produce progeny than those without it; hence selection would be toward the favorable gene. While we have a great deal of information concerning anatomical mutations we know almost nothing about biochemical mutations (see p. 701). Nevertheless, such physiological changes must have been and must continue to be very important in their evolution.

Mutations occur at random both in nature and as a result of mutagenic agents (chemicals or high energy radiations). They bear no relationship to the needs of the organism and they are unpredictable, at least in our present state of knowledge. It may be possible someday to mutate specific genes but much more must be learned about the techniques of handling DNA than is presently known, before this can be done. Almost 100 per cent of the mutations are harmful, a fact that is understandable since all organisms alive today have gone through millions of years of selection. Only the best traits are preserved; hence any further change is likely to be less desirable than those already in existence.

Under different circumstances a mutation could be unfavorable and be preserved —for example, a mutation that rendered an amphibian partially or totally blind. In its normal environment death would be certain. However, if it wandered into a cave where vision was of little advantage, its chance for survival might be as good as that of a normal animal. Indeed, it may even be better since eyes are apt to be injured in such dark caverns. If such were true, blind amphibians would have a selective advantage over those with functional eyes, and would then increase in the population until the entire population would be sightless. This has actually happened in certain caves. The sickle-cell trait in man, mentioned earlier (p. 705) is also a case in which a mutation has an advantage in a particular environment.

Since mutations occur only very rarely it is difficult to study enough cases to understand what part they play in evolution. However, by studying large populations of organisms, it is possible to determine the frequency of genes in such populations.

FIG. 27-3. Three mutations occur commonly in animals. Curled wings in Drosophila is recessive to normal wings. Hornless (polled) condition in cattle is dominant to horned. Fused or webbed toes (syndactyly) and extra toes (polydactyly) in man are dominant to normal toes.

Such studies come under the heading of **population genetics** and have received more and more attention in recent years.

The question, why is the frequency of genes in a population relatively constant from generation to generation, stimulated two men in the early part of this century to propose a theory which has become a law. They were G. H. Hardy, an English mathematician, and W. Weinberg, a German physician who, working independently, formulated the basic law of population genetics now known as the Hardy-Weinberg Law. This law states that **the proportion of genes and genotypes in any large biparental population will remain constant generation after generation providing there is random mating, equal fertility, no mutations, no selection and no environmental change.** It fails with small populations, but in large populations it works regardless of whether the genes are dominant or recessive. This, then, gives us a base from which to determine the effect of mutations, selection, or gene flow, because they are all superimposed upon this equilibrium.

At the outset one might wonder why recessive blue eyes in human populations do not give way to dominant brown eyes with the passing of time. We know they do not, and this is not because of any association of the genes within the chromosome. It is because there is normally no

ploid, cross-fertilizing individuals the frequency of any pair of genes, A and a, must appear in each individual as one of the three combinations, AA, Aa, and aa. The number of times each combination appears in a population can be determined in the following fashion: The number of times the gene A appears in the population (frequency) can be defined as the frequency of the homozygous dominant individuals AA plus $\frac{1}{2}$ of the frequency of the heterozygous individuals Aa, and this can

TABLE 1

Mating		Frequency		Percentage Offspring		
MALE	FEMALE	SPERM	EGGS	AA	Aa	aa
AA x AA		All A	All A	100		
AA x Aa		All A	$\frac{1}{2}$ A : $\frac{1}{2}$ a	50	50	
AA x aa		All A	All a		100	
Aa x AA		$\frac{1}{2}$ A : $\frac{1}{2}$ a	All A	50	50	
Aa x Aa		$\frac{1}{2}$ A : $\frac{1}{2}$ a	$\frac{1}{2}$ A : $\frac{1}{2}$ a	25	50	25
Aa x aa		$\frac{1}{2}$ A : $\frac{1}{2}$ a	All a		50	50
aa x AA		All a	All A		100	
aa x Aa		All a	$\frac{1}{2}$ A : $\frac{1}{2}$ a		50	50
aa x aa		All a	All a			100

Totals   225 : 450 : 225
Ratio $\frac{1}{4}$: $\frac{1}{2}$: $\frac{1}{4}$

selection for either eye color and so long as this happens the genes for both will combine so as to give the same proportion of brown and blue eyes in each succeeding generation. Let us see why this is so.

In any population the distribution of a pair of genes, A and a, either of which can occupy a given locus, each individual will possess one of the following genotypes and no other: AA, Aa, or aa. Let us suppose these exist in the population in the typical Mendelian ratio of $\frac{1}{4}$ AA: $\frac{1}{2}$ Aa: $\frac{1}{4}aa$. Now assuming that random mating occurs and comparable offspring are produced, the next generation will consist of the same proportion of genotypes, as will be seen by recording all of the possible combinations in the next generation (Table 27-1).

In any population consisting of dip-

be designated p. Likewise, the frequency of the gene a may be defined as the frequency of the homozygous recessive individuals aa plus $\frac{1}{2}$ the heterozygous individuals, Aa; this can be designated q. We know that the sum of the three genotypes, AA, Aa, aa, equal 1.00; therefore, $p + q = 1.00$. In random mating the sperm cells carrying gene A or a will unite in accordance with their relative frequencies. As you will see from Table 2, the three

TABLE 2

Sperm Cells

Eggs	A (p)	a (q)
A (p)	AA (p²)	Aa (pq)
a (q)	Aa (pq)	aa (q²)

Results: p^2 (AA) + $2pq$ (Aa) + q^2 (aa)

genotypes have the frequencies, $p^2 + pq = p$ and $q^2 + pq = q$, and we know that $p + q = 1.00$; then it becomes obvious that the frequencies of the genotypes AA, Aa, and aa in the second and all subsequent generations will be the same as in the original population.

Mendel's Laws, it will be observed, represent the special example of the Hardy-Weinberg Law where p and q are equal, each being 0.5. If p is dominant, the phenotypic ratio is 3:1. Actually Mendel used the binomial theorem $(a + b)^2 = a^2 + 2ab + b^2$ to express his famous F_2 generations.

It is possible with this information to compute the frequencies of genotypes in the population providing one of the frequencies is known. It is usually easier to obtain figures for recessive genes, aa (q^2), because they are more obvious. With this information it is possible to compute the frequencies of the other genotypes in the population. An excellent example of this comes from humans.

The trait albinism (p. 675) occurs in white populations in the ratio of 1 in 20,-000. It is recessive and is inherited as a single pair of genes; therefore, an albino has the genotype, aa. In order to determine how many individuals in the population are carriers for the trait, that is, how many are heterozygous (Aa), it is possible to use the Hardy-Weinberg Law to find the answer. The frequency of aa, represented by q^2, is $\frac{1}{20,000}$. By taking the square root of this figure we get about $\frac{1}{141}$ which represents q. We know that if $p + q = 1.00$, it follows that $p = 1 - q$. Substituting $\frac{1}{141}$ for q, $1 - \frac{1}{141} = \frac{140}{141}$ which is the value of p. Now we know the value of both q and p and from this information we can calculate the heterozygotes in the population because we know the number is represented by $2pq$, thus, $2 \times \frac{140}{141} \times \frac{1}{141} = \frac{1}{70}$. This means that heterozygous condition Aa is present in one person in every 70, even though only

1 person in 20,000 is homozygous and has the defect.

Another example of how the Hardy-Weinberg Law operates may be taken from studies of the blood antigens M and N, again in human populations. Because of usage we shall employ the letters M and N, although this is misleading because only a single pair of alleles are involved. (Correctly, we should use M and m or N and n). Neither allele is dominant and there is no differential selective value associated with them. Most people do not know nor care whether they possess M, N, or MN. The genotype can be distinguished by simple serological tests.

Studies of 6,129 white people in the United States have demonstrated the following proportion of phenotypes (also given in percentages): $M = 1787$ (29.16%); $N = 1303$ (21.26%); and $MN = 3039$ (49.58%). By using the Hardy-Weinberg Law we can calculate that $q = 0.46$, which when subtracted from 1.00 gives us $p = 0.54$. Then $p^2 = 0.29$ and $2pq = 0.49$, rather close to the proportions established by actual serology tests. The agreement between theoretical calculations and observations establishes the likelihood that the blood antigens are under the control of a single pair of genes in which neither is dominant to the other.

From these examples we have seen the usefulness of the Hardy-Weinberg Law. We must remember, however, that it is entirely theoretical. It assumes random mating, the lack of migration of organisms in and out of a population, the absence of differential mortality among the various genotypes, and an infinitely large population without chance gene frequency fluctuations. In spite of these exceptions the law is most important to an understanding of evolution. It demonstrates that there is nothing built into Mendelian inheritance that can alter gene frequencies in populations. If alterations do occur, they must be ascribed to other factors such as natural selection, migration, chance and mutations, both forward and backward. Evolution, then is a result of these factors.

Natural Selection. Darwin's thoughts on the part natural selection plays in evolution have been largely retained and enlarged upon as a result of new information that has become available since his time. One of the most interesting cases of the operation of natural selection has been observed in the last one hundred years in Darwin's own England. It concerns moths belonging to the species *Biston betularia,* and the phenomenon is called *industrial melanism.*

These moths occurred in two different forms in Europe, a normal light *peppered* form and a dark form (Fig. 27-4). The first dark moth was found near Manchester, England, in 1848, and in the years that followed it increased in numbers until today it is the only form present in areas where a great deal of heavy industry exists. What is the relationship between industrialization and the predominance of the dark form?

A careful study of the tree trunks by H. B. D. Kettlewell reveals that as the gaseous by-products in industry increase the mottled lichens are poisoned and disappear from the tree trunks leaving them dark as a result of the accumulated soot from the factories. Thus the *peppered* moth is clearly visible on the dark trunk, which was not the case when the moth rested on lichens. Consequently, the light-colored moths were easily observed and eaten by birds, whereas the dark-colored moths were protected because they matched the dark background

FIG. 27-4. Industrial melanism illustrated by the moth, *Biston betularia.* The *melanic* and *peppered* forms are shown in both photographs. The one above is of a tree trunk covered with lichens. Find the two *peppered* moths. The dark form is very conspicuous. The lower photograph shows the blackened tree trunk of an industrial area. Note how conspicuous the *peppered* moth is, whereas the dark form blends into the background.

of the blackened trunks and were thus inconspicuous. As a result the light moths disappeared in the industrial regions, though they have been able to maintain their numbers in the rural areas of England.

We can explain these observations utilizing our knowledge of genetics and applying the rules of natural selection. Gene mutations must have always occurred in the population of these moths producing an occasional dark form, but these were immediately preyed upon owing to their conspicuous coloration. When metropolitan areas became industrialized, the gases and soot belching forth from the factory chimneys killed the lichens, thus changing the background upon which the moths rested. Now the dark color became an advantage and the light color a disadvantage, hence the dark-colored moths were selected for and preserved in the population. The light moths, on the other hand, were selected against and disappeared from the population. This phenomenon has been observed to occur in many other species of moths in those areas of Europe and the United States where industry is heavily concentrated. This demonstrates natural selection in action and results from man's efforts to change the face of the earth.

Attempts have been made to classify natural and artificial selection into several types. The first type of selection has been called **directional;** that is, those individuals which vary in one general direction are favored whereas those that vary in the opposite direction are eliminated. The classical case of this type of selection is horse evolution which is described later (p. 763).

The second type is known as **stabilizing selection** which tends to keep down the numbers of deleterious mutant genes and gene combinations. This stabilizes and protects the normal development pattern of the species. It is anti-evolutionary in its effects because it tends to stop change. Examples of this type of selection are the

most common and are responsible for the stability of a species. Buck deer with too large antlers would be as disadvantageous as one with too small antlers, although for different reasons. In any environment there is an optimum antler size that promotes success of its owner. Mutants either way would tend to be eliminated and the population would maintain the optimal antler size. This demonstrates the fact that most mutations are harmful.

A third type is **dynamic selection** which permits the species to maintain itself in its changing environment and to take advantage of new ecological opportunities as they become available. Alterations of climate, contact with new parasites, predators, or competitors, destruction of food sources, all bring pressure to bear on the species. If new genotypes are not available the species fails to survive. Therefore dynamic natural selection involves the establishment of new genotypes that provide the animal with the means to adapt to the new environmental conditions. Even though we know that new genotypes are a result of mutation and recombination, it is reasonable to say that new genotypes are *produced* by selection. Over a long period of time selection is the principle force which directs evolution because it determines which genotypes survive, and these are the only ones in which mutations can occur.

Genetic Drift. Chance also plays an important part in evolution. Not all populations are large; some small segment of a larger population becomes isolated frequently by accident, and of necessity interbreeds. Thus by chance heterozygous gene pairs become homozygous for one allele or the other. This is called **genetic drift** and is an exception to the Hardy-Weinberg Law which holds only for large populations. The differences noted within small populations of the same species may be explained by genetic drift.

Large populations possess a great many

genes in their *gene pool* and no small group would possess all of them in the same proportion as they exist in the large population. Therefore, if a small group, by accident, became transported to some distant land their composite gene pool more than likely would not be representative of the entire population. Interbreeding through subsequent generations would tend to emphasize the genes they possess and in the proportion that existed in the original small population.

An example of genetic drift can be drawn from *Homo sapiens*. A small group (28 persons) of Germans, called the Dunkers, migrated to Pennsylvania in the early part of the eighteenth century. Owing to strict religious beliefs they have remained segregated up the present time. A number of characteristics of this group were studied and it was found, for example, that there was a high percentage of the ABO blood groups among them. The results were compared with those taken from the original stock from which the Dunkers came, still living in Germany, and the general American population. The outcome demonstrated evidence for genetic drift as regarding the percentage of type A blood. The Dunkers show 59.3 per cent, the original stock, 44.6, and the American population as a whole, 39.2 per cent. Obviously, the early migrants possessed a higher percentage of genes for blood type A than the German population from which they came, and have maintained it since. There seems to be no evidence that selection has played a role, since there is no advantage of one type of blood over another. It seems that pure chance was the only factor involved.

Genetic drift may operate in other ways. Frequently when the population of a species becomes extremely high, disease of one sort or another becomes epidemic, killing off a large proportion of the population. Natural selection operates by preserving those that possess resistance to the disease. It does not matter how selectively

advantageous other genes are if the individual which possesses them does not have the genes that control the production of antibodies against the disease. He dies and is eliminated from the population. The resistant animals that remain may possess quite a different frequency of genes when compared to those in the original large population. Genetic drift may then operate and the following generations possess characteristics in proportions quite different from those in the original population.

Isolation

Darwin realized, as have most biologists since, that isolation played a very important part in the origin of new species, but it was not until inheritance was thoroughly understood that the full meaning of isolation became apparent. It is known now that in addition to **geographic isolation, genetic isolation** is also essential for the origin of new varieties and eventually new species. Genetic isolation may even be the more important. Let us consider each of these briefly.

Geographic. Darwin and many other naturalists noted very early that animals living on an island were frequently quite different from those on the neighboring mainland. Other barriers, such as a mountain range, a deep canyon, a wide body of water, or a desert, have been known to separate members of a species long enough for differences to be detected between the two groups. For example, there are two closely related species of squirrels on the two opposite rims of the Grand Canyon, different only in color markings. Undoubtedly, at one time they migrated freely from one rim to the other but eventually, because of the great depth of the canyon and the turbulence of the Colorado River, they were unable to mingle as they had in the past. Today they are gradually changing, though slightly, in spite of the fact that the environment is almost identical.

It is understandable that when a barrier occurs in the range of a given species so that groups of individuals of that species are completely separated, the continual occurrence of mutations and the slightly different environments acting selectively upon them will eventually bring about divergence of the two groups. If the barrier continues for a sufficiently long period of time, the differences may become sufficient to constitute two species. If the barrier is then removed so that the two groups once again intermingle they will probably maintain their identity as different species. However, if the barrier is removed at a time when they have not changed enough, that is, while they are still varieties, it is possible that the differences may be lost through interbreeding. The latter instance is illustrated by the human species, *Homo sapiens.* Although he has occupied nearly all portions of the earth's surface and does show some marked physical variations, the various races have not lost their ability to interbreed. The barriers that have been set up between races have not been effective sufficiently long to bring about infertility. With the intervention of modern means of transportation those original geographic barriers can be overcome, so theoretically man should lose what changes have been produced by this isolation, providing there is a free mingling of all races. But such, as we all know, is not the case. Society places barriers that can be as effective as infertility or vast geographical obstacles. However, while it is possible it seems highly improbable that such practices will lead to a new species of mankind. Indeed, the social barriers seem likely to continue to grow less as time passes, with the resultant merging of existing races.

It is interesting to note that under natural conditions hybridization is only rarely observed among closely related species of animals. To be sure, it has been possible to effect it under laboratory conditions—the biscow, for example, as a result of the mating of a bison and a cow—but such cases are unusual and do not normally occur in nature. Since the animals occupy the same environment and are therefore subject to the same conditions, why do they not mate freely and thus reverse the differences established earlier through isolation, inducing reverse evolution in this way? This question can best be answered from a study of genetics.

Genetic. When two species or even varieties mate the genes are not as perfectly compatible as they were in the common ancestor. This results in low fertility or in most cases complete sterility. Thus such crosses under natural conditions would be unfruitful if they did occur and the hybrid would have little chance of establishing itself. Also, the hybrid itself is often sterile, as is true of the mule previously referred to (p. 683). Furthermore, slight differences in the mating season might act as a barrier even though the animals were fertile. These and many other slight differences act as barriers to keep the two species distinct and separate.

Many kinds of gene changes occur, from slight modifications in the gene itself to an alteration in the arrangement of the genes on the chromosomes, any of which may make fertility impossible. Under laboratory conditions these changes sometimes occur spontaneously in a species that in all other respects is like the parent form. Such genetic changes are as effective in isolating animals as any physical barrier could be. Many biologists agree that interfertility is the acid test of a species. No matter what other characteristics two species may have in common, they are distinct species if they lack interfertility. The problem of establishing species on such a basis is almost hopeless at the present time because of our lack of information concerning the genetic constitution of all but a few species of animals. These are the animals extensively used in the laboratory, such as Drosophila, mice, rats, and paramecium.

Neotony. A long-known observation among different groups of animals may well be one of the important forces that brings about evolutionary change. This is the curious phenomenon of **neotony** where sexual maturity occurs during the larval or juvenile stage of the animal. It occurs among insects, the early vertebrates, and may explain how man came to be the strange animal he is. Great steps in evolution, called *macroevolution,* may be explained by neotony.

The classical case among vertebrates is the Mexican axolotyl (p. 361). Normally a salamander breathes by means of external gills during the larval stage but develops lungs in the adult. The axolotyl becomes sexually mature during the larval stage and never does acquire air-breathing lungs. Thus an animal has drastically changed by the simple procedure of becoming sexually mature at a time in its life cycle when its body is quite unlike the normal adult. This could account for a major step in evolution, perhaps in a very short time and without the usual microevolutionary steps by which it is believed most evolution takes place. This observation becomes quite startling when applied to man.

Adult man in physical appearance is more similar in many ways to a young ape than to the adult ape. Such physical characteristics as the relatively huge brain, the form of the teeth, the flatness of the face, hairlessness, angle of the head with the trunk, and the sutures between the bones of the skull, all resemble those in the baby ape. These observations led Bolk in 1926 to call man a neotonous primate. Perhaps man has simply lost the capacity to mature and remains, in part, in the juvenile stage.

Cooperation

Such phrases as "struggle for existence" and "survival of the fittest" appealed to the emotions of many people of Victorian England and spurred them on to provide such other phrases as "eat or be eaten" and "nature red in tooth and claw." This idea of rugged competition seemed to reflect the attitude of industrialists of this period and helped justify their methods. However, in the current century, with the advent of genetics and a better perspective of the problem of evolution, it became clear not only that biological theories could not be used to explain (much less justify) economic or social phenomena but that the fierceness of the struggle for existence leading to natural selection was greatly overemphasized as well. It became apparent that the *fit* survived, not the *fittest,* which implied that only one survived. And this survival could be the result of cooperation as well as competition. Fighting, pugnacity, and aggressiveness are often less conducive to biological success than cooperation. To "live and let live" promotes the welfare of species as much as mortal combat. Indeed, success depends on both cooperation and competition; at one time struggle may be important, at another cooperation. Survival of the offspring of a species may depend on parental care as well as fierce defense. Today we are inclined to interpret natural selection as including both cooperation and competition.

DIRECTION OF EVOLUTION

At the beginning of life there must have first existed only one species. After a time this must have varied as a result of mutations, thus giving natural selection an opportunity to initiate evolution. It is conceivable that evolution might have proceeded in any or all directions, and perhaps it did at first, but after a time it seems to have headed in a certain rather general but definite direction, which has continued more or less uninterrupted ever since. This is as one would expect, because genes, being chemical entities, would be apt to change in fairly similar ways. Because of their structural nature it would seem impossible for them to change in any or all directions. Similar mutations do appear repeatedly, as a matter of fact, indicating that the same gene changes again and again. Since mutations can occur only within certain limits, the resulting organisms will then be able to change only in certain ways. This would have the effect of guiding any possible mutations in a general direction so that evolution could proceed in that direction and no other. While evolution may have been random at first, it has since become oriented or directed so that today

it is occurring along specific lines. This idea is often referred to as **orthogenesis** or **straight-line evolution.** While, in general, it does occur and evolution is not totally random, it is not as directional as was once thought. One of the classic evidences for straight-line evolution is that of the horse.

Horse Evolution

The modern horse has had an interesting evolution and one that can be followed better than most because of the abundance of fossils left from the Eocene to the present and because most of them were found in North America where much digging has

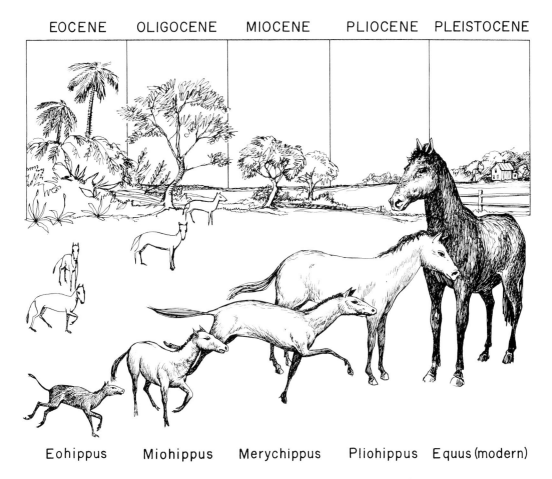

EOCENE   OLIGOCENE   MIOCENE   PLIOCENE   PLEISTOCENE

Eohippus   Miohippus   Merychippus   Pliohippus   Equus (modern)

FIG. 27-5. The evolution of the horse illustrates orthogenesis. Probably these animals did not progress along a direct path from the tiny Eophippus to Equus but rather there were many deviations along the way. Progress was in a general way toward the present-day horse, but there were many paths that led to extinction.

been going on during the past 200 years.

Eohippus, the earliest known ancestor of the horse, and perhaps the tapirs and rhinoceroses as well, occurred in early Eocene times and was anatomically quite remote from *Equus,* our modern horse (Fig. 27-5). It was about the size of a jackrabbit and possessed functional toes on each appendage, four in front and three behind. There were rudiments of others which, when accounted for, demonstrated that the animal had descended from an ancestor with five digits, the usual number among vertebrates. In the forefeet only the inside or "thumb" was rudimentary while in the hind feet both the thumb and the "little finger" were missing but could be seen as functionless splints along the next foot bone. The teeth of *Eohippus* were also quite different from those of the modern horse. They had short crowns and long roots nicely adapted for browsing in and around the edges of forests. The face was short, the eyes placed well over the teeth. These tiny mammals apparently lived in seclusion, feeding on succulent leaves and avoiding contact with the huge mammals of this period.

In the Oligocene we find a somewhat larger animal, *Miohippus,* with only three toes on the forefeet, although a rudiment of a fourth remained. The middle toe on each foot apparently bore the brunt of the weight of the animal because it was much larger than those on either side. Otherwise, there were few changes from *Eohippus.*

During the Miocene *Merychippus* came into prominence, still with three toes but with added emphasis on the middle one which bore all of the body weight. The other two toes, while externally visible, appear to have been of little or no use to the animal. The molar teeth possessed rather high crowns and the flat nature of the upper surfaces indicates that these animals were grazers rather than browsers, that is, they fed on grasses in the open

prairie lands rather than on leaves in the forests. The face was longer, thus displacing the orbit posteriorly. *Merychippus* was larger than any of the horses up to that time, standing about 3 or 4 feet in height.

This gradual tendency toward greater size and reduction of the number of toes continued into the Pliocene, where *Pliohippus* was without external lateral toes, although retaining splints indicating the historic loss. Thus, in *Pliohippus* we see only a single toe or hoof, a character which has remained unchanged up to the present. This animal also possessed teeth better adapted for chewing grass and its general anatomy resembled that of the modern horse.

Horses that appeared in the Pleistocene had acquired essentially the same proportions as the modern horse. There is a single hoof on each foot, although paired lateral splints give evidence of the ancient toes of its forebears. On rare occasions a colt is born with the two lateral toes visible externally, thus reminiscent of its ancestors. The tendency toward a longer face has continued with the result that the eye is located at the edge of the most posterior molars. The teeth are beautifully adapted for grinding grasses, which form the principal diet of these animals. The size is larger than any of the earlier horses, and by selective breeding man has produced the kinds of horses he desires, from Shetland ponies to draft horses.

Through a period of 60 million years, the horse has evolved from a tiny animal living in the forest for protection and feeding on succulent leaves to a huge grass-eating beast roaming the prairies where fleet-footedness is essential for survival. This seems to be a case of straight-line evolution. Without going into a lengthy discussion of the reasons, it is now becoming clear that the evolution of the horse has not been as straight-line as might appear. Simpson, for example, believes that horses as well as other animals have never gone straight toward a goal but, instead, have pushed out in many directions at succeeding stages in their evolution, with one part of the anatomy such as the teeth going forward more rapidly at times than other parts. In other words, there have been many lines of horse evolution all along the way, each evolving in different directions but in the general direction of the modern horse. Some of these survived to give rise to the next great step whereas others became extinct. Indeed, he believes that the most direct line from *Eohippus* was not to the modern horse but to an extinct horse called *Hypohippus*. Apparently, then, the direction from *Eohippus* to *Equus* has not been a straight one but rather one with many deviations, jogs left and right, some paths leading to extinction, others carrying on to the next, perhaps only then to become extinct.

What, then, keeps this whole trend delimited to one general progressive course? There must be forces operating continuously to bring about this over-all trend, forces that seem forever to "nudge" the line in a general direction. Environment alone cannot be the answer because we know from genetics that mutations occur regardless of environmental changes, although it undoubtedly does play a part. When neither of two factors is the whole answer, both must operate simultaneously; both the environment and the functional capacities of the organism interact, resulting in the ultimate fitting of the latter to the former. This we call **adaptation,** the most significant outcome of evolution, about which we shall have more to say later.

Opportunity in Evolution

Another feature that is probably important in oriented evolution, which also involves the relation of organisms and environment, is the relative time or coincidence with which these impinge upon one another. When the environment is just right for an animal to evolve in a certain direc-

tion, the animal must not only be present but must also be sufficiently adaptable (have sufficient mutations available) to take advantage of the opportunity. Simpson called this "Opportunism of Evolution." Because of these environmental opportunities, animals follow within certain restricted limits, progressing toward an apparent goal, as in the case of the horse. As the environment changes, the organisms change with it. Living things themselves constitute more opportunities by providing a new environment; the body of a vertebrate as a home for a blood parasite is an illustration. Thus new environments are constantly being created (and others destroyed) which open up more and more opportunities for a greater variety of living things. This has produced an untold number of kinds of animals, of which probably over a million are alive today. Evolution constantly operates with materials available. Frequently a structure is produced that may not be perfect but serves a purpose more or less satisfactorily. Perhaps there is no structure in the body of any animal that performs its function to a perfect degree. Why, then, are not all of the organs of animals perfect, or more broadly, why is the animal itself more or less imperfect in every detail? There is constant selection among physical variations after they appear and a constant process of adaptation, but complete and absolute fitness to the environment in every conceivable way seems quite impossible to attain.

To illustrate this point, any one of hundreds of examples in any animal or group of animals might be chosen. The matter of photoreception, which was reviewed previously in the various animal groups, is a good illustration of how all groups of animals have devised some method of receiving light rays. This is an important adjunct to orientation in the environment and, accordingly, every animal can make good use of an organ for photoreception. Among all of the photo-

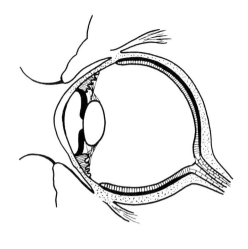

FIG. 27-6. There is a remarkable similarity between the molluscan (cuttlefish, left) and vertebrate (human, right) eyes, yet they have evolved along two quite different pathways. This type of evolution is called convergent evolution and is abundantly illustrated among animals.

receptors there is none that we might call a perfect photoreceptor. The primate eye is one of the best and we are all aware of its imperfections. We have been able to build a better one in the laboratory—one that will do things the human eye cannot approach. Furthermore, our eyes seem to do a rather good job during adolescence and early maturity but fail in the later years. Evolution has tended toward the production of a satisfactory animal body that can reach maturity after which it becomes more imperfect, eventually dying due to the failure of its separate parts.

There are various types of photoreceptors among animals from the very simple eye spots in the protozoa to the complex molluscan and vertebrate eyes. All gradations are found from those that merely record light and darkness to those that form crude images and finally to those that produce clear, distinct images. We need only recall the crude patches of pigmented cells in planaria (p. 231) to see a photoreceptor that is very primitive yet sufficient for the species to survive. A better eye would be of no value because the animal does not possess a nervous system adequate to record such impressions if they were received.

Hence, the eye has paralleled the development of other organs of the body, and has usually been as good as needed to maintain the species. We might argue that man could conveniently use an eye with the speed of perception that is possessed by a photoelectric cell, but our brains could not receive and interpret the impressions that would come through such eyes.

From the planarian eye we see steady improvement concomitant with the development of organ systems until finally among the mollusks, arthropods, and vertebrates we see the best eyes of all. It is interesting to note that each of these types has faced the same problem but has solved it differently. The arthropod eye consists of many tiny units aggregated into a compound structure which forms many images, giving a composite picture (p. 307). Thus, the problem of receiving light has been satisfactorily solved but in an entirely different manner from that of the mollusk or vertebrate. On the other hand, the likeness of the vertebrate and squid or cuttlefish eye (Fig. 27-6) is amazing. The fact that two such distantly related groups of animals could solve photoreception in almost identical ways seems incredible. Each animal had different materials at hand to build a photoreceptor and each built it differently, but both came out with essentially the same organ, varying only in the placement of the sensory cells of the retina (the rods and cones in the vertebrate are directed away from the light source, whereas in the molluscan eye they are reversed). The pathways by which these eyes were formed is entirely different in the two groups, which merely proves the earlier contention that animals solve similar problems in different ways.

Divergence and Convergence in Evolution

As opportunities have presented themselves, animals have evolved in many directions with respect to certain organs in order to take advantage of all possible en-

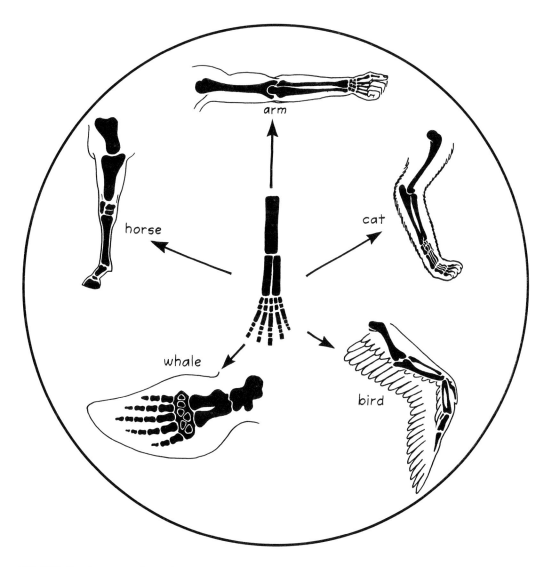

FIG. 27-7. The front appendage of vertebrates illustrates divergent evolution. The hypothetical vertebrate appendage was a five-toed structure which has been modified in many ways as represented by the arm of man, the front leg of the cat, the wing of the bird, the flipper of the whale, and the front leg of the horse. Each modification satisfies the needs of the particular animal living in an environment that requires such an appendage for survival.

vironments. This is called **divergent evolution** or **adaptive radiation.** At some later time some members of various groups have evolved toward life in a particular environment; this is called **convergent evolution.** The manner in which these two types of evolution operate can best be understood by following a specific structure or organ through its evolution in several groups of animals. A good example is the forefoot of land vertebrates.

The ancestral land vertebrate appendage was a five-toed structure designed for surface locomotion. As new environments became available the forefoot underwent **divergent evolution,** becoming highly modified for locomotion in many ways. For example, it became a single-toed leg in horses, a five-toed clawed leg in cats, a flipper in whales, an arm in man, and a bird's wing (Fig. 27-7). This fundamental five-digited structure has become an effective instrument for locomotion in water, on land, and in the air. This is the situation in which we find vertebrates today. But long before vertebrates reached their present state, ancestral forms, even after they became adapted to land life, had the opportunity of taking to the air which has some obvious advantages over locomotion on land. Members of three groups took advantage of this opportunity and underwent **convergent evolution** toward locomotion in the air. These were: first, the reptiles (pterodactyls), then the birds, and finally the mammals (bats) (Fig. 27-8). They all produced wings which were essentially the same, although varying slightly in minor details. None of them are perfect instruments of flight, yet they are sufficiently good to permit both the birds and the bats very real success, the former more than the latter. The pterodactyls became extinct for unknown reasons, but it seems unlikely that the ability to fly was a contributing factor.

Another case of convergent evolution is illustrated by still other members of these same three groups (reptiles, birds, and mammals) which returned to the water and became modified in many ways for an aquatic life (Fig. 27-8). The primitive reptile *Ichthyosaurus* took on the shape of a modern fish and its appendages became fin-like. The whale, a mammal, developed fish-like appendages and body form. The penguin, a bird, lost its ability to fly but became a proficient swimmer, using its wings as flippers.

Finally divergent evolution is nicely illustrated in Australia where the ancient marsupial stock gave rise to a variety of animals that closely parallel the placental mammals on other continents (Fig. 27-9). For example, there are shrew-like marsupials, squirrel-like marsupials, dog-like marsupials and many others. It appears that, given only marsupials to begin with and no carnivores to destroy them, divergence has been commensurate with the possible niches, paralleling similar situations where placental mammals were the starting point. There are many similar cases of divergent and convergent evolution among animals that could be cited. They confirm one of the fundamental features of evolution, namely, that all opportunities are exploited with the materials at hand. How far the diversification goes depends on the animal and its supply of mutations, as well as the number of environments in which the animal can survive.

EVOLUTION THROUGH EXPERIMENTATION

Under natural conditions, animal hybridization probably is of little significance in evolution, although there are cases in which new species of plants have apparently arisen as a result of such natural crossing. Domestication among animals was carefully studied by Darwin and he used the results of these studies as a potent argument in favor of natural selection. He observed, as we all have, that under the influence of selective breeding a wide variety of ani-

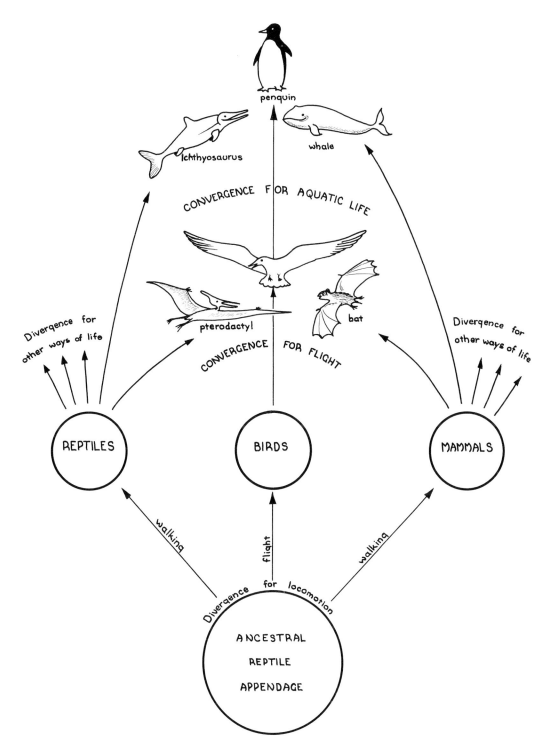

FIG. 27-8. Divergent and convergent evolution can be illustrated by a study of the anterior appendages of three different groups of vertebrates. The ancestral reptile appendages diverged for locomotion (walking and flying) at a very early time. Some members of each class (reptiles, birds, mammals) subsequently underwent convergence toward flight and life in the water by modifying their anterior appendages to function more effectively in these environments.

FIG. 27-9. A comparison of placental (left) and marsupial (right) mammals illustrating divergent evolution in both groups based on their modes of life. (Top to bottom) Those that are adapted for feeding on ants (*Tamandua tetradactyla* and *Myrmecobius fasciatus*), the mole-like forms that are adapted for burrowing (*Parascalops breweri* and *Motoryctes typhlops*), squirrels that are modified for soaring (*Glaucomys volans* and *Petaurus sciureus*), and wolf-like carnivorous animals (*Vulpes vulpes* and *Thylacinus cynocephalus*).

mals can be produced and if such forms appeared in nature, they certainly would be assigned different species names. Darwin argued that new species could come into being by substituting man as the selective agent. Since the environment was not endowed with reasoning powers, the tendency would be to select in many different directions with the ultimate goal always the adaptation to the particular environment in which the animal found itself.

Under the guiding hand of man a prodigious variety of animals have been produced to satisfy his whims, whether it be for food, as in the case of chickens and cattle, or for entertainment, as in the case of canaries and racing horses. He has done a notable job in the chicken, for example, which varies from the cocky Bantam to the tremendous Brahmin and is a far cry from the Oriental jungle fowl from which present-day chickens are largely or wholly descended. This ancestor laid perhaps two dozen eggs per year, whereas some present-day breeds equal that number in a month. The domestic chicken would soon become extinct if suddenly removed from the protection of domestication and set free in a natural environment. Domesticated animals seem to preserve their interfertility, quite contrary to conditions found in nature. The reason why they do is that man plans it. Sterile animals are of no use to him, so he has selected them for high fertility along with other traits that he wishes to accentuate. Even with some of his domestic animals the beginnings of infertility have been evident. For example, some crosses between dogs are all but impossible, as between a very large one and a very small one. Furthermore, some crosses often produce malformed animals that soon die, or again the number of offspring may be small. The incompatibilities noted now, after several hundred generations, may, perhaps, become so great that a strict genetic barrier will be placed between certain varieties of dogs alive today, inaugurating a new

FIG. 27-10. A case of protective coloration. Find the chipmunk.

species. If that happens, man will have created a new species and thus controlled evolution under his own guidance. We must conclude, therefore, that in the domestication process, man has within his grasp the very mechanism by which evolution proceeds.

THE END RESULT OF EVOLUTION: ADAPTATION

Out of all this should come animals remarkably adapted to their environment but, as we have already seen, this is not completely so. In spite of the rather careless way in which most animals are keyed to their environments, certain examples of adaptation forever intrigue the naturalist and the layman. Among these, color adaptations are particularly interesting.

The matter of camouflage is an important factor in survival and is used almost universally by animals. Such concealing or **protective** coloration has been selected for, and the outer coverings of some animals match their background astoundingly well

771

FIG. 27-11. These two snakes demonstrate mimicry in animals. The poisonous coral snake (*Micrurus fulvius tenere*), in the top picture, is mimicked by the false coral snake (*Oxyrhopus baileyi*). Note the remarkable resemblance between the two.

carries a potent defensive or offensive weapon, such as a venomous snake or a honeybee, for example (Fig. 27-11). Such well-equipped animals are frequently highly colored; this advertises their danger and warns unsuspecting predators that might take them by mistake. Hence a much lesser creature that might be a choice morsel finds distinct value in resembling the more formidable one. Some animals mimic living or dead leaves, and certain butterflies are so faithful in such resemblance that they may go unobserved even by a careful naturalist (Fig. 27-12). Even the veins of the leaves are portrayed by similar markings in the wings of the insect. These adaptations and many others undoubtedly have a marked effect on survival, but every such case is open to question and should be interpreted in the light of actual observations.

Things of much greater importance than color, body shape, horns, claws, and similar characters are such physiological qualities as ability to resist disease, high or low temperatures, desiccation, and so on. Fitness for a specific environment involves many qualities, and it is the product of all of them that makes for survival. It follows that most of them must be favorable, although an animal may survive and be rather successful while carrying along some unfavorable traits. When the weight of the adverse qualities exceeds that of the favorable ones the animal becomes extinct. This has happened to millions of races in the distant past and has happened in recent times, as in the case of the passenger pigeon.

Adaptations tend toward better and better fitness for the environment which results in specialization (Fig. 27-13). When this has been carried to the extreme, the animal is said to be "overspecialized," a fact which biologists have long considered important in the extinction of certain species and even large groups of animals. Specialization is inevitable, and all animals are specialized, some much more than

(Fig. 27-10). Most animals, particularly those that fly or swim, are dark on the dorsal side and white or lighter in color on the ventral side. Thus potential predators from beneath looking up will be less apt to see them because they blend with the sky and those from above would experience the same difficulty because of blending with the darker earth or stream bottom. Other animals, such as fish, frogs, and lizards, can change their skin color to match the background upon which they happen to find themselves. Such concealing coloration is also advantageous to the predator because it can go unobserved until the prey moves into striking range. The positive survival value of such colorations has been shown by experimentation in which the prey with colors most in contrast to the background is always picked up first by the predators.

Some animals have found survival value in **mimicking** another species that

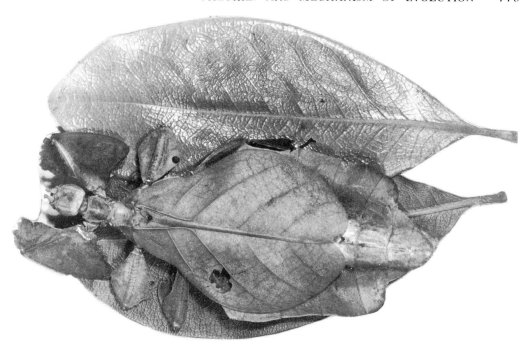

FIG. 27-12. Certain insects resemble leaves upon which they rest, a circumstance which obscures them from their enemies.

FIG. 27-13. This is a photograph of the attachment organ of the shark sucker, a bony fish that adheres to the ventral surface of sharks, thus getting a free ride. This is not only a remarkable case of adaptation but also one of commensalism.

FIG. 27-14. A case of "overspecialization." This is the skull of a wild boar. The upper canine teeth have grown upward through the top of the snout and curved so that they could have little function as defensive weapons. The lower canines might have a little more value in this regard.

others (Fig. 27-14). Land animals, for instance, are adapted for obtaining oxygen from air, and if the earth were suddenly covered with water they would all be eliminated. This is specialization in a broad sense. As adaptation proceeds, animals become adapted to narrower and narrower limits of their environments and some, such as ruminants, have become adapted to eating grass and probably could not survive if all grasses of the earth were destroyed. Thus survival is intricately linked with consistency of specific environments.

The more an animal becomes specialized, the more closely it is forced to live in the environment for which it is fitted. Therefore, the more generalized types are less apt to become extinct. For example, omnivores are more apt to survive under conditions where the food is likely to change than strict herbivores or carnivores. If food becomes scarce and the omnivorous animal can no longer exist as a predator it can subsist on vegetable matter, or it may devour some vegetable matter and some meat as the situation demands. This is one of the reasons why the crow is so successful, since it feeds on carrion, grain, leaves, or almost any other form of food. Obviously, then, as animals become more specialized they are endangering their possibility of survival.

The Irish elk is often used to illustrate this point. While its overspecialized antlers were undoubtedly an important factor in its extinction, they probably were not the whole story. It seems that with each succeeding generation of this animal the antlers became larger and more complex until they became so fantastic that it is difficult to understand how the animal could manage them at all. It must have required much of the elk's metabolic output to supply materials for their construction, to say nothing of the burden of supporting them. Here is a case of progressive adaptation for a structure which had decided survival value when it first appeared, but which eventually became a factor in eliminating the species. However, our information is not complete and one must be cautious in drawing conclusions because other factors in its environment may have been equally important. For example, a sudden increase in wolves or a virulent disease, in addition to its cumbersome antlers, could have hastened the departure of this beautiful animal.

EVOLUTION AND THE FUTURE

Some believe that evolution has run its course and that all of the niches of the world have been filled so that no further change is possible. Furthermore, others contend that the apotheosis of evolution, namely, man, has been attained and there is now "no place to go." One might be inclined to agree with these contentions if there were no evidence of evolution going on around us and if man had become perfect in every respect, leaving no room for improvement. Most of us would not sub-

scribe to either of these statements. From what we know of the past it seems likely that as long as there is life on earth there will be continuing change or evolution. The directions it will take are unpredictable to us now, but that it will continue seems assured.

To be sure, the abundance of life in existence now might suggest that all of the possible environments capable of supporting life have been taken, leaving no room for any more forms. A similar situation might have seemed to be true even in the Cambrian, where all of the present phyla had their representatives. There were fewer niches then but all of them were probably filled, and as ages passed new niches appeared and new species filled them. There is no reason to believe that a similar process is not going on at the present time. New environments are constantly being created and those animals with an ample supply of mutations move into them, with the aid of natural selection. There will come a time, perhaps a billion or so years in the future, when all life will cease, but up to the end living things will undoubtedly attempt to adapt.

It is highly probable that the evolution of certain groups could be repeated if the ones living today were wiped out. Many of the "immortals" such as *Sphenodon* and the opossum are still with us and perhaps they could radiate once again, giving rise to new groups of reptiles and mammals. Undoubtedly the new forms would not be exactly like the ones we see today, but they might be as diversified. One might ask why the opossum has not done this very thing today, why it is still essentially the same creature that lived in the Cretaceous. The most obvious reason is that placental mammals have occupied nearly all of the environments that are available to it and the competition gives it little opportunity to crowd in. Hence it has been able only to maintain itself up to the present. But if the placental mammals were suddenly re-

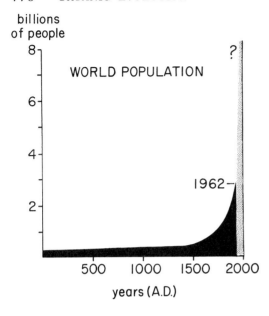

billions
of people

WORLD POPULATION

1962

500   1000   1500   2000

years (A.D.)

FIG. 27-15. Human populations follow the logarithmic growth curve just as other organisms do. This graph shows the curve for the entire world population from the beginning of the Christian Era to the year 2000. The extrapolated curve beyond 1962 indicates a population of over 8 billion by the year 2000.

moved, the descendants of the opossum would soon fill the spaces left and there would be rapid evolution among the various forms, just as there was in Australia.

Likewise, if the human species came to an abrupt end, the spaces left would be filled by other forms, perhaps not exact duplicates but certainly some possessing the unique qualities of man. The entire trend in evolution has been toward a more intricate coordinating system, and there is no reason to believe that such a trend would cease if there were no animals possessing those qualities on the earth. To be sure, no other groups are likely to usurp that position among animals so long as man maintains his present place. Unless he retrogresses, it is highly improbable that any other group could match or excel him in reasoning power.

What does future evolution hold for man? Can he profit by what he knows about this grand drama of evolution, can

he control its future trends with respect to the animals around him, and most important, can he control it with respect to his own destiny? These are the really important problems that scientists and laymen alike wish to understand and, of course, they are the most difficult to answer. We might speculate briefly about them in the closing sentences of this book.

The evolution of man has placed him in a unique position among animals in that he is the first and only animal who can control his environment to a greater or lesser extent. He builds shelters, clothes his body, plans his food needs and provides for them, and in general improves his physical environment wherever his own ingenuity and available materials will permit. He knows enough about evolution to take advantage of it in controlling animal and plant life around him, which enhances his own chances for survival. In other words, he can give evolution direction with a goal. He is rapidly gaining greater and greater control over his environment in all respects, so that his continued existence is more assured from that point than it ever has been. However, there is a sinister aspect to all of this because, while he has acquired sufficient knowledge to direct evolution to a certain extent in the organic world about him, he has done almost nothing in directing his own evolution, either physical or social. Further confusing the issue, he has at his disposal means by which he can annihilate himself, in which respect he is unique among animals. Moreover, he seems to be little concerned about either the quality or the quantities of his members. Man, like all animals, has the capacity to reproduce himself far beyond his food supply, if no checks intercede. In all parts of the world populations are "exploding," primarily as a result of a drop in death rates. At the present time approximately 270,000 babies are born each day and only 142,000 people die, leaving a daily increase of 128,000. This means that each year approximately 47,000,000 individuals are added to the total world population. As you will observe from Figure 27-15 by the year 2,000 the population will reach between 6 and 8 billion as compared to 2.9 billion in 1960. Since this is a logarithmic curve (p. 129), the situation will be compounded with each year thereafter until human protoplasm will crowd everything else off the earth. It has been estimated that if the present rate continues by the year 2,500 there would be 5 square yards of the earth's surface for each person. The heart of New York City has one person for every 35 square yards today, and most people would agree that even this concentration covering deserts and mountain peaks would hardly be compatible with the "good life." There seems little doubt that the "population problem" must be dealt with as hastily as possible. Even now sociologists, as well as biologists, are deeply concerned and many already fear it is too late to bring about effective controls.

Because man's social evolution has not kept pace with his ability to control his physical environment, he may destroy himself either by breeding himself "out of house and home" or by physical destruction through modern warfare, neither of which are inevitable. It seems that a creature with such a remarkable nervous system, who is able to control his earthly environment, and contemplate extraplanetary excursions, should be able to manage his own development, the facts for which he has before him. But there is the matter of time, even if the earnest intention is there. Will we act soon enough? If we do, *Homo sapiens* could evolve into a better adapted man both physically and socially; if we do not, our place will be taken by some lesser creature.

SUGGESTED SUPPLEMENTARY READINGS

BATES, M., and HUMPHREY, P. S., *The Darwin Reader* (New York, Charles Scribner's Sons, 1956).

CARTER, G. S., *Animal Evolution: A Study of Recent Views of Its Cause* (London, Jidgwick and Jackson, 1951).

CROW, J. F., "Ionizing Radiation and Evolution," *Scientific American,* 201(3) (September, 1959), 138.

DARWIN, C., *On the Origin of Species by Means of Natural Selection, or The Preservation of Favored Races in the Struggle for Life* (New York, Appleton-Century-Crofts, 1875).

DOBZHANSKY, T., "The Genetic Basis of Evolution," *Scientific American,* 182(1) (January, 1950), 32.

LACK, D., "Darwin's Finches," *Scientific American,* 188(4) (April, 1953), 66.

SIMPSON, G. G., *The Meaning of Evolution* (New Haven, Yale University Press, 1951).

Classification of the
Animal Kingdom

[Rather detailed and intended for reference only]

SUBKINGDOM—PROTOZOA

PHYLUM PROTOZOA. Protozoa. Mostly unicellular, some colonial. Habitat moist or aquatic, fresh water and marine. Free-living or parasitic. Sexual and asexual reproduction. Classification is based on methods of locomotion.

    SUBPHYLUM PLASMODROMA. Possess flagella at some stage of the life cycle, some have pseudopods and show amoeboid movement. Adult sporozoa immotile. Sexual reproduction in some.

        Class Mastigophora. Move by means of flagella. Mostly free-living, some parasitic. Chlorophyll present in some, thus demonstrating primitiveness. *Euglena, Chlamydomonas, Volvox, Trypanosoma.*

        Class Sarcodina. Move by means of pseudopods, a few by flagella. Mostly free-living, some parasitic. *Amoeba, Entamoeba, Actinophrys, Peneroplis.*

        Class Sporozoa. Adult immotile. All parasitic, most with complex life cycles involving sexual stages. *Plasmodium, Eimeria, Nosema.*

    SUBPHYLUM CILIOPHORA. Move by means of cilia or cirri (fused cilia). Macronucleus (metabolic) and micronucleus (genetic) present in most. Sexual reproduction.

        Class Ciliata. Mostly free-living, a few parasitic. Sexual reproduction by conjugation in many. *Paramecium, Tetrahymena, Stylonychia, Stentor, Vorticella.*

        Class Suctoria. Mature forms possess tentacles used in obtaining food. Adults are stalked and immotile, young forms are free-swimming and ciliated. Mostly free-living. *Podophrya, Tokophrya, Acineta.*

SUBKINGDOM—METAZOA

PHYLUM MESOZOA. Simplest of all metazoa. Consist of outer cellular layer, commonly ciliated, which encloses one or more reproductive cells. All parasitic. *Dicyemida.*

PHYLUM PORIFERA. Sponges. Adults are sedentary and the larvae flagellated. Loosely diploblastic but not true ectoderm and endoderm. Choanocytes. Spicules give support to body. Various canal systems.

    Class Calcispongiae. Spicules composed of calcium carbonate. Marine, shallow water. Ascon, sycon, and rhagon canal types. *Sycon, Leucosolenia, Scypha.*

    Class Hyalospongiae. Spicules composed of silicic acid (silica), hence known as "glass sponges." Deep-water, marine. Rhagon canal system. *Euplectella, Hyalonema.*

779

Class Demospongiae. Soft sponges. Skeletons of siliceous spicules and spongin fibers. Spicules absent in some species. Rhagon canal system. Fresh-water and marine. Value as sponges for man. *Spongia, Spongilla.*

PHYLUM COELENTERATA. Coelenterates. Basically two-layered animals (diploblastic), some show mesoglea cells. Single gastrovascular cavity with one opening. All are aquatic, mostly marine. Radially symmetrical. Nematocysts. Colonial forms demonstrate polymorphism.

Class Hydrozoa. Both polyps and medusae in life cycle. Velum in medusae. Variable size. Fresh and salt-water. *Hydra, Obelia, Gonionemus, Physalia.*

Class Scyphomedusae. Jellyfishes. Polyps reduced or absent. Umbrella margin of medusae notched, no velum. Cells in the mesoglea. *Pelagia, Cyanea.*

Class Anthozoa. Sea pens, sea anemones, corals. Polyps only, individual or colonial. Septa, mesenteries, and tentacles conspicuous. *Astrangia, Metridium, Cribrina.*

PHYLUM CTENOPHORA. Ctenophores (comb jellies, sea walnuts, cat's-eyes). Pelagic (floaters) and marine. Biradial symmetry. Comb-like structures a typical characteristic. All are free-swimming. *Cestum, Beroë.*

PHYLUM PLATYHELMINTHES. Flatworms. Dorsoventrally flattened and bilaterally symmetrical. Well-developed mesoderm, hence triploblastic. Mostly parasitic, some terrestrial, fresh-water, and marine. Mostly hermaphroditic (monoecious). Excretory system composed of flame-cells.

Class Turbellaria. Free-living flatworms. Externally ciliated. Mouth ventral. Fresh-water, marine, and terrestrial. *Planaria, Phagocata, Dugesia.*

Class Trematoda. Flukes. Cuticle forms external covering. Suckers present and mouth usually anterior. Parasitic. *Opisthorchis, Fasciola, Schistosoma.*

Class Cestoda. Tapeworms. Cuticle forms external covering. Scolex with suckers and (usually) hooks. Few to many proglottids. Parasitic. *Taenia, Echinococcus.*

PHYLUM NEMERTINEA. The nemertines. Possess a circulatory system, an anus, and an eversible proboscis enclosed in a tubular cavity called the rhynchocoel. Body form slender, flat and soft. Mostly marine. *Amphiporus.*

PHYLUM ASCHELMINTHES. Diverse group of animals. All possess pseudocoel. Simple digestive tract with muscular pharynx.

Class Rotifera. Wheel animals. Sexes separate (dioecious). Bilaterally symmetrical. Primitive flame-cells. Mostly free-living, some parasitic. Grinding organ, the mastax with well-developed jaws and wheel-like cilia on anterior end. *Epiphanes, Asplanchna.*

Class Nematoda. Round worms. External covering smooth. Cilia absent. Bilaterally symmetrical. Mostly dioecious. Complete digestive tract, mouth to anus. Tube-within-a-tube body plan. *Ascaris, Trichinella, Necator, Wuchereria.*

PHYLUM ACANTHOCEPHALA. Spiny-headed worms. Possess a pseudocoel. Slightly flattened. Proboscis present, usually bearing hooks. Dioecious. Parasitic in the intestines of vertebrates. *Gigantorhynchus.*

PHYLUM ENTROPROCTA. Small group of animals, mostly colonial, attached by a stalk. Ciliated tentacles. Pseudocoel is present. Mostly marine. *Pedicellina.*

PHYLUM ECTOPROCTA. Permanently attached animals which form arborescent or encrusting colonies. Possesses a special structure the lophophore. *Bugula.*

PHYLUM BRACHIOPODA. Lamp shells. Possess bivalve shell and stalks. Resemble mollusks. Marine. *Magellania.*

PHYLUM CHAETOGNATHA. Arrow worms. Mouth contains stout, chitinous teeth, which give it its name. Relation to other phyla doubtful. Marine. *Sagitta.*

PHYLUM MOLLUSCA. Mollusks. Snails, clams, squid, octopuses, and others. Shell or shells usually present. A ventral muscular foot characteristic. Segmentation absent. Mantle in some forms. 90,000 species, the third largest phylum.

> **Class Amphineura.** Chitons. Eight dorsal body plates in most species. Body bilaterally symmetrical. Large flat foot, strongly adhesive. Marine, on rocks near shore. *Cryptochiton, Mopalia.*

> **Class Scaphopoda.** Tooth-shells. Foot modified for burrowing. Shell shaped like a tooth and open at both ends. Fine, threadlike tentacles. Marine and bottom dwellers. *Dentalium.*

> **Class Gastropoda.** Snails, slugs, and whelks. Single, strong, flat ventral foot. Special feeding organ, the radula. Head faintly distinct, tentacles prominent. Trochophore larvae in some species. Both fresh- and salt-water. Economically important to man. *Haliotis, Littorina, Helix.*

> **Class Pelecypoda.** Clams. No radulas or tentacles. Functional mantle present. Foot spade-shaped adapted for digging in sand and mud. Fresh- and salt-water. *Venus, Ostrea, Anodonta.*

> **Class Cephalopoda.** Squids, octopuses, and nautiluses. Foot divided into arms or tentacles which vary in number among the different species and which possess adhesive sucking cups or disks. Some possess internal or external shell. Radula and siphon present. All marine. *Loligo, Nautilus, Sepia.*

PHYLUM ANNELIDA. Segmented worms. Serially arranged segments or metameres. Bilaterally symmetrical. Well-developed digestive, circulatory, nervous, muscular, and reproductive systems. Tube-within-a-tube body plan well developed. Coelom present. Some marine forms possess a trochophore larva. Marine, fresh-water, terrestrial, a few are parasitic.

> **Class Archiannelida.** Small simple marine annelids. *Polygordius.*

> **Class Polychaeta.** Clamworms. Parapodia on each segment and bearing setae. Tentacles in head region. Usually dioecious. Mostly marine. *Nereis, Aphrodite, Chaetopterus.*

> **Class Oligochaeta.** Earthworms. Parapodia and head absent. Setae small. Monoecious. Damp soil and fresh-water. *Lumbricus, Tubifex, Enchytraeus. . . .*

> **Class Hirudinea.** Leeches. Parapodia, setae, and head absent. One or two suckers. Segments subdivided into annuli. Fresh-water and parasitic. *Hirudo, Placobdella, Hemopis.*

PHYLUM ONYCHOPHORA. Peripatus. Rare group showing both annelid and arthropod characteristics. Short unjointed appendages. Body annelid-like. Breathing and circulatory systems resemble arthropods, also coelom. Probably similar to arthropod ancestors. *Peripatus.*

PHYLUM ARTHROPODA. Arthropods. Most distinguishing characters are the jointed appendages and chitinous or limy exoskeleton. Basic body regions are head, thorax, and abdomen (modified in some). Heart dorsal, nervous system ventral. Bilateral symmetry. Largest number of species of all phyla—750,000.

SUBPHYLUM TRILOBITOMORPHA. Trilobites. All extinct.

SUBPHYLUM CHELICERATA. Without antennae and first pair of appendages modified into pincerlike chelicerae. Six pairs of appendages.

    Class Xiphosurida. Horseshoe or King crab. Very ancient forms with few living representatives. Marine. *Limulus.*

    Class Eurypterida. Sea scorpions. All extinct.

    Class Pycnogonida. Sea spiders. Shortened body and very long legs. Marine. *Nymphon.*

    Class Arachnida. Spiders, scorpions, ticks, and mites. Breathing organs are book lungs in scorpions and spiders. *Lactrodectes, Centrurus, Eutrombicula, Dermacentor.*

SUBPHYLUM MANDIBULATA. Appendages near mouth modified into mandibles or jaws.

    Class Crustacea. Crustaceans (crabs, lobsters, crayfish, barnacles, sowbugs). Limy skeleton. Breathe with gills. Two pairs of antennae. Mostly fresh-water or marine; head and thorax fused into a cephalothorax. *Cambarus, Callinectes, Balanus.*

    Class Diplopoda. Millipedes. Cylindrical bodies of many segments, each with 2 pairs of legs (50 to 200 pairs). Short antennae. No poison glands. *Julus, Spirobolus.*

    Class Chilopoda. Centipedes. Many segments, each bearing a pair of legs, which range in number from 15 to 170 in different species. Prominent segmented antennae. Possess poison glands. *Scolopendra, Lithobius.*

    Class Insecta. Insects. Three pairs of walking legs and usually wings at some stage. A pair of antennae. Three body regions: head, thorax, and abdomen. Graded metamorphosis (complete, incomplete, gradual, or none). Many orders, some of which are listed below.

        Order Thysanura. Bristletails or silverfish. No metamorphosis. Wingless. Chewing mouth parts absent. Long caudal bristles. *Lepisma, Thermobia.*

        Order Neuroptera. Ant lions, lacewings, doodlebugs. Metamorphosis complete. Biting mouth parts. Wings with cross veins. Adults and larvae terrestrial and carnivorous. *Chrysopa, Myrmeleon.*

        Order Orthoptera. Grasshoppers, locusts, crickets, cockroaches, and others. Gradual metamorphosis. Biting mouth parts. Usually two pairs of wings, many with leaping legs. Called the singing insects. *Mantis, Romalea.*

        Order Odonata. Dragonflies and damsel flies. Metamorphosis incomplete. Two pairs of membranous wings and large compound eyes. Name derived from tooth-like biting mouth parts. Larval forms are aquatic and breathe by means of rectal gills. *Gomphus.*

        Order Ephemeroptera. Mayflies. Incomplete metamorphosis. Two pairs of wings, hind ones small. Rudimentary chewing mouth parts. Adults live very short periods. *Ephemera, Polymitarcys.*

        Order Anoplura. Sucking lice. Gradual metamorphosis. Wingless. Sucking and piercing mouth parts. Ectoparasites of the hairy regions of mammals. *Pediculus, Phthirius.*

        Order Hemiptera. True bugs. Gradual metamorphosis. Piercing and sucking mouth parts. Two pairs of wings in some, others are wingless. *Cimex, Lygus.*

        Order Homoptera. Cicadas, aphids, leaf hoppers, and others. Metamorphosis gradual. Sucking and piercing mouth parts. Mostly with two pairs of wings held dorsally. Parasitic on trees and shrubs. *Aphis, Magicicada.*

        Order Coleoptera. Beetles, fireflies, weevils, and others. Metamorphosis complete. Chewing mouth parts. Forewings usually heavy and protective. Exoskeleton horny or leathery. Largest order: 250,000 species. *Leptinotarsa, Dytiscus.*

Order Lepidoptera. Butterflies and moths. Complete metamorphosis. Larvae with chewing mouth parts, adults with sucking. Usually four membranous scaly wings. Compound and simple eyes. Proboscis long and coiled in most. Larvae spin cocoons from silk and make other provisions for pupae. Antennae are feathery in adult moths and knobbed in adult butterflies. Moths hold wings horizontally when at rest, whereas butterflies hold wings vertically. Some larvae do serious damage to crops. *Carpocapsa, Hibernia, Anosia, Papilio.*

Order Siphonaptera. Fleas. Metamorphosis complete. Piercing and sucking mouth parts. Small head, body flattened laterally, and leaping legs. Ectoparasites on birds and mammals. *Ctenocephalides, Pulex.*

Order Hymenoptera. Bees, ants, wasps, and others. Referred to as the social insects. Complete metamorphosis. Chewing and sucking mouth parts. Four membranous wings. Some possess a sting, saw, or a piercing organ. Of great economic significance. *Apis, Bombus, Pheidole.*

Order Diptera. Flies, mosquitoes, and others. Metamorphosis complete. Two wings. *Culex, Musca.*

PHYLUM ECHINODERMATA. Echinoderms. Starfish, sea urchins, and others. Endoskeleton and water vascular system characteristic. Also ·pentamerous body plan. Adults radially symmetrical. All marine.

SUBPHYLUM PELMATOZOA. Primitive stalked forms. Only one living class.

Class Crinoidea. Sea lilies. Stalked forms attached to ocean floor. Adults usually pentamerously branched to form arms with pinnules. Madreporic plate absent. Tube-feet without suckers. *Pentacrinus, Antedon.*

SUBPHYLUM ELEUTHEROZOA. Free-moving unattached forms. All marine.

Class Asteroidea. Starfishes. Most are prominently pentamerous. Madreporic plate and pedicellariae present. Numerous tube-feet lying in ambulacral grooves. Most possess powers of autotomy and regeneration of lost arms. *Asterias, Solaster.*

Class Ophiuroidea. Brittle stars. Arms markedly flexible and set-off from central body. No ambulacral grooves. Autotomy and regeneration marked. No pedicellariae. *Ophioderma, Aphiothrix.*

Class Echinoidea. Sea urchins, sand dollars and others. Body rounded or extremely flattened. Madreporic plate aboral. Arms absent. Tube-feet, spines, and pedicellariae present. Skeletal tests present. *Arbacia, Strongylocentrotus.*

Class Holothuroidea. Sea cucumbers. Soft cylindrical bodies. Much reduced skeleton, spicules only embedded in body wall. Anal respiration by means of respiratory trees. Arms, pedicellariae, and spines absent. Madreporic plate internal. Muscular body wall, Autotomy and regeneration marked. *Thyone, Cucumaria.*

PHYLUM HEMICHORDATA. Acorn worms. Well developed enterocoelom and gill slits. Primitive dorsal nervous system and internal skeleton in form of a notochord. Prominent proboscis. Wormlike. All marine. *Saccoglossus.*

PHYLUM CHORDATA. Chordates. All possess, at some stage in their life cycle, well developed gills or gill slits, dorsal tubular nerve cord, and a notochord.

SUBPHYLUM UROCHORDATA. Tunicates (sea squirts). Larvae show chordate characteristics whereas the adults become sedentary and lose the neural tube and notochord. Adults possess primitive circulatory system. All marine. *Styela, Amaroucium.*

SUBPHYLUM CEPHALOCHORDATA. Amphioxus. Fusiform body shape showing prominent muscle segments (myotomes). Coelom well developed. Circulatory system without discrete heart. Marine. *Branchiostoma.*

SUBPHYLUM VERTEBRATA. Vertebrates. Internal skeleton of cartilage or bone (both in some), the main axis being the spinal column composed of overlapping vertebrae. Nervous system with brain dorsal to the digestive tract. Two pairs of appendages. Red blood.

Class Agnatha. Lampreys and hag fish. Scales, jaws, and appendages absent. Mostly ectoparasitic on bodies of other vertebrates. Both monoecious and dioecious in different species. Some have rasping tongue and more than seven pairs of gills. Most primitive of vertebrates. Marine and fresh-water. *Petromyzon, Bdellostoma.*

Class Chondrichthyes. Sharks, rays, skates, and chimaeras. Cartilaginous endoskeleton. Placoid scales in most species. Rudimentary notochord. Spiral valve in intestine. No opercula over gills in most. Mostly marine. *Squalus, Raja.*

Class Osteichthyes. Bony fishes. Scales are never placoid. Endoskeleton of bone and cartilage. Caudal fin effective in locomotion. Swim bladder present, becomes lungs in some species. Paired pectoral and pelvic fins, highly modified in some. Operculum present. Marine and fresh-water.

Subclass Choanichthyes. Lobe-finned and lungfishes. Nostrils open into mouth cavity. Paired fins possess enlarged median lobes. Most species fossils. *Protopterus, Latimeria.*

Subclass Actinopterygii. Ray-finned fishes. Nostrils not connected with mouth cavity. Variable body form, mostly streamlined. *Acipenser, Amia, Perca.*

Class Amphibia. Frogs, toads, salamanders, and others. Larvae usually aquatic, adults usually terrestrial. Metamorphosis in most. Adult skin glandular and soft. Usually four walking legs on adults. Eyelids usually present. Adult heart with two auricles and one ventricle; larvae possess one auricle and one ventricle. None marine. Poikilothermal.

Order Apoda. Caecilians. Legless, worm-like. Short tail, or completely lacking. Tiny scales in some. *Ichthyophsis.*

Order Caudata. Newts, salamanders, hellbenders, mud puppies. Tailed forms. Front and hind legs about equal in size. No scales. *Triturus, Ambystoma, Necturus.*

Order Salienta. Frogs and toads. Tailless forms. Front legs small, hind legs large for leaping. Eggs laid in jelly masses and strings. Metamorphosis clearly indicated. No scales. *Rana, Bufo.*

Class Reptilia. Lizards, snakes, turtles, alligators, and others. Scales or bony plates form external covering. Poikilothermal. The heart ventricle partially separated in most species. Air-breathing throughout life.

Order Squamata. Lizards and snakes. Scales smooth on snakes, horny and thick on lizards. Cloacal opening transverse. Copulatory organs paired. *Agkistrodon, Anolis.*

Order Testudinata. Turtles, terrapins, and tortoises. Beaks, bony plates to form box-like shell, and short legs are the chief characteristics. Turtles live in either fresh or salt water, terrapins live in fresh water, and tortoises live on land. Some reach great size and age. *Chelonia, Terrapene.*

Order Crocodilia. Alligators, crocodiles, and others. Body form lizardlike and large. Crocodiles have elongated pointed snouts whereas those of alligators are rounded. Two complete ventricles present. Bony plates overlying heavy skin. Valves in nostrils and ears which are closed when under water. *Crocodylus, Alligator.*

Order Rhynchocephalia. A "living fossil" possessing characteristics of primitive reptiles. Found in New Zealand. Possesses a parietal eye in roof of skull. *Sphenodon.*

Class Aves. Birds. Feathers characteristic. Wings usually present for flight. Light skeleton. Beak present. Homiothermal. Heart consisting of two auricles and two ventricles. Ubiquitous in distribution. 30,000 species and subspecies. Many orders. The student is referred to bird books for classification. *Pelecanus, Gallus.*

Class Mammalia. Mammals. Mammary glands which secrete milk for nourishing the young. Hair present on at least part of the body. Sweat and sebaceous glands, red blood, young usually born alive (viviparous), and homiothermal. Over 17,000 species and subspecies.

Subclass Prototheria. Monotremes. Egg-laying and possessing reptilian characteristics, particularly in the urogenital system and the intestinal openings into the cloaca. *Echidna, Ornithorhynchus.*

Subclass Theria. Marsupials and placental mammals.

Infraclass Metatheria. Opossum, kangaroo, and others. Possess primitive placenta and abdominal pouches which house mammary glands. *Didelphis, Macropus.*

Infraclass Eutheria. Placental mammals. Embryos develop in uterus of female. All viviparous.

Order Insectivora. Shrews, moles, and others. Shrews smallest living mammals. Nocturnal, usually terrestrial, and insect-eating. *Sorex, Scalopus.*

Order Chiroptera. Bats. Forelimbs modified into wings for flight. Sharp teeth and claws. Usually nocturnal. Variable diets, from fruit to blood of vertebrates including man (Vampire bats). *Myotis, Desmodus.*

Order Primates. Monkeys, lemurs, gibbons, and many others including man. Large hands and feet with opposable "thumb." High intelligence. Usually arboreal. *Ateles, Gorilla, Homo.*

Order Carnivora. Mostly flesh-eating. Dogs, cats, bears, mink, seals, and others. Canine teeth large. Usually five clawed toes. Terrestrial and widespread. *Canis, Felis, Procyon.*

Order Perissodactyla. Horse, rhinoceros, tapir, and others. Hoofed mammals with odd number of toes. Long legs and large body size. *Equus, Tapirella.*

Order Artiodactyla. Cow, camel, deer, and others. Hoofed mammals with even number of toes. Ruminants have four-chambered stomachs. Hoofs on two or four toes. *Bos, Camelus.*

Order Proboscidea. Elephants. Extension of upper lip and nose into a "trunk." Upper incisor teeth greatly enlarged to form tusks. Massive animals with thick skull and skin. *Elephas.*

Order Sirenia. Sea cows—manatee and dugong. Aquatic mammals. Hind legs are lost and front ones developed into flippers. Transverse tail. *Manatus.*

Order Cetacea. Whales, porpoises, and others. Aquatic, primarily marine. Anterior appendages modified into paddles for swimming. Neck absent, small ear-openings, smooth body, and very little hair (modified in some to form whalebone). Usually large, one (the blue whale) is largest animal that has ever lived. *Physeter, Mesoplodon.*

Order Edentata. Anteaters, sloths, and others. Teeth absent in some (anteaters) and others (armadillos and sloths) possess no incisors and canines and no enamel on any teeth. All members highly specialized. Many extinct forms, such as the giant sloth and armadillo. *Bradypus, Dasypus.*

Order Rodentia. Gnawing mammals. Squirrel, hamster, and others. Incisor teeth well developed and chisel-like, canine teeth absent. *Mus, Rattus.*

Order Lagomorpha. Rabbits, conies, and others. Chisel-like incisor teeth, canines absent. *Lepus, Ochotona.*

Acknowledgments for Illustrations

Glossary and Index

Glossary

The glossary is included as an aid in not only defining biological terms, but also in helping the student pronounce them. Their origin is indicated as follows: Gr., Greek; L., Latin; M. E., Middle English; A.S., Anglo-Saxon; Fr., French. Words that do not appear here may be found by referring to the index.

Long words with two accented syllables contain both the primary accent (") and the secondary accent (').

Ab-do'men (L. *abdere*, to hide). The belly region of animals, specifically in mammals that part which extends from the diaphragm to the pelvis.

Ab-duc'tor (L. *ab*, from; *ducere*, to lead). A muscle which pulls a structure away from the median line of the animal.

Ab'i-o-gen''e-sis (L. *a*, not; *bio*, life; *genesis*, birth). The doctrine whereby life originates from the non-living world.

Ab-o'ral (L. *ab*, from; *oris*, mouth). The side opposite the mouth.

Ab-sorp'tion (L. *ab*, away; *sorbere*, to suck in). The taking up of fluids or other substances by living systems.

A-byss'al (L. *abyssus*, bottomless). The bottom waters of the deep sea, marked by the absence of light and hence of plants; where carnivores live.

Ac-cre'tion (L. *accrescere*, to increase). The addition of material to an inert mass of the same material.

Ac'e-tyl-cho''line. A chemical substance produced at or near para-sympathetic nerve endings which is thought to be involved in conduction of nerve impulses across synapses.

A-coe'lo-mate (Gr. *a*, not; *koilos*, hollow). Animals without a coelom.

Ac'ro-meg''a-ly (Gr. *akron*, point, peak; *megas*, big). An organic disease caused by the hypersecretion of the anterior pituitary after the long bones have reached maturity.

Ad-ap-ta'tion (L. *ad*, to; *aptare*, to fit). A process by which an organism becomes better suited to its environment.

Ad-duc'tor (L. *ad*, to; *duco*, lead). A muscle which pulls a structure toward the median line of the animal.

Ad'e-nine. A pyrimidine component of nucleic acids and nucleotides.

Ad-he'sion (L. *adhaerere*). A molecular force at surfaces causing unlike molecules to cling together.

Ad'i-pose (L. *adeps, adipis*, fat). Pertaining to fat.

Ad-re'nal gland (L. *ad*, to; *renes*, kidneys; *glans*, acorn). A double endocrine gland located on or near the kidney; consists of the cortex and the medulla, each secreting different hormones.

Ad-re'nal-in. A hormone produced by the medullary portion of the adrenal glands.

Ad-sorp'tion (L. *ad*, to; *sorbere*, to suck in). The attachment of molecules of one substance to the surface of other substances.

A'er-o''bic (Gr. *aer*, air; *bios*, life). Growing only in air or free oxygen.

Af'fer-ent (L. *affere*, to bring). Carrying toward. An afferent artery carries blood to the lungs.

Ag-glu'ti-nin (L. *ad*, to; *glutinare*, to glue). A substance in the blood which causes cells or microörganisms to clump.

Al'bi-nism (L. *albus*, white). A condition in which the normal pigment of the skin, hair, and eyes is lacking.

Al-i-men'tary (L. *alimentum*, from; *alere*, to nourish). Pertaining to the digestive tract.

Al-lan'to-is (Gr. *allas*, sausage; *eidos*, form). An extra embryonic membrane arising as an outgrowth of the cloaca in reptiles, birds, and mammals.

Al-lele' (allelomorph) (Gr. *allelon*, of one another). The alternative forms of a gene having the same locus in homologous chromosomes which influence "alternative" characters.

Al′ler-gy (Gr. *all, ergy, ergon,* work). A condition in which substances that are normally harmless cause a marked hypersensitivity or reaction.

Al-ve′o-lus (L. dim of *alveus,* pit). A small cavity, such as the alveoli of the lungs or the socket of a tooth.

A-mi′no ac′id (from amine NH_2). An organic compound resulting from protein breakdown; it must contain at least one amino group (NH_2) and one acid group (COOH).

Am′i-to″sis (Gr. *a,* without; *mitos,* thread). Direct nuclear division without formation of condensed chromosomes or spindle fibers.

Am′ni-on (Gr. dim. of *amnos,* lamb). A transparent membrane surrounding the embroyos of reptiles, birds, and mammals.

Am′ni-o″ta (Gr. dim. of *amnos,* lamb). A group of vertebrates possessing an amnion and an allantois—reptiles, birds, and mammals.

A-moe′boid (Gr. *amoebe,* change). Cell movements resembling those of the amoeba.

Am′phi-as″ter (Gr. *amphi,* both sides of; *aster,* star). A figure formed by the spindle fibers and the two asters in the dividing cell.

Am-phib′i-a (Gr. *amphi,* of both kinds; *bios,* life). Class of vertebrates including frogs, toads, and salamanders which usually spend their larval life in water (water breathers) and their adult life on land (air breathers).

Am′y-lase (L. *amylum,* starch; Gr. *opsis,* appearance). A carbohydrate-splitting enzyme produced by the pancreas.

An-ab′o-lism (Gr. *ana,* up; *bole,* stroke). Constructive metabolism.

An′aer-o″bic (Gr. *an,* negative; *aer,* air; *bios,* life). Growing only in the absence of air or free oxygen.

A-nal′o-gous (Gr. *ana,* up; *logos,* ratio, proportion). Body parts with similar functions but usually genetically dissimilar.

An-am′ni-o″ta (Gr. *a,* not; *amnion,* inner membrane around the fetus). A group of vertebrates without an amnion—cyclostomes, fishes, and amphibia.

An′a-phase (Gr. *ana,* up; *phasis,* appearance, aspect). A stage in mitosis following metaphase when chromosomes migrate from the equatorial plate to the poles of the cell.

A-nas′to-mo″sis (Gr. *ana,* up; *stoma,* mouth). The union of two or more blood vessels, nerves, or other structures.

A-nat′o-my (Gr. *ana,* up; *temnein,* to cut). The study of the structure of animals and plants.

An-nel′i-da (L. *annulus,* ring; Gr. *eidos,* resemblance). A phylum of animals.

An-ten′na (L. a sailyard). Tactile sense organs on the heads of arthropods.

An-ten′nules (L. dim. of antenna). Tactile sense organs located near the antenna of many arthropods.

An-te′ri-or (L. comp. of *ante*). Toward the head end of an animal.

An″ti-bod′y (Gr. *anti,* against; M.E. *bodi,* body). A substance produced in the body as a result of the presence of a foreign body (antigen).

An′ti-gen (Gr. *anti,* against; *genes,* born). A substance which, when introduced into the body, stimulates the production of antibodies.

An′ti-tox″in (Gr. *anti,* against; L. *toxicum,* poison). A substance in the body fluids naturally occurring or induced which neutralizes specific poisons or toxins.

A′nus (L. *anus*). The exit of the alimentary canal opposite the mouth.

A-or′ta (Gr. *aeirein,* to lift). The large artery carrying blood away from the heart.

Ap′er-ture (L. *aperire,* to uncover). An opening.

Ap′i-cal (L. *apex,* summit). The top or apex.

Ap-pend′age (L. *ad,* to; *pendere,* to hang). A part of the body that extends some distance, such as an arm or leg.

Ar-ach′nid-a (Gr. *arachne,* spider). A class of the Arthropoda, including the spiders, ticks, mites, and scorpions.

Ar-bo′re-al (L. *arbor,* tree). Tree-living.

Ar-chen′ter-on (Gr. *arche,* beginning; *enteron,* gut). The primitive gut of an embryo produced by gastrulation.

Ar′tery (L. *arteria,* windpipe, artery). A blood vessel carrying blood away from the heart.

Ar′thro-pod-a (Gr. *arthron,* joint; *pous,* foot). A phylum of animals.

Ar-tic′u-la-tion (L. dim. of *articulus,* joint). A joint.

A-sex′u-al re-pro-duc′tion (L. *a,* not; *sexus,* sex; L. *re,* again; *productio,* production). Reproduction without involving sex cells.

As-sim′i-la″tion (L. *ad,* to; *similis,* like). The conversion of the end products of digestion into protoplasm.

As′ter (Gr. *aster,* star). The star-shaped structure formed around the centriole in mitosis.

A-sym′me-try (Gr. *a,* without; *syn,* with; *metron,* measure). Without symmetry.

At′a-vism (L. *atavus,* ancestor). Resemblance to a remote ancestor.

At′ro-phy (Gr. *a,* not; *trephein,* to nourish).

The gradual regression of the whole body or of its parts.

Au'di-to-ry (L. *audire*, to hear). Pertaining to hearing or ears.

Au'ric-le (L. *auris*, ear). Ear-like projection, as on the head of planaria, or a heart chamber into which the veins empty.

Au-to-nom'ic (Gr. *autos*, self; *nomos*, law). Self-operating.

Au'top-sy (Gr. *autos*, self; *optos*, seen). The dissection of a body (post-mortem) to determine the cause of death.

Au'to-some (Gr. *autos*, self; *soma*, body). The chromosomes other than the sex chromosomes.

Au-tot'o-my (Gr. *autos*, self; *tomos*, cutting). The automatic breaking off of a part of the body, such as in arthropods.

A'ves (L. *avis*, bird). A class of Vertebrata to which the birds belong.

Ax'is (L. *axis*, axle). An imaginary line through an animal, about which the organism is oriented; also, it refers to the anterior second vertebra.

Ax'on (Gr. *axon*, axle). The nerve fiber that conducts the impulse away from the cell body.

Bar'na-cle. A crustacean.

Ber'i-ber'i. A disease resulting from thiamine deficiency.

Bi'ceps (L. *bi*, two; *caput*, head). A muscle with two parts at one end, as the flexor muscle of the human arm.

Bi-cus'pid (L. *bis*, twice; *cuspis*, point). A structure with two cusps or points, as a bicuspid tooth or biscuspid valve between the left auricle and ventricle of the mammalian heart.

Bi-lat'er-al sym'me-try (L. *bis*, twice; *latus*, side; Gr. *syn*, with; *metron*, measure). The arrangement of body parts so that the right and left halves are mirror images of each other.

Bile pig'ments (L. *bilis*, bile; *pingere*, to paint). The colored pigments of bile (bili rubin, bili verdin) resulting from hemoglobin breakdown.

Bi'na-ry fis'sion (L. *bi*, two; *fissus*, cleft). The type of reproduction (asexual) in which division into two parts is approximately equal.

Bi-no'mi-al no'men-cla-ture (L. *bis*, twice; *nomen*, name; *calare*, to call). The international system of naming animals whereby two names are used. The first is generic, the second specific.

Bi-o-gen'e-sis (Gr. *bios*, life; *genesis*, birth). The doctrine that life comes only from pre-existing life.

Bi-ol'o-gy (Gr. *bios*, mode of life; *logos*, discourse). The science of plant and animal life.

Bi-o-lu'mines'cence (Gr. *bios*, mode of life; L. *lumen*, light). The emission of light by living organisms.

Blas'to-coel (Gr. *blastos*, bud; *koilus*, hollow). Cavity of the blastula.

Blas'to-pore (Gr. *blastos*, bud; *poros*, passage). The opening into the archenteron of the gastrula.

Blas'tu-la (Gr. *blastos*, bud). The early embryo in which the cells form a hollow ball.

Bow'man's cap'sule (named after Sir Wm. Bowman, English physician. L. *capsula*, a little box). The cup-like structure at the end of the kidney tubule which surrounds the glomerulus.

Bra'chi-al (L. *brachium*, arm). Pertaining to the arm of a vertebrate.

Bra'chi-ate (L. *brachium*, arm). A manner of swinging from limb to limb in trees with the hands, such as apes employ.

Brack'ish. Water intermediate in salt content between sea water and fresh water.

Bron'chi-ole (Gr. *bronchos*, windpipe). A tiny air tube in the lung.

Bron'chus (Gr. *bronchos*, windpipe). One of the two main air passages of the trachea.

Bruise. A blood clot in the tissue.

Buc'cal (L. *bucca*, cheek or mouth cavity). The mouth cavity.

Bud'ding (M.E. *budde*). Reproduction by the splitting off and subsequent development of a small portion of the original animal.

Cae'cum (L. *caecus*, blind gut). A blind sac.

Cal-ca're-ous (L. *calcarius*, limestone, limy.) Containing lime or calcium carbonate.

Cal'or-ie (L. *calor*, heat). The amount of heat energy equal to that used in raising a kilogram of water from 14.5 to 15.5 degrees centigrade. A calorie, when written with a small *c*, is one thousandth of a Calorie.

Can'cer (L. crab, ulcer, sign of the zodiac). One of a variety of malignant tumors.

Ca'nine. (L. *canis*, dog). Pertaining to the pointed tooth next to the incisors, and so named because of its dog-like characteristics.

Cap'il-la-ry (L. *capillus*, hair). Tiny blood vessel

with walls of one cell layer which connects arterioles to venules.

Cap′sule. (L. *capsula,* little box). Any fibrous or membranous envelope, covering a part or the whole of an organism.

Car′bo·hy″drate (L. *carbo,* coal; Gr. *hydor,* water). An organic compound (starch, sugar) containing carbon, hydrogen, and oxygen in which the last two atoms are in the same proportions as in water (H_2O).

Car′di·ac (Gr. *kardia,* the heart). Pertaining to the heart.

Car·niv′o·ra (L. *caro,* flesh; *vorare,* to devour). Flesh-eaters.

Car′ti·lage (L. *cartilago,* gristle). A white elastic secretion forming certain skeletal structures of vertebrates, particularly of embryos and the very young.

Cas·tra′tion (L. *castratio*). The act of removing the sex glands, usually from males.

Ca·tab′o·lism (Gr. *kata,* down; *ballein,* to throw). Destructive metabolism.

Cat′a·lyst (Gr. *kata,* down; *lysis,* a loosing). A substance that alters the rate of a chemical reaction, which would go very slowly or not at all without it.

Cau′dal (L. *cauda,* tail). Pertaining to the tail.

Cen′tri·ole (Gr. *kentron,* a center). A small body in the centrosome around which the asters form during mitosis.

Cen′tro·some (Gr. *kentron,* a center; *soma,* body). A tiny differentiated area of a cell near the nucleus containing the centriole. Also called cell center.

Ce·phal′ic (Gr. *kephale,* the head). Pertaining to or near the head.

Cer′e·bel″lum (L. diminutive of *cerebrum,* brain). The part of the brain in higher vertebrates which controls muscular coordination.

Cer′e·brum (L. *cerebrum,* brain). The anterior part of the brain, which is conspicuous in man, and is the seat of thought, memory, and reasoning.

Cer′vi·cal (L. *cervix,* neck). Pertaining to the neck.

Char′ac·ter (Gr. *charassein,* to engrave). Used specifically in biology to designate any trait, function, or structure of an organism.

Chi′tin (Gr. *chiton,* a kind of garment, tunic). A horny substance forming the skeleton of arthropods and other animals.

Chlo′ro·phyll(Gr. *chloros,* green; *phyllon,* leaf). A green pigment in plants essential for photosynthesis.

Cho′a·no·cyte (Gr. *choane,* funnel; *kytos,* hol-

low). Flagellated cells with collars, typical of porifera.

Chor′date (L. *chorda,* cord). An animal possessing a notochord which subsequently may be replaced by backbone (tunicates, vertebrates, etc.).

Chro′ma·tin (Gr. *chroma,* color). The dark, staining material of the chromosomes.

Chro′ma·to·phore (Gr. *chroma,* color; *pherein,* to bear). Pigment-containing cells or bodies in the skin of certain animals, such as the frog and some reptiles which are able to change their skin color.

Chro′mo·mere (Gr. *chroma,* color; *meros,* part). One of the many linearly arranged bead-like structures found on a chromosome.

Chro·mo·nem′a (Gr. *chroma,* color; *nema,* thread). Thread-like strands of chromatin visible in the nucleus during mitosis and in some cells during interphase.

Chro′mo·somes (Gr. *chroma,* color; *soma,* body). Deeply staining rod-shaped bodies within the nucleus and conspicuously visible during cell division. They contain the genes.

Cil′i·a (L. *cilium,* eyelid). Microscopic, hair-like projections from certain cells which vibrate, causing movement.

Class (L. *classis,* collection). Principal subdivision of a phylum.

Cleav′age (A.S. *cleofan,* to cut). Divisions of the fertilized egg.

Cli′to·ris (Gr. *chleio,* close). An organ of the female mammal homologous with the penis of the male.

Clo·a′ca (L. *cloaca,* sewer). A common receptacle for digestive and excretory wastes and the reproductive cells of lower vertebrates.

Clone (Gr. *klon,* twig). A group of animals produced by asexual reproduction from a single individual.

Co·ag′·u·la″tion (L. *cogere,* to drive together). A process of changing a sol into a gel.

Co·coon′ (Fr. *cocon,* shell). A protective covering for eggs, larvae, pupae, or adult animals.

Coe′lom (Gr. *koilus,* hollow). The body cavity lined with tissue of mesodermal origin in which the digestive and other organs lie.

Co·en′zyme. A relatively simple substance which is involved in the transfer of hydrogen atoms during oxidative reactions in protoplasm.

Col′loid (Gr. *kolla,* glue; *eidos,* form). A system in which particles larger than molecules of one substance are suspended throughout a second substance.

Co'lon (Gr. *kolon*, the colon). The part of the large intestine which extends from the caecum to the rectum.

Com-men'sal-ism (L. *cum*, together; *mensa*, table). The intimate association of two species in which one is benefited and the other is neither helped nor harmed.

Con'ju-ga"tion (L. *cum*, together; *jugare*, to join, marry). A sexual process in unicellular organisms where two individuals unite temporarily and exchange their nuclear material, later dividing.

Con-trac'tile vac'u-ole (L. *cum*, together; *trahere*, to draw; *vacuus*, empty). A space in the cytoplasm of certain species of protozoa where fluids collect before being periodically discharged to the outside.

Cop'u-la"tion (L. *copulare*, to couple). The union of two individuals in which spermatozoa are transferred from the male to female.

Cor'ne-a (L. *cornu*, horn). The transparent outer covering of the anterior part of the eye.

Cor'o-na-ry (L. *coronarius*, crown).• Encircling in the manner of a crown; applied to nerves, vessels, etc.

Cor'pus (L. *corpus*, body). A body.

Cor'tex (L. *cortex*, bark). The outer layer

Cra'ni-um (Gr. *kranion*, the head). The portion of the skull which envelops the brain.

Cross'ing o'ver. The process in which homologous chromosomes break and exchange corresponding parts.

Cu-ta'ne-ous (L. *cutis*, the skin). Pertaining to the skin.

Cyst (Gr. *kystis*, a bladder). The stage of an organism where it is encased in a resistant wall.

Cy-tol'o-gy (Gr. *kytos*, hollow; *logos*, discourse). The science that deals with cell structure.

Cy'to-plasm (Gr. *kytos*, hollow; *plasma*, something molded). The protoplasm of a cell, exclusive of the nucleus.

Dac'tyl (Gr. *daktylos*, finger). Pertaining to the finger.

De-am'i-na"tion (L. *de*, from; *amino*, amino group). The process by which the amino group is removed from the amino acid.

Def-e-ca'tion (L. *de*, from; *faecis*, dregs). The evacuation of the bowels.

De'glu-ti"tion (L. *de*, down; *glutire*, to swallow). The act of swallowing.

Den'drite (Gr. *dendron*, tree). The branching protoplasmic outgrowth of a nerve cell.

Der'mal (Gr. *derma*, skin). Pertaining to the skin, especially the deeper layers.

Der'mis (Gr. *derma*, skin). The inner layer of the skin.

Di-al'y-sis (L. *dialysis*, separation). The process by which crystalloids and colloids are separated in solution. This involves a natural or artificial membrane through which unequal diffusion takes place.

Di'a-phragm (Gr. *diaphragma*, midriff). The internal muscular layer found between the mammalian thoracic and abdominal cavities.

Di-as'to-le (Gr. *dia*, through; *stellein*, to set, place). The relaxation phase of the cardiac cycle.

Di-en-ceph'a-lon (Gr. *dia*, between; *engkephalon*, brain). An area of the vertebrate brain immediately posterior to the cerebrum.

Dif'fer-en'ti-a"tion (L. *differre*, to carry apart). Specialization of cells and tissues as a result of growth and development.

Dif-fu'sion (L. *diffundere*, to pour). The movement of molecules as a consequence of their kinetic energy.

Di-ges'tion (L. *digestio*, digestion). The conversion of food into materials that can be absorbed and assimilated.

Dig'it (L. *digitus*, finger). A finger or a toe.

Di-hy'brid (Gr. *dis*, twice; L. *hibrida*, mixed offspring). The offspring of parents differing in two characters.

Di-mor'phism (Gr. *dis*, twice; *morphe*, shape). Having two forms.

Di-oe'cious (diecious) (Gr. *dis*, twice; *oikos*, house). Having the sexes in separate individuals.

Dip'lo-blas"tic (Gr. *diploos*, double; *blastos*, bud). Having two germ layers.

Dip'loid (Gr. *diploos*, double). The number of chromosomes in somatic cells.

Dis'tal (L. *dis*, apart; *stare*, to stand). Most distant from the point of attachment.

Di-ur'nal (L. *dies*, day). Associated with daylight.

Di'ver-tic"u-lum (L. *de*, away; *vertere*, to turn). A pouch or pocket leading out from a tube.

D N A. Abbreviation for desoxyribose nucleic acid.

Dom'i-nant. A gene which expresses its effect even in the presence of a different gene for the same character.

Dor'sal (L. *dorsum*, back). The upper surface of any animal.

D P N. Abbreviation for diphosphopyridine nucleotide.

Duct (L. *ducere,* to lead). A tube for the passage of metabolic products.

Duct′less gland. A gland which pours its secretion directly into the blood stream.

Du′o-de″num (L. *duodeni,* 12 each). The first part of the small intestine posterior to the stomach (about as long as the width of 12 fingers).

Du′ra ma′ter (L. *dura,* hard; *mater,* mother). The tough outer covering of the brain and nerve cord.

Dys-gen′ic (Gr. *dys,* hard, ill; *gignesthai,* to be born). Tending to bring about genetic degradation of a species.

Ec-cen′tric (L. *ex,* without; *centrum,* center). Away from center.

Ec′dy-sis (Gr. *ek,* out; *dyein,* to enter). To shed the exoskeleton, as in arthropods.

E-col′o-gy (Gr. *oikos,* house; *logos,* discourse). The division of biology dealing with the relation of plants and animals to their environment.

Ec′to-derm (Gr. *ektos,* outside; *derma,* skin). The outermost germ layer of the gastrula which gives rise to the nervous system.

Ec′to-par″a-site (Gr. *ektos,* outside; *para,* beside; *sitos,* food). A parasite which lives on the outermost surface of its host.

Ec′to-plasm (Gr. *ektos,* outside; *plasma,* something molded). The outer layer of cytoplasm in a cell.

Ec′to-sarc (Gr. *ektos,* outside; *sarx,* flesh). The outer layer of certain protozoa.

Ef-fect′or (L. *effectus,* to effect). A nerve end organ which serves to distribute impulses which activate muscle contraction and gland secretion.

Ef-fer′ent (L. *efferre,* to bear out). Conveying away from, as motor nerves that conduct impulses away from the cord.

Egg (L. *ovum,* egg). The animal gamete or ovum formed by the female.

E-jac′u-la-tion (L. *ejaculatus,* to throw out). The emission or discharge, as of sperm cells.

E-lec′tro-lyte (Gr. *electron,* amber; *lytos,* dissolved, dissoluble). A substance which, when in solution, dissociates into ions and thus conducts an electric current.

El-ec′tron. The part of an atom having a negative charge.

El′e-ment (L. *elementum,* of obscure origin). A simple substance which cannot be decomposed by ordinary chemical means and consisting of one kind of atom.

Em′bry-o (Gr. *embryon,* embryo). The organism in an early stage of development.

Em′bry-ol″o-gy (Gr. *embryon,* embryo; *logos,* discourse). The science of the development of the organism.

E-mul′si-fi-ca″tion (L. *e,* out; *mulgere,* to milk). The process of dividing fat into particles of very small size.

En-cyst′ (Gr. *en,* in; *kystis,* bladder). To become enclosed in a cyst.

En-der-gon′ic. A reaction that requires energy.

En′do-crine (Gr. *endon,* within; *krinein,* to separate). Pertaining to a ductless gland.

En′do-derm (Gr. *endon,* within; *derma,* skin). The innermost germ layer of the gastrula which gives rise to the lining of the digestive tract and its derivatives.

En′do-par″a-site (Gr. *endon,* within; *para,* beside; *sitos,* food). A parasite living within the body of its host.

En′do-plasm (Gr. *endon,* within; *plasma,* something molded). Inner cytoplasm surrounded by ectoplasm.

En′do-sarc (Gr. *endon,* within; *sarx,* flesh). Inner mass of protoplasm in a protozoan.

En′do-skel″e-ton (Gr. *endon,* within; *skeletos,* hard). Internal bony and cartilaginous structure of animals.

En′do-the″li-um (Gr. *endon,* within; *thele,* nipple). Epithelial lining of the circulatory organs.

En′er-gy (Gr. *energein,* to be active). The capacity to do work.

En-ter-o-ki′nase (Gr. *enteron,* gut; *kinein,* to move). Intestinal enzyme which activates pancreatic trypsinogen.

En′ter-on (Gr. *enteron,* gut). That part of the digestive tract derived from endoderm.

En′to-derm. See Endoderm.

En′to-mol″o-gy (Gr. *entomon,* insect; *logos,* discourse). The study of insects.

En-vi′ron-ment (Fr. *environ,* about, thereabouts). External or internal surroundings.

En′zyme (Gr. *en,* in; *zyme,* leaven). Organic catalyst.

Ep-i-der′mis (Gr. *epi,* upon; *derma,* skin). The outermost layer of the skin.

Ep′i-gen″e-sis (Gr. *epi,* upon; *gignesthai,* to be born). The concept that development begins with an undifferentiated cell.

Ep-iph′y-sis (Gr. *epi,* upon; *phyein,* to grow). The tip of a bone separated in early development by cartilage but later becoming a part of the bone.

Ep′i-the″li-um (Gr. *epi,* upon; *thele,* nipple). A sheet of cells covering either external or internal parts of body surfaces.

E′qua-to″ri-al plate (L. *aequator,* one who equalizes). The plate-like arrangement of chromosomes formed at the equator during cell division.

E-rep'sin (L. *eripere*, to set free). A mixture of peptone and proteose-splitting enzymes produced by the intestinal mucosa.

E-soph'a-gus (Gr. *oisophagos*, gullet). The tube extending from the pharynx to the stomach.

Es'ti-va''tion (L. *aestivus*, pertaining to summer). Inactivity brought about by extreme dryness and heat.

Es'tro-gen (L. *aestus*, fire, glow). A hormone produced by the ovarian follicle which, together with one of the pituitary hormones, influences estrus.

Es'trus (L. *aestus*, fire, glow). The mating period in female mammals marked by intensified sexual urge.

Eu-gen'ics (Gr. *eu*, well; *genos*, birth). The science of applying genetic knowledge for the improvement of the human species.

Eu-sta'chi-an tube (named after *Eustachi,* Italian physician. L. *tuba*, pipe). A tube leading from the pharynx to the middle ear.

Eu-then'ics (Gr. *euthenein*, to thrive). The science of improving the human race by improving the environment.

E-vag'i-na''tion (L. *e*, out; *vagina*, sheath). An out-pocketing of some part or organ.

E-vis'cer-ate (L. *ex*, out; *viscera*, entrails). To remove the internal organs.

Ev'o-lu''tion, organic (L. *evolvere*, to unroll; Gr. *organon*, instrument, tool). Descent with modification.

Ex-cre'tion (L. *ex*, out; *cernere*, to sift). Discharge of wastes of metabolism.

Ex-er-gon'ic. A reaction which yields energy.

Ex'o-skel''e-ton (Gr. *exo*, outside; *skeletos*, hard). The hardened external structure of animals.

Ex'pi-ra''tion (L. *ex*, out; *spirare*, to breathe). To breathe out.

Ex-ter'nal res'pi-ra''tion. The exchange of gases between the alveoli of the lungs and the blood.

Fac'et (L. *facies*, face). A sub-division of the compound eye in arthropods.

Fam'i-ly (L. *familia*, from *famulus*, servant). The main sub-division of an order.

Fas'ci-a (L. a band). A sheet of connective tissue which covers and binds parts together.

Fau'na (L. *faunus*, a god of the woods). The animal life characteristic of a region.

Fe'ces or **fae'ces** (L. *faeces*, dregs). Undigested, unabsorbed food residue.

Feedback. Stimuli passing from the effector to the receptor indicating that some action has taken place.

Fer'ti-li-za''tion (L. *fertilis*, from *ferre*, to bear). The fusion of the sperm with the egg to produce a zygote.

Fe'tus (L. a bringing forth). The unborn young of any viviparous animal.

Fi'brin (L. *fibra*, band). The essential insoluble protein found in the blood clot.

Fi-brin'o-gin (L., *fibra,* band; Gr. *gignesthai,* to produce). The soluble protein material which is converted to fibrin during clotting.

Fis'sion (L. *fissus*, cleft). Asexual reproduction in which the cell divides into two parts.

Fis'sure (L. *fissus*, cleft). Any groove, furrow, cleft, or slit.

Fla-gel'lum (L. *flagellum*, whip). A mobile, whiplike process.

Fol'li-cle (L. *folliculus*, small sac). A small excretory or secretory sac or gland.

Fo-ra'men (L. *foramen*, an opening). A hole in a bone or membrane.

Fos'sa (L. *fossa*, ditch). A pit or depression found in bone.

Fos'sil (L. *fossilis*, from *fodere*, to dig). Any naturally preserved record of prehistoric life.

Func'tion (L. *fungi*, to perform). Plant or animal action.

Gam'ete (Gr. *gametes*, spouse). A mature germ cell.

Gam'e-to-gen''e-sis (Gr. *gametes*, spouse; *genesis,* birth). The development of gametes.

Gan'gli-on (Gr. *ganglion,* enlargement). A mass of nerve cell bodies.

Gas'tric (Gr. *gaster,* belly). Pertaining to the stomach.

Gas'tro-vas''cu-lar (Gr. *gaster,* belly; L. *vasculum*, vessel). A cavity used both for digestion and circulation.

Gas'tru-la (Gr. *gaster,* belly). The early embryonic stage following the blastula in which the embryo consists of two germ layers.

Gas'tru-la''tion (Gr. *gaster,* belly). The process of invagination of the blastula to form the gastrula.

Gene. Hereditary units located on the chromosomes.

Ge-net'ics (Gr. *gignesthai,* to be born). The science of heredity.

Gen'i-tal (L. *gignere,* to beget). Pertaining to the reproductive organs.

Gen'o-type (Gr. *genesthai,* to be produced; *typos,* impression). Genic constitution.

Ge'nus (L. *genere,* to beget). Taxonomic sub-division of a family.

Ge-ot′ro-pism (Gr. *ge*, earth; *repein*, to turn). Response to gravity.

Germ lay′er (L. *germen*, germ). An embryonic primary cell layer.

Germ plasm (Gr. *plasma*, something molded). Reproductive and hereditary substance of individuals which is transmitted in direct continuity to the germ cells of succeeding generations.

Ges-ta′tion (L. *gerere*, to carry). The period of pregnancy.

Gill (Gr. *cheilos*, lip). An aquatic respiratory organ.

Gill arches (Gr. *cheilos*, lip; *arcus*, bow). The walls bearing the gills.

Gill slit (pharyngeal cleft) (A.S. *slitan*). Paired openings in the wall of the pharynx of chordates which permits the water that entered through the mouth to escape externally during breathing.

Giz′zard (Fr. *giser*, gizzard). An enlarged muscular part of the digestive tract.

Gland (L. *glans*, acorn). A cell or collection of cells which produces a specific product.

Glo-mer′u-lus (L. *glomare*, to make a ball). A tuft or cluster of blood vessels projecting into the capsule of each uriniferous tubule.

Glot′tis (Gr. *glotta*, tongue). Opening from the pharynx into the larynx.

Gly′co-gen (Gr. *glykus*, sweet; *gen;* producing). A carbohydrate stored in many parts of the body; also known as "animal starch."

Goi′ter (L. *gutter*, throat). An enlargement of the thyroid gland, usually resulting from a deficiency of iodine in the diet.

Golgi body. A cytoplasmic particle which probably functions in the production of secretory products.

Go′nad (Gr. *gonos*, reproduction). A gamete-producing reproductive organ.

Go-nan′gi-um (Gr. *gone*, seed; *angeion*, vessel). The reproductive individual of a hydroid colony.

Gre-gar′i-ous (L. *gregarius*, from *grex*, a herd). The property of animals of flocking together.

Gul′let (L. *gula*, gullet). Esophagus.

Hab′i-tat (L. *habitare*, to dwell). Environment of an organism.

Hap′loid (Gr. *haploos*, single; *eidos*, form). The reduced number of chromosomes found in the gametes; half the diploid number.

He′mo-coel (Gr. *haima*, blood; *koilus*, hollow). A body cavity functioning as a part of the circulatory system.

He′mo-cy″a-nin (Gr. *haima*, blood; *kyanos*, a dark-blue substance). An oxygen-carrying pigment, copper-bearing and blue in color, found in the blood of mollusks and arthropods.

He′mo-glo″bin (Gr. *haima*, blood; L. *globus*, globe). Oxygen-carrying red pigment of blood.

He′mo-phil″i-a (Gr. *haima*, blood; *phil*, to love). A hereditary condition in man in which blood clotting is abnormally slow.

He-pat′ic (Gr. *hepar*, liver). Pertaining to the liver.

Her-biv′o-rous (L. *herba*, herb; *vorare*, to devour). Subsisting on plants.

Her-ed′i-ty (L. *hereditas*, heirship). Organic resemblance based on descent.

Her-maph′ro-ditic (Gr. *Hermes, Aphrodite*). Possessing both male and female reproductive organs.

Het′er-o-zy″gote (Gr. *heteros*, different; *zeugon*, yolk). A hybrid formed from gametes having different genes for the same trait.

Hi′ber-na″tion (L. *hiems*, winter). The dormant state in which some animals spend the winter.

His′ta-mine. An organic compound which is a powerful dilator of the capillaries and a stimulator of gastric secretions; found in all plants and animals.

His′to-gen″e̩-sis (Gr. *histos*, tissue; *gignesthai*, to be born). The origin, development, and differentiation of tissues from undifferentiated cells of the embryonic germ layers.

His-tol′o-gy (Gr. *histos*, tissue; *logos*, study). The study of the microscopic structure of tissues and organs.

Hol′o-zo″ic (Gr. *holos*, whole; *zoion*, animal). Nutrition involving the ingestion and digestion of organic material.

Ho-mol′o-gy (Gr. *homos*, same; *logos*, study). The study of organs which result from common embryonic origin. They may or may not have the same function.

Ho′mo-zy″gote (Gr. *homos*, same; *zeugon*, yolk). An organism formed from gametes containing like genes for a given character.

Hor′mone (Gr. *hormon*, from *hormaein*, to arouse or excite). Chemical substance produced by an endocrine gland which, when transported to another area, produces a specific effect.

Host (L. *hostis*, stranger). The organism upon which a parasite lives.

Hy′a-line (Gr. *hyalos*, clear). A translucent, albumenoid material.

Hy′brid (L. *hybrida*, mongrel). An organism

formed from the union of gametes differing in one or more genes; a heterozygote.

Hy′dranth (Gr. *hydra*, water serpent; *anthos*, flower). A vegetative branch of a hydroid colony.

Hy′dro-car″bon (Gr. *hydor*, water; L. *carbo*, coal). An organic compound formed only of hydrogen and carbon.

Hy-drol′y-sis (Gr. *hydor*, water; *lysis*, a loosing). Chemical decomposition by reaction with water.

Hy′men (Gr. *Umen*, membrane). A membranous fold which usually partially or wholly occludes the external orifice or vagina during virginity.

Hy′oid (Gr. *hyoides*, Y-shaped). A Y-shaped group of bones at the base of the tongue.

Hy′per-ton″ic (Gr. *huper*, beyond; *tonikos*, strength). High osmotic pressure in reference to another solution.

Hy-poph′y-sis (Gr. *hupo*, under; *physis*, growth). The pituitary gland.

Hy-poth′e-sis (Gr. proposal). Tentative solution or proposal concerning a problem.

Hy′po-ton″ic (Gr. *hupo*, under; *tonikos*, strength). A lesser osmotic pressure in reference to another solution.

I-den′ti-cal twins. Twins arising from the same fertilized egg and therefore having the same genetic constitution.

Il′e-um (L. grain). The most posterior portion of the small intestine.

Il′i-um (L. flank). The dorsal bone of the pelvic girdle.

Im-mu′ni-ty (L. *immunis*, free). The power which a living organism possesses to resist and overcome infection.

In″breed′ing. The crossing of closely related animals.

In-fun-dib′u-lum (L. *infundibulum*, funnel). A stalk-like evagination of the diencephalon.

In-gest′ (L. *ingestus*, from *ingerere*, to put in). To take in food.

In′or-gan″ic (L. *in*, not; Gr. *organikos*, instrument). Pertaining to substances of non-organic origin.

In-ser′tion (L. *insertus*, from *inserere*, to connect, insert). Point of attachment of a muscle to the movable part.

In′su-lin (L. *insula*, island). Hormone secreted by the pancreatic Islets of Langerhans.

In-teg′u-ment (L. *integumentum*, covering). The outermost covering of an organism; skin.

In′ter-cel″lu-lar (L. *inter*, between; *cellula*, cells). Between cells.

In-ter′nal se-cre′tion. Secretion into the blood stream.

In′ter-sti″tial (L. *inter*, between; *sistere*, to set). Pertaining to intercellular spaces.

In-tes′tine (L. *intestinus*, internal). Part of the digestive tract posterior to the stomach.

In′tra-cel″lu-lar (L. *intra*, within; *cellula*, cells). Within cells.

In′tus-sus-cep″tion (L. *intus*, within; *suscipere*, to receive). Growth by the addition of new materials within protoplasm.

In-vag′i-nate (L. *in*, in; vagina, sheath). An inpushing of a cellular layer into a cavity.

In-ver′te-brate (L. *in*, not; *vertebra*, joint). An animal without a vertebral column.

In′vo-lu″tion (L. *in*, in; *volvere*, to roll). A rolling or turning inward of cells over a rim.

I′on (Gr. *ion*, going). A portion of a molecule in solution carrying a charge.

Ir′ri-ta-bil″i-ty (L. *irrito*, excite). Ability to respond to a stimulus.

Is′chi-um (Gr. *ischion*, hip). The posterior ventral bone of the pelvic girdle.

I′so-ton″ic (Gr. *isos*, equal; *tonikos*, strength). Having the same osmotic pressure.

Je-ju′num (L. *jejunus*, empty). The digestive tract lying between the duodenum and the ileum.

Jug′u-lar (I. *jugulum*, collar bone). Pertaining to the neck (jugular) vein.

Kid′ney. The major excretory organ in vertebrates.

La′bi-al (L. *labium*, lip). Pertaining to lips.

Lab′y-rinth (Gr. *labrys*, double ax). Part of the inner ear in higher vertebrates, composed of semicircular canals, utriculus, sacculus, and cochlea.

Lac′ri-mal (L. *lacrima*, tear). Pertaining to tears.

Lac′te-al (L. *lac*, milk). Pertaining to milk; also referring to lymph vessels in the small intestine.

La-cu′na (L. *lacuna*, cavity). A small pit, hollow, or cavity, as in bone or cartilage.

La-mel′la (L. small plate). A thin layer.

La-nu′go (L. *lanuginosus*, wool). The soft woolly hair covering the human fetus, usually shed shortly before birth.

Lar′va (L. *larva*, ghost). An immature, free-living stage of an animal.

Lar′ynx (Gr. *larynx*, larynx). A structure containing the vocal cords located at the top of the trachea and below the root of the tongue in all vertebrates except birds.

Lat′er-al (L. *latus*, side). Toward the side.

Le′thal gene (L. *lethum*, death). A gene capable of bringing about the death of the organism.

Leu′co-cyte (Gr. *leucos*, white; *kytos*, cell). A white blood cell.

Lig′a-ment (L. *ligamentum*, bandage). A tough, fibrous band of connective tissue.

Lin′gual (L. *lingua*, tongue). Pertaining to the tongue.

Link′age (M.E. *linke*). Phenomenon occurring when a series of genes are passed on as a unit.

Li′pase (Gr. *lipos*, fat). Fat-splitting enzyme.

Lip′id (Gr. *lipos*, fat). Pertaining to fat.

Lum′bar (L. *lumbus*, loin). Pertaining to the region of the back between the thorax and the pelvis.

Lu′men (L. cavity). The internal cavity within a structure.

Lymph (L. *lympha*, water). Fluid found in the lymph vessels containing fat, white blood cells, and plasma.

Mac′ro-nu″cle-us (Gr. *makros*, large; L. *nucleus*, kernel). The large nucleus of a ciliate (such as paramecium) as distinguished from the micronucleus.

Ma-la′ri-a (L. *mal*, bad; *aria*, air). An infectious disease caused by protozoa (sporozoa) and transmitted by certain mosquitos.

Man′di-ble (L. *mandere*, to chew). The lower jawbone in vertebrates or either jaw in arthropods.

Man′tle (L. *mantellum*, cloak). A sheet-like tissue enclosing soft structures of an animal, such as a mollusk.

Ma-nu′bri-um (L. *manus*, hand). The uppermost part of the sternum; also the structure bearing the mouth in the medusa.

Ma-rine′ (L. *marinus*, from *mare*, the sea). Pertaining to the sea.

Mas′ti-ca″tion (L. *masticare*, to chew). Referring to chewing.

Ma-ter′nal (L. *maternus*, of a mother). Referring to the mother.

Mat′u-ra″tion (L. *maturus*, ripe). The final stages in the production of gametes in which the number of chromosomes is reduced to one-half (diploid to haploid) the number characteristic of the species.

Me′di-an (L. *medius*, middle). Pertaining to the mid-line.

Me-dul′la (L. *medulla*, marrow). The distinct inner portion of a structure.

Me-dul′la ob-lon-ga′ta (L. oblong medulla). The most posterior portion of the brain.

Med′ul-la-ry plate, groove, or **tube** (L. *medullaris*, narrow). Neural plate, groove, or tube found in the embryonic development of the vertebrate nervous system.

Med′ul-lat-ed. A nerve fiber with a myelin covering or sheath.

Mei-o′sis (Gr. to make smaller). See Maturation.

Mem′brane (L. *membrana*, membrane). Any thin cellular sheet or layer.

Me-nin′ges (Gr. *meninx*, membrane). The three membranes enveloping the brain and the spinal cord.

Men′o-pause (Gr. *Men*, month; *pausis*, cessation). The period when menstruation normally ceases; change of life.

Mes′en-chyme (Gr. *mesos*, middle; *engchein*, to pour in). A loose embryonic connective tissue derived chiefly from mesoderm.

Mes′en-ter-y (Gr. *mesos*, middle; *enteron*, intestine). A membrane supporting an organ in the abdominal cavity; also a partition found in certain coelenterates.

Mes′o-derm (Gr. *mesos*, middle; *derma*, skin). The mid-layer of embryonic cells found between the ectoderm and the endoderm.

Mes′o-gle″a (**mesogloea**) (Gr. *mesos*, middle; *gloia*, glue). A non-cellular, jelly-like substance found in coelenterates.

Mes′o-neph″ros (Gr. *meso*, middle; *nephros*, kidney). A kind of vertebrate kidney found in all embryos and in certain adult fish and amphibians.

Me-tab′o-lism (Gr. *meta*, beyond; *ballein*, to throw). The sum total of the chemical and physical processes occurring in protoplasm.

Met′a-gen″e-sis (Gr. *meta*, over; *genesis*, origin). Alternation of sexual and asexual generations.

Met′a-mere (Gr. *meta*, over; *meros*, part). Homologous segment of the body.

Me-tam′er-ism. The possession of a succession of homologous parts.

Met′a-mor″pho-sis (Gr. *meta*, over; *morphe*, form). The structural changes taking place in the transformation of a larva to an adult.

Met′a-phase (Gr. *meta*, after; *phasis*, appearance). The midstage of mitosis during which there is a lengthwise separation of chromosomes at the equatorial plate.

Met′a-zo″a (Gr. *meta*, over; *zoion*, animal). The multicellular animals in which there is a differentiation of the somatic cells.

Mi′cron (Gr. *mikros*, small). One thousandth part of a millimeter.

Mi′cro-nu″cle-us (Gr. *mikros*, small; L. *nucleus*, kernel). The small reproductive nucleus of certain protozoa.

Mi·gra′tion (L. *migratio*). Moving from place to place.

Mil′li·li″ter (L. *mille,* one thousand; Fr. *litre,* liter). Thousandth part of a liter.

Mit′o·chon″dri·a (Gr. *mitos,* thread; *chondros,* grain). Small granules or rod-shaped structures found in the cytoplasm, thought to contain enzymes.

Mi·to′sis (Gr. *mitos,* thread). Nuclear division.

Molt (M.E. *mouten,* from L. *mutare,* to change). To shed an outer covering.

Mo·noe′cious. Containing both sexes in the same organism, hermaphroditic.

Mon′o·hy″brid (Gr. *monos,* single; L. *hybrida,* mongrel). The offspring of parents differing in one character.

Mor·phol′o·gy (Gr. *morphe,* form; *logos,* discourse). The study of form and structure.

Mu′cous (L. *mucus,* slime). Pertaining to mucus.

Mu′cus (L. *mucus,* slime). A watery secretion which covers mucous membranes.

Mu′tant (L. *mutare,* to change). A variation which breeds true.

Mu·ta′tion (L. *mutare,* to change). A permanent transmissible change in the character of an offspring.

My′e·lin (Gr. *myelos,* marrow). A fat-like substance forming a sheath around the axis of a medullated nerve.

My′o·fi″bril (Gr. *mys,* muscle; L. *fibrilla,* a small fiber). One of the slender, protoplasmic threads found in the muscle fiber which runs parallel with the long axis.

Na′res (L. *naris,* nostril). Openings of the air passages in vertebrates, both external and internal.

Na′sal (L. *nasus,* nose). Pertaining to the nose.

Nem′a·to·cyst (Gr. *nema,* thread; *kystis,* a bladder). A stinging body found in coelenterates.

Ne·phrid′i·o·pore (Gr. *nephros,* kidney; *poros,* passage). The external opening of the invertebrate excretory organ.

Ne·phrid′i·um (Gr. *nephros,* kidney). An invertebrate excretory organ.

Neph′ro·stome (Gr. *nephros,* kidney; *stoma,* mouth). The funnel-shaped opening at the inner end of the nephridium.

Neu′ral (Gr. *neuron,* nerve). Pertaining to the nervous system.

Neu′ri·lem″ma (Gr. *neuron,* nerve; *lemma,* covering). The outermost nerve fiber sheath.

Neu′ron, or **neu′rone** (Gr. *neuron,* nerve). The nerve cell.

No′to·chord (Gr. *notos,* back; *chorde,* string). The cylindrical rod of supportive tissue found in chordates, dorsal to the digestive tract and ventral to the nerve cord.

Nu·cle′ic acid. A group of molecules composed of nucleotide complexes, the important types being desoxyribose nucleic acid (DNA) and ribose nucleic acid (RNA).

Nu·cle′ol·us (L. diminutive of *nucleus*). A round, conspicuous body found within the nucleus of most cells.

Nu′cleo protein. A giant molecule containing nucleic acid and protein.

Nu′cleo·tide. A molecule containing phosphate, five-carbon sugar (ribose or desoxyribose), and a purine or a pyrimidine.

Nu′cle·us (L. kernel). A dense spheroid body, containing chromatin, found within the cell.

Nu·tri′tion (L. *nutrimentum,* nourishment). Sum total of the processes involved in food assimilation.

Oc·cip′i·tal (L. *occiput,* back of the head). Pertaining to the back of the head.

O·cel′lus (L. a little eye). The simple eye found in invertebrates.

Oc′u·lar (L. *oculus,* an eye). Pertaining to the eye; also the eyepiece of a microscope.

Ol·fac′to·ry (L. *olfacere,* to smell). Pertaining to the sense of smell.

Om·ma·tid′i·um (Gr. *omna,* eye). A small rod-like unit in the invertebrate compound eye.

Om·niv′o·rous (L. *ominis,* all; *vorare,* to devour). Subsisting on food of all types.

On·tog′e·ny (Gr. *onto,* being; *genos,* birth). The evolution of developmental history of an organism.

O′o·cyte (Gr. *oon,* egg; *kytos,* cell). The original cell of the ovarian egg before the formation of polar bodies.

O′o·gen″e·sis (Gr. *oon,* egg; *genesis,* origin). The origin and development of the ovum.

O′o·gon′i·um (Gr. *oon,* egg; *gonos,* offspring). The primordial cell which gives rise to the ovarian egg.

Oph·thal′mic (L. *ophthalmia,* the eye). Pertaining to the eye.

Op′tic (Gr. *optikos,* sight). Pertaining to the eye or vision.

O′ral (L. *os,* mouth). Pertaining to the mouth.

Or′bit (L. *orbis,* circle). The bony eye socket.

Or′gan (Gr. *organon,* an instrument). A group of tissues associated to perform one or more functions.

Or′gan·elle″. A minute organ found in protozoa.

Or·gan′ic com′pound (Gr. *organon,* an implement; L. *componere,* to put together). A carbon-containing molecule.

Or′gan·ism (Fr. *organisme*). Any living thing.

Or'ga-nog"e-ny (Gr. *organon*, an instrument, implement; *genesis*, birth). The developmental processes involved in the formation of specialized tissue and organ systems.

Or'i-gin (L. *orior*, rise, become visible). Part of the muscle attached to an immovable structure.

Or'tho-gen"e-sis (Gr. *orthos*, straight; *genesis*, descent). Progressive evolution in a given direction.

Os-mo'sis (Gr. *osmos*, pushing). Diffusion through a semi-permeable membrane.

O'to-lith (Gr. *ous*, ear; *lithos*, stone). A small calcareous mass found in the auditory organ of many animals.

O'va-ry (L. *ovarium*, ovary). The primary female sex gland in which the eggs are formed.

O'vi-duct (L. *ovum*, egg; *ducere*, to lead). The tube through which the eggs are carried from the ovary to the uterus or outside the body.

O-vip'a-rous (L. *ovum*, egg; *pario*, to produce). Producing eggs which hatch outside the body.

O'vi-pos"i-tor (L. *ovum*, egg; *ponere*, to place). An organ found in female insects for depositing eggs.

O'vo-vi-vip"a-rous (L. *ovum*, egg; *vivus*, alive; *parere*, to bear). Producing eggs which hatch within the body.

O-vu-la'tion (L. *ovum*, egg). The discharge of the unimpregnated ovum from the ovary.

O'vum (L. egg). The mature female gamete.

Ox'i-da"tion (Gr. *oxys*, acid). An increase of positive charges on an atom, or the loss of negative charges.

Pae'do-gen"i-sis (Gr. *pais*, a child; *genesis*, origin). Reproduction while in the immature or larval stage.

Pa'le-on-tol"o-gy (Gr. *palaios*, old; *ons*, being; *logos*, discourse). Study of fossils.

Palp (L. *palpare*, to feel). One of the pointed sense organs attached to the mouth of some invertebrates.

Pan'cre-as (Gr. *pan*, all; *kreas*, flesh). A digestive gland located behind the stomach and opening by a duct into the duodenum.

Par'a-site (Gr. *para*, beside; *sitos*, food; or *parasitos*, eating beside another). An organism which lives on or in another living organism from which it receives an advantage without compensation.

Par'a-thy"roid (Gr. *para*, near; *thyreoeides*, shield-shaped). A small endocrine gland located near the thyroid.

Pa-ren'chy-ma (Gr. *para*, beside; *enchyma*, infusion). Loose, spongy connective tissue.

Pa-ri'e-tal (L. *parietis*, a wall). Pertaining to the coelomic wall.

Par'the-no-gen"e-sis (Gr. *parthenos*, virgin; *genesis*, origin). Reproduction by development of the egg without its being fertilized by the male element.

Pa-ter'nal (L. *paternus*, from *pater*, father). Pertaining to a father.

Path'o-gen"ic (Gr. *pathos*, suffering; *genesis*, to produce). Disease-producing.

Pa-thol'o-gy (Gr. *pathos*, disease; *logos*, study). The study of abnormal structures and processes.

Ped'al (L. *pes*, foot). Pertaining to the foot or feet.

Pe-lag'ic (L. *pelagicus*, from *pelagus*, sea). Inhabiting the open sea.

Pel'li-cle (L. *pellicula*, small skin). A thin skin, or film.

Pe'nis (L.). The male organ of copulation.

Pen'ta-dac"tyl (Gr. *pente*, five; *daktylos*, finger). Having five digits.

Pep'sin (Gr. *pepsis*, a cooking, digesting). The protein-splitting enzyme of the gastric juice.

Per'i-car"di-um (Gr. *peri*, around; *cardia*, heart). The membranous sac surrounding the heart.

Per'i-os"te-um (Gr. *peri*, around; *osteon*, bone). The tough, fibrous membrane surrounding bone.

Pe-riph'er-al (Gr. *periphereia*, from *peri*, around; *pherein*, to bear, carry). Pertaining to the surface.

Per'i-stal"sis (Gr. *peri*, around; *stalsis*, constriction). The wave of contraction by which the alimentary canal propels its contents.

Per'i-to-ne"um (Gr. *peri*, around; *tenein*, to stretch). The thin epithelial membrane which lines the coelom and invests the viscera.

pH. Symbol which represents the concentration of hydrogen ions in a solution.

Phag'o-cyte (Gr. *phagein*, to eat; *kytos*, cell). A type of white blood cell which ingests foreign substances.

Pha-lan'ges (Gr. *phalanx*, long line of battle). Digital bones.

Phar'ynx (Gr. *pharynx*). The portion of the digestive tract located between the mouth and esophagus.

Phe'no-type (Gr. *phaino*, show; *typto*, strike). The total of visible and physiological traits common to a group of individuals.

Phos'phor-y-la'tion The addition of a phosphate group to a compound.

Pho'to-syn"the-sis (Gr. *phos*, light; *synthesis*, a putting together). The chemical combination, in the green plant, of carbon dioxide and water, to form carbohydrate, in the presence of light and chlorophyll.

Phy·log'e·ny (Gr. *phylon*, race, branch; *geny*, become). The evolutionary history of a race or group.

Phy'lum (Gr. *phylon*, tribe). One of the main divisions of the animal or plant kingdom.

Phys'i·ol"o·gy (Gr. *physis*, nature; *logos*, study). The study of functions of organisms.

Pig'ment (L. *pingere*, to paint). Coloring matter.

Pin'e·al (L. *pinea*, pine cone). An evaginated structure on the roof of the brain.

Pi·tu"i·tar'y bod'y (L. *pituita*, phlegm; A.S. *bodig*). An endocrine gland.

Pla·cen'ta (L. *placenta*, a flat cake). The round, flat organ within the uterus of mammals formed during embryonic development and attached to the embryo by means of an umbilical cord.

Plan'u·la (L. *planus*, flat). The ciliated, free-swimming larva found in the development of certain invertebrates.

Plas'ma (Gr. something molded). The liquid part of the blood or lymph.

Plas'ma mem'brane (L. *membrana*, skin covering). The external cytoplasmic membrane of a cell.

Plas'tid (Gr. *plastides*, to form). A pigmented cytoplasmic inclusion.

Plat'y-hel·min"thes (Gr. *platy*, flat; *helmins*, worm). A phylum of animals.

Pleur'al (Gr. *pleura*, side). Pertaining to the cavity in which the lungs are contained.

Plex'us (L. interwoven). A nervous or vascular network.

Po'lar bod'y (L. *polaris*, axis). The non-functional cell formed during the maturation of the egg cell.

Pol'y-mor"phism (Gr. *polys*, many; *morphe*, form). The occurrence of more than two types of individuals in the same species.

Pol'yp (Gr. *polypous*, many-footed). The attached form of a coelenterate usually possessing a mouth and tentacles at the free end.

Pos·te'ri·or (L. latter). Situated behind.

Pre·co'cious (L. *praecox*, ripe before its time). Characterized by early maturity.

Pre·da'ceous (L. *praedo*, prey). Capturing of live animals for food.

Pri·mor'di·al (L. *primordium*, beginning). Original or primitive.

Prin'ci·ple (L. *principium*, beginning). Scientific fact, theory, or law.

Pro·bos'cis (Gr. *proboskis*, trunk). Tubular extension of the lips, nose, or pharynx.

Proc'to-de"um (Gr. *proktos*, anus; *hodos*, way). The most posterior part of the digestive tract near the anus, lined with ectoderm.

Pro·neph'ros (Gr. *pro*, before; *nephros*, kidney). A primordial kidney.

Pro·nu'cle·us (Gr. *pro*, before; L. *nucleus*, kernel). The nucleus of either the egg or sperm cell during the interval existing between the penetration of the sperm into the egg and the subsequent union to form the germinal nucleus.

Pro'phase (Gr. *pro*, before; *phasis*, appearance). The first stage of mitotic division during which the chromosomes become visible.

Pros'tate gland (Gr. *prostates*, one who stands before; L. *glans*, an acorn). An accessory sex gland found in the male surrounding the neck of the bladder and urethra.

Pro'te·in (Gr. *protos*, first). An organic compound composed of amino acids forming an essential part of the protoplasm.

Pro'to·plasm (Gr. *protos*, first; *plasma*, something molded). The colloidal living substance constituting the physical basis of life.

Pro'to·zo"a (Gr. *protos*, first; *zoion*, animal). A phylum of animals.

Prox'i·mal (L. *proximus*, next). Near the point of attachment of an organ.

Pseu'do-coel (Gr. *pseudo*, false; *koilia*, body cavity). A body cavity not completely lined with mesoderm, as found in the round worm.

Pseu'do-po"di·a (Gr. *pseudo*, false; *pous*, foot). A temporary protoplasmic projection found in amoeba or in some amoeba-like cells.

Pty'a·lin (Gr. *ptyalon*, spittle). Salivary enzyme which acts on starch.

Pu'bis (L. *pubes*, mature). The pubic bone, one of the three bones forming the pelvis.

Pul'mo·nar·y (L. *pulmo*, lung). Pertaining to the lung.

Pu'rine. A characteristic substance in nucleic acids. The two common ones are adenine and guanine.

Py·lor'ic (Gr. *pylorus*, gate). Pertaining to the posterior portion of the stomach or the pylorus.

Py'rim·i·dine A characteristic substance in nucleic acids. The three common ones are thymine, cytosine, and uracil.

Quad'ru-ped (L. *quattuor*, four; *pes*, foot). Four-footed animal.

Ra'di·al sym'me·try (L. *radius*, ray). The condition in which similar parts are regularly arranged around a central axis, for example, as seen in starfish.

Ra'mus (L.). A branch, as of a blood vessel, bone, or nerve.

Re-cep'tor (L. *receptor*, receiver). A sensory end-organ.

Rec'tum (L. *rectus*, straight). The most posterior portion of the large intestine.

Re-gen'er-a"tion (L. *re*, again; *generare*, to beget). The renewal or repair of a structure.

Re'nal (L. *renes*, kidney). Pertaining to the kidney.

Ren'nin (A.S. *gerinnan*, to curdle, coagulate). Enzyme secreted by the stomach wall which causes the coagulation of casein in milk.

Re'pro-duc"tion (L. *re*, again; *pro*, forth; *ducere*, to lead). The production of offspring.

Res'pi-ra"tion (L. *re*, again; *spirare*, to breathe). The gaseous metabolism at the cellular level.

Re-sponse' (L. *re*, again; *spondere*, to promise). Reaction to stimulus.

Ret'i-na (L. *rete*, net). The innermost layer of the eye containing the light sensitive receptors.

Rh fac'tor (the Rhesus factor). A chemical factor found in the blood of some individuals which has genetic significance.

Rho-dop'sin (Gr. *rhodon*, rose; *opsis*, sight). Visual purple. A substance found in the retina and associated with vision.

RNA. Abbreviation for ribose nucleic acid.

Ru-di-men'ta-ry (L. *rudis*, unwrought, rude). Imperfectly developed, or having no function.

Ru'mi-nant (L. *rumen*, throat). A group of cud-chewing animals including the cow, goat, and deer, which have a stomach with four complete cavities.

Sap'ro-zo"ic (Gr. *sapros*, rotten; *zoion*, living being). Living on dead or decaying organic matter.

Sar'co-lem"ma (Gr. *sarx*, flesh; *lemma*, covering). The elastic sheath investing each striated muscle fiber.

Sar'co-plasm (Gr. *sarx*, flesh; *plasma*, liquid). The fluid protoplasmic matter of striated muscles.

Se-ba'ceous glands (L. *sebum*, tallow, grease; L. *glans*, an acorn). Small skin glands associated with hair follicles which produce a waxy secretion for lubrication of the skin.

Se-cre'tin. A hormone produced by the intestinal wall which controls the secretion of pancreatic juice.

Se-cre'tion (L. *secretio*, from *secernere*, to separate). The process of separating various substances from the blood for use by the organism; also the material produced.

Sed'en-tar-y (L. *sedere*, to sit). Permanently attached form.

Seg'ment (L. *segmentum*, a piece cut off). A portion of a metameric organism.

Self'-fer-ti-li-za'tion. Fertilization of an egg by a sperm from the same individual.

Se'men (L. *serere*, to sow). The sperm-containing fluid of male animals.

Semi'i-cir"cu-lar ca-nals' (L. *semi*, half; *circulus*, circle). Canals in the inner ear of the vertebrate which make up an essential part of the sense organ of equilibrium.

Sem'i-nal (L. *semen*, seed). Pertaining to the semen.

Sem'i-nal re-cep'ta-cles (L. *semen*, seed; L. *recipere*, to receive). Sac-like receptacles in the female used for the storage of sperm after copulation.

Sem'in-al ves'i-cles (L. *semen*, seed; L. *vesica*, bladder). Sac-like structures in the male used to store sperm.

Sem'i-nif"er-ous tu'bule (L. *semen*, seed; *ferro*, to carry; *tubules*, small tube). A small duct used to convey seminal fluid.

Sen'so-ry cell (L. *sensus*, sense). Any receptor cell.

Sep'tum (L. *septum*, partition). A partition between adjoining cavities.

Ser'i-al ho-mol'o-gy (L. *series*, join; Gr. *homos*, same; *logos*, discourse). The serial repetition of structures having the same embryonic origin.

Se-rol'o-gy (L. *serum*, liquid). The study of serums and their actions.

Ses'sile (L. *sedere*, to sit). Attached, as opposed to free-living.

Se'tae (L. *seta*, bristle). Stiff bristle, as, for example, the setae in the parapodia of *Nereis*.

Si'nus (L. cavity). A cavity or hollow space.

Sol'ute (L. *solvere*, to loosen). The dissolved substance in a solution.

Sol'vent (L. *solvere*, to loosen). The substance in which the solute is dissolved. It is the continuous liquid portion of a solution.

So'mite. A serial segment or metamere of an animal.

Spe'cies (L. appearance). A primary subdivision of a genus.

Sperm (Gr. seed). Male sex cell.

Sper'ma-ry. Male reproductive gland, testis.

Sper'ma-tid. The male germ cell just prior to the formation of the sperm.

Sper'ma-to-gen"e-sis (Gr. *sperma*, seed; *genesis*, origin). The process by which spermatozoa are formed.

Sper'ma-to-zo"on (Gr. *sperma*, seed; *zoion*, animal). A mature male reproductive cell, sperm.

Sphinc'ter (Gr. *sphingein*, to bind tightly). A ring-like muscle surrounding a natural orifice; the opening is closed by its contraction.

Spic'ule (L. *spiculum*, a little point). A sharp, needle-like body, characteristic of sponges.

Spi'nal col'umn (L. *spina*, thorn, spine). A continuous series of vertebrae in vertebrates which houses the spinal cord.

Spi'nal cord. The tubular part of the central nervous system which extends posteriorly from the brain throughout the length of the spinal column.

Spin'dle (A.S. *spinnan*, to spin). The spindle-shaped threads or fibers associated with the chromosomes in mitosis, radiating out from the centrosomes.

Spi'ra-cle (L. *spiraculum*, air hole). A breathing orifice of insects and the first gill slit in cartilaginous fishes.

Spleen (Gr. *splen*, spleen). A large organ situated in the upper part of the abdomen on the left side and lateral to the stomach having to do with red blood cell disintegration.

Spore (Gr. *spora*, seed). A special encapsulated reproductive body of one of the lower organisms.

Spor'u-la"tion (Gr. *spora*, seed). Reproduction by multiple fission, forming spores.

Stat'o-cyst (Gr. *statos*, stationary; *kystis*, sac.) An organ of equilibrium found in invertebrates.

Stat'o-lith (Gr. *statos*, standing; *lithos*, stone). The solid body within a statocyst.

Ster'num (L. breastbone). Breastbone.

Stig'ma (Gr. a pricked mark). A light-sensitive pigment spot in certain protozoa.

Stim'u-lus (L. *stimulare*, to incite). An environmental change which causes a response.

Strat'i-fied (L. *stratum*, a covering). Arranged in layers.

Stri'at-ed (L. *stria*, channel). Cross-striped, such as in skeletal muscle.

Sub-cu-ta'ne-ous (L. *sub*, under; *cutis*, skin). The region immediately beneath the skin.

Sub'mu-co"sa (L. *sub*, under; *mucosus*, mucus). One of the layers of tissue in the wall of the digestive tract.

Su'ture (L. *sutura*, from *suere*, *sutum*, to sew). The point of fusion between two bones.

Swim'mer-et (A.S. *swimman*). Paired biramous appendage of the crayfish, just posterior to the walking legs.

Sym'bi-o"sis (Gr. *syn*, together; *bios*, living). Living together of two species.

Sym"me'try (Gr. *syn*, together; *meton*, measure). The regular or reversed disposition of parts around a common axis, or on each side of any plane of the body.

Syn'apse (Gr. *syn*, together; *hapto*, unite). The region of contact of two adjacent neurons.

Syn-ap'sis. Temporary union of maternal and paternal homologous chromosomes prior to the first maturation division.

Syn-cyt'i-um (Gr. *syn*, together; *kytos*, cell). A multinucleate mass of protoplasm.

Sys'tem (Gr. *syn*, together; *histanai*, to place). A group of organs having the same general function.

Sys'to-le (Gr. *syn*, with; *stellein*, to set, place). The contraction phase of the cardiac cycle.

Tac'tile (L. *tangere*, to touch). Pertaining to the sense of touch.

Tax-on'o-my (Gr. *taxis*, arrangement; *nomos*, law). The science of the classification of living things.

Tel'o-phase (Gr. *telos*, end; *phasis*, aspect). The last stage in mitotic division.

Ten'don (L. *tendere*, to stretch). A fibrous cord of connective tissue which binds a muscle to a bone or to other structures.

Ten'ta-cle (L. *tentare*, to touch, feel). A slender, whip-like organ for feeling or motion found in invertebrates.

Ter-res'tri-al (L. *terra*, earth). Living on the ground.

Tes'tis (L. *testis*). The sperm-forming male gonad.

Tet'rad (Gr. *tetra*, four). The four chromosomes which arise during maturation from the pairing and splitting of a homologous pair of chromosomes.

The'o-ry (Gr. *theoria*, a beholding, speculation). A formulated hypothesis.

Tho-rac'ic (Gr. *thorax*, chest). Pertaining to the chest or thorax.

Tho'rax (Gr. chest). The chest.

Throm'bin (Gr. *thrombos*, clot). A substance produced in shed blood when prothrombin comes in contact with thromboplastin. It is essential in clot formation.

Throm'bo-plas"tin (Gr. *thrombos,* clot; *plastikos,* to form, mold). A substance released from injured cells or platelets that initiates blood clotting.

Thy'mus (Gr. *thymos,* thymus). A ductless gland-like body situated ventral and anterior to the heart and below the thyroid.

Thy'roid (Gr. *thyreos,* shield; *eidos,* resemble). An endocrine gland located in the neck of vertebrates which secretes thyroxine.

Thy-rox'ine. The hormone secreted by the thyroid.

Tis'sue (L. *texere,* to weave). A collection of cells, usually similar, organized for the performance of a specific function.

Tox'in (Gr. *toxicon,* poison). A poisonous substance of plant or animal origin.

Tra'che-a (Gr. *tracheia,* windpipe). The breathing tube or windpipe of vertebrates and the tiny air tubes of certain arthropods.

Trait (L. *tractus,* a drawing). An inherited character.

Trans-duc'tion. The passage of genetic material from one bacterium to another by means of a virus.

Trip'lo-blas"tic (Gr. *triplax,* triple; *blastos,* bud). Having three germ layers.

Tryp'sin (Gr. *truein,* rubbing down; *pepsis,* digesting). A protein-splitting pancreatic enzyme.

Tym-pan'ic mem'brane (Gr. *tympanon,* eardrum; L. *membrana,* skin covering). The eardrum.

Um-bil'i-cal cord (L. *umbilicus,* navel). The cord-like connection between the placenta and the fetus of mammals.

U-re'a (Gr. *ouron,* urine). A nitrogenous metabolic waste of mammals found in urine.

U're'ter (Gr. *oureter,* ureter). The tube which carries urine from the kidney to the bladder or to the cloaca.

U-re'thra (Gr. *oureter,* ureter). The tube that carries urine from the bladder to the surface, and in the male conveys the seminal fluids.

U'rine (L. *urina,* urine). The fluid secreted by the kidney.

U'rin-if"er-ous tu'bule (L. *urina,* urine; *ferre,* to bear; *tubulus,* any small tube). One of the excretory tubules in the kidney of higher vertebrates, consisting of a coiled tube and a capsule.

U'ro-gen"i-tal (u'ri-no-gen"i-tal sys'tem) (Gr. *ouron,* urine; *gignesthai,* to produce). Pertaining to both the excretory and reproductive systems.

U'ter-us (L. womb). The hollow muscular posterior end of the oviduct where the developing animal is contained and nourished.

Vac'u-ole (L. *vacuum,* empty). Small space in the cytoplasm.

Va-gi'na (L. sheath). The canal in the female reproductive tract which receives the penis in mating.

Va'gus (L. wandering). The tenth cranial nerve.

Va-ri-a'tion (L. *variare,* to change). Difference in structure or function exhibited by individuals of the same species.

Va-ri'e-ty (L. *varietas,* difference). One of the sub-divisions of the species.

Vas de'fer-ens (L. vessel; L. carrying down). The tube or duct which conveys sperm away from the testis.

Va'sa ef'fer-en"ti-a (L. vessels; L. *efferens,* bringing out). Small ducts which carry sperm from the testis to the epididymis in higher vertebrates.

Vas'cu-lar (L. *vasculum,* little vessel). Pertaining to vessels.

Vein (L. *vena,* vein). A blood vessel that carries blood to the heart.

Ven'tral (L. *venter,* belly). The lower surface, opposite to dorsal.

Ven'tri-cle (L. *ventriculus,* little belly). A lower muscular pumping chamber of the heart, also a brain cavity.

Ver'mi-form ap-pen'dix (L. *vermis,* worm; *forma,* form; *ad,* to; *pendo,* hand). A small, blind pouch projecting from the caecum in some mammals.

Ver'te-bral col'umn (L. *vertere,* to turn). See Spinal column.

Ver'te-brate (L. *vertebratus*). Animal with a backbone.

Ves-tig'i-al (L. *vestigium,* footstep). A rudimentary or degenerate structure which at one time was functional or better developed.

Vil'lus (L. *villus,* hair). A very small, finger-like projection, especially found in the vertebrate intestinal lining for increasing absorption.

Vi'rus (L. slimy liquid, poison). The simplest living organism composed almost entirely of nucleoprotein. They are capable of reproduction only within cells and are visible only under the electron microscope.

Vis'cer-a (L. internal organs). Internal organs of the body cavity.

Vi'ta-min (L. *vita,* life; M.E. *amine,* a chemical radical). A general term for a number of unrelated organic substances found in many foods and necessary, in small quantities, for normal metabolic activity.

Vi·tel′line (L. *vitellus,* yolk). Pertaining to egg yolk.

Vi·vip′a·rous (L. *vivus,* alive; *parere,* to bear). Producing young that receive nourishment for their development from the uterine wall of the mother.

Warm′-blood′ed. Animals possessing a temperature regulating device which enables them to maintain a constant body temperature.

Zo′o·ge·og″ra·phy (Gr. *zoion,* animal; *ge,* earth; *graphein,* to write). A branch of zoology dealing with the geographic distribution of animals.

Zy′gote (Gr. *zygotos,* united). The fertilized egg.

Index